CONTRIBUTORS

FRANKLIN P. ADAMS

NELSON ALGREN

BORIS ARTZYBASHEFF

WILLIAM ATTWOOD

HOWARD BAER

FREDERIC A. BIRMINGHAM

RAY BRADBURY

FREDERICK HAZLITT
  BRENNAN

T. K. BROWN III

ERSKINE CALDWELL

E. SIMMS CAMPBELL

JIMMY CANNON

IRWIN CAPLAN

ILKA CHASE

ERNEST CHIRIAKA

STUART CLOETE

SAM COBEAN

BARNABY CONRAD

PARKE CUMMINGS

CLARENCE DARROW

ABNER DEAN

ANDRE DE DIENES

ELDON DEDINI

PIETRO DI DONATO

JARO FABRY

F. SCOTT FITZGERALD

COREY FORD

FRED FREEMAN

PAUL GALLICO

MARTHA GELLHORN

NAIAD GIBLAN

BURT GLINN

WILLIAM LINDSAY
  GRESHAM

JOHN GROTH

PHILIPPE HALSMAN

ERNEST HEMINGWAY

ROBERT HENDERSON

ROBERT HOLLEY

SYD HOFF

LANGSTON HUGHES

CYRIL HUME

ALDOUS HUXLEY

RONNIE JACQUES

JAMES JONES

FRED C. KELLY

GERALD KERSH

ERIC KNIGHT

MANUEL KOMROFF

RICHARD E. LAUTERBACH

HELEN LAWRENSON

WILLIAM J. LEDERER

RICHARD LITWIN

WALLACE LITWIN

WILLIAM MARCH

MORRIS MARKEY

WILLIAM MOULTON
  MARSTON

EDGAR LEE MASTERS

ANDRÉ MAUROIS

MARTIN MAYER

JOHN MCDERMOTT

DOROTHY MCKAY

GEORGE A. MCNAMARA

JOHN MCPARTLAND

H. L. MENCKEN

JAMES A. MICHENER

AL MOORE

FRANK NAGY

GEORGE JEAN NATHAN

JOHN NOVOTNY

FRANK O'CONNOR

ROBERT OSBORN

BOB PATTERSON

ELLIOT PAUL

LOUIS PAUL

GEORGE PETTY

JAMES W. POLING

GARRETT PRICE

GARDNER REA

ROBERT RIGGS

HENRY MORTON ROBINSON

IRVING ROIR

ROBERT C. RUARK

WILLIAM SAROYAN

MARK SCHORER

BUDD SCHULBERG

FRANK SCULLY

IRWIN SHAW

BARBARA SHERMUND

MAX SHULMAN

BETTY SOUTH

BEN STAHL

JOHN STEINBECK

CARL STEPHENSON

LELAND STOWE

JESSE STUART

ROBERT SWITZER

ARTHUR SZYK

J. K. TAUSSIG, JR.

RAEBURN VAN BUREN

VARGA

EDMUND WARE

HENRY WAXMAN

JAMES WECHSBERG

THOMAS WOLFE

HERMAN WOUK

ALEX YOUNG

The
ESQUIRE
Treasury

THE BEST OF TWENTY YEARS OF ESQUIRE
FACT, FICTION, AND LAUGHTER
INCLUDING SEVENTY-THREE STORIES AND ARTICLES,
EIGHTY-FOUR DRAWINGS, CARTOONS, AND PHOTOGRAPHS
BY SOME OF THE MOST DISTINGUISHED AMERICAN WRITERS,
ARTISTS, AND PHOTOGRAPHERS

EDITED BY

ARNOLD GINGRICH

19 53

SIMON AND SCHUSTER : NEW YORK

FIRST PRINTING

Library of Congress Catalog Card Number: 53-10809

To the memory of
DAVID A. SMART
1892–1952

Thanks are due to all the publishers who, having acquired book rights in many of these stories and articles since their first appearance in *Esquire*, have graciously consented to their reappearance here. And a special citation is in order for Thomas Bruce Morgan, of *Esquire's* staff, for having performed at least nineteen-twentieths of the actual work of preparing this volume for press.

A. G.

CONTENTS

·III·
GRAPHICS SECTION
follows page 352

·IV·
FACT AND FANCY

Contents

· V ·
LARGELY ABOUT WOMEN

Introduction

ESQUIRE appeared, for the first time, in October 1933. Conceived at the darkest moment of the depression (in fact, our salesmen first went out with dummies of the first issues on March 4, 1933, the day the Bank Holiday began) and born at the dawn of the New Deal, we characterized it in our first promotional efforts as a magazine devoted to "the art of living and the new leisure."

By "new leisure" we meant, of course, the five-day, forty-hour week that had just become "not merely every man's right but virtually every man's duty."

We had first planned it as a sort of male counterpart of Vogue and Harper's Bazaar, expecting its sale to be confined largely to those "first buyers" who constitute the best customers of the nation's best men's stores. And we had intended to distribute it only through those stores, figuring that we would thus be establishing a pipeline to the prime prospects for advertisers of everything of especial or exclusive interest to men.

In every city and town there are "spenders" who are six months to a year ahead of the mob in getting the new things. They are the first to buy the new styles in clothes, the new models in automobiles, to take up the new vogues in sports and amusements. They are the first, the freest and readiest buyers. And their influence upon their fellows is incalculable.

We knew this, not just in theory, but for a fact, because we had built a business on the knowledge. We had been reaching this depression-proof "phalanx of first buyers" for several years during which we had broadened a small direct-mail business into a styling and marketing service for men's stores across the country.

Throughout that first phase we were in the publishing business, so to speak, but not of it. We were producing booklets, catalogs, folders, broadsides, and brochures, but had not yet ventured into the periodical field. This next step had been taken, however, at the beginning of the depression, in October 1931, with the publication of Apparel Arts, the trade magazine that fathered Esquire.

Knowing that we were assured of a certain irreducible minimum of sales through our store contacts, we consulted with news company officials and with outside circulation experts, during the summer of 1933, to determine how many copies of Esquire we might expect to sell on the newsstands. They assured us that under existing economic conditions we could not hope to sell more than twenty-five thousand copies of any fifty-cent item. Esquire was a runaway success. The first twenty-five thousand copies lasted less than half a day on the newsstands. One key newsstand in a metropolitan station, which had been allotted one hundred copies in the advance estimate of newsstand distribution, sold two thousand copies the first week.

From a quarterly basis, on which we had begun with the first issue, we were kicked upstairs into becoming a monthly virtually overnight. The second issue, dated January 1934, and bearing the legend "now issued every month," appeared on December 5, 1933, the day of Repeal.

Accustomed as we have always been to thinking of it as a new magazine—the way even a grandpa keeps on thinking of his son as a boy—it is something of a shock to realize that Esquire is sufficiently grown up to remember such things of the far away and the long ago as the Hoover (and the Hindenburg) administrations and, yes actually, Prohibition.

But it was certainly an unhousebroken pup back there twenty years ago this month when the "awkwardly edited" first issue came out, that curiously inept first issue whose cover might more suitably have graced a sporting goods catalog than a magazine, and whose general layout, with its odd-sized illustrations and staggered carry-over pages, ran off like Guido Gimlet's horse, "madly in all directions." There were some of those continuation pages in the back of the book on which there appeared portions of as many as five or six different stories or articles. And there were stories and articles which were carried over on as many as five or six of these pages. It was a regular snipe hunt. There was point to the gag employed by a Philadelphia columnist, to explain the occasional nonappearance of his column, that he was "out looking for the ending of an *Esquire* story."

There was no point at all, however, to nine-lived rumor that sprang up in the late thirties to the effect that copies of that first issue of *Esquire* were worth three thousand dollars. Time and again we had to take editorial notice of that one, before we could put a stop to the letters, telegrams, and even long distance calls, from people who had just unearthed copies after hearing the exciting news and expected to collect that legendary collectors' price from us.

Esquire was called "Esky" from the first week of its life. We never called it that; in fact we rather cordially disliked that diminutive, which sounded sissy to our ears as an epithet for a magazine that was self-consciously cultivating the hair on its chest, but the public spontaneously accorded it that nickname and it stuck. Newsdealers, in reordering the first issue of *Esquire*, commented on the fact that their customers kept calling for it by that odd abbreviation. And then, with the second issue, when the little pop-eyed man appeared, to begin cutting his capers on the front cover, he simply was "Esky" in person, and so he remains to this day. This too, despite the fact that we never called him anything at all, in print, until after he had been on the cover for over a

year. And it wasn't until he had begun to be imitated far and wide that we finally went through the formality of adopting our pop-eyed runt, legally, as our trademark. In other words, the public had recognized him, as our trademark, before we did ourselves.

More or less the same was true of the secondary meaning acquired by the word "esquire" after the magazine was born. Before that, the obsolescent word lay in the dictionary, all but forgotten. Except for lawyers' correspondence, the once general practice of addressing men by mail as John Jones, *Esq.* as opposed to *Mr.* John Jones, had gone out with the quill pen. Before the common use of typewriters, tradesmen generally addressed their patrons as *Esq.* In America there was never the hairsplitting accuracy that prevailed in England over the use of *Esq.* and *Mr.*, limiting the use of the former designation to a landed gentleman. Over here it was simply considered a more respectful way of saying *Mr.* to address a man as *Esq.* But it had been dying out fast ever since the turn of the twentieth century.

Then along came *Esquire*, the Magazine for Men, and breathed new life into a moribund word. Suddenly there began a lively burgeoning of *Esquire Thises and Thats*, all under the banner of this word which had theretofore been barren of all appeal to entrepreneurs.

That this had taken place as an after-the-fact development, following upon the launching of *Esquire*, as the first magazine of general appeal to devote a measurably large portion of its content to masculine fashions, was made a matter of record in the New York courts as early as 1935. In a consent decree in that state, recognition was accorded the magazine as having endowed the word "esquire" with the secondary meaning of smartness and distinction as relating to things of especial interest and appeal to men.

We had hoped, of course, that some such acceptance would ultimately accrue to the title of the magazine, but we hadn't foreseen that it would occur so quickly. We had hit upon the name in the course of making up one list of possible titles after another, only to have a patent lawyer in Washington return all our wanted titles with the notation that they had already been used. It was while staring at a blank pad that lay over the lawyer's latest letter, telling us that the word "trend" was not available for our use as a title, that we noticed the abbreviation "Esq." following our name and peeping out from under the edge of the pad.

Nor have we ever for a moment pretended that we knew beforehand that our magazine-making formula would capture the imagination of the public as it did. We thought of it only as "a new measure of magazine money's worth," and so described it at the time. One catch-phrase we used was "all you can read for fifty cents."

Another of our early word-plays was "nobody knows what the public wants, except its money's worth, and in the magazine business as in any other, his money's worth is what nobody can ever get too much of."

When *Esquire* was a-borning, business was in the doldrums and the country in the dumps. A Hollywood executive arose, in one of those What's-Wrong-With conferences that were even more frequent then than they have been of late, to say, "There's nothing wrong with picture business that good pictures can't cure." The remark has a bromidic overtone like "The country is fundamentally sound" or even "Build a better mousetrap."

But it was an inspiration to us, flirting as we were at the time with the temptation to take a flier into the magazine publishing business with the vague general notion of "a magazine for men." For translating that remark into terms of magazine publishing we chose to make it mean, "There's nothing that will put over a magazine that won't put itself over."

In other words, hard times or boom times, nothing that you can say or do about a magazine will do any good anyway unless the magazine will say and do for itself about ten times as much as you could possibly say or do about it.

Up to that point there had been much wondering and worrying about the high cost of "putting a new magazine over." But once convinced of the soundness of that fatalistic truism, the whole thing looked simple. There was no point in worrying about the high cost of high-pressure promotion experts, circulation wizards, publicity or advertising mugwumps or any of the other mysterious medicine men of the publishing field. There was, in fact, no point in worrying about anything that couldn't get between the covers of the magazine itself. That was the only place where high pressure could do any good.

Esquire went over. Nobody, and nothing, put it over. It proved that there was nothing wrong with the magazine business, even in 1933. Then and since, it had no more complicated formula than "as big a money's worth as possible."

The Alpha and Omega of our editorial practice was to say that the magazine would be "edited with a standing broad grin" and that our ideal of editing was that which Jefferson defined for government: "He edits best who edits least."

Analyzing the content of a living magazine is somewhat like that sport in which university professors indulge for the amusement of the press when they analyze the physical makeup of a living person's body. The list of ingredients is simple, but putting them all together in the indicated proportions is not enough to create a new life. A certain spark will still be missing. Nobody knows what it is—nobody can tell how it can be captured. It can only be recognized, not duplicated.

At any rate, something made *Esquire* catch on with the public as few magazines in publishing history have ever caught on.

Maybe it was the number, as well as the luster, of the "big names," of which this book's table of contents will give you some idea. Or maybe it was the then startling innovation of cartoons in full color. Maybe it was the sheer size and diversity of the magazine's contents. Or maybe it was the fact that it took as long to leaf through *Esquire* as it took to read some of the weeklies of the day from cover to cover. Whatever it was, it was something more than mere novelty, or *Esquire* would have slipped back quickly after its first rocket-like leap to success.

The prophets of doom were never lacking to predict just such an eventuality. Throughout the first year we had constantly heard, "You'll never make it." Then, after the magazine's circulation had gone up one year after another in almost geometrical progression, that tune merely changed to "You made it too fast—you can't possibly last."

Well, maybe it is possible, theoretically, for a magazine to live forever, but actually magazines do have a way of wearing out. Like people, they are prone to such afflictions as growing old or going stale or just plain getting tired. Times change, and with the changing times there are bound to be changing tastes. And it is changing tastes that govern the rise and fall in the popularity of magazines.

The public's mood is changing all the time, but the change is so gradual that it is hardly perceptible from week to week or even from month to month.

The human being effects a complete change of skin every seven years, but unlike the lower forms of life, the snake for example, man is not forced to make this change so abruptly as to be aware of it. We don't have to crawl out of our skins, spectacularly, at any one time at any one given season. The change is so gradual that nobody but a dermatologist is constantly and consciously aware of it. And the public changes its thinking, its tastes and moods, as gradually and imperceptibly

as it changes its skin. Only a small class of specialists, editors for instance, need be constantly and consciously aware of it. And of those who are, not all are in a position to do anything about it anyway.

Periodical publications must be cut to a pattern, and very rare is the pattern that permits constant change, so gradual as to be imperceptible. That's why you see magazines being reorganized, reissued with a "new policy" and often with a new name. Magazines that are cut to a narrow pattern must accomplish their "skin-change" with an abrupt metamorphosis. Some magazines refuse to change, and that is why we have the familiar sight of once-great journals, bearing proud and venerable names, now fallen not merely in advertising but in circulation and influence, too.

Looking back over twenty years, it seems to us that *Esquire*'s one basic success secret lies in its self-regenerating publishing formula, made possible by the breadth of its editorial pattern. If you look at it, as a casual reader, from month to month, you will not be aware of its constant change. But if you have occasion to compare issues of the same month or same general season, one or two years apart, the differences will astonish you.

Even with magazines that are confined to no missionary function, wedded to no set political or crusading attitude, and restricted to no narrowly specialized vein of subject matter, there is still a very real and constant danger of getting into a groove, falling into a rut, and becoming "typed." A time arrives when inspiration tires, when the zest for the job loses its first fine edge, when success induces smugness and complacency, and the performance as a whole takes on a certain weariness of tone. One issue begins to look too much like another, and before long an alert and exacting public begins to find the whole show as old and worn as a radio comedian's joke book. Of course, this may yet happen to *Esquire*. We've seen it happen to the best and the brightest, and we have as yet discovered no heaven in which to arrange for any special immunity for ourselves. But we have at least taken cognizance of this natural tendency, in implementing our original formula upon which *Esquire* was founded twenty years ago. Ours is the sort of variety show that makes a virtue and a feature out of the constant uncovering of new talent, and the only consistency about *Esquire's* editorial pattern is its constancy of gradual change.

This is perhaps more logical than it sounds, when you remember that the magazine's prime purpose, in the original planning state—the hidden pill beneath the sugar coating of amusement and entertainment features—was the stimulation of a desire for change, the whetting of the appetite for novelty and/or innovation, in all the pursuits of the "new leisure."

We wanted, always, to feel that the reader could never feel sure, as he turned from one page to the next and from one issue to the next, of what might be coming up.

What we said about the magazine, in a greeting to new subscribers back in 1936, could equally apply to the book you are now holding in your hands:

It is a magazine for men to which, through circumstances beyond its control, a considerable number of women seem to have become addicted. It has learned most of the accepted rules and practices of publishing only in the course of breaking them. The magazine is, as its name implies, not for children. Nor is it, on the other hand, a dirty magazine, as some may have falsely told you. It is dedicated to the literate, if not the literary, and to the intelligent if not the intellectual. Politically it is nonpartisan, as concerns the two major American parties. Otherwise it is something of an anomaly, because it is both anti-fascist and anti-communist. It will probably puzzle you. It might help to explain that its conception of the true and ideal American way of life lies in every man's right to misspend his life as and if he sees fit. Editorially it is broad-minded in every sense of the term. If you have tender prejudices it will probably step on at least one of them. It isn't, and it never will be, the magazine for everybody.

Perhaps all this has told you rather more than you cared to hear about the magazine out of which this book's contents have been taken. But it seemed sensible, before turning you loose in a book that skims the cream of *Esquire's* first two hundred and forty issues, to try to tell you something definitive about the magazine itself.

Here you have, then, the first comprehensive collection of writings from *Esquire* in the thirteen years since *The Bedside Esquire,* a book that sold over six hundred thousand copies despite getting off to a very bad start when its original publication date happened to coincide with the Nazi invasion of Holland.

Here you have, also, the first cross-section of *Esquire's* pictorial elements ever to be issued in the magazine's twenty years, although there was a scattering of its cartoons through the pages of last year's volume entitled *The Girls from Esquire.*

Twenty years ago, when *Esquire's* prospects were all still in the future conditional tense, we wrote that "our most important dividends, this year and next, will be in enjoyment of our job. If we were getting out the *Congressional Record,* conceivably we might not feel that way, but *Esquire* is the kind of magazine that it's actually fun to work on."

It was and it still is. And by that same token, so was this book.

SECTION ONE

Extra Base Hits

INTRODUCTION

EACH OF THE PIECES presented in the following section made the audience get up out of their seats and either yell with excited delight or groan with outraged anguish.

The extra excitement they provoked at the time of their original appearance is their only common denominator. Yet each represents in some way a deviation from that sacred rule of Safety First which has made Caution the most debilitating of all the occupational diseases of magazine editors.

We think it was Havelock Ellis who somewhere once referred to Safety First as "the most ignoble of mottoes." In any case, the exceptions to its worship by Hollywood and the common run of commercial magazines have been comparatively few. To be sure it's an unwritten rule, but as spelled out in the nightmares of editors it could well read about like this:

If you must have a villain, see that he is a raceless creature of no discernible religious or national persuasion, and if you must reveal his origin or habitat, see that he hails from an unrecognizable section of a wholly imaginary city in an utterly fictitious country and that he practices, apart from his villainy, no particular trade or profession.

Following this rule strictly might not get many new subscriptions but it is obviously the only way to avoid losing any by the "Sir, you cur, cancel my subscription" route.

Away back when the magazine was new we promised never to give grounds for offence, knowingly, on either religion or race. At the same time, we foresaw that the pursuit of editorial happiness in a magazine devoted to sophisticated adult amusement and entertainment would inevitably involve giving offence, cheerfully and consciously, to many peoples' prejudices, sensibilities or special interests. As a consequence of this relatively uninhibited editorial policy authors have enjoyed in our pages a rare degree of freedom of expression.

We let the author say his say, as long as he says it well, whether or not it happens to square with our own pet peeves and prejudices, tastes and likes. And short of unavoidable deletions necessitated by the laws of libel and obscenity, we edit scripts as little as possible on their way into print in *Esquire's* pages.

As a further safeguard to the magazine's freedom of expression we installed a safety valve, after the first issue, in the form of *The Sound and the Fury*, where offended, shocked, outraged and variously infuriated readers have been allowed to howl to high heaven in protest against the opinions and attitudes of the authors and artists who displeased them.

This outlet has afforded satisfaction to some and sport to many, these twenty

1

years. Also it has served us as a sort of cross between a lie detector and an applause meter. Nobody's ever actually got hurt, for all the threats of mayhem that have enlivened that column's contents. And whenever one of Esquire's authors has attacked anybody or anything unfairly, the truth has come out in that column like murder. Since the readers have the last word, they have yet to come off second best in such instances.

The current *Sound and Fury* championship was won by a Mr. Bernard Dorrity for having posed the interesting proposition: *Let's Secede from Texas.* He won it by the obvious device of taking in more territory than had been attempted by any one of our assorted opinion provokers in all the seventeen years since the uproar over the declaration that *Latins Are Lousy Lovers.* The latter is undoubtedly the best remembered single article in *Esquire's* life to date. But each of the other contributions in this section made the same kind of sensational impression, in different degree, in its season. Editors' notes, in this and the other sections, have been added only where there seemed to be some need for them, and are not meant to indicate any special preference for the piece so annotated. After all, the whole book is our treasury.

PIETRO DI DONATO'S
"Christ in Concrete"

THIS STORY, which grew into the highly successful novel of the same name, was greeted in our March 1937 issue with a whoop-de-do that we have never exceeded and only a couple of times equaled. Here's just a lift from it, as the whole thing would be much too long to quote: *This month, with no disrespect to all our Discoveries of these past three years, we find ourselves wishing for a stronger word with which to introduce the first published writing of Pietro di Donato, an almost incredibly talented* young Italian bricklayer lately turned author.

As we say in a prefatory note to the story itself, not once in the last three years have we felt the spine-tingling thrill of "discovery" so strongly as in reading "Christ in Concrete," not once since the night three years ago when we came across a story called "No More Trouble for Jedwick." On that occasion we wrote the then utterly unknown Louis Paul an excited letter in which we said among other things that we were confident he was going places. And go places he did. "Jedwick" won the O. Henry Memorial Award as the best short story of that year. Within a few months Louis Paul's stories were appearing in the big-money "slicks," and within the year his first novel was a Literary Guild selection.

This time, just back from a month out of the country, we were tunneling our way through the mountains of accumulated manuscripts and, a little after four in the morning, had reached that point where the going was a bit tough. We had caught ourselves nodding two or three times in the course of reading one script, and were weighing the wisdom of taking time out for black coffee before tackling the next one, which happened to be "Christ in Concrete." The title had turned into an exclamation before we had finished the first page, and no coffee was needed to keep us awake.

Finishing the story, which left us limp, we looked to see if the author had appended any word about himself. And came across the following: "What can I say, other than—I am twenty-five—been a bricklayer since thirteen—support a large family—I am alive—and yet dead—have died a thousand times in the guts of great Job, who has weighted my life and rises everywhere before me—he's not human—my soul scene is a maelstrom of bricks, mortar, goading foremen, leering suckers, whore-faced bosses, shouts, sweat, madness and mute death on Job."

This was tantalizing and not alto-

gether reassuring. *It seemed to us to have a slightly phony ring, a note of arty self-dramatization that had not sounded once in the story itself. We were skeptical, too, of all this prodigious bricklaying.* Meyer Levin, who had read the story before we had and who happened to be New York-bound the next day, offered his expert services as reporter and investigator on the case. He would look up, and over, Mr. di Donato and confirm or deny our cynical suspicion that all this breast-beating about bricklaying and bosses was just a Union Square or Greenwich Village gag.

Anyway, Meyer Levin concluded his dossier on di Donato with these prescient words:

"I think he is completely emotionalized and future work is utterly unpredictable. In any case a terrific fuss about this story might upset him and harm his development especially if we advertise it startlingly."

Whether the terrific fuss we made over the story harmed him is hard to say. We did what we hadn't done since "No More Trouble for Jedwick," issued "Christ in Concrete" in the form of a small book, calling this dual publication our "gesture of respect to its author's talent, whether or not he ever writes another line."

Well, he did go on to finish the novel, and it was a book club selection. But after that all we were ever able to get out of him was a succession of scripts that, with one exception, proved to be simply further adumbrations of that one first story. We published the exception, and have been hoping, ever since, that there might be others.

HELEN LAWRENSON'S
"Latins Are Lousy Lovers"

PRESERVING OUR POLICY of protecting the anonymity of authors who do not choose to sign their works, we held out valiantly against every sort of pressure from news services, columnists, news-magazines, and assorted Latin interests, refusing for many months to tell who wrote the article that set back the Good Neighbor Policy halfway to its own goal line. Meanwhile, five female authors coyly refused either to confirm or to deny its authorship.

We were still holding out, in fact, when the better part of a year later a piece came out in another magazine, under the by-line of Helen Brown Norden, to which by-line was appended the legend, "Author of *Latins Are Lousy Lovers.*"

So now at this late date we feel no compunction about saying that she was. Her by-line has since changed, by the way, to Helen Brown Lawrenson.

The Cuban police (as we duly reported in our issue for November 1936, the month following the article's appearance) *promptly clapped eight unoffending (and presumably equally offended) Havana newsdealers into the dungeon. There they would be held, said the Cuban police, "pending an investigation."* What kind of investigation do you suppose the Cuban police wanted to hold? Or do you suppose they were misquoted in the Havana dispatches that were so gleefully played up by most American papers? *Maybe they wanted to hold a contest, instead of an investigation. In any event, the fact that the military police chose to take any official notice of such a peculiarly unspeakable affront to the composite national manhood struck Americans as being both funny and surprising. All that the Cuban police accomplished, in protesting the interestingly debatable and obviously unprovable generality that Latins may be lousy lovers, was to furnish food for further thought on Latin peculiarities. By confiscating the magazines they made it very hard for some subsequent researcher to attempt to prove a Latin sense of humor. And by jailing the eight newsdealers they*

virtually obviated the necessity for
further research to justify the conclusion
that Latins Are Lousy Logicians. Could
the Cuban police possibly have suspected
either any one, or all eight, of the newsdealers wrote the article in question? Or
even that, as representative Cubans, they
were more pleased than the police with
the arguments that the article advanced?
Stumped by our rhetorical questions, we
can only say that we hope the investigation proves whatever the national police
want it to prove. Meanwhile, we live and
learn. We have assisted in advertising to
the world that there is one place where
Sex, as such, is sacred. It should help,
rather than hinder, the tourist business.

T. K. BROWN'S
"*The Valley of the Shadow*"

HERE'S WHAT WE SAID, among other
things, about The Valley of the Shadow
in our issue for August 1945: We hope
you'll read it and we hope you'll like it.
But if you'll read it, whether or not you
"like" it as a story, we feel sure that you
will put it down, after finishing it, with
the feeling of having just had a terrific
emotional experience. Our own feeling,
after reading it in manuscript, was a hol-
lowed-out exhausted sensation, with difficulty in catching our breath such as we
had some years ago at the moment of
realization that we had succeeded in
swerving out of what had a few seconds
before appeared to be an absolutely inevitable and guaranteed fatal highway accident.

We put stress on the matter of reading it all the way through, although it
wouldn't have occurred to us to do so
just on the basis of our own reading of
the story. We read it right through, our
attention held like that of a rabbit by a
rattlesnake. But we showed the story in
galley proofs to a female of whom we are
very fond, perhaps because she has never
yet been invited to lecture at any insti-

tutions of higher learning, and she had
to be reassured, a couple of times, that
we had not mixed the galleys up, and
that the galley with which we asked her
to begin was indeed the one with which
the story began. She seemed to find the
beginning sort of "impressionistic or
something," but she liked it fine after
being prevailed upon to persevere.

(Long-memoried old Esquire addicts
will recall that we had a peck of trouble,
when this magazine was young, over the
plaints of the plain readers who were
bothered by the "goofy endings" of so
many of our stories. But bedad and be-
divil if this isn't the first time we ever
had any complaint from any reader, plain
or fancy, about a story's beginning.)

So take it easy, if by any chance you
find the going bumpy as you start the
story, because we're willing to bet that
before you end it you'll find it turning
you inside out.

The story was reprinted in Martha
Foley's Best American Short Stories of
1946, but the novel of which it was expected to be a part has not yet appeared.

LANGSTON HUGHES'
"*A Good Job Gone*"

THIS STORY was the great sensation of
Esquire's extreme youth, hard as it may
be to believe today, when in the interim
such books as Strange Fruit have appeared to make it seem pale by contrast.
In our second issue (January 1934) we
described this story to our readers and
asked them to vote on whether we
should run it. The violence of both the
yeas and the nays so amazed us that we
felt impelled in the next issue to remind
our readers that ushers at the old melodramas sometimes had to ask overrespon-
sive customers to put their six-shooters
away during the villain's big scene, and
at the movies young children must be
reminded, now and then at hectic moments, that "it's only a story."

The vote went nine to one in the story's favor (not without challenges to duels between Sound and Furyites), and we printed the story in our fifth issue, April 1934.

Westbrook Pegler, then just leaving his sports writing job in Chicago to become a columnist in New York, was among those who warned us that if we printed the story, the magazine would .not survive its appearance by more than six months.

J. K. TAUSSIG'S
"My Crew at Pearl Harbor"

FROM THE EDITORIAL PAGE of our issue for March 1943: Today, January 11, we're writing this page on the "Century," between Chicago and New York, which is where we usually write it, because this particular page happens to be the last one to go to press, and we usually start for New York before this page starts for press. We get on the train and begin scribbling furiously, trying to win the standing bet that we won't get it finished in time to mail back to Gus from Toledo. (Why we use this page, every so often, as a confessional of all our weaknesses is something we don't understand any better than you do, but it's a habit of some nine years' running.)

Well, last month, as it happened, we finished our page long before Toledo, and began looking through our briefcase to see what other train chores it might contain. Nothing we ever find in that old briefcase surprises us any more. Some very strange things have been in it, and it's been lost, more than once, in some strange places, and found its way back in strange ways. We're so used to it that we walk with a portside list whenever, which is seldom, we walk without it.

But this time it turned up one of the events of an editorial lifetime. Because this time what turned up, next to some urgent memos for August 1941, was a pair of manuscript envelopes, clipped together with a note from our office better half, saying something to the effect that we might want to read these two scripts on the train if we had time.

So, wondering what was so special about them, we began reading one of them. As we read the first one, we still wondered. Halfway through it, we turned back to the beginning to see if the accompanying letter might give any clue. There we found that this script, while more or less promised to some magazine with a deadline of the umpteenth, was nevertheless offered to us if we could reach a decision within a day or so because, etc., etc. Well, that explained why we had to read it, but it didn't tell us a thing about why we had to like it. We finished it, nevertheless. But it was a reeking whiffer. All very subtle and sophisticated and meant to be just too profound, a dreary fantasy in the vein of what the German aestheticists used to term the als ob, but you and we would have dubbed the so what or what of it. You wouldn't have been able to stand it, believe us who know that you've been able to stand for a lot these last nine years.

So we finished reading it with a mental note to tell our secretary not to believe everything she reads in these well-meant letters attached to scripts by willing authors. Then we debated between the probable pleasure to be found in the other script as against that of going back to the club car for a drink. Well, it was pretty far back to the club car, and the other script was right at hand, so we decided to give it a look, on the off chance that it might average things out so that the time spent on the other one might not remain a total loss.

This second one, too, we began in the middle of things, without first reading the accompanying letter.

"In the middle of things" is the precise, if not exactly novel, descriptive phrase—and what things we found our-self in the middle of! It was Pearl Harbor, to the life and death. And it lifted us out of our lethargy in a leap. We read it through in one gasping gulp. As we finished we noticed, unbelieving, that the last page of the script bore the number seventeen. We'd have sworn it was about five pages in all.

Then, avid for every last available detail, we turned back to read the letter that was attached to the script. This only increased our excitement, because the letter, like the script itself, bore the unmistakable earmarks of authenticity in every line. So it wasn't until we neared the letter's end, by which time we were feeling a lot like Little Jack Horner in our smug satisfaction over finding this under our thumb, that we suddenly bit, hard, on the pit of the plum. For only there did we discover that this script was not ours.

The author had, it developed, sent this same script out in triplicate, to three different magazines, and while he paid us the compliment of hoping that it would end up in Esquire, because that was "more of a man's proposition" and would reach more of the fellows he wanted to tell his story, still he realized that time was of the essence in any story about Pearl Harbor, since the Navy had just taken the lid off the details a few days before, and he would have to place the story quickly, he presumed, to place it at all.

In other words it was first come first served, and it was ours only if we won the race to come and get it.

So we waited until it had been a full twenty-four hours after sending the telegram, and then we decided that we simply had to call up about it.

We asked for him by name, at the Naval Hospital in Newport. It's a famous Navy name. But it evoked no recognition. What was his grade, they wanted to know at the hospital switchboard. Lieutenant, we remembered. What was his number, they wanted to know next,

because the hospital's a big place. How should we know that? Well then, what was the nature of his illness or injury? Now they were getting to where we knew the answers as well as you will know them after reading the piece. We told all about what happened to him at Pearl Harbor, and that soon got us switched to another voice. A very polite, friendly and efficient voice, a very Navy voice, explaining that of course it was impossible to talk direct on the phone to a man who has been lying in a cast for fifty-three weeks, but offering to act as go-between in carrying questions and answers back and forth down the corridor to and from the lieutenant's bed and the telephone. Would we care to try that? What message did we want to convey? All this with a "sir" between every other breath; competent as a machine gun, but cordial as a handclasp.

We were struck dumb for a long moment. The whole thing suddenly hit us hard. Yes, what did we want to know? What, besides the glorious truth that our flag was still there? What message could we have for that man in that bed we couldn't see, when we could visualize the beds, and cots and stretchers he had been on ever since that terrific twenty-four hours at Pearl Harbor over a year ago, back to that first bed from which he looked up to see darkness through the skylight and wondered whether it was night or whether that was the pall of smoke from the Arizona? What could we have to say to him, what could any of us who weren't there ever have to say to those who were, and lived?

We finally mumbled something about wondering whether our offer was acceptable, and winced as we heard the question repeated by that friendly Navy voice.

Then in a minute we heard all we wanted to know.

The lieutenant, as it happened, had just been writing a wire to tell us, but now we could hear his message without waiting for it. Yes, he had heard from all three magazines, and one of them had made a better offer, and the other had made an offer that wasn't more than a bit better than half as good. But the magazine that had made the better offer was a magazine that the lieutenant felt that Navy men didn't especially like, so he had decided that he would prefer to see his story told in Esquire.

Was that what we wanted to know?

Boy, was it!

PIETRO DI DONATO

Christ in Concrete

MARCH whistled stinging snow against the brick walls and up the gaunt girders. Geremio, the foreman, swung his arms about, and gaffed the men on.

Old Nick, the "Lean," stood up from over a dust-flying brick pile, and tapped the side of his nose.

"Master Geremio, the devil himself could not break his tail any harder than we here."

Burly Vincenzo of the walrus mustache and known as the "Snoutnose," let fall the chute door of the concrete hopper and sang over in the Lean's direction. "Mari-Annina's belly and the burning night will make of me once more a milk-mouthed stripling lad. . . ."

The Lean loaded his wheelbarrow and spat furiously. "Sons of two-legged dogs . . . despised of even the devil himself! Work! Sure! For America beautiful will eat you and spit your bones into the earth's hole! Work!" And with that his wiry frame pitched the barrow violently over the rough floor.

Snoutnose waved his head to and fro and with mock pathos wailed, "Sing on, oh guitar of mine. . . ."

Short, cheery-faced Joe Chiappa, the scaffoldman, paused with hatchet in hand and tenpenny spike sticking out from small dicelike teeth to tell the Lean as he went by, in a voice that all could hear, "Ah, father of countless chicks, the old age is a carrion!"

Geremio chuckled and called to him. "Hey little Joe, who are you to talk? You and big-titted Cola can't even hatch an egg, whereas the Lean has just to turn the doorknob of his bedroom and old Philomena becomes a balloon!"

Coarse throats tickled and mouths opened wide in laughter.

Mike, the "Barrel-mouth," pretended he was talking to himself and yelled out in his best English . . . he was always speaking English while the rest carried on in their native Italian. "I don't know myself, but somebodys whose gotta bigga buncha keeds and he alla times talka from somebodys elsa!"

Geremio knew it was meant for him and he laughed. "On the tomb of Saint Pimplelegs, this little boy my wife is giving me next week shall be the last! Eight hungry little Christians to feed, is enough for any man."

Joe Chiappa nodded to the rest. "Sure, Master Geremio had a telephone call from the next bambino. Yes, it told him it had a little bell there instead of a rose bush. . . . It even told him its name!"

"Laugh, laugh all of you," returned Geremio, "but I tell you that all my kids must be boys so that they some day will be big American builders. And then I'll help them to put the gold away in the basements for safe keeping!"

A great din of riveting shattered the talk among the fast-moving men. Geremio added a handful of "Honest" tobacco to his corncob, puffed strongly, and cupped his hands around the bowl for a bit of warmth. The chill day caused him to shiver, and he thought to himself, "Yes, the day is cold, cold . . . but who am I to complain when the good Christ himself was crucified?

"Pushing the job is all right (when has it been otherwise in my life?), but this job frightens me. I feel the building wants to tell me something; just as one Christian to another. I don't like this. Mr. Murdin tells me, 'Push it up!' That's all he knows. I keep telling him that the underpinning should be doubled and the old material removed from the floors, but he keeps the inspector drunk and . . . 'Hey, Ashes-ass! Get away from under that pilaster! Don't pull the old work. Push it away from you or you'll have a nice present for Easter if the wall falls on you!' . . . Well, with the help of God I'll see this job through. It's not my first, nor the . . . 'Hey, Patsy number two! Put more cement in that concrete; we're putting up a building, not an Easter cake!' "

Patsy hurled his shovel to the floor and gesticulated madly. "The padrone Murdin-sa tells me, 'Too much, too much! Lil' bit is plenty!' And you tell me I'm stingy! The rotten building can fall after I leave!"

Six floors below, the contractor called. "Hey Geremio! Is your gang of dagos dead!"

Geremio cautioned to the men. "On your toes, boys. If he writes out slips, someone won't have big eels on the Easter table."

The Lean cursed that "the padrone could take the job and shove it . . . !"

Curly-headed Sandino, the roguish, pigeon-toed scaffoldman, spat a clod of tobacco juice and hummed to his own music. . . . "Yes, certainly yes to your face, master padrone . . . and behind, this to you and all your kind!"

The day, like all days, came to an end. Calloused and bruised bodies sighed, and numb legs shuffled towards shabby railroad flats. . . .

"Ah, *bella casa mio*. Where my little freshets of blood, and my good woman await me. Home where my broken back will not ache so. Home where midst the monkey chatter of my piccolinos I will float off to blessed slumber with my feet on the chair and the head on the wife's soft full breast."

These great child-hearted ones leave each other without words or ceremony, and as they ride and walk home, a great pride swells the breast. . . .

"Blessings to Thee, oh Jesus. I have fought winds and cold. Hand to hand I have locked dumb stones in place and the great building rises. I have earned a bit of bread for me and mine."

The mad day's brutal conflict is forgiven, and strained limbs prostrate themselves so that swollen veins can send the yearning blood coursing and pulsating deliciously as though the body mountained leaping streams.

The job alone remained behind . . . and yet, they too, having left the bigger part of their lives with it. The cold ghastly beast, the Job, stood stark, the eerie March wind wrapping it in sharp shadows of falling dusk.

That night was a crowning point in the life of Geremio. He bought a house! Twenty years he had helped to mold the New World. And now he was to have a house of his own! What mattered that it was no more than a wooden shack? It was his own!

He had proudly signed his name and helped Annunziata to make her x on the wonderful contract that proved them owners. And she was happy to think that her next child, soon to come, would be born under their own rooftree. She heard the church chimes, and cried to the children, "Children, to bed! It is near midnight. And remember, shut-mouth to the *paesanos!* Or they will send the evil eye to our new home even before we put foot."

The children scampered off to the icy yellow bedroom where three slept in one bed and three in the other. Coltishly and friskily they kicked about under the covers; their black iron-cotton stockings not removed . . . what! and freeze the peanut-little toes?

Said Annunziata, "The children are so happy, Geremio; let them be, for even I, would a Tarantella dance." And with that she turned blushing. He wanted to take her on her word. She patted his hands, kissed them, and whispered. "Our children will dance for us . . . in the American style some day."

Geremio cleared his throat and wanted to sing. "Yes, with joy I could sing in a richer feeling than the great Caruso." He babbled little old-country couplets and circled the room until the tenant below tapped the ceiling.

Annunziata whispered, "Geremio, to bed and rest. Tomorrow is a day for great things . . . and the day on which our Lord died for us."

The children were now hard asleep. Heads under the cover, over . . . moist noses whistling, and little damp legs entwined.

In bed Geremio and Annunziata clung closely to each other. They mumbled figures and dates until fatigue stilled their thoughts. And with chubby Johnnie clutching fast his bottle and warmed between them . . . life breathed heavily, and dreams entertained in far, far worlds, the nation builder's brood.

But Geremio and Annunziata remained for a while staring into darkness, silently.

"Geremio?"

"Yes?"

"This job you are now working . . ."

"So?"

"You used always to tell me about what happened on the jobs . . . who was jealous, and who praised. . . ."

"You should know by now that all work is the same. . . ."

"Geremio. The month you have been on this job, you have not spoken a word about the work. . . . And I have felt that I am walking into a dream. Is the work dangerous? Why don't you answer . . . ?"

Job loomed up damp, shivery gray. Its giant members waiting.

Builders quietly donned their coarse robes, and waited.

Geremio's whistle rolled back into his pocket and the symphony of struggle began.

Trowel rang through brick and slashed mortar rivets were machine-gunned fast with angry grind Patsy number one check Patsy number two check the Lean three check Vincenzo four steel bellowed back at hammer donkey engines coughed purple Ashes-ass Pietro fifteen chisel point intoned stone thin steel whirred and wailed through wood liquid stone flowed with dull rasp through iron veins and hoist screamed through space Carmine the Fat twenty-four and Giacomo Sangini check. . . . The multitudinous voices of a civilization rose from the surroundings and melded with the efforts of the Job.

To the intent ear, Nation was voicing her growing pains, but, hands that create are attached to warm hearts and not to calculating minds. The Lean as he fought his burden on looked forward to only one goal, the end. The barrow he pushed, he did not love. The stones that brutalized his palms, he did not love. The great God Job, he did not love. He felt a searing bitterness and a fathomless consternation at the queer consciousness that inflicted the ever mounting weight of structures that he HAD TO! HAD TO! raise above his shoulders! When, when and where would the last stone be? Never . . . did he bear his toil with the rhythm of song! Never . . . did his gasping heart knead the heavy mortar with lilting melody! A voice within him spoke in wordless language.

The language of worn oppression and the despair of realizing that his life had been left on brick piles. And always, there had been hunger and her bastard, the fear of hunger.

Murdin bore down upon Geremio from behind and shouted:

"Goddamnit Geremio, if you're givin' the men two hours off today with pay, why the hell are they draggin' their tails! And why don't you turn that skinny old Nick loose, and put a young wop in his place!"

"Now listen-a to me, Mister Murdin—"

"Don't give me that! And bear in mind that there are plenty of good barefoot men in the streets who'll jump for a day's pay!"

"Padrone—padrone, the underpinning gotta be make safe and . . ."

"Lissenyawopbastard! If you don't like it, you know what you can do!"

And with that he swung swaggering away.

The men had heard, and those who hadn't knew instinctively.

The new home, the coming baby, and his whole background, kept the fire from Geremio's mouth and bowed his head. "Annunziata speaks of scouring the ashcans for the children's bread in case I didn't want to work on a job where . . . But am I not a man, to feed my own with these hands? Ah, but day will end and no boss in the world can then rob me of the joy of my home!"

Murdin paused for a moment before descending the ladder.

Geremio caught his meaning and jumped to, nervously directing the rush of work. . . . No longer Geremio, but a machine-like entity.

The men were transformed into single, silent, beasts. Snoutnose steamed through ragged mustache whip-lashing sand into mixer Ashes-ass dragged under four by twelve beam Lean clawed wall knots jumping in jaws masonry crumbled dust billowed thundered choked. . . .

At noon, Geremio drank his wine from an old-fashioned magnesia bottle and munched a great pepper sandwich . . . no meat on Good Friday. Said one, "Are some of us to be laid off? Easter is upon us and communion dresses are needed and . . ."

That, while Geremio was dreaming of the new house and the joys he could almost taste. Said he, "Worry not. You should know Geremio." It then all came out. He regaled them with his wonderful joy of the new house. He praised his wife and children one by one. They listened respectfully and returned him well wishes and blessings. He went on and on. . . . "Paul made a radio—all by himself mind you! One can hear Barney Google and many American songs! How proud he."

The ascent to labor was made, and as they trod the ladder, heads turned and eyes communed with the mute flames of the brazier whose warmth they were leaving, not with willing heart, and in that fleeting moment, the breast wanted so, so much to speak, of hungers that never reached the tongue.

About an hour later, Geremio called over to Pietro. "Pietro, see if Mister Murdin is in the shanty and tell him I must see him! I will convince him that the work must not go on like this . . . just for the sake of a little more profit!"

Pietro came up soon. "The padrone is not coming up. He was drinking from a large bottle of whiskey and cursed in American words that if you did not carry out his orders—"

Geremio turned away disconcerted, stared dumbly at the structure and mechanically listed in his mind's eye the various violations of construction safety. An uneasy sensation hollowed him. The Lean brought down an old piece of wall and the structure palsied. Geremio's heart broke loose and out-thumped the floor's vibrations, a rapid wave of heat swept him and left a chill touch in its wake. He looked about to the men, a bit frightened. They seemed usual, life-size, and moved about with the methodical deftness that made the moment then appear no different than the task of toil had ever been.

Snoutnose's voice boomed into him. "Master Geremio, the concrete is re—ady!"

"Oh yes, yes Vincenz." And he walked gingerly towards the chute, but, not without leaving behind some part of his strength, sending out his soul to wrestle with the limbs of Job, who threatened in stiff silence. He talked and joked with Snoutnose. Nothing said anything, nor seemed wrong. Yet a vague uneasiness was to him as certain as the foggy murk that floated about Job's stone and steel.

"Shall I let the concrete down now, Master Geremio?"

"Well, let me see—no, hold it a minute. Hey Sandino! Tighten the chute cables!"

Snoutnose straightened, looked about, and instinctively rubbed the sore small of his spine. "Ah," sighed he, "all the men feel as I—yes, I can tell. They are tired but happy that today is Good Friday and we quit at three o'clock—" And he swelled in human ecstasy at the anticipation of food, drink, and the hairy flesh-tingling warmth of wife, and then, extravagant rest. In truth, they all felt as Snoutnose, although perhaps, with variations on the theme.

It was the Lean only, who had lived, and felt otherwise. His soul, accompanied with time, had shredded itself in the physical war to keep the physical alive. Perhaps he no longer had a soul, and the corpse continued from momentum. May he not be the Slave, working on from the birth of Man—He of whom it was said, "It was not for Him to reason?" And probably He, who, never asking, taking, nor vaunting, created God and the creatable? Nevertheless, there existed in the Lean a sense of oppression suffered, so vast, that the seas of time could never wash it away.

Geremio gazed about and was conscious of seeming to understand many things. He marveled at the strange feeling which permitted him to sense the familiarity of life. And yet—all appeared unreal, a dream pungent and nostalgic. Life, dream, reality, unreality, spiraling ever about each other. "Ha," he chuckled, "how and from where do these thoughts come?"

Snoutnose had his hand on the hopper latch and was awaiting the word from Geremio. "Did you say something, Master Geremio?"

"Why yes, Vincenz, I was thinking—funny! A—yes, what is the time—yes, that is what I was thinking."

"My American can of tomatoes says ten minutes from two o'clock. It won't be long now, Master Geremio."

Geremio smiled. "No, about an hour . . . and then, home."

"Oh, but first we stop at Mulberry Street, to buy their biggest eels, and the other finger-licking stuffs."

Geremio was looking far off, and for a moment happiness came to his heart without words, a warm hand stealing over. Snoutnose's words sang to him pleasantly, and he nodded.

"And Master Geremio, we ought really to buy the seafruits with the shells—you know, for the much needed steam they put into the—"

He flushed despite himself and continued. "It is true, I know it—especially the juicy clams . . . uhmn, my mouth waters like a pump."

Geremio drew on his unlit pipe and smiled acquiescence. The men around him were moving to their tasks silently, feeling of their fatigue, but absorbed in contemplations the very same as Snoutnose's. The noise of labor seemed not to be noise, and as Geremio looked about, life settled over him a gray concert—gray forms, atmosphere and gray notes. . . . Yet his off-tone world felt so near, and familiar.

"Five minutes from two," swished through Snoutnose's mustache.

Geremio automatically took out his watch, rewound, and set it. Sandino had done with the cables. The tone and movement of the scene seemed to Geremio strange, differently strange, and yet, a dream familiar from a timeless date. His hand went up in motion to Vincenzo. The molten stone gurgled low, and then with heightening rasp. His eyes followed the stone-cementy pudding, and to his ears there was no other sound than its flow. From over the roofs somewhere, the tinny voice of *Barney Google* whined its way, hooked into his consciousness and kept itself a revolving record beneath his skull-plate.

"Ah, yes, Barney Google, my son's wonderful radio machine . . . wonderful Paul." His train of thought quickly took in his family, home and hopes. And with hope came fear. Something within asked, "Is it not possible to breathe God's air without fear dominating with the pall of unemployment? And the terror of production for Boss. Boss and Job? To rebel is to lose all of the very little. To be obedient is to choke. Oh dear Lord, guide my path."

Just then, the floor lurched and swayed under his feet. The slipping of the underpinning below rumbled up through the undetermined floors.

Was he faint or dizzy? Was it part of the dreamy afternoon? He put his hands in front of him and stepped back, and looked up wildly. "No! No!"

The men poised stricken. Their throats wanted to cry out and scream but didn't dare. For a moment they were a petrified and straining pageant. Then the bottom of their world gave way. The building shuddered violently, her supports burst with the crackling slap of wooden gunfire. The floor vomited upward. Geremio clutched at the air and shrieked agonizingly. "Brothers, what have we done? Ahhhh-h children of ours!" With the speed of light, balance went sickeningly awry and frozen men went flying explosively. Job tore down upon them madly. Walls, floors, beams became whirling, solid, splintering waves crashing with detonations that ground man and material in bonds of death.

The strongly shaped body that slept with Annunziata nights and was perfect in all the limitless physical quantities, thudded as a worthless sack amongst the giant debris that crushed fragile flesh and bone with centrifugal intensity.

Darkness blotted out his terror and the resistless form twisted, catapulted insanely in its directionless flight, and shot down neatly and deliberately between the empty wooden forms of a foundation wall pilaster in upright position, his blue swollen face pressed against the form and his arms outstretched, caught securely through the meat by the thin round bars of reinforcing steel.

The huge concrete hopper that was sustained by an independent structure of thick timber, wavered a breath or so, its heavy concrete rolling uneasily until a great sixteen-inch wall caught it squarely with all the terrific verdict of its dead weight and impelled it downward through joists, beams and masonry until it stopped short, arrested by two girders, an arm's length above Geremio's head; the gray concrete gushing from the hopper mouth, and sealing up the mute figure.

Giacomo had been thrown clear of the building and dropped six floors to the street gutter, where he lay writhing.

The Lean had evinced no emotion. When the walls descended, he did not move. He lowered his head. One minute later he was hanging in mid-air, his chin on his chest, his eyes tearing loose from their sockets, a green foam bubbling from his mouth and his body spasming, suspended by the shreds left of his mashed arms pinned between a wall and a girder.

A two-by-four hooked little Joe Chiappa up under the back of his jumper and swung him around in a circle to meet a careening I-beam. In the flash that he lifted his frozen cherubic face, its shearing edge sliced through the top of his skull.

When Snoutnose cried beseechingly, "Saint Michael!" blackness enveloped him. He came to in a world of horror. A steady stream, warm, thick, and sickening as hot wine bathed his face and clogged his nose, mouth, and eyes. The nauseous syrup that pumped over his face, clotted his mustache red and drained into his mouth. He gulped for air, and swallowed the rich liquid scarlet. As he breathed, the pain shocked him to oppressive semi-consciousness. The air was wormingly alive with cries, screams, moans and dust, and his crushed chest seared him with a thousand fires. He couldn't see, nor breathe enough to cry. His right hand moved to his face and wiped at the gelatinizing substance, but it kept coming on, and a heart-breaking moan wavered about him, not far. He wiped his eyes in subconscious despair. Where was he? What kind of a dream was he having? Perhaps he wouldn't wake up in time for work, and then what? But how queer; his stomach beating him, his chest on fire, he sees nothing but dull red, only one hand moving about, and a moaning in his face!

The sound and clamor of the rescue squads called to him from far off.

Ah, yes, he's dreaming in bed, and far out in the streets, engines are going to a fire. Oh poor devils! Suppose his house were on fire? With the children scattered about in the rooms he could not remember! He must do his utmost to break out of this dream! He's swimming under water, not able to raise his head and get to the air. He must get back to consciousness to save his children!

He swam frantically with his one right hand, and then felt a face beneath its touch. A face! It's Angelina alongside of him! Thank God, he's awake! He tapped her face. It moved. It felt cold, bristly, and wet. "It moves so. What is this?" His fingers slithered about grisly sharp bones and in a gluey, stringy, hollow mass, yielding as wet macaroni. Gray light brought sight, and hysteria punctured his heart. A girder lay across his chest, his right hand clutched a grotesque human mask, and suspended almost on him of him was the twitching, faceless body of Joe Chiappa. Vincenzo fainted with an inarticulate sigh. His fingers loosed and the bodyless-headless face dropped and fitted to the side of his face while the drippings above came slower and slower.

The rescue men cleaved grimly with pick and axe.

Geremio came to with a start . . . far from their efforts. His brain told him instantly what had happened and where he was. He shouted wildly. "Save me! Save me! I'm being buried alive!"

He paused exhausted. His genitals convulsed. The cold steel rod upon which they were impaled, froze his spine. He shouted louder and louder. "Save me! I am hurt badly! I can be saved I can—save me before it's too late!" But the cries went no farther than his own ears. The icy wet concrete reached his chin. His heart appalled. "In a few seconds I will be entombed. If I can only breathe, they will reach me. Surely, they will!" His face was quickly covered, its flesh yielding to the solid sharp-cut stones. "Air! Air!" screamed his lungs as he was completely sealed. Savagely, he bit into the wooden form pressed upon his mouth. An eight of an inch of its surface splintered off. Oh, if he could only hold out long enough to bite even the smallest hole through to air! He must! There can be no other way! He is responsible for his family! He cannot leave them like this! He didn't want to die! This could not be the answer to life! He had bitten half way through when his teeth snapped off to the gums in the uneven conflict. The pressure of the concrete was such, and its effectiveness so thorough, that the wooden splinters, stumps of teeth, and blood never left the choking mouth.

Why couldn't he go any farther?

Air! Quick! He dug his lower jaw into the little hollowed space and gnashed in choking agonized fury. "Why doesn't it go through? Mother of Christ, why doesn't it give? Can there be a notch, or two-by-four stud behind it? Sweet Jesu! No! No! Make it give. . . . Air! Air!"

He pushed the bone-bare jaw maniacally; it splintered, cracked, and a jagged fleshless edge cut through the form, opening a small hole to air. With a desperate burst the lung-prisoned air blew an opening through the shredded mouth and whistled back greedily a gasp of fresh air. He tried to breathe, but it was impossible. The heavy concrete was settling immutably and its rich cement-laden grout ran into his pierced face. His lungs would not expand and were crushing in tighter and tighter under the settling concrete.

"Mother mine—mother of Jesu-Annunziata—children of mine—dear, dear, for mercy, Jesu-Giuseppe e' Maria," his blue foamed tongue called. It then distorted in a shuddering coil and mad blood vomited forth. Chills and fire played through him and his tortured tongue stuttered, "Mercy, blessed Father—salvation, most kind Father—Savior—Savior of His children help me—adored Savior —I kiss Your feet eternally—you are my Lord—there is but one God—you are my God of infinite mercy—Hail Mary divine Virgin—our Father Who art in heaven hallowed be Thy—name—our Father—my—my Father," and the agony excruciated with never-ending mount, "our Father—Jeus, Jesu, soon Jesu, hurry dear Jesu Jesu! Je-sssu. . . !" His mangled voice trebeled hideously, and hung in jerky whimperings.

The unfeeling concrete was drying fast, and shrinking into monolithic density. The pressure temporarily desensitized sensation; leaving him petrified, numb, and substanceless. Only the brain remained miraculously alive.

"Can this be death? It is all too strangely clear. I see nothing nor feel nothing, my body and senses are no more, my mind speaks as it never did before. Am I or am I not Geremio? But I am Geremio! Can I be in the other world? I never was in any other world except the one I knew of; that of toil, hardship, prayer . . . of my wife who awaits with child for me, of my children and the first home I was to own. Where do I begin in this world? Where do I leave off? Why? I recall only a baffled life of cruelty from every direction. And hope was always as painful as fear, the fear of displeasing, displeasing the people and ideas whom I could never understand; laws, policemen, priests, bosses, and a rag with colors waving on a stick. I never did anything to these things. But what have I done with my life? Yes, my life! No one else's! Mine—mine—MINE—Geremio! It is clear. I was born hungry, and have always been hungry for freedom—life! I married and ran away to America so as not to kill and be killed in Tripoli for things they call, 'God and Country.' I've never known the freedom I wanted in my heart. There was always an arm upraised to hit at me. What have I done to them? I did not want to make them toil for me. I did not raise my arm to them. In my life I could never breathe, and now without air, my mind breathes clearly for me. Wait! There has been a terrible mistake! A cruel crime! The world is not right! Murderers! Thieves! You have hurt me and my kind, and have taken my life from me! I have long felt it—yes, yes, yes, they have cheated me with flags, signs and fear. . . . I say you can't take my life! I want to live! My life! To tell the cheated to rise and fight! Vincenz! Chiappa! Nick! Men! Do you hear me? We must follow the desires within us for the world has been taken from us; we, who made the world! Life!"

Feeling returned to the destroyed form.

"Ahhh-h, I am not dead yet. I knew it—you have not done with me. Torture away! I cannot believe you, God and Country, no longer!" His body was fast breaking under the concrete's closing wrack. Blood vessels burst like mashed flower stems. He screamed. "Show yourself now, Jesu! Now is the time! Save me! Why don't you come! Are you there! I cannot stand it—ohhh, why do you let it happen—it is bestial—where are you! Hurry, hurry, hurry! You do not come! You make me suffer, and what have I done! Come, come—come now—now save me, save me now! Now, now, now! If you are God, save me!"

The stricken blood surged through a weltering maze of useless pipes and exploded forth from his squelched eyes and formless nose, ears and mouth, seeking life in the indifferent stone.

"Aie—aie, aie—devils and Saints—beasts! Where are you—quick, quick, it is death and I am cheated—cheat—ed! Do you hear, you whoring bastards who own the world? Ohhh-ohhhh aie-aie—hahahaha!" His bones cracked mutely and his sanity went sailing distorted in the limbo of the subconscious.

With the throbbing tones of an organ in the hollow background, the fighting brain disintegrated and the memories of a baffled lifetime sought outlet.

He moaned the simple songs of barefoot childhood, scenes flashed desperately on and off in disassociated reflex, and words and parts of words came pitifully high and low from his inaudible lips, the hysterical mind sang cringingly and breathlessly, "Jesu my Lord my God my all Jesu my Lord my God my all Jesu my Lord my God my all Jesu my Lord my God my all," and on as the whirling tempo screamed now far, now near, and came in soul-sickening waves as the concrete slowly contracted and squeezed his skull out of shape.

LELAND STOWE

←——————————————————————————————→

What's Wrong with Our Women?

I GIVE YOU: the American woman." My friend Jacques raised his glass, pausing just enough to emphasize the slight touch of arsenic in his voice. He smiled a double-edged smile, and then added with just a shade more emphasis: "You can have her."

"But, Jacques," I protested. "But really, Jacques. The best-looking woman in the world—the most modern—the most intelligent. The most beautiful legs—the best figure. Why, you Europeans are the first to admit it."

"I know," said Jacques. "I know. We're the first to be fascinated—and, after a little experience, the first to get cured. Of course your women have wonderful figures. Of course they look superb—providing one doesn't look too closely, you understand. But let's be fair. As a novelty, the American woman is incomparable. For a brief flirtation, or perhaps for a week-end excursion, she has much charm. She can be amusing and decorative. All that is quite evident. But don't take her seriously. You mustn't make that mistake. Your women, they are much too spoiled. Marry one of them? No, thanks. You can have them."

One thing about Jacques. He had not merely sampled the wine; he was a connoisseur of it. Yet he was announcing his withdrawal from competition on this side of the Atlantic. For observant, cosmopolitan males, that has become a pretty common occurrence. Our renowned American Eve may still boast of a rather fabulous collection of superlatives, but a lot of the lure and polish seem to have vanished from her original apple. In more discerning masculine circles today, men constantly conduct a sort of unofficial, nonstop Gallup poll on the relative merits of women. And our star-spangled contestant has come a cropper. Even though she is generally recognized as the most glamorous of the world's women, her rating in this quality poll has been declining steadily for a number of years. Maybe men are getting around more, and getting a bit more perceptive as they get around. Anyhow, the more that men get around (outside the U.S.A. as well as in it), the less importance they attach to the good looks and other superficial assets of American women.

A famous French masculine film star, sailing for home after two years in Hollywood, exclaimed with unconcealed relief: "At last! At last I shall have the pleasure of being together with a *homely* woman." His sardonic comment obviously intimated his anxiety to get somewhere where women are chiefly interesting for considerably more than their looks. There are, it seems, many different ways for women to be appealing.

Of course, the American woman thinks of herself as "different." She glories in her difference. America's Eve has been indiscriminately praised and pampered by her men ever since she first became conscious that she was developing curves where females benefit by them. Our enraptured Adams have showered their attentions upon her and made her the most ballyhooed female in the world. In the process, they have hoisted her on a pedestal—from which it is every male's privilege to try to bribe her into sneaking off, once in a while. Our Eve has scarcely needed to polish her apple. Any guy, she thinks, is a cinch to take a bite, if he gets half a chance.

It's doubtful whether any other nation's women have ever been so idolized. The first objective of the average young American male is to corral a personal Eve for his private pedestal. That not having been too difficult, the bewitched and bedazzled captor-turned-captive waves his hand toward the stunning creature on her elevated perch and exclaims: "There she is—our American woman! There's nothing like her in the world. Venus di Milo couldn't hold a candle to her. Isn't she wonderful?"

Being American, naturally she has to be wonderful.

And, admittedly, she does look the part. On a pedestal, I mean.

But our American woman can't stay on a pedestal all the time. She's got too much vitality, too many ideas, and too many wants. Being a dream girl—a symbol of the ultimate in womanhood—can get monotonous, both for her and the fellow who worships her. After all, except for the art-lovers, who in hell is interested in a woman on a pedestal? America's Eve is an extremely practical female. None, certainly, has done any better for herself. Whatever the altitude of her symbolic perch, you will notice that she always keeps her feet quite solidly on the ground. Everyone admits that she is well worth looking at. Enough, then, of dream-girl concepts. Let's look at her as a woman.

A clinical, down-to-earth inspection of America's Eve is long overdue. What Mr. Average American still does not perceive about his native-grown "deadlier of the species" is little short of astonishing. If few women care to be seen without their make-up on, most American men are even more anxious to preserve their illusions. In their minds, apparently, the American woman is—*American*. What more need be said? Yet there does exist a serious, sociological need to get a much more balanced and rounded assortment of facts about her—especially since she's becoming, as I've pointed out, the subject of increasing criticism.

During twenty years as a foreign correspondent, I've lived and traveled on five continents. I've naturally got in the habit of comparing men and women of other nationalities with our own; and I've come to some interesting conclusions. One of them is that my friend Jacques knows what he's talking about. Professional experts and amateur globe-trotters agree our Eve is neither all she thinks she is nor much that American men assume she is. Compared with her overseas sisters, she doesn't, they find, score as many top points as might be expected. She has become the victim of too much ballyhoo. The pedestal pose, encouraged by her men, has thrown her out of focus. In short, she has been looked at too much—but *looked into* far too little. You can't blame Eve for that. It's the American Adams who cling to their rose-tinted spectacles.

At this point, gentlemen, can you take it?

Kindly sit on your emotions. Try to relax into the judicious mood of lordly males who are accustomed to a calm weighing of evidence. Bear in mind that objectivity was never more necessary. Dismiss the personal, and seek the common denominator. For present purposes, you are entitled to make any exceptions you choose. Here, I am concerned only with what some regard as the average characteristics of the supposedly average American woman, since there's no way of making an investigation of our women except in terms of the majority of their sex. And let's rule out patriotic prejudice. This is to be no dance of adoration around a symbolic pedestal. It's a quest for facts. Let's begin, then, with a simple question—a question so simple that Mr. Average American rarely asks it:

What are our women like?

Almost everyone knows the obvious half of the answer. Certain orchids unquestionably belong to America's Eve, and there's astonishingly little disagreement about them. By something approaching general consent, she is described as:

The best-looking woman in the world.

The most modern woman in the world.

Among the world's best-dressed women.

Also, she has a remarkably fine figure; she is exceptionally intelligent; she is the most independent and free of women anywhere; she has more power over her men than do women of other nations; she enjoys the most privileges of any women anywhere; on the whole, she has more legal rights than women elsewhere; she has more initiative than most; and, finally, she owns more property and wealth—both collectively and individually—than women have held in any other country, at any time in history.

That's as brilliant an assortment of orchids as anybody's Eve might hope to win. In addition, the American woman wears this handsome corsage with befitting gestures and with few intimations of embarrassment. If false modesty ill befits a queen, she prefers to act the queen. But the trouble is that our Eve's orchids, however unique, do not begin to supply a complete answer to what—exactly—she is like. Probing, cold-blooded realists, not overly impressed by her flattering corsage, are likely to unwrap a supplementary bonquet for the American woman; and the bouquet looks suspiciously like poison ivy. Each branch bears a precise label, something like this: "Our woman is also—"

The most spoiled and self-centered woman in the world.

The most aggressive.

The most unhappy and dissatisfied.

She is less feminine and less interested in men than are women of other lands;

she is less interested in husband, home and family; she is the world's most expensive woman; she is more restless and bored than other women; she is, in general, less spiritual and she possesses less individuality.

"Who says so?" roars a chorus of indignant American males.

Please, gentlemen. Your seats! These are the conclusions of a distinguished array of psychologists, psychoanalysts, sociologists, and such. Lined up behind them are most foreigners (male or female) who have spent much time in the United States—and also an increasing number of traveled Americans. You may prefer to dismiss the amateurs; but the experts are specialists. Experience has made them prudent fellows: they shy clear of public forums where they might be lynched. But the scientific urge compels them to examine all kinds of evidence and to publish the results of their researches in such weighty volumes as *Modern Woman: The Lost Sex*. What they reveal may be embarrassing or annoying, but you can't ignore or underestimate their accumulated facts. The specialists can't be accused of malice. Nor can their findings be waved lightly aside.

On the evidence, one fundamental fact should be plain. Something pretty awful has happened to our good-looking, head-strong, self-satisfied American Eve. She has fallen off her pedestal!

As yet, she herself and a host of her unanalytical admirers may be only dimly aware of it, but the question has long ceased to be whether something, just possibly, might be amiss with her. Today the question is phrased only in one way: "What's wrong with our women?" When that becomes a dominant query, danger signals are flying, helter-skelter, all over our social landscape.

Mr. Average American is an incurable idealist about women—especially about "our women." But if millions of American Adams are still unprepared for the realists' candid portrait, millions of our Eves are caught in a more desperate plight. Suppose their men begin to open their eyes, for a change? Suppose they begin to look closely and listen attentively? Obviously, women can't change years of habit in a few weeks or months. What, if anything, could be expected to blast American females out of being themselves?

Well, it has happened—if only to a degree. For a brief period during the war, America's Eves succumbed to a revolutionary change, both out-of-character and significant. Suddenly they lost their long-established habit of playing "hard to get." When I came home from China, Burma, India, and Russia at the end of 1942, I could scarcely believe my eyes. In one year of war an amazing thing had happened. American women, right out in public, were walking the main streets of our cities *holding hands* with their men in uniform. In restaurants, on trains, almost anywhere, you saw American Eves—completely off pedestal, publicly showing affection for their husbands or boy friends. The entire American scene had taken on an unaccustomed warmth and humanness. The change was so tremendous that it was wryly amusing—but also decidedly ironic. Never, before or since, have I seen American women demonstrate *en masse* so unabashed an interest in mere man.

Of course they reverted swiftly to normal, once the war ended. Within a year after V-J Day, Eve was back in the saddle, pushing toward whatever she thought she wanted and dragging her unprotesting male after her. In most foreign countries women do not need a national draft act or mobilization to prompt or excuse a natural show of affection toward the men of their choice. But it will probably take another world war to blast the American woman into treating her man, publicly, as anything more than a convenient door opener or check payer.

The war had another upsetting effect on American women. And, from their viewpoint, this one was truly menacing. Millions of American men got a once-in-a-lifetime opportunity to compare their women with those of other nations. For the first time in U. S. history, the American female encountered large-scale competition from foreign women; and the competition proved almost as deadly as it was real. If vast numbers of our men had been kept overseas for another two or three years, heaven knows what inferiority complexes and neuroses America's vaunted Eves might have developed. They were caught completely off base. They were thrown on the defensive—a situation that simply wasn't in their book. Most alarmingly, a very considerable percentage of American males abroad indicated plainly that what they discovered both intrigued and pleased them.

This is where America's Eves began to wobble visibly on their previously unthreatened pedestals. Those foreign creatures were shamelessly without scruples. They gave every evidence that they recognized a good thing when they saw it. As for our boys overseas, whether in Australia, the Orient, the Near East, or Europe, they were pretty well embarked on learning new things about women—or was it more things about a different kind of women?

It wasn't the women of easy virtue who made a lasting impression on them, either. The vast majority of American boys who married foreign girls fell in love with decent, respectable persons—girls or women who represented the average in their country and community. Among the Americans, the percentage of those who were free to marry and *did* marry foreign girls was impressively high. They took the vows with 55,000 British women alone. Tens of thousands more married women from all parts of Europe, the Far East and Australia. The Yankee Lochinvars brought their war brides home with great pride; and most of these supposedly rash ventures appear to be working out very satisfactorily.

"I'll take my dishonorable discharge and get out of my own country if they send my girl back to Italy," declared a corporal recently. When a girl puts a guy in that frame of mind, she must have something. What made so many American youths fall so hard for the women they met overseas? The answer to that question should be highly educational for many of the girls they left behind—and left. Talking about their non-American fiancées, Americans overseas have been heard to make the following remarks:

"You oughta see how my French gal can cook and sew."

"Say, these Australian women are really okay. They're so natural and un-spoiled. They appreciate any little thing you do for them."

"You know—my girl can do everything. Every time I see her, she's fixing my socks or my uniform or something."

"I'll say these women over here are different. Why, they're always asking what you want to do. Imagine that!"

"They don't expect you to spend a lot of money on them. They know how to have a good time."

I remember an Air Force lieutenant, reassigned from England to a special training job in Texas. Somehow he managed to have his English bride join him. "You ought to see how my wife has got our quarters in the barracks fixed up," he told me. "It takes a British girl to make a place cozy with next to nothing. The American wives at camp can't hold a candle to her. Most of them are griping and complaining. They're all jealous of her, too. Betty just buckles down with what she's got, and shows them up. British girls really know how to make a home. For one thing they're not spoiled dolls."

The war-brides' husbands fairly oozed with glowing testimonials. Sex appeal and the mating technique did not seem to be major elements in their happy state of mind—at any rate, not what aroused most comment. One conclusion was inescapable: by and large, these foreign women possessed a lot of qualities that the average American girl apparently lacked, either in toto or to a noticeable degree. You can sum the whole situation up pretty accurately in this fashion: *most women of non-American background and nationality are brought up to please men.* And most males, including Americans, are so egotistical or perverse as to greatly relish being pleased.

Our servicemen merely discovered overseas what almost all cosmopolitan, traveled observers have long known. They learned that, on the average, the women of other continents are considerably more interested than American girls—1) in men as men; 2) in their own personal lifetime jobs of being suc-cessful as women, wives, and homemakers. As a result, foreign women know a good deal more about cooking, sewing, and housekeeping than the cocksure, somewhat willful, and much more self-promoting American women do. The overseas woman attaches at least as much importance to what she can do in her feminine sphere as she does to how she looks. She grows up with an acute consciousness that her chief asset is her femininity; the more intrinsically fem-inine she is, the better. In her different civilization, culture and code, it is an accepted axiom that the woman demands less and gives more. She regards this as natural. All she needs to do is to understand that her own feminine weapons are unbeatable. The more she sticks to her own ground, to her own weapons and instincts, the greater are her prospects of genuine fulfillment as a woman. These things are ABC's for most women throughout the world—except in the United States.

The most important differences between foreign and American women are those you hear the least about. There's a popular idea that foreign women excel in such items as greater vivacity of expression, more exotic complexions, and more zestful performance after the lights are out. All of which is sometimes true. But to assume that these are their chief distinctions is unsophisticated, inaccurate, and beside the point.

The basic ways in which a majority of foreign women differ from Americans are—1) in their attitude and mentality; 2) in their acceptance of woman's position in society; 3) in their essential femininity. And so America's Eve is left in a rather lonely place of her own. Why, she wonders, do these foreign women rate so highly anyhow? They are not nearly so independent. They do not have so many varieties of careers. Their lives are narrower. On the whole they possess far fewer legal rights. Even if they give more, they get less—so far as the eye can see. Yet the experts now hand these women a surprising number of laurels— and at the expense of the very females who have collected more fancy adjectives and adulation than any others on earth.

At this critical point, many American pedestal-worshippers are doubtless being blown off their chairs by their patriotic emotions. These are mere generalities, they say wrathfully. If the psychologists and the rest of these so-called, self-designated "experts" wish to level a wholesale indictment against our American women, let them be specific. What facts can they produce to back up their unchivalrous, uncalled-for accusations? Probably most of these professional "detractors of American womanhood" are frustrated intellectuals, namby-pamby professors, or shameless ex-patriots. Let them put up, or shut up!

Which is reason enough to get down to cases. So let's consider the main charges that the realists bring against America's Eve when they attempt to balance the picture and put her in perspective.

1. *Our women, they say, are the most spoiled and self-centered in the world.*

That reminds me of Mary Garden's classical comment: "American women don't worship their men. They merely skin them." (Now really, Mary. Aren't you carrying it to extremes?) Being a reporter by training, I would prefer to let American women speak for themselves. I wonder if you've heard very much of what they've been saying, from coast to coast, for a good many years?

"I just adore Robert Taylor," says Mrs. Smith, "so Bill and I went to the movies."

"Dick really wanted a Buick, but I *had* to have a Packard," explains Mrs. Johnson brightly.

"I can't stand Chinese food. You can go there some other time."

"I've found a wonderful place for our vacation. We always go to the mountains. You know *I* like them much the best."

"And really," says Mrs. Perry (just as if her husband hadn't the remotest connection with the matter), "they offered $30,000 for my house. But of course, *I* wouldn't consider selling it for that."

In the United States, the over-all feminine chant emphasizes the perpendicular pronoun. Our women betray themselves when they talk about what they prefer, what they want, what they've got, or what they are out to get. Listen for a while and you can't escape the impression that it's the men's first obligation to please their women in practically everything—and that this is an operation which should be reversed only under exceptional circumstances. There is no other country in the world where women wait so presumptuously for some male to light their cigarette. And this is the only country where obliging males frequently get not so much as a slight nod for their pains. America's Eve takes most of the daily little courtesies as her imperial due. She parades her feminine priorities and often ignores the existence of any masculine priorities. In general, she exudes a deeply entrenched conviction that woman comes first and goes through life much as she goes through a doorway. No women are more waited upon. Yet no women anywhere are more indifferent or oblivious to what reciprocal graciousness can mean.

2. *Our women are exceptionally aggressive.*

Spend an hour or two trying to get near bargain counters in your local department store. Watch the "lady" shoppers pushing into commuters' trains or city busses. Observe how they capitalize on the "women-first" tradition—in railroad stations, elevators, or anywhere. In American ticket lines or queues, notice how, almost invariably, it is some female who pushes callously ahead of dozens of waiting people.

In the New York subway the other day a determined Amazon nearly knocked a man off his feet as she barged into a train. In any foreign city, the woman would have excused herself graciously—certainly, if she were as well-dressed as this female was. Did she turn around? Did she beg the fellow's pardon? Not she! For all she cared, the man she had crashed into might have been a bag of meal. The venom in his eyes was really something. It is only in America that it is woman's special prerogative to be rude. We have more female pushers, shovers, grabbers, and go-getters than any other section of the globe. There remain only a minority of exceptions, ladies who are nobly aware that "aggressive" is not synonymous with "lady-like." But the only place for our average Eve is out in front. She gets there.

3. *Our women are the most unhappy and dissatisfied.*

The realists waste few words on this question. "Look at their faces," they say.

That's pertinent advice. The faces of American women tell a great deal. They merit much study and more reflection. Negatively, they are very interesting. I say negatively because our women's faces, on the average, are unusual for what they do *not* have rather than for what they have. In general, they lack mobility and expression. They also lack the range of individuality that differentiates the features of most women abroad. In the American woman's countenance, as in her voice, it is exceptional to discern something truly distinctive, a real personality. And her face too often mirrors discontent; in repose it is likely to be metallic, without inner light.

When American women are alone and not called upon to put on a social act, their faces reveal a great deal. Traces of contentment, let alone happiness, are rarely to be observed. But the evidence of widespread unhappiness among our women is not only written in their faces. They themselves are the first to admit the depths of their discontent. By the frankness of their confessions they continue to appall and alarm psychiatrists and other doctors. In no other country do women reveal their spiritual uneasiness so publicly as in the United States. By scores of thousands, their letters are published yearly in "advice to the love-lorn" columns and read by millions of other women—who presumably are interested for similar reasons. Dorothy Dix, Beatrice Fairfax, and many other confessional columnists are assured of handsome lifelong incomes simply because such a great percentage of their fellow countrywomen are excessively unhappy.

An eminent psychiatrist, backed by many of his colleagues, says American women "have gone *too far too fast* . . . They haven't developed emotionally in keeping with their economic and social advancement." Pearl Buck offers an extremely perceptive observation. She says: "I have never seen in any country . . . such unsatisfactory relationship between men and women as there is in America. No, not even in Japan, where women as a class are depressed as women never were."

That's straight from the shoulder, and fundamental. The American woman may enjoy remarkable privileges and exceptional power. Nevertheless, and by and large, she confesses herself to be spiritually and emotionally adrift. In her actions, as in her face, she reveals an unparalleled inner hunger and uncertainty.

4. *Our women are less feminine and less interested in men.*

It's notorious that women "wear the pants" in the average American household. But it's equally evident that the trousers chafe them sorely. America's Eve is the undisputed boss in nine out of ten of our homes, and equally so in virtually all our elementary and secondary schools. European observers have no doubt (and neither should any half-conscious American male) that women run almost everything in the U.S.A.—except, occasionally, their husband's offices. That demonstrates the pronounced ability of American women. But it also greatly reduces the field in which men are essential to them. American husbands intrude upon or share in only a minor portion of their wives' major activities. Maybe this makes it inevitable that our women show a limited and minimum interest in men.

As a minor test, try this one. Walk along Fifth Avenue or any comparable thoroughfare in any larger American city at any time between mid-morning and nightfall. Watch the steady procession of women. The majority of them would not see Clark Gable or the handsomest man in the world if he passed by, or even if they almost bumped into him. It couldn't happen in Stockholm, Paris, Rome, Rio—or Geneva, Switzerland. Not that "honest" women in other lands actually invite sidewalk flirtations. They don't. But wherever foreign women go, they carry with them a subtle awareness of men as men. They are too feminine to be capable of spending several hours in public places without occasionally noticing a man who has some quality that, however fleetingly, focuses their attention. In similar circumstances, most American women simply do not see men at all. They have more important things to think about. Men are reserved for certain times and places—a matter of the women's own convenience. At other times and places, men do not, as a rule, exist for them. In no other part of the world have I observed this phenomenon to a like degree.

This brings up a paradox. Certainly no other women spend such enormous amounts of money on beauty treatments, coiffeurs, "uplifts," and other paraphernalia to enhance either appearance or sex appeal. You might think this expensive ritual demonstrates the American woman's interest in males. In males as a convenience to have around? Or in males *as such?* Or is she chiefly interested in attracting attention and admiration for herself? I leave it to you to figure out the percentages on this delicate subject. But this much is sure: femininity is a quality which cannot be measured by what a woman puts on. Femininity is what any woman has got on the inside—what she *is.* Could it, by any chance, be true that the more feminine a woman is on the inside, the less she feels the need of excessive indulgence in make-up rituals, "slenderizers," and innumerable other "come-on" devices? Could it be that when women strain so desperately to create a romantic appeal they admit subconsciously that what femininity they possess rather badly needs bolstering? . . . I'm just a chap who looks—and wonders.

Most of the world's women have precious little cash to spend on beauty treatments. But there's no discernible shortage of femininity among them. If they believe in enhancing their appearance, they seldom go to the American extremes. Where sex appeal is concerned, they do not confuse artificial accessories with the fundamental article. As for being feminine, it remains for America's Eve to assume that what goes on the outside can be equivalent to the quality of femininity itself. Judged by their efforts and actions, our women desperately want to be more feminine. They gild the lily—and how! But if they were not essentially less feminine than they ought to be, would they feel the need of making such efforts to get that way?

Femininity also means staying on women's ground. This is the last thing most of our women seem satisfied to do—and the last thing many of their men will let them do. Our superindustrialized civilization demands that women compete with men in many of their own fields. They have done it, aggressively and with ability. More and more they have had to compete with men—as a result of which they have taken to aping men and acting like men. In the process, they have become increasingly less feminine—in their habits and actions, in their minds and instincts. No cosmetic house will ever invent a formula or penetrating cream that will come within a billion light-years of the seat of the dislocation.

5. *Our women are less interested in their husbands, home, and family.*

Why waste space on the obvious? Close to 100,000 American war grooms have already brought home the vital evidence and testimony. They fell for foreign women chiefly because these unfamiliar creatures were surprisingly interested in woman's job and woman's sphere.

6. *Our women are excessively expensive.*

When foreign men start squiring almost any star-spangled Eve, they reach this conclusion promptly. In our near-matriarchy, the female customarily does the choosing, and she is rarely reticent about her tastes and preferences. After a brief exposure to our female tourists in prewar Paris, many a European ruefully made the comment that it's largely the American woman's fault she is losing her power over men. The idea is getting around that women want a lot for what they give. When our boys went overseas, they discovered the same thing, by comparison.

Of course many of our women manage to keep their demands within reason. But the notion has nevertheless got around that the American feminine article is, on the whole, about the most expensive known to man. It isn't merely because of what she expects for entertainment and clothes. It's because of *what she expects*—namely, plenty. Maybe masculine overindulgence and false pride are partly responsible. It's human for the girls to take what they can get. The emphasis on material things and comforts in our society is certainly another factor. In any case, the upshot is that America's Eves are pretty demanding darlings. Far more hard cash is spent on their material comfort, adornment, pleasure or whims than on those of any other women. American men make a cult of encouraging this situation. Why blame the women? Here we merely recognize a fact.

7. *Our women are more restless and bored.*

In general, they have more leisure than women elsewhere. Time-saving inventions, from electric washing machines to God knows what, have conspired to leave an increasing vacuum in the daily routine of most of our middle- or upper-middle-class women. A great many have gone into women's clubs and other social or charitable activities. Even so, they often have more time than they know what to do with, or are bored with the uses to which they put their time.

This may apply specifically only to a minority. But this minority sets the pattern and exercises an influence much beyond its numerical size. Man or woman, we Americans are restless animals. But the restlessness of American women, according to psychiatrists, goes much deeper than that of men. America's average Eve seems always to be seeking desperately, but not finding. She is the antithesis of the relatively fulfilled, inwardly secure woman who exists in impressive numbers in most foreign lands.

8. *Our women are less spiritual and have less individuality.*

Here again perhaps our assembly-line civilization is largely to blame. Something is criminally responsible for the terrible standardization of American women. Anyone with a slight degree of artistic discrimination must be aware of the deplorable sameness of females from one end of the U. S. A. to the other. The majority of our women look the same, dress the same, act the same, and sound much the same. Any real incentive to make new acquaintanceships with women is lower in this country, I believe, than in any other. An intelligent Chinese writer, Helena Kuo, says (in *The American Mercury*):

"American city women, with their standardized faces, legs, shoes, and figures, seem so uniform that we of the East cannot recognize them individually . . . They seem to come off the production line so rapidly that they look like members of a Rockette dancing chorus."

In most countries women aspire to be distinctive, in personality and appearance. The opposite is true here. America's Eve has the naïve idea that she should ape here sister-competitors as much as possible. The fashion magazines, the beauticians, and Hollywood exert a diabolical influence. The combined result levels down our women of all ages. The conception of a woman *being herself* is regarded as outlandish. Only the most discriminating and strong-minded succeed in resisting terrific pressures toward conformity.

If our women are not even a fraction as interesting as they could be and ought to be, they themselves are largely to blame. They refuse to grasp a simple fact—*when a woman is different she has really got something.* The element of the unsuspected, the unlike, or the mysterious is totally absent in most American women. If you meet them in Boston or Atlanta, the odds are that you've already met them in Chicago or Seattle. Whatever the labels on the bottle, the wine is much the same. What a wasted opportunity! What a neglect of fine material!

With the loss of her individuality, the American woman inevitably loses a certain indefinable spiritual spark as well. For some reason, the humble American waitress is a notable exception. But good repartee, the skillful art of fencing with words, is too rarely the forte of the American Eve. Perhaps our civilization overstresses the exterior and sadly neglects what is interior and personal. Individuality comes from the inside and feeds on spiritual fires within. But this, precisely, is what most of our women seem determined to have as little of as possible. It is our great loss as well as theirs.

By this time it must be apparent that the orchids collected by our American Eves do not stand up well under a Klieg-light inspection. The glamour and the beautiful (standardized) figure may suit her posture well, but they are only one aspect of a rounded-out composite portrait. The American woman's attention and efforts have been recklessly concentrated on appearances—on what she can get, have, or use—on externals. For far too many years, she has occupied herself feverishly with almost everything except those things that would most develop her femininity and would give her the deepest satisfactions that women can have. It is small wonder that, on the average, she gives every indication of not knowing what she wants. How can she know what she wants, when, in our mechanized and extroverted civilization, she does not know where she belongs?

Have American men been of any real, intuitive help to her in her confusion, perplexity, and frustration? Far from it. They keep pushing her deeper into the squirrel cage of her quandary. If there is one song that all the women in the United States of America ought to sing in chorus, it is this: "You made me what I am today—I hope you're satisfied."*

The odd thing is that an amazing proportion of America's males actually seem to be fairly well satisfied. It doesn't make sense, and it's no tribute either to their awareness or their intelligence. After all, the specialists agree that there is a good deal which has gone haywire in our women; and the reason isn't simply that those cantankerous, feminine creatures really wanted to go haywire. They never could have succeeded without a lot of unconscious or intentional help from their men.

But that's another problem, and it requires another investigation. If you don't know what or how much has gone wrong with your women, Mr. Average American, it's time to take a long look in your mirror—whether before or after shaving is of minor importance.

HELEN LAWRENSON

Latins Are Lousy Lovers

First of all, I want to make it clear that this is not the wail of a downhearted frail who was scorned and is therefore taking a cad's revenge. The following observations are not based on personal experience alone, but on the testimony of other disillusioned damsels, as well. I have listened to their plaints in ladies' rooms, night clubs, tearooms, boudoirs, on boats and on beaches; and I wish to acknowledge my indebtedness to those unwept, unhonored and unsung American women who have trusted and Given All in Cuba and Mexico, Central and South America, Spain and Puerto Rico—not to mention various encounters with visiting Latins on their own hearthstones in Ohio, Maine, Mississippi and both Dakotas. I, myself, have just returned from five months in Cuba, where I did a little field work on my own; and I believe that it is high time someone exploded the mythical superiority of Latins as lovers and relegated it to its proper place, along with other half-baked, but quaint, traditions, such as the saying that ashes in your coffee make you drunk, that if you don't save all your baby teeth, your second set will be puppies' teeth, or that if you don't move, the bee won't sting you. (Ah, so you've been caught on that one, too!)

It is a common belief all over the world that Latin men are the best lovers and Americans the worst. With an American flag of washable bunting draped prominently—but with careless grace—around my chest, and balancing an American eagle on my head, I hereby rise to state that this is a hoax. I will not only state it; hell, I will prove it. In order to facilitate matters, let us divide the subject into three parts: The Latin at Large, The Latin at Home, and The Latin in Bed. All right, Miss America, take it away!

THE LATIN AT LARGE

From now on, I will say Cubans, because I have taken a special course in Cubans, but you can substitute Venezuelans or Andalusians or Argentines, because, from what the rest of the girls say, they are practically interchangeable as far as this subject is concerned.

In the first place, they are generally short in stature. When anyone asks you if you want to meet another Cuban, it's customary to say, "All right. Is he over

five foot four?" (She Stoops to Conquer Cubans can be taken physically, therefore, as well as morally and spiritually.) They are not only short; they are thin,
too, with narrow shoulders and wide hips: in other words, like the Flapper
Age trousers—bell-bottomed. Their teeth—if any—are either frayed stumps or
dazzling with gold. They wear straw Kellys too large or too small, badly fitting
suits, and shoes that pinch their feet—and they have little feet. Of course, they
do have nice eyes—that is, when they aren't cross-eyed. Their hair is oily and
usually needs cutting. They spit a great deal. They are always scratching
themselves.

That is the typical Cuban for you. That is, that is what they're like if they
look like Cubans. Most Cubans don't look like Cubans. They look like Germans,
Italians, Swedes, Polacks, and clerks from Yonkers. It makes my heart bleed
to think of the boatloads of hopeful females who go down there every year
on cruises, trusting to find a nation of Cesar Romeros. If they do find one,
the odds are ten to one that he's another American tourist. As one more
disappointed maiden put it, on her return to Manhattan, "The worst
Americans are better than the best Cubans. I mean, the Americans you see
here digging ditches or driving ice wagons or riding in the subways are all
handsomer and better built than the most highly publicized Don Juans in
Havana."

In the second place, although part of their claim to superiority in amorous
dalliance is based on an assumption of gallantry, they are not gallant in a
practical way. They meet you at a bar for cocktails at five-thirty, make violent
love to you—and then go home for dinner. They will meet you afterward and
renew their spirited attack, but for the space of a couple of hours, their mad love
is abated. They appreciate their home cooking, and, of course, foreign young
women cannot be invited—or, at any rate, they aren't—into the sanctity of the
typical Cuban home. They pay you fantastic compliments that no half-wit
would believe, but they never send you flowers or give you presents. I take that
back. A South American gave a girl I know an old coin, and a New York blonde
once got a clock and an Eversharp pencil from a Cuban who said he was en-
slaved by her eyes, that he was blinded by the golden sunshine of her hair,
that he would cut off his right arm for her, in short, that he would die for her.
(They are fond of fancying themselves as impetuous, violent folk, ready to
draw their machetes at the drop of a sombrero.) They are, however, great on
photographs and practically the moment they meet you, will pull out their
pictures, inscribe them passionately, and present them to you, blissfully confident that forever afterward you sleep with their images under your pillow by
night and plastered on to your mirror by day, where you can spend long hours
in adoration.

They are convinced that all American women worship them; and they love
American women because they're so free and easy. With their money, they
forget to add. There are very few who object to acting as amiable escorts to
American girls who foot the bills. In fact, some of them can be said really to

live only during the tourist season, when they emerge like butterflies to meet all incoming ships. The rest of the year, they just languish around, recounting their exploits and saving their strength.

They are good dancers, as a rule, although the belief that every Cuban is a born hoofer is a fallacy. When they are good, they are superlatively so, but there are plenty of them who can step on your feet just as often and just as heavy as the boys back home. They are definitely not good drinkers. A couple of highballs and they are sitting on top of the world. One more, and they slip down in their chairs, practically parallel with the floor. All Latins have trouble with their livers and if they drink too much they get very sick. One Cuban says, "When I drink more than two drinks, my kidneys resent it, and my liver abets them." Their sense of humor expresses itself for the most part in jokes which were thrown out of the Minsky circuit ten years ago. They adore American slang but are always five to ten years behind. (Last winter I met a Cuban who had just caught up with "It's the cat's pajamas!") Anything approaching subtlety will leave them blankfaced and untouched, but the simplest reference to the bathroom and the elimination processes of the digestive tract will plunge them into uncontrollable hysterics. They also appreciate any suggestion of sex, provided it is elementary enough. Judged by their standards, the greatest wits in the world have been the little boys who scribble on fences and the comfort station wall decorators. The national type of joke most prevalent is a charming little game known as the *pega*. It is couched in the form of question and answer and is the ultimate in obscene simplicity. Naturally, examples cannot be given at this time, but the question is frequently something like, "Have you got a few minutes to spare?" And when the victim answers, "Yes, why?"—and they always answer, even though they've been hearing this form of joke daily all their lives, they never seem to catch on)—the answer is, "Well then, do thus and so"—(fill in with any of the dirtier phrases you remember from your childhood.) This will render them incapacitated by laughter for ten minutes.

While the above may seen irrelevant, I believe it to have a bearing on the general subject, since it depicts sidelights on the qualities of the Latin at Large as a companion. And after all, a certain amount of companionship—sometimes known as the preliminaries—is customary before getting down to the brass tacks of *amor*.

THE LATIN AT HOME

In his own home, the Cuban man is absolute king, lord and master. He demands service and he gets it—hand and foot. Although he practically never takes his wife out—and seldom stays home with her—he is insanely jealous and keeps constant tab on her by bribing the servants, tapping the telephone wires, and a general spy system as elaborate as that of the Jesuits. He telephones his home every hour or so as part of the check-up. If his wife says she is going to the hairdresser's, the modiste's or the milliner's, he makes sure to telephone there, too. If she goes to a movie, he runs over and sees the same picture so that he can question her on it during dinner that night. When he stays out all night, he almost never notifies his wife, but if he telephones and says he won't be home, he makes a point of going home within an hour.

The Cuban husband is practically never at home, except for meals. He goes out night after night, to political meetings, the club, poker games, jai-alai games, cock fights, cabarets, dances, parties, dinners, sidewalk cafés—or to visit his mistress—and his wife stays home. Once a month, he may spend an evening at the movies with her; a couple of times a year he takes her to large charity fiestas; and on special occasions, like the Fourth of July or the President's Saint's Day, he may invite her out and buy her a glass of sherry. One man I know married his wife when she was sixteen and has never let her out at night since. She is now thirty-two. She has never even been permitted to go alone in the daytime to do her shopping or to a beauty parlor or to the movies. Although she is the mother of three children, the only person she can go to these places with is her older sister, and then she must travel in a closed automobile, never in a street car or bus, where other men might look at her. Her husband initiated her into this regime immediately after they returned from their honeymoon. Right then, he began leaving her in the house while he went out; and night after night, she used to sit at an upstairs window alone and watch him sitting in a gay party at the sidewalk café across the street. Nor is he an ignorant country yokel. He is a member of Congress; he has traveled in the United States and in Europe; he likes music, dancing and night life; and he is considered worldly and charming by the women he meets outside of his home.

This is by no means an isolated case, although not all Cubans carry the system to such extremes. However, they do not take their wives to night clubs, cabarets or public restaurants. When they go out for a good time—which is about six nights out of the week—their helpmates stay at home. As one man said, "Certainly my wife stays home where she belongs. Furthermore, I never allow her to have girl friends. When she starts to become friendly with another woman— go to the movies with her or to the hairdresser's, right away I forbid her to see her any more. Women together talk and breed trouble. My wife must live for me alone and for what time I can find to give her." Which might be said to be the definitive word on the subject.

THE LATIN IN BED

And now we come to the point of the piece. God knows, the Cuban man spends enough time on the subject of sex. He devotes his life to it. He talks it, dreams it, reads it, sings it, dances it, eats it, sleeps it—does everything but do it. That last is of course not literally true, but it is a fact that they spend far more time in words than in action. Sitting in their offices, rocking on the sidewalk in front of their clubs, drinking at cafés, they talk hour after hour about sex. When the University of Habana had a football team, they used to drive their American coach crazy by sitting in the dressing-room before a game and describing their exploits—play by play—with the girls they took out the night before. A smart American who makes an appointment to discuss business with a Cuban at a café always makes the Cuban sit with his back to the street because if he does not, the Cuban will eye every woman who passes, and, like as not, at a crucial point of the business transaction, will interrupt to make anatomical comments on some pretty who is just going by. They telephone each other at their offices during business hours to describe in minute detail a new conquest. According to them, they always had their first affair at the age of two. This may account for their being all worn out at twenty-three. Makers of aphrodisiacs do a thriving business: Spanish fly, yohimbim, marihuana cigarettes, cocaine, Baume Bengué. (Even the horses at Oriental Park have ginger put under their tails.) You can pick up any Cuban newspaper and see, on the second or third page, right smack in the middle of the news, a big ad—"Men! Let Science help you! Merely a matter of the hormones. Etc., etc."

This lack of masculine energy does not prevent them from talking a great game. They boast of their prowess, their anatomical proportions, and their methods. (To hear them talk of what is known to Drs. Van der Velde, Stopes, *et al.* as the love-play, you'd think they invented it. Certain they are, at least, that it has been revealed to them alone out of all mankind in a sort of divine and mystic annunciation kept secret from the rest of the world.) But if you believe the testimony of their women-folk, when it actually comes to the test, they apparently suffer from tropical amnesia. In other words, they're talkers, not doers.

According to Cuban technique, love is a game of chess. Now it's your move; now it's mine—whoops, I caught you! If I do this, she will do that. If she says that, it means I should do this. They will spend hours figuring out unnecessary progressive steps in an amorous campaign, and when their objective is finally obtained, they are apparently too exhausted by strategy to do much about it. Through the years, they have managed to work out an extraordinarily and elaborately complicated system of sexual attack, which only they know the meaning of; and they are perfectly happy to putter around with this for months at a time, making telephone calls, writing notes, conferring with their friends (they are inveterate gossips and cannot make an amorous move without running off beforehand and afterward to consult with all their male friends), and making a great to-do about symbols and signals and point counter point.

They believe in quantity, not quality, also. Every man has his wife and his mistress of the moment. In addition, he has to find time to attend to the demi-mondaines (dancers, singers, nightclub hostesses or just women about town), the concubines (maids, dance-hall girls, little *achinadas* and *mulaticas*), and to the regular professional prostitutes. (They are great frequenters of houses of ill fame, making their rounds as a matter of course, and Mr. Dewey would have a difficult time in Habana. He certainly would lack the taxpayers' wholehearted support.) Besides this, in each one of these classes of women, he has someone he's working up to the proper pitch of surrender—dropping in to see occasionally, buying a glass of beer for, calling on the telephone—and, also in each class, he has someone he's got marked out to start paying attention to when he gets around to it, or when a vacancy occurs in the regular lists or on the scrub team. You can easily see how all of this keeps him extremely busy— he even has to devote afternoons, and frequently mornings, to it—so that he doesn't find quite so much time for actual practice.

Nevertheless, living in this constant aura of sex, the Cuban grows serenely sure that he is more adept amorously than other men—particularly Americans. In this impenetrable vanity of theirs, they are unlike any other nation. The elderly American, at least, occasionally lets a bit of cynicism slip into his attitude. He admits that the gift of a diamond bracelet, a mink coat or a car may possibly have influenced the young lady of his choice, but the Cuban, be he ever so ancient, fat, bald and wrinkled, is perpetually convinced that his personal charms alone are what render him irresistible. To see him is to love him, he reasons.

They are a curious mixture of Spanish tradition, American imitation and insular limitation. This explains why they never catch on to themselves. I think the reason for their initial vanity is that, early in life, they start frequenting what, for want of a better word, are known as fancy women. (I know a better word but I won't use it here.) These women, for obvious business reasons, flatter them extravagantly, make them think they're superlative lovers—and the men never find out otherwise. I suppose no one ever has the heart to tell them. And everything with which they come in contact the rest of their lives serves to perpetuate the myth: the books they read, the songs they sing, the testimony of their fellow countrymen—who are, as I have said, anything but reticent—and the continued plaudits of their womenfolk. One case I heard of—submitted by a fellow field worker—had to do with a noted Casanova, famed not only in Habana but as far as Pinar del Rio for his amatory skill. When subjected to an impartial test, it turned out that his routine could be classified as Amateur College Boy, Class G-6, but that immediately on completion of said simple routine, he sat up in bed and exclaimed delightedly, "Am I not wonderful? Am I not wonderful?"

In short, as the result of an extensive female survey, my conclusions are that offhand I would swap you five Cubans, three South Americans and two slightly used Spaniards for one good Irish-American any night in the week. I feel sorry for the women of Cuba. Theirs not to reason why, theirs but to try and try.

I am hereby offering a plea for Latin womanhood. Too long have they suffered under adversity's rod. Any upstanding American man who wants to do a humane deed knows where to go now. My advice to the American male is, Go South, young man, Go South. It's open season for putting the horns on Cuban manhood. They'll look like a race of moose when you get through with them, and you will have served to remove a national stigma and explode a world-wide myth.

If this all sounds like an embittered and chauvinistic diatribe against Cubans, I can only say that I did not mean it as such. It is merely that I happen to like American men, and I have been aroused to a high pitch of indignation by hearing them constantly maligned. You cannot spend an hour in the society of any Latin male without hearing what bad lovers Americans are. "Of course, American men know nothing of sex!" is the theme song of the tropics. I thought that our own home boys might like to know that they've been severely underrated and that they no longer need tremble before foreign competition in the most popular of all indoor sports.

T. K. BROWN III

The Valley of the Shadow

A LADY in a white gown took his hand and led him past the dragon. She was a kind lady.

"I never thought I'd see a real dragon," he said anxiously. But he mustn't let the lady know he was afraid.

He looked back: the dragon was gone. Rocks and sand and ragged steep places, a blazing desert, just what he had supposed it would be, like the picture of Death Valley in his geography book. It was very hot.

"This is the Valley of the Shadow of Death," he told the lady, and his words were caught up in a hollow wind and sent booming across the wastelands; they rolled in all directions, thundering hoops of sound, as big as a house. They knocked down the cliffs.

"Of death, of death, of death," the rocks shouted, and the whole vault of the sky rang with echoes, and the air shed bright scalcs of quartz. Phrases of the psalm flitted about him, birdlike: I will fear no evil, he leadeth me beside the still waters; and that strange one: surely good Mrs. Murphy shall follow me all the days of my life.

"Is thee Mrs. Murphy?" he asked. "Did thee follow me into this valley?"

"No, child," she answered. "I am another."

"A mother?" Had she said "a mother"? There was such a roaring in the air, like a storm; but it was hot and he felt giddy. He'd better say something. "I can do long division," he stated. "My papa taught me."

"I'm taking you home, child," the kind lady said.

"To the eyes?"

They sat on the horizon and looked at him, whatever he did, two great sad eyes, like his mother's. They swept the whole dead land with their slow and melancholy gaze and returned always to him as soon as he moved, and they said sadly, "You are lost, little boy, you know."

He was afraid of them.

"To the eyes," the kind lady said. "Cool sleep."

Right in front of them was a terrible goblin.

"Excuse me," he said, "but there's another griffin. Couldn't we go around?" But the griffin was gone.

"Where the sea is," she replied. "Like Atlantic City."

July, 1945

38

Salt water taffy and the man who made a racer car out of red sand.

"But I don't live there." The sun was burning white on all the rocks and sand and he saw nothing that he recognized, and he felt quite faint and sick. "I think we're lost," he said.

"Yes," the lady said, but now she was like cruel Miss Watson the penmanship teacher. "We are lost, we are lost, we are lost. Up and down, up and down, stroke, stroke, wrist loose, arm loose, up and down."

There was a crow in the cornfield once.

He burst into tears. (But no tears came.) And now he was a very small little boy, very afraid indeed, and he wished he was home in bed.

"My name is Timmie Walton," he recited, the way his mother had taught him if he should ever get lost. "I am six years old and I live in New York City on Seventy-Eighth Street and our name is in the telephone book. Please take me home."

But she led him straight on, though he stumbled. When he looked up at her fearfully she was gone, and his hand held a starfish, and ahead of him the two great jelly eyes stared at him solemnly from the horizon, and rolled over backwards; and the lady's voice fell over him like a tent, saying, "That's where the cool green sea is. That's where Ran lives, she draws drowned sailors to the bottom of the sea. Go to her. Go, go quickly."

His father had told him about Ran. She was a goddess. He knew more than anyone else in the whole world, except this terrible lady. His father had told him about Sir Patrick Spens.

> Half-owre, half-owre to Aberdour,
> 'Tis fifty fathoms deep,
> And there lies gude Sir Patrick Spens,
> Wi' the Scots lords at his feet

That was the cool green sea.

"Of death, of death," the cliffs muttered.

"Is thee an angel?" he asked in a small voice, looking all around the shimmering desert for her. "Is thee an angel?"

And the desert wind flung his words against the walls of the Valley of the Shadow of Death and into their eternal arguing, and the two echoes came back to him together with the sound of his own voice, immeasurably more vehement.

"Angel . . . Angel . . . of death."

"The child will be dead before this day is dead," the doctor said to the nurse. He was somewhat of a poet and wished to impress the nurse. Moreover he hated people.

The year was 1922 and the child was six years old. His temperature was 108° and the meningococci were feeding on the nerves of his spine. He was delirious and kept calling, "Lady, lady!"

The boy's father was waiting in the hallway. He had been waiting for eight hours, since early morning; he had seen his son wheeled out of the operating room, where they had cut a hole in his head the size of a silver dollar. Now, when he saw the doctor coming down the hall toward him, he rose to his feet, holding his hat in his fist. He saw the doctor assume the expression which doctors assume in the presence of the parents of dying children.

"There is still hope," the doctor said gravely.

Mr. Walton asked: "Do you think he will live?"

The doctor considered his various responsibilities, toward truth and toward people. Because of his hatred of people he answered, "I cannot say that I think he will live. But there is still some reason to hope."

Mr. Walton said, "Thank you." He stood facing the doctor, twisting his hat in his hands.

The doctor looked at this strange innocent Quaker man who did not know what to do with his hat, and was attacked by a sort of loathing.

"There's no use your waiting here," he said harshly. "Your worry isn't going to save his life. Go out and get drunk and come back in the evening. If your boy is still alive, then he will stay alive. If he is dead, I am afraid he will stay dead."

Mr. Walton said again, in a whisper, "Thank you."

He went down the stairs of the hospital to Amsterdam Avenue, looked distractedly about him; walked slowly up the avenue. At 116th Street he turned right, and when he reached Morningside Drive he crossed it to the bay which looked out over the rooftops of Harlem. He sat down on the stone bench. It was as fitting a place as any to wait for his son to complete the formality of dying.

That was what he said to himself.

He pressed his lips together and contemplated minutely the knuckles and fingernails of his right hand. The doctor had said that there was still some reason to hope. That meant that there was no hope whatsoever. If a doctor thinks that a patient may live he says that there is a fifty-fifty chance, but if he knows that a patient will die he says there is still reason to hope.

"What shall I do?" he asked aloud.

Mr. Walton was a man who had difficulty fitting deep emotions into his soul. He had learned many imperatives about right and wrong during his lifetime, and many rules of conduct, Quaker honesty and plain dealing and whatnot; but when he was confronted with the simple and terrible fact of death he was lost. There was no provision in his system for the dull seething in his bowels at this moment and no answer to the mute question which would be drawn in his wife's face when she met him in the hall.

"Our boy is dead."

And then? Plain dealing? Truth in all particulars? Our boy is dead, had died, is gone. We had built our lives around him, but now he is dead.

"We of the Meeting are moved to express our profound sympathy with thee in thy bereavement and to hope that thee will find the strength in Jesus . . ."

Yes, thank you all; but our Timmie is dead, thank you, death has got at him.

What can you build with words and gestures which will erase this fact from the minutes of the Meeting and from the headstone in your yard?

Timothy L. Walton
1916—1922

So tiny a grave.

Three little girls on roller skates swarmed into his bay and pursued one another around its circumference.

"You're it! You're it!"

"Sheila is a monkey! Sheila is a donkey!"

Shrieks and laughter.

"Excuse me, mister."

He watched them gravely; and when he saw that he was in their way he arose and walked to the stairhead. Below him lay a shabby park, and beyond it a patchwork of tenements under a haze of smoke, and far in the distance, over invisible waters, the faint shape of a bridge.

He had told his son about Bifrost, the rainbow bridge to Asgard, about the Æsir and the Vanir and the giants of Jötunheim, who lived on the very edge of the world, and about Hymer, the giant of the winter sea, whose cattle were the icebergs; and he remembered his child's wide, wondering eyes as he had heard about these things.

"Tell me about Balder and the mistletoe, papa."

"Well, Balder was the god of brightness and wisdom, and Loki hated him . . ."

And at once he saw his son as a little cosmos, perfect like a bean sprout, a microcosm in the fertile earth of life, ready to flower and to grow toward completion and to produce; a little living plant, compounded of wondering, thinking eyes and of hands that tried already to fashion things and of other qualities; and it struck him as a savage brute act of destruction that such a beginning should be blighted by the mildew which is called death; and he wondered, with a dreadful constriction of his vitals, what larger purpose lay in such ruin.

The little girls skidded close to his heels and squealed their terror at being caught, and the smoke hung eternal over Harlem.

He looked down again at his knotty hands.

Lord God, he said to himself and to Another, praying, he wasn't an accident. We wanted him. We had thought he was part of Thy will. He would have been brought up in the knowledge of Christ and would have served Thee as best he could. He would . . .

"Tell me about Thor and the sea serpent, daddy."

And the way Timmie had grasped his thumb in his whole little hand.

Mr. Walton stumbled back to the stone seat and sat down; plunged his face into his hands. He could not understand what had broken down in him.

Almighty God, he said silently, with an immediate human passion, as if, for the first time, he were appealing to his God as to a friend, Almighty God, it is simply this, that we love him. Don't take him away from us.

That was the word that had been fighting in him during these days: love. We love him. Helen and I, we love him deeply.

And in this moment it seemed to him that he had achieved a unique vision: it was as if the rocks of his scholasticism had been cleft asunder, to lay open a pulsing living heart, and as if this were a singular discovery: that God was a friend, a puissant comrade, who could in His human kindness save the life of his child.

His faith could not encompass this miracle, that he should now believe that his son would live.

A quiet joy took possession of him. He looked up, smiling a silly smile.

This is the way the ladies ride. That was their favorite game: the boy trotting on his father's knees, already half frightened by the jouncing that was to follow. Their eyes met in a bright understanding.

This is the way the gentlemen *ride.* An easy canter now, becoming gradually more lively. Now it was going to happen.

This is the way the HUNTERS *ride.* And he tumbled the boy as high as he could, again and again, whoopsy-daisy, *this is the way the* HUNTERS *ride*—until they were pitched to the floor and lay laughing, laughing in each other's arms. Then Timmie tried to pull off daddy's mustache.

Mr. Walton, still smiling, stood up. Goodness, how could a baby like that die?

A little girl, looking behind her, skated full tilt into him. He caught her before she fell. Her grimy face looked up at him.

"Well, little girl, that was quite a bump, wasn't it?"

He wanted to be friends with this little girl.

"Are you playing tag?"

The other two stood apart, waiting for Sheila.

"Yes."

"Have you ever played leapfrog?"

"Yes."

"I mean, on skates."

"No."

"That's lots of fun, on skates—What's your name, child?"

"Sheila."

"Hey, Sheila, come on!"

"That's a very pretty name—Sheila. I have a little boy about your age. His name is Timmie."

"Hey, Sheila, stop flirtin' with that man!"

"I gotta go, mister," Sheila said. She darted away: the three little girls clattered off down the sidewalk in the gathering dusk. Mr. Walton watched them benignantly. It did not occur to him that he had driven them away. In none does the flame of life leap so inextinguishably, he thought, as in small children.

Mr. Walton took out his watch. Eight-thirty.

Evening.

"Come back in the evening. If your boy is still alive, then he will stay alive. If he is dead, I am afraid he will stay dead."

In the gathering twilight, which had already obscured the ugliness of Harlem and had rendered the distant bridge invisible, Mr. Walton realized that he had reached an hour of decision. A quarter mile from him, in a square building, in a white room, his son was either dead or alive, a corpse or a living organism; his little boy: alive, or perhaps quite dead.

And as he started his journey back to the hospital he was confronted again in his spirit with a reality which seemed to have very little to do with God: that spinal meningitis is fatal seventy times out of a hundred; that a temperature of 108° is a clinical phenomenon; that it would need a most especial miracle to save the life of his son and that miracle, quite simply, would not come to pass.

He thought he could hear the doctors in the hospital restaurant.

"Yeah, the kid in 608 kicked off about seven, seven-thirty. Kept hollering 'Lady' and then went into a coma. Little devil had a temp of 108° for about twelve hours—never saw anything like it."

"With 108° I'd holler 'Lady' myself. The bread, please, doc."

Such would have been the pattern of the passing of his son.

As he walked down Amsterdam Avenue Mr. Walton devoted himself soberly to the task of composing his mind to the humility he would need in this hour.

Black night fell over the desert as if the whole world had fallen into a well. He had never seen anything so black. He was only a short distance from the big eyes when this happened, a block or two; and now they glowed in the darkness. They were as big as the two round gas tanks you saw from the ferry, higher than all the houses; their gaze stretched out straight ahead of them, high over his head, so strong he could see it, two luminous cables across the sky. It was like walking up to the pier of a ghostly bridge.

He hurried toward them.

Suddenly it was much cooler, with a presentiment of rain; and somehow he felt about him things he knew. Wasn't that Mrs. Borden's dog barking?

He bumped into a big man.

"Where are ye goin' at all, little boy?"

Brass buttons on a blue uniform, a large head bent over him, an enormous big mustache, twinkling eyes. It was nice Sergeant Mulvaney, the Irish policeman. He saw with surprise that he was on a street, and all around him were houses he knew.

"Were you lost on the desert too, Sergeant Mulvaney?"

The policeman laughed the way they do in the funnies: a white balloon issued from his mouth and in it were the words "Ho! Ho! Ho!"

"Sure and I've been on me beat the whole day," he said. "And now where d'ye think ye're goin', me little man?"

"To the eyes."

"Sure and I think ye're makin' a mistake now," Sergeant Mulvaney said. "Now where ye really want to go is down *there*."

He looked again: this wasn't Sergeant Mulvaney at all, it was his papa pretending to be Sergeant Mulvaney, with a funny false mustache and a funny accent and using "you." That was very funny.

"Thee's my daddy," he shouted, "and I'm going to pull off thy mustache." He made a grab for it.

But his daddy wanted to keep on being Sergeant Mulvaney.

"No, me laddy, 'tis Sergeant Mulvaney, the policeman, and what I say is the law. And what I say is, ye should turn off here and go down this here street till ye reach your own house, which is right at the end of this here street."

"But the eyes?"

"Never ye mind the eyes—they'll wait for ye till ye're old enough to go visitin' around alone. Now please to take this here tricycle o' mine and race off home, because it's goin' to rain and they're waitin' supper for ye."

There was a tricycle.

Then he knew what this was: this was a dream, the kind you have just before you wake up, so you can fix it to come out the way you want it.

"This is *my* tricycle," he said. "Santa brought it last Christmas."

"Maybe it is and maybe it isn't," his daddy said with his funny accent. "Now off with ye—and if I can still see ye when I've counted ten—sure and I'll shoot me revolver at ye. One!"

His daddy was playing a dream-game. He jumped on his tricycle.

"Two!"

"Thee doesn't have a revolver!"

"Three!"

Boy, he'd better hurry! He pedaled furiously down the sidewalk. There was Mrs. Borden's dog, all right, and the big apartment house with its awning to the curb, and there, sure enough, was his house.

"Four!"

And then there was an orange sheet of lightning behind him, and a crack of thunder, and the blatter of fat drops of rain on him; and he forgot the game with his daddy and frowned with all his might, trying to swing the dream around to the way he wanted it to end, quickly, before it was too late, trying to arrange it so that he would be running up the steps of his house and would see the lights in the windows and his mama and papa sitting at the dining table, waiting for him, and could tell them all about the terrible desert and the lady and the eyes.

So that when he woke up he would be home.

LOUIS PAUL

No More Trouble for Jedwick

JEDWICK smiled at the woman drawing water from the well. "Kin I have me a drink, ma'am?" he drawled, his broad shoulders drooped shyly in a half bow.

She was tall and dark. The sun blazed down on the white hot Virginia highway. Jedwick's clothes were saturated with sweat. Scintillant beads shone like translucent jewels against his shiny skin. The black man shook his head like a hound dog coming up out of a creek.

"I reckon," she nodded. The Negro woman, lighter than Jedwick, was not wholly at ease. Her husband was in the village getting groceries. Roamin' niggers . . .

"Yas ma'am," Jedwick said, and dipped into the barrel.

The woman dried her hands on her apron. "Y'all f'om round hyeah?"

Jedwick stared at her a moment. "I ain't f'om hyeah," he murmured between immense gulps, "ner neither I ain't gonna stay hyeah. Whereat I git to Alexandria?"

"Right smart piece yonder."

"How fur?"

She speculated. "Eight-twelve mile."

Jedwick finished his water and looked at the blue and gold cauldron over his head. "Hot, ain't it?"

"Do git hot."

"Yo' man wuk in town?"

"No. He after groceries."

Jedwick glanced down the hill toward the little village. The view was empty. She understood his movement.

He smiled. He had fine healthy teeth. She was aware of a frightened sensation in the pit of her stomach. Jedwick bent and rubbed his ankle as though that were an habitual gesture. The flaming orb in the sky shone down remorselessly. Something about the Negro's beautiful black arms hypnotized her. She stood poised, enchanted, like a statue: made to flee, but forever motionless. The midday silence was oppressive, like the sun. She waited.

"I ain't seed no woman fo' a long time," Jedwick said, almost in apology.

"He after groceries."

March, 1934

Closer to hers, his face was more strikingly handsome than ever. His lips were very cool, strangely. Perspiration came off on her mouth and cheeks. . . .

Later he said, "Thank you sho' nuff fo' that there water, ma'am. Ain't they some law gin doin' much wawkin' thisyere state highways?"

"Is," she looked up at the stranger, embarrassed, "if them troopers ketches you."

Jedwick nodded and suddenly disappeared down the embankment. Couldn't trust the road from here in. Stick to the tracks.

He wrapped a long red handkerchief around his shoulders to keep his neck from frying, and stepped gingerly along the single-tracked roadbed, trying to pace the ties to his long swinging gait. Oughta lay these hyeah ties out even, so's a man could wawk. Wa'nt no cinder path like usual. Say ten mile. 'Bout fo' hours in thisyere sun. Should be makin' up a string o' boxes fo' Manhattan Junction in Alex some'rs round six.

He wanted after an hour to crawl under the shade of some green leafy trees. Lay out yo' legs an' sleep. Thoughts that came like hunger or dreams, unwanted; but they were only a whip-flick to sting the flesh of his determination. Gits me out o' the sun in one o' them boxes in Alex, yassuh! There I rests. He visualized a phrase: Jedwick escapes.

Waves of hypnotic steel-grey heat shimmered up off the two metal radiators that converged in the distance. His eyes began to burn. He thought it would be nice to be rich. He would buy a boat with a motor in it, all covered with a striped canvas canopy, and sail out of sight of land. There would be a breeze off in the ocean. Nice gal, that there brown lady by the highway crossin'. Like a scared cottontail. She liked him. They all liked Jedwick. Lovin' ain't harmin' no gal, he thought.

Bugs. Chrissakes! Little gnats and fuzzy things and leg-squirming beetles popped up in front of him; some kind of a locust whanged with a flat noise on his chest, and he slapped it down. Flies and ticks smelled your sweat. A breath of wind floated lazily over the treetops, but died itself of the heat. Jedwick sighed.

Sighing wasn't natural to him. He thought he'd sing. He bugled a tentative air. A slick-tawkin' man f'om Bumminham . . .

The plaintive lyric echoed magnificently between the banks of woods. Jedwick's cello-like bass rose through the dazzling, brain-sizzling heat to heaven, and he laughed about some dimly-felt deliciousness in solitude's freedom. His voice took up the lilt.

> A slick-tawkin' man f'om Bumminham
> Come up my way, an' his name was Sam,
> I pay no attention, ner I din give a damn,
> Till he stoled my gal away.

He hummed the rest of the melody: it was too hot to think of the words.

A little garter snake, sunning itself under the vast ceiling of broiling light, was startled and jiggled off noisily into the brush. Maybe, he confided to the vanished reptile, maybe tomor' I gonna be in New York. Yassuh. Wonder how fur they is after me? Think they can ketch thisyere Jedwick? Yo' completely crazy. How fur I is to Alex, I wonder? Damn me! but it do git hot!

Three miles an hour, 'bout. 'Thout stoppin' I git me in them yards fo sundown. Yassuh. Sundown. Don't seem like ole sun ever gone go down.

> I hates t' see
> Thet evenin' sun go down . . .

Nossuh. Man said that jes crazy's that snake.

There was a shack directly around a bend, and the white man saw him first. "Where you going to, boy?"

He had a wrinkled skin and sandy grey hair and wore grey uniform pants.

"I goin' t' ask you fo' some water, has you got any?" Jedwick smiled brightly with his thick lips.

"Where you goin'?" the man repeated.

"Well, y'see, cap'n, well, suh, I'm goin' in t' the Districk. Yassuh. Dassit."

"Washin'ton? What you traipsin' up here for?"

"Don't like to wawk on the highway, cap'n boss. 'S y'all got a little water?"

"Alexandria's along up hyeah. You makin' for one of them boxes?"

"Nossuh, nossuh! Ain't layin' over no place, cap'n suh. Ole friend in town gonna ride me into the Districk.

"You must be runnin' away, boy," the man in the shack said, squinting lowered eyes at the big sweating Negro.

"Me? I ain't runnin' no place, suh, cap'n," he protested. "Why fo' I gonna run any place?"

The white man fetched up an iron pail and handed him a different dipper. "Too hot," he said, shaking his head, "to hit them ties 'less yo-all runnin' away. Why ain't you takin' a sleep in some cool place?"

"Me, suh? I gotta git in D. C. Yassuh. I got me friends in the Districk, suh."

The wrinkled man glanced down at Jedwick's right ankle.

"Goin' git me a job," Jedwick stammered uncertainly, "in—like, suh, now, a 'partment house. Dassit," he said, "Yassuh."

"Take all you want," the other said about the water; "they's a crick below here. Ain't my business where-at you're runnin' to."

"Nossuh, cap'n. I ain't runnin'."

"Matter o' fact, they's some empties makin' up in Alexandria about seven tonight. You going t' New York," he stated.

Jedwick was amazed. "How you figger that there, boss?"

"If'n I don't know a chain-gang nigger," he told Jedwick calmly, "I'll go and jump in that there crick."

The big Negro's face curled into a magnificent smile. "Come f'om thataway?"

"Been around," the man said expressionlessly.

"Yassuh," murmured Jedwick. He added, "Thank y'all fo' that water."

"Not 'tall."

"Thank y'all," he repeated.

The man drew himself in out of the heat. Jedwick started off toward Alexandria, but caught a phrase which he thought was the man calling him back—until he analyzed it.

"I want Colonel Saunders, yessum," he was saying, "the police chief in—"

Jedwick sauntered back, and the man in the shack stepped away from the phone when he saw him. His hand slipped into a drawer and the Negro saw a pearl butt come out. Jedwick muttered softly as he crashed over the flimsy table, rolling the white man backward out of his chair. He twisted, and leapt again. They bowled heavily through the door, rocking the flimsy shack. The leather-faced, wiry man struggled up almost successfully, but Jedwick got his feet on him. The black kicked scientifically, as a boxer uses his hands.

In a moment the white man lay still, his head battered. His shirt was torn where his stomach had been gashed. Jedwick felt very sorry for him. How foolish the man had been. Jedwick hated to hurt anybody.

He stopped long enough to bundle the body inside the shack, take another drink and dip his face in the bucket of cool water. It seemed hotter in the sun than ever.

Now he dumped the pail empty and resumed his trek in the oily tropical sun's glare. In a few moments the water he had drunk sank through the pores of his skin and oozed out in driblets. If it's hotter down in Africa, he joked to himself, I'm glad my folks done been slaves. Yassuh.

Slaves.

At least it wasn't too hot to whistle. Instead of his bit of excoriation of a slick-tawkin' man from Bumminham the great black figure chanted a whistley refrain as he trudged on tirelessly toward his destination. He loped along, picking the ties carefully. The song was a monotonous, fugitive melody about a man named Joe, who

> —Done his Susie wrong, yassuh,
> But he love her all the same.

He seemed almost to skip along the ties to that repetitious lilt.

Jedwick was, as he saw the shacks of Alexandria's outskirts loom glaringly in the terrific blaze of afternoon, neither blithe nor desperate, neither coward nor cruel. He was escaping. A criminal—or any man—would. He felt very sorry for the grey-haired man, did he not? Of course. Glimpsing the freight-yards of Alexandria, Virginia, he lapsed into the weakness of a sigh again. Like when the cap'n blowed his whistle at sundown and yo' pick drapped outn yo' fingers . . . like when the las' sack o' cotton was drug down t' the baler, an'—, yassuh. He shook these memories off. Jedwick wasn't really a sighing man.

He hadn't eaten for forty hours. You travels light and fast and lives offn yo' flesh. But yo' gits hongry. Whereat you kin promote a vittle or that in Alex? Better crawl in one of them cars. They gonna trace that phone cawl. Find that wrinkled man an' they gonna be hell poppin' round Alex.

Down in behind the fence. That was the place. He saw a bum duck between two cars and hop over the coupling, coming toward him.

"Hi," he greeted this specimen.

"Know what time d'Junction empties goin out t'night?" the bum screwed up a weather-scarred face.

"Yassuh. Seven."

"You eat?"

"No suh!"

"Where ya come in?"

Jedwick thumbed his hand back.

"Leggin'—you out in that there sun?"

"Sho nuff, likely, brother," Jedwick answered.

"Got a coupla hours," said the bum. "They's a jungle overn 'em weeds. Some liver here, an' haffa loaf o'bread."

Jedwick thanked the man from the North.

They toasted the liver. The bum, whose name was Sully, dug some whole coffee beans out of a bag, battered them on a rock, and had a can going. They split the 'breard' and the big Negro was very grateful. After the meal Sully pulled a razor from a leather bag around his neck and began to shave a light beard. Jedwick, in payment for the bum's life-giving coffee, related the incidents of his story. The man shaving exhibited a great curiosity concerning the details of Jedwick's encounter with the brown up on the hill yonder. He chuckled, vicariously amused.

Jedwick added that he had killed the trackman.

Sully squinted. "You must be one o' dese tough black boys."

"Nossuh," said Jedwick, particular not to be misunderstood. "Whut else I gonna do?"

"Coulda flattened him, or tied him up." Sully put away his razor.

"Sho'. You figger out jes' whut to do. That man had a big gun. He gonna blow off my haid ifn I don't git him."

"Every man fur himself, sonny," the bum shrugged his shoulders. "You set?"

"Les go git stowed away fo some no-count railroad bull git rampagin' round."

They idled through the yard, trained soldiers expertly taking cover back of every bump in the topography. Jedwick pried a loose door. Sully was boosted half way up. A metallic voice startled them.

"What you guys doin'?"

Sully's wits left him and he stared up at the man blankly. Jedwick grinned with silly surprise. "We's jes' gonna ride in, suh."

"Oh, yer jist gonna ride in?"

"Yassuh," he said innocently.

"Just gonna ride in." The voice was pregnant with unpleasant suggestions.

Jedwick wrinkled his brow into a puzzled expression. "Yassuh, cap'n, boss. Ain't it aw right?"

"Ain't it aw right!" he mimicked, and spat. "Where you two bums from?"

"We, suh?"

"Who the hell y'think I'm talkin' to?"

"Yassuh. I got a frien' in New York, boss," he explained. "He gits me a job in a big apartment house. Sully hyeah goin' try to git a job too, cap'n."

"Well, maybe I don't know stiffs no more," the man said. "Don't you know you can't ride on no freight train?"

"Can't ride on no freight train?" Jedwick almost believed in this innocence himself. "Nossuh, boss, nossuh. Is thisyere a freight train? Look like they is all epty. I never know they is hahm in ridin' in epty car. Never would come in hyeah did we knows that, suh. Dassit." He was talking fast—for his life. "Yassuh, boss, gentman, suh."

The train-bull shook himself impatiently. "Better take yourselfs outa here big and pronto," he said with positiveness, "or you'll be gittin' about sixty days apiece for vags."

"'Scuse us, mister cap'n, boss, suh, yassuh," Jedwick murmured with elegant unctuousness, "we is goin'."

The law swung himself up the side ladder and disappeared momentarily along the line of cars.

"You gittin' in?" the black man whispered to Sully coolly.

Sully backed away. "Not me!" he exclaimed hoarsely.

Jedwick shook a finger, said "Hi!" got his belly up on the platform, clipped the door to, and disappeared into the black interior.

He heard the bull coming back, tapping on each door. "Hey, you, come outa there!" He got to Jedwick's door and cried, "Hey, you, come outa there!" There was only silence inside. Footsteps crunched away along the gravel.

Jedwick lay motionless for an unconscionable time. At last the train gave three bone-rattling jerks that knocked him into another corner. The couplings shrieked, another gentle bump, and the train moved slowly out of the yards. The engineer's hoot-hoot sounded to Jedwick's ears like a wild pæan to freedom. The car was like a furnace, but of course he didn't care.

He crawled over to the door and lay with his head to the floor crack, afraid to push the thing ajar.

Wonder and excitement to freedom! The train rattled on, carriages hitting track-cracks with ever-increasing crescendo. Fool, anyone who risked life unnecessarily. That trackman. Why hadn't he let well enough alone? Dead now, and nothing gained. Never would *he* risk the quickness of life except in the defense of his own.

On into the night the bumping freight train sped. North. Where he could achieve that departure from the old and sink into the blissful anonymity of its millions, renascence, born again, with only dead memories to remind him of the past. Yassuh, he speculated. Dassit. Goin' git free in New York. But gotta watch out fo' that bull. Whereat I wonder is fust division stop on thisyere line? Some'rs 'long hyeah. He pried the door open a crack. The sun had set and blue darkness had fallen over the countryside that bobbed swiftly by his limited vision. A hot wind blew in his face.

Yassuh. Like sho' nuff git me a little sheteye, can't takin' no chances. Bull goin' look in these hyeah cars fust crack outn the box do we make a division stop. We git in the Junction mornin' sometime . . . then, nigger, you is free. Yassuh. Dassit—free! The thought made his brain spin airily. No more trouble for Jedwick!

Well, no more later; but just now the cars pulled up under brakes and came to a jerking halt. He shoved open the door and glanced out. Blackness. Tall brush alongside the cinder roadbed. Lucky. Jedwick was always lucky. He jumped down and squatted behind the weeds. Sure enough. The bull had a flash, and he peered into the recesses of every car. Another train, a passenger, thundered on past in the opposite direction. Jedwick waited until the freight train began to move, then he hopped out like a big rabbit scooting across an open space, and swung himself up into the car. That was all right. He was good for another hour.

That hour found him asleep. Fatigue fells all men. Jedwick fell asleep, woke when the train stopped again—which was too late. He was on his knees when the light flashed in.

"What the hell you doin' in there?" the bull shouted.

Jedwick, a thinking animal in danger, murmured in a much broader accent than his own, "Cain't po' man rahd in disyere train, yo' honah?"

"Comin' outa there?"

"Sho gwine come out, yassuh."

He jumped down, but squatted his great frame into a much smaller figure. The railroad bull clicked his light into Jedwick's face. "Say, ain't you the same nigger I chased in Alexandria?"

"Whut Alesandria?"

"Din I tell yer to stay outa them cars?"

"Me, yo' honah? Nossuh," Jedwick exhibited surprise.

"Hell I ain't!"

"Nossuh," Jedwick said gently but firmly.

"Where'd y'git on?"

"Bout a nour back yander, yo' honah, suh. Ah bo'd de train when de cyahs stoppin' sahd them there weeds. Scuse me, suh."

"Well," said the man, not exactly satisfied, "git on outa here. You can't ride in these here trains. An' I ketch y' ridin' agin," he showed Jedwick an army Colt strapped to his trousers, "I'm gonna plug ya." He meant it. "I see you agin," the white man added, "you git it."

Jedwick hunched his shoulders. "I'se so'y, yo' honah. Ah gone git away f'om hyeah jes lahk y'all say. Gone right now." He started off toward the rear of the train. "Ain't meant nary hahm, suh," he murmured.

"See you stay 'way," the bull called after him.

When the freight train pulled out again Jedwick was on it. After the next stop the bull knew he was on it. It was a game of hide and seek. At each stop the Negro ran for cover in the weeds, and thanked the night for being darker than the ace of spades. He saw the blue steel of a gun behind the flash as the detective prowled through the cars.

Jedwick wondered why the man wouldn't let well enough alone. Damn me, but people sho' huntin' trouble wid big guns. Why fo' ever body come messin' 'round me? What I wanna harm nobody fo'? They keeps messin' 'round stid leavin' me be, an' mo' trouble happen fo' you know it. That man goin' kill me ifn he ketches me, he thought, or I goin' try to kill him. Why anybody want kill someone else?

The bull wouldn't, of course, let well enough alone. He knew there was only one way to nab the black bastard—that was on the moving train. There was some danger in that, but the bull didn't consider danger. His job was to get that pernicky nigger the hell and gone off his train.

Crawling along the tops of the cars, he swung himself down over the one he suspected. He gently wedged it open and slipped in. Jedwick sat square in front of the door, his legs spread and tensed, waiting. The bull plopped between the black man's outstretched legs, and Jedwick caught him full in the face with a large but cunning heel. The man's pistol cracked against the side of the car, and the white bull's body dropped out like a sack of potatoes and hit the cinders with a thud. Jedwick sighed as at the completion of an unpleasant duty. Trouble, he thought philosophically; why people allus huntin' 'round fo' trouble?

The sunrise got pink in the east. He sized up the land about him. Wasn't but a few minutes out of the Junction. Better slip off before that cop was missed. Shortly the freight slowed. He hopped it from the ladder.

It was a mile or so to the highway. The sun was just blazing up properly. Another boiling day. A truck was the thing.

Free. Escape was almost certain now. They couldn't pin the railroad bull's accident on him. And Alabama would never get him if he reached New York. Of course he'd reach New York. One of those wonderful red vans came chugging up the highway. By God, this was luck! A colored chauffeur was at the wheel. Going right into the city. Jedwick's luck was an enchanted affair. When the truck approached he flicked his hand and smiled teethily. The driver jammed his brakes. Didn't he say his luck was magic?

"Sho' nice of you," he said as he skipped up on the seat. He sank into the leather cushion blissfully. "Yassuh."

"Goin' into New York?"

"Yassuh."

"Where you from?"

"Been bummin' my way up from the Districk," said Jedwick. "Ole feller goin' far as the las' town in a little Fo'd brang me thus far."

"I got a samdwich I ain't et," said the driver. "You're perfectly welcome to it."

"Sho' nice of you," he repeated. He took the sandwich and swallowed it whole. "My name Jedwick," he grunted past the last mouthful.

At Canal and Sixth Avenue the driver said, "Like you to drop off here, buddy. I get caught ridin' anybody in, it's jes' too bad fo' me."

"Yassuh," said Jedwick gratefully. "Sho' nice of you." He dropped down and the truck turned up Sixth Avenue.

LANGSTON HUGHES

A Good Job Gone

It was a good job. Best I ever had. I got it my last year in high school and it took me damn near through college. I'm sure sorry it didn't last. I made good money, too. Made so much that I changed from City College to Columbia my Sophomore year. Mr. Lloyd saw to it I got a good education. He had nothing against the Negro race, he said, and I don't believe he did. He certainly treated me swell from the time I met him till that high brown I'm gonna tell you about drove him crazy.

Now, Mr. Lloyd was a man like this: he had plenty of money, he liked his licker, and he liked his women. That was all. A damn nice guy—till he got hold of this jane from Harlem. Or till she got hold of him. My people—they won't do. They'd mess up the Lord if he got too intimate with 'em. Poor Negroes! I guess I was to blame, too. I should of told Mr. Lloyd she didn't mean him no good. But I was minding my own business, and that time I minded it too well.

But that was one of the things Mr. Lloyd told me when I went to work there. He said, "Boy, you're working for me—nobody else. Keep your mouth shut about what goes on here, and I'll look out for you. You're in school, ain't you? Well, you won't want to have to worry about money to buy books and take your girl-friends out—not if you stay with me."

He paid me twenty-two dollars a week, and I ate and slept in. He had a four-room apartment, as cozy a place as you'd want to see, looking right over Riverside Drive. Swell view. In the summer when Mr. Lloyd was in Paris or Berlin, I didn't have a damn thing to do but eat and sleep, and air the furniture. I got so tired, that I went to summer school.

"What you gonna be, boy?" he said.

I said, "A dentist, I reckon."

He said, "Go to it. They make a hell of a lot of money—if they got enough sex appeal."

He was always talking about sex appeal and lovin'. He knew more dirty stories than any man I ever saw, Mr. Lloyd did. And he liked his women young and pretty. That's about all I did, spent my time cleaning up after some woman he'd have around, or makin' sandwiches and drinks in the evenings. When I did something extra, he'd throw me a fiver anytime. I made oodles o' money. Hell

April, 1934

53

of a fine guy, Mr. Lloyd, with his 40-11 pretty gals—right out of the Follies or the Scandals, sweet and willing.

His wife was paralyzed, so I guess he had to have a little outside fun. They lived together in White Plains on a big estate. But he had a suite in the Hotel Stuyvesant, and a office down on Broad. He says, when I got the job, "Boy, no matter what you find out about me, where I live, or where I work, don't you connect up with no place but here. No matter what happens on Riverside Drive, don't you take it no further."

"Yes, sir, Mr. Lloyd," I said, because I knew where my bread was buttered. So I never went near the office or saw any of his other help but the chauffeur—and him a Jap.

Only thing I didn't like about the job, he used to bring some awfully cheap women there sometimes—big timers, but cheap inside. Didn't know how to treat a servant. One of 'em used to nigger and darkie me around, but I got her told right quietly one time, and Mr. Lloyd backed me up.

The boss said, "This is no ordinary boy. True, he's my servant, but I got him in Columbia studying to be a dentist, and he's just as white inside as he is black out. Treat him right, or I'll see why." And it wasn't long before this dame was gone, and he had a little Irish girl with blue eyes that he treated mean as hell.

Another thing I didn't like, though. Sometimes I used to have to drink a hell of a lot with him. When there was no women around, and Mr. Lloyd would get one of his blue spells and start talking about his wife, and how she hadn't walked for 18 years, just laying flat on her back. After about an hour of this, he'd want me to start drinking with him. And when he felt good from licker, he'd start talking free about women in general, and he'd ask me what they were like in Harlem. Then he'd tell me what they were like in Montreal and Havana and Honolulu. He'd even had Gypsy women in Spain.

Then he would drink and drink, and make me drink with him. And we'd both be so drunk I couldn't go to classes the next morning, and he wouldn't go to the office maybe all day. About four o'clock he'd send me out for some clam broth and an American Mercury, so he could sober up on Mencken. I'd give him a alcohol rub, then he'd go off to his suite in the Stuyvesant and have dinner with the society folks he knew. I might not see him again for days. But he'd slip me a greenback usually.

"Boy, you'll never lose anything through sticking with me! Here." And it would be a fiver.

Sometimes I wouldn't see Mr. Lloyd for weeks. Then he'd show up late at night with a chippie, and I'd start making drinks and sandwiches and smoothing down the bed. Then there'd be a round o' women, six or eight different ones in a row, for days. And me working my hips off keeping 'em fed and lickered up. This would go on till he got tired and had the blues again. Then he'd beat the hell out of one of his women and send her off. Then we'd get drunk again. When he sobered up he'd telephone for his chauffeur to drive him to White

Plains to see his old lady, or down to the hotel where he lived with a private secretary. And that would be that.

He had so damn much money, Mr. Lloyd. I don't see where folks get so much cash. But I don't care so long as they're giving some of it to me. And if it hadn't been for this colored woman, boy, I'd still be sitting pretty.

I don't know where he got her. Out of one of the Harlem night clubs, I guess. They came bustin' in about four o'clock one morning. I heard a woman laughing in the living room, and I knew it was a nigger laugh—one of ours. So deep and pretty, it couldn't have been nothing else. I got up, of course, like I always did when I heard Mr. Lloyd come in. I broke some ice, and took 'em out some drinks.

Yep, she was colored, alright. One of these golden browns, like an Alabama moon. Swell looking kid. She had the old man standing on his ears. I never saw him looking so happy before. She kept him laughing till daylight, and hugging and kissing. She had a hot line, that kid did, without seeming to be serious. But he fell for it. She hadn't worked in Harlem speakeasies for nothing. Jesus! She was like gin and vermouth mixed.

We got on swell, too, that girl and I. "Hy, Pal," she said when she saw me bringing out the drinks. "If it ain't old Harlem, on the Drive." She wasn't a bit hinkty like so many colored folks when they're light-complexioned and up in the money. If she hadn't been the boss's girl, I might have tried to make her myself. But she had a black boyfriend—a number writer on 135th Street—so she didn't need me. She used to talk to me about him all the time. She was in love with him. Used to call him up as soon as the boss got in the elevator bound for the office.

"Can I use this phone?" she asked me that very morning.

"Sure, Miss," I answered.

"Call me Pauline," she said, "I ain't white." And we got on swell. I cooked her some bacon and eggs while she called up her sweetie. She told him she'd hooked a new butter and egg man with bucks.

Well, the days went on. Everytime, the boss would show up with Pauline. It looked like blondes didn't have a break. A sugar-brown had crowded the white babies out. But it was good for Mr. Lloyd. He didn't have the blues. And he stopped asking me to drink with him, thank God! He was crazy about this Pauline. Didn't want no other woman. She kept him laughing all the time. She used to sing him bad songs that didn't seem bad when she was singing them. Only seemed funny and good-natured. She was nice, that girl. A gorgeous thing to have around the house.

But she knew what it was all about. Don't think she didn't. "You've got to kid white folks along," she said to me. "When you're depending on 'em for a living. Make 'em *think* you like it."

"You said it," I agreed.

And she really put the bee on Mr. Lloyd. He bought her everything she wanted, and was as faithful to her as a husband all winter. Used to ask me when she wasn't there, what I thought she wanted. I don't know what got into him. He loved her like a dog.

She used to spend two or three nights a week with him. And the others with her boy-friend in Harlem. And it was a hell of a long time before Mr. Lloyd found out about this colored fellow. When he did, it was a pure accident. He saw Pauline going in the movies at the Roxy one night with him—a tall black good-looking guy with a diamond on his finger. And it made the old man sore.

That same night Mr. Lloyd got a ring-side table at the Cabin Club in Harlem. When Pauline came dancing out in the 2 o'clock revue, he called her, and told her to come there. He looked mad. Funny, boy, but that rich white man was jealous of the colored guy he had seen with her. Mr. Lloyd, jealous of a jig! Wouldn't that freeze you?

They had a hell of a quarrel that morning when they came to the apartment. First time I ever heard them quarrel. Pauline told him finally he could go to hell. She told him, yes, she loved that black boy, that he was the only boy she loved in the wide world, and the only man she wanted.

They were all drunk, because between words they would drink licker. I'd left two bottles of Haig & Haig on the tray when I went to bed. I thought Pauline was being stupid, talking like that, but I guess she was so drunk she didn't care.

"Yes, I love that colored boy," she hollered. "Yes, I love him. You don't think you're buying my heart, too, do you?"

And that hurt the boss. He'd always thought he was a great lover, and that women liked him for something else besides his money. Because most of them wanted his money, nobody ever told him he wasn't so hot. His girls all swore they loved him, even when he beat them. They all let *him* put *them* out. They hung on till the last dollar.

But that little yellow devil of a Pauline evidently didn't care what she said. She began cussing the boss about dawn. Then Mr. Lloyd slapped her. I could hear it way back in my bedroom where I was sleeping, with one eye open.

In a minute I heard a crash that brought me up on my feet. I ran out, through the kitchen, through the living-room, and opened Mr. Lloyd's door. Pauline had thrown one of the whiskey bottles at him. Now they were battling like hell in the middle of the floor.

"Get out of here, boy!" Mr. Lloyd panted. So I got. But I stood outside the door in case I was needed. If she wanted help, I was there. But Pauline was a pretty tough little scrapper herself. It sounded like the boss was getting the worst of it. Finally, the tussling stopped. It was so quiet in there I thought maybe one of them was knocked out, so I cracked the door to see. The boss was kneeling at Pauline's feet, his arms around her knees.

"My God, Pauline, how I love you!" I heard him say. "I want you, child. Don't mind what I've done. Stay here with me. Stay, stay, stay."

"Lemme out of here!" said Pauline, kicking at Mr. Lloyd.

But the boss held her tighter. Then she grabbed the other whiskey bottle and hit him on the head. Of course, he fell out. I got a basin of cold water and put him in bed with a cloth on his dome. Pauline took off all the rings and things he'd given her and threw them at him, laying there on the bed like a ghost.

"A white bastard!" she said. "Just because they pay you, they always think they own you. No white man's gonna own me. I laugh with 'em, and they think I like 'em. Hell, I'm from Arkansas where the crackers lynch niggers in the streets. How could *I* like 'em?" She put on her coat and hat and went away.

When the boss came to, he told me to call his chauffeur. I thought he was going to a doctor, because his head was bleeding. But the chauffeur told me later he spent the whole day driving around Harlem trying to find Pauline. He wanted to bring her back. But he never found her.

He had a lot of trouble with that head, too. Seems like a piece of glass or something stuck in it. I didn't see him for eight weeks. When I did see him, he wasn't the same man. No, sir, boy, something had happened to Mr. Lloyd. He didn't seem quite right in the head. I guess Pauline dazed him for life, made a fool of him. He drank more than ever and had me so high I didn't know B from Bull's Foot. He had his white women around again, but he'd got the idea from somewhere that he was the world's great lover, and that he didn't have to give them anything but himself—which wasn't so forty for the little Broadway gold diggers who wanted diamonds and greenbacks. Women started to clearing out early when they discovered that Mr. Lloyd had gone romantic— and cheap. There were scandals and fights and terrible goings on when the girls didn't get their presents and checks. But Mr. Lloyd just said, "To hell with them," and drank more than ever, and let the pretty girls go. He picked up women off the streets and then wouldn't pay them, cheap as they are. Late in the night he would come in and start drinking and crying about Pauline. The sun would be rising over the Hudson before he'd stop his crazy carryings on— making me drink with him and listen to the nights he'd spent with Pauline.

"I love her, boy! And she thought I was trying to buy her. Some black buck had to come along and cut me out. Fooling her. But I'm just as good a lover as that black boy any day." And he would begin to boast about the white women he could have—without money, too. (Wrong, of course.) But he sent me to Harlem to find Pauline.

I couldn't find her. She'd gone away with her boy-friend. Some said they went to Memphis. Some said Chicago. Some said Los Angeles. Anyway, she was gone—that kid who looked like an Alabama moon.

I told Mr. Lloyd she was gone, so we got drunk again. For almost a week, he made no move to go to the office. I began to be worried, cutting so many classes staying up all night to drink with the old man, and hanging around most of the day. But if I left him alone, he acted like a fool. I was scared. He'd take out women's pictures and beat 'em and stamp on 'em and then make love to 'em, and tear 'em up. Wouldn't eat. Didn't want to see anybody.

Then one night, I knew he was crazy—so it was all up. He grabs the door like it was a woman, and starts to kiss it. I couldn't make him stop, so I telephoned his chauffeur. The chauffeur calls up one of Mr. Lloyd's broker friends.

And they take him to the hospital. That was last April. They've had him in the sanatorium ever since. The apartment's closed. His stuff's in storage, and I have no more job than a snake's got hips. Anyway I went through college on it. But I don't know how the hell I'll get to dental school. I just wrote ma down in Atlanta and told her times was hard. Ain't many Mr. Lloyd's, you can bet your life on that.

And the chauffeur told me yesterday he's crazy as a loon now. Sometimes he thinks he's a guy named Don Juan. Again, he thinks he's a stud-horse chasing a mare. Sometimes he's a lion. Poor man! The padded cell! He was a swell guy when he had his right mind. But a yellow woman sure did drive him crazy. As for me, well, it's just one good job gone.

Say, boy, give me a smoke, will you? I hate to talk about it.

JOHN McPARTLAND

◄──►

For These Are the Bedeviled

The fellow who has the desk next to yours at the office is friendly—a little too friendly, perhaps. He seems anxious to please you; maybe he talks too much; his gestures are nervous and a bit exaggerated. The suspicion comes slowly: can the guy be "queer"? Or maybe you have a younger brother or a nephew, someone for whom you feel a special kind of personal responsibility. The kid has always seemed a good sort, although just a trifle flighty and prone to fits of temper or unnecessarily tense emotional responses. Lately, though, he has picked up a collection of pretty odd characters as friends. You don't like their looks and you've begun to suspect that they're a bunch of what, for want of a better word, you've always called "pansies." You wonder what to do about the kid.

Or—let's face the possibility—you suddenly find that you yourself are thinking brief, surprising, unwanted thoughts, making unplanned gestures, or unexpectedly saying foolish and silly things. You may be just an adolescent or you may be a fat old codger with a trunkful of memories of women you've known. At such a moment, if you can talk to yourself honestly, you may think, with a flash of revulsion, "Is there something wrong with me? Maybe I'm not completely normal. . . ." Psychologists believe that a great many men have to face a situation of this sort at some time in their lives. Some experts even insist that the subject of homosexuality is unpleasant and repulsive to most of us chiefly because we've had these disturbing periods of uncertainty about ourselves.

There is nothing to be gained by shrugging off the very existence of homosexuality. It exists; we meet it only too often in everyday life. How, then, should you, as a decent and civilized man, react to the overfriendly fellow at the office, to your kid brother or nephew and his questionable friends, to your own occasional shocking impulse? The best way, probably, of approaching all three of these situations is to try to understand the causes of homosexuality. Inversion is not necessarily the sinful fault of the individual concerned—nor, on the other hand, is it something to accept as a minor personality flaw. It often has its nasty

July, 1950

FOOTNOTE: Recent public statements concerning the incidence of homosexuality have underlined more than ever before the need for open discussion on this subject which has for too long been obscured by hush-hush and antiquated taboos. This article was offered as another step forward in the evolution of a healthy approach to an increasingly critical problem in present-day society.

and degenerate aspects, but too often, also, do we laugh or sneer at it. So let's try for the middle course. Let's try to remember that the homosexual is less likely to be a sinful man than a desperately sick one.

For these are the bedeviled. If you know one hundred men, you are almost certain to know one of these. These are the men who look at other men as you look at women. These are the men whose emotional and sexual maladjustments cause them to be both preyers and preyed upon.

Without your being aware of it, the man at the desk next to you, the clerk at the drugstore, or your next-door neighbor may be homosexual, and the probabilities are that he is trying to lead a normal life either consciously or unconsciously and that his daily existence is one of quiet frustration. Many homosexuals, though, play an active role in our society; let's take a quick look at the tense, precarious lives they lead, especially as those lives come in contact with the vicious underworld and violent death.

If we examine the careers of three different men, we can discern the boundaries of the dark homosexual world in their separate existences. A young man is beaten to death in a Chicago apartment; a world-famous producer pays a thousand dollars to a cold-eyed man in a white silk gabardine suit as the two sit in a dark booth of a Los Angeles café; a plump youth with a peach-bloom face and not a penny in his pocket walks into a New York cafeteria and loads his tray with turkey and cranberry sauce, knowing that before he has finished his meal some strange man with hungry eyes will come to his table, start a conversation, and pay his bill.

Let's look first at the young man, whom the police found in a blood-spattered bedroom, some hours after his roommate had killed him.

Paul, as we'll call him, grew up in a small town about a hundred miles from Chicago, one of a family of four. Through childhood he was what his mother called "high-strung," overly excited and happy at times, raging in tantrums at others. The school records show him to have been an unpredictable student. Teachers who remember say that he would show interest only if he liked his teacher; if the teacher—man or woman—seemed unsympathetic to him, he would sulk through the course. His mother, to whom he was overdevoted, blamed the teachers when her son did badly, praised him when he did well.

In the short-pants stage, Paul was not too different from the boys in his town. He stayed home more than was usual and he quarreled during games more often than his companions, but there was nothing obviously pathological about him. In his senior year at high school, he began running with a crowd of half-a-dozen boys who prided themselves on being the intellectual elite. These boys all seemed to be nice kids, on the surface. But they hung around too close together, their jokes were too much among themselves, and they regarded the other kids as apart from themselves. There was a kind of hysteria when they were together; they were more shrill than other boys; they giggled a good deal; they mimicked the other students with cruel ability to find the ridiculous.

One night, the father of one of Paul's friends found his son and another boy of the same set in the family car together. The group was investigated, and it was discovered that they had all been indulging in pretty general sex play. The gang was broken up, and Paul's mother sent him to boarding school. There, Paul was homesick and unbearably lonely, until he fell in love with an instructor. This instructor was used to handling cases like Paul's. He was sympathetic and found, through conversation, that Paul was already familiar with the mechanics of homosexuality. He went to the headmaster with Paul, not as a denouncing prosecutor but as a good teacher who had discovered a dangerous and contagious disease in one of his pupils. The headmaster wrote Paul's mother a decent and helpful letter, but she responded by flouncing into the school, accusing the faculty of shameful things, and removing Paul.

Instead of putting her son in the hands of a competent psychiatrist, Paul's mother let him go away to an art school in Chicago, where, after three months, he began to live with two other young men of his age and an older man, the latter a known homosexual with a police record. Paul began to spend more money than he could afford on clothes, jewelry, and entertainment. His demands on the older man became exorbitant and he was thrown out, bodily, from the apartment. Frightened and in money trouble, he went home to his mother.

For the next three years Paul repeated this process of leaving home for a time and then, finding himself in difficulties, returning to his mother, whose emotional shielding of him progressed to a clearly pathological point. At last, though, he settled down in Chicago, where he got a job as an assistant in an art and antique shop whose proprietor was an elderly man who liked to have boys like Paul around much as an old roué might like pretty girls as assistants. Paul learned from him, as he had begun to learn from the older man in his first Chicago experience, what might be called the social rules of the homosexual world. He began to realize that his employer had been preyed upon by blackmailers and extortionists until he had worked out methods of protecting himself, and that he would not permit Paul, or any other homosexual, to force money from him. The youth learned to be suspicious of approaches by strangers and to regard other homosexuals both as secret members of his lodge and as possibly dangerous predators.

He found a friend to live with, but theirs was a loose arrangement in which they quarreled over other men, pretended mutual faithfulness, and were both homosexual prostitutes. Both boys learned to range the meeting places of the brotherhood—the bars, the restaurants, the certain corners of beaches and parks. They were given jewelry and money, and over these gifts they quarreled in bitter jealousy—not so much over the indicated unfaithfulness as in envy over each other's success.

Paul died because of a childish quarrel over a wrist watch, which had been given to his roommate by an elderly admirer. It was an ornate affair with a diamond-set dial, and Paul became literally sick with envy. One evening, while his roommate was asleep, he stole the watch. When the other one asked for it back he refused to return it, and there was a violent, hysterical quarrel. In spitting rage, the roommate picked up an iron from the fireplace and beat Paul to death.

And so the sordid tragedy came to its climax. Whom can we blame for it? Paul's mother? Paul himself, for remaining an infant, for sliding easily from a little boy with tantrums to an adult parasite? Some men with the same unfair start in life become alcoholics, others express their childishness in different ways. Many physicians now believe that over half of all *practicing* homosexuals are totally unnecessary inverts—there is no innate cause, they have become what they are because of external factors, usually parental. And Police Commissioner Valentine of New York once attributed twenty per cent of all crimes of passion to homosexuals.

The story of our Hollywood producer—let's call him Leon—is a very different one. Leon today is a slender, silver-haired man in his late forties with a gentle, expressive face, and soft, dark eyes. He was seduced when he was sixteen years old by the concert master of a famous orchestra. The concert master cannot be blamed entirely, for Leon was as intentionally seductive as a stage-struck girl. He had been, until then, completely inexperienced—but he had been aware of the strength of men, their handsomeness, and their charm since the age of twelve. He stayed with the concert master for five years and he left him only because the old man was no longer his intellectual equal.

Whatever the sin may be, the root of it in Leon is in the secret stuffs of his body; he is essentially a strong, intelligent and charming woman in the body of a man. As a woman Leon might have led a tempestuous life with many loves, but essentially a successful and full one. As a man, Leon is a damned soul, a dangerous man to the normal and healthy young men his soft eyes smile upon.

There were other great loves in Leon's life after the concert master. There were a couple of actors, a ballet dancer, a playwright. In the purely theatrical world, where Leon gained prominence as a director, such relationships were understood. Not until he came to Hollywood did Leon discover the more vicious aspects of the homosexual world. A grapevine had spread the news of Leon's peculiarity before he arrived in Hollywood, and hard-eyed people he had never heard of were planning to take advantage of his professional prestige by making capital of his sexual aberrations. They succeeded—succeeded in spite of his cleverness, his carefulness, his experience.

In Hollywood, Leon had his first contact with the horrors of blackmail. He was caught in a compromising situation by a "detective" and a photographer in a San Fernando Valley motel; a woman star threatened to sue him for alienation of her husband's affections; he even found himself having to cast a young man in a star part for which he was unqualified—blackmail of an insidious and morale-destroying sort.

But in the dark booth of the Los Angeles café, where we saw him at the beginning of this article, Leon was not paying the thousand dollars as blackmail. His self-respect and dignity gone, Leon was dealing with a procurer of homosexuals.

If he had not been given the opportunity to approve men and women for quarter-of-a-million-dollar salaries, if he had not been charged with the responsibility for million-dollar pictures, if he had not been sincere in his appreciation of artistry, the fact that Leon loves as a woman in a man's body might not have destroyed the fabric of his integrity. But he is a man under intense pressures, and the further pressures of his homosexuality have been too much for him. He no longer permits his longing for the swaggering young men he sees on the lots to affect his decisions; he buys his love now like an elderly rich Oriental.

What to do about Leon, or the thousands of others like him? Apart from the whole question of therapy for incipient and actual homosexuals, there is the problem of damage done by a man like Leon. Not only does he debauch decent young men, but he now acts as a source of money for one of the most vicious of all rackets—the supplying of young men to elderly and middle-aged homosexuals. With all due sympathy for Leon, for his talent, his ability, his sensitivity, he is now a consort of criminals, a criminal of the worst sort himself.

It is interesting that this combination of artistic ability and homosexuality is not uncommon. It's by no means true, though, that all artistic men are homosexual, nor need we assume that talent justifies sexual variation. We ought, however, to be prepared to give further sympathy and understanding to the men of unusual talent who are also homosexuals. We might in some way be able to save them from a fate like Leon's.

Now, how about the plump young man in the New York cafeteria? His is a hard career to define, and yet he marks as much of a type in the nightmare world of the homosexual as does the battered young man in the Chicago flat or the burned-out genius. Mark again, these are the boundaries of the homosexual; there are possibly several *million* potential and actual homosexuals in this country who are living through their lives in fear of violence, of blackmailers, or more often of only their own inhibited desires, but who are never actually touched by the sordid realities. It is particularly on these that our plump youth preys, a mild little predator.

Wilmar—let's call him that—is a lonely lad living in a dream world of his own, a marked-down Casanova. He tells great stories of himself to stupid-eyed little girls, who make much of him for a while and then, when they begin to notice his gilt is thinning, he moves on. He works as a soda man in drugstores, a bellhop, or any other job that fits a drifter. At intervals he finds himself without money, without a job, and quite often without a place to sleep. Then he heads for one of the meeting places of the homosexual brotherhood—the urban type that Wilmar represents seems able to smell out such places even in a strange town.

Wilmar is both a little ashamed and a little proud of his ability to get money from homosexuals. Being an unadmitted homosexual himself, he feels guilt over any contact with them, but his ego is soothed by their attentions and by his ability to urge money out of them. And so he fills his tray and knows that someone else will pay his bill.

The crime here is utterly cruel. Wilmar is a hustler with the shallowness and greed of the hustler masked by ingenuousness. He must represent some warped, horrible dream of love to the men upon whom he preys, and it is pitiful that he will debase himself and allow them to be debased for the price of an eighty-cent cafeteria check. This debasement is not physical; as a rule, Wilmar does nothing more than lead men on for a few minutes, but his crime is much worse than physical perversion—it is a perversion of dignity.

Wilmar will get in trouble one day—bad trouble. He is confident of his ability to get out of situations, and he will sometimes go to a man's apartment or hotel room, drink his liquor, and try to steal his money—it is probable that some of these incidents have involved actual perversion, although he denies it —and the police records show that sooner or later ill will come to him.

Those, then, are the boundaries of the shadow society. Paul, the pouting, infantile youth, a homosexual prostitute who was murdered over a wrist watch, the crime rooted in the same emotional causes that made him and his friend homosexuals. Leon, the artist, intelligent and talented—whose inverted love is used to the advantage of others. Wilmar, the boy who hides his own inversion from himself and who sells his own integrity for a few dimes.

These men face three constant threats. They may be ostracized, condemned, and even imprisoned by the normal world; they are the easy prey of the criminal; worst of all, they are at the mercy of their own kind.

The belief by psychologists that most active homosexuals are the products of an unhealthy infancy seems well-confirmed by the latest studies. The young men who hang around the crowded big-city bars which are the meeting places for homosexuals are almost entirely *false* homosexuals—young men who should be normal by right of birth and body but who are not. Let's look at a typical one. Let's try to find out how he has become what he is today.

This man is thirty but looks somewhat younger. He is fairly tall, an inch or two under six feet; he is slender, weighing about a hundred and fifty. His hair is dark and wavy, his face is handsome, and his eyes are strikingly attractive. He has worked as an interior decorator and a florist's assistant, and has spent four years in the Army. Given to wearing bright-colored shirts and similar apparel, he is usually recognized as a "pansy" upon sight. He talks with all the affectation popularly associated with homosexuals—giggling, wrist and hand movements, rolling eyes. He seems to be a real one, all right.

What made him that way? Where did he come from? What does he do? And how many of his kind are there? The answer to the last question is easy: too many of them, and our society is making more of them every day.

This one seems to be of familiar background—the all-female family. A smothering mother, sisters that treated their little brother as another sister, too much protection from the world, lack of whatever strength of character it is that makes some boys rebel against such pink cotton wool—these all bear at least partial responsibility for the simpering and giggling parody who sits at the bar of a homosexual joint and mouths clever obscenities.

Mark the last factor, the lack of resistance to a smothering environment. That is the intangible that makes it difficult to place the blame. He can't be blamed for the way his mother and sisters spoiled him as a little boy, but then what about the little boy of similar environment who fights back to become the toughest little kid on the block? Nature is ruthless. For this lack of the intangible quality that makes a boy fight back, she harasses these false inverts with an array of psychic and physical punishments.

By the time this boy was in his early teens he was a sissy. Then society—you and I, that is—took over the job of making him into a homosexual. We normal adolescents, with our instinctive cruelty that makes a hate-maddened Apache seem like a Quaker minister, turned on the gentle little sissy and teased him, tormented him, and drove him away from us. It's so easy to think up jokes that can be played on a slender boy of thirteen who giggles like a girl, who won't fight back, and who cries when he's tormented. We helped do it, and the creature in the bright shirt is almost as much of our manufacture as he is of that terrible mother who directed self-pity and self-love into a smothering stickiness that engulfed her son.

So the boy grew older. He retreated from the world of men and accepted the world of girls. Furtive playing around with other boys who had abnormal sexual tendencies became a self-admitted pattern of sexual satisfaction.

Older men found him. He got presents of jewelry and clothes, and he began to regard himself as desirable. The feeling of guilt and shame was there, too, but it showed up now in typical homosexual style as a flaunted bitter pride in his homosexuality, a pride that wasted itself in obscene jokes about "queers" and "aunties," an hysterical pride in shamefulness.

It may be that such manufactured homosexuals perform some psychosomatic transformation upon themselves, for they often seem to become less masculine as they grew older, as if their bewildered bodies were trying to rectify the situation. This one soon began to drift from job to job, from one shallow "love affair" to another, and even to a kind of amateur homosexual prostitution. Sick in mind and believing himself sick in body, he is today uncertain and unhappy, in spite of his superficial shell of gaiety.

Every culture has produced men of his type. It is possible that there are more homosexuals in the latter stages of a civilization, when life is easier and cities have been built, yet there is evidence that the roughest kind of masculine life also produces homosexuals. When there are no women at all around, man's need for a sexual outlet finds satisfaction as best it can. The actual history of the western frontier of our own country is filled with incidents of homosexuality; there were inverts on the Chilkoot during the gold rush. The unfortunate reputation for an easy tolerance of sexual abnormality which our folklore attributes to France is guessed by some to be a result of the homosexuality rampant in Napoleon's mighty and far-ranging armies. The male prostitute, a rather common figure of Berlin's night life in the '20s, was manufactured by the Kaiser's *feldgrau* hordes from a strapping *Jüngling*. Isolate any great mass of men in an army, subject them to the great emotions and greater boredom of war, keep them milling around for several years, and you produce not only homosexuals but also a homosexual tradition.

These young men who flock around the "queer" joints of our cities today are, in the main, the results of a different kind of emotional chemistry. Their sickness can generally be traced to their childhood environments. And it isn't always the pink and sticky mother, so well-reviled by Philip Wylie, that plants the seed of homosexuality in the young boy. Quite often a strong, dominant, and self-sufficient father will cause his son to subconsciously reject the male role out of a feeling of sheer inadequacy in comparison to the old bull.

Talk to these well-dressed lads who flock by the scores around those special cocktail bars on Hollywood Boulevard, or along Chicago's Division Street, or the equivalent places in your own town. Most of them come from what are loosely called "good families." They are likely to have completed college, and they are well-informed on the clinical facts of their condition. They'll insist, most of the time, that their homosexuality is principally a matter of choice; they like being queer. They're almost hysterically happy about it.

"You think you're normal," one of them might say to you. "Well, you aren't. You're all bound up inside—you're afraid to let yourself go. That's where we've got it all over you, we know what real excitement and real feeling are like. Your kind of love is pale and colorless, you do everything by habit, there's no emotion. You've got to be one of us to know how to enjoy life."

What this boy means is that there is an hysterical release in homosexual relationships which is certainly not common among normal couples. Some appreciable percentage of all homosexuals become so because of sexual failures in normal relationships; they have suffered from bad marriages, sordid relationships with prostitutes or near-prostitutes or a sense of sexual inadequacy. Here they feel a companionship as an integral part of the sexual connection, a sense of mutual abandonment of the restrictions and inhibitions of morality and mores.

But is it true that they prefer their lot and have made a free choice of it? Well, what, after all, is free choice? Certain psychic traumas—emotional or mental injuries—may be responsible for some cases of homosexuality. Glandular or organic insufficiency and disbalance can cause homosexual tendencies. More and more, though, it seems likely that the vast majority of homosexuals are psychic rather than physical misfits. Hormone therapy is frequently used as a help even in those cases that seem to be caused solely by emotional instability, but psychiatric treatment is apparently necessary in *all* cases of sexual abnormality.

We won't be far wrong, then, if we think of homosexuality as a sickness. Sure, it's a particularly virulent and unpleasant one, but it *can* often be cured—if the patient himself wants to be cured and will help the doctor along. Unfortunately, though, cures cost money. Psychiatrists to cleanse the mind come high, and endocrine treatments—the introduction into the patient's body of glandular substances called hormones, which are not naturally present in sufficient supply —are expensive. Yet, if you are worried about your kid brother or some other young person you know and there seems to be no way of paying for the services of a reputable psychiatrist or physician, the story of a young man we'll call Leslie might interest you.

At nineteen, Leslie knew nothing about life. His mama had taken care of that. He was a skinny and vaguely unhappy mother's boy, afraid of girls. He found himself curiously uninterested in women and curiously fond of neighbor boys. Give Leslie credit, though—at nineteen he woke up. He started wondering one evening, lay awake all night shivering with worry, went to the medical room of the library early next morning, and found out about himself. What to do then? His problem was a tough one.

It has taken Leslie years to break away from the insidious influence of his mother, who always hovered about him like a great psychopathic hen, not knowing what a horrible thing she was doing to her son—and how could one explain it to her? Leslie had to break his own habit patterns, to stop worrying about his health like an old woman and fretting like a sewing-club member. He made a supreme effort to overcome his fear of girls and to seek their companionship.

Leslie isn't well yet. He's fighting a brave fight to be a normal man—something a lot of us take for granted—and he's doing it alone and under difficulties. If outside pressures get too great, he may yet slip into the hysteric warm pool of homosexuality, but the boy is trying. And if he keeps on, maybe he and others like him may prove that it can be done.

So there you are. We're back to that fellow next to you who seems to be on the make. Of course you can get rough with him and punch him in the nose. You might be surprised, though; some homosexuals are very rough characters, and at the best you won't teach him anything and you won't really prove anything to yourself. The homosexual fellow, if he really is one—and he might be no more than a friendly, awkward guy—will only think that you are covering up a guilt feeling of your own. And that may be true.

Possibly the best thing to do in the situation is to ignore the man. He'll probably leave you alone in time, and no harm done. Or else, sort of gently stress the fact that you like girls. He won't be likely to bother you once he realizes you don't want to play.

But supposing the young fellow for whom you feel a big-brother responsibility starts showing some suspicious signs? First of all—don't start talking until you've done some listening. Find out what the lad is thinking about, and if he has learned to trust you, he'll be willing to talk to you. If he doesn't trust you, you won't be very successful at the big-brother act. Boys grow up at differing rates, and one of the normal phases of the pre-adolescent period in all boys is essentially homosexual, though not viciously so. The gang with its secrets and its inherent contempt for girls is a part of that phase. Maybe the young fellow is merely going through this phase.

If, however, you are quite sure that the boy is getting into dangerous ground, you had better act. Find the source of contamination—another boy, maybe a group of boys. Don't try to be a policeman and don't do your boy harm by making a fuss; get him away from the point of contamination by finding something better for him. If this one step is not enough, take him to a doctor—but don't tell him that you're taking him for treatment because you think he might be going queer. Talk it over with the doctor first and then send the boy for a general over-all checkup. Your doctor will tell you what to do from that point on.

Now let's be honest. As we said at the beginning, a lot of men wonder at some time or another about themselves. Men who have seemed perfectly normal do go sour, even after years of healthy marriage. Older men get worried about a fancied decline in sexual powers and kick themselves into a false and destructive inversion. These things happen and they can be faced like any other problem; we unfortunately tinge them with a kind of slimy secrecy. We all of us do have some normal homosexual tendencies, about as important and useful as our set of nipples.

If it's more than this that has set a man to do a little shameful wondering, there are two things he can do. First, he can realize that what he's going through is neither new nor particularly uncommon, and he can try to trace whatever is going on to its source. There is a current bad habit of using psychiatrists as crutches. Most of us have sense enough and guts enough to at least make a stab at understanding ourselves without going to a psychiatrist. If, however, the self-searching doesn't do the trick, he can tell his physician the story. The physician will, if necessary, recommend a psychiatrist.

Meanwhile, let's stop refusing to face the facts. Homosexuality as such is shameful only when it is a product of self-defeat and self-destruction, and self-defeat and self-destruction are shameful in any form. You can't help resenting the infantile Pauls and the slimy little Wilmars. But don't forget that for every Paul or Wilmar there is a Leon, who can be appreciated for his talents and pitied for his soft inability to first real friendship or normal sexual satisfaction. And for every lost Leon, there is a Leslie, who is at least making a brave effort to become a valuable and normal member of society.

If we can find some way to bring the shadow world of homosexuality into the light, we will remove much of the viciousness and violence. The homosexual is properly the concern of the physician and the sociologist rather than of the police. Incipient Pauls can be spotted in grammar school and given special attention, incipient Leons can be discovered by the family doctor and assisted into a normal physical reference, incipient Wilmars might be helped in something like the CCC Camps of the '30s. We harm them and ourselves most by refusing to admit their existence, or by laughing them off as "pansies"—just something to make jokes about.

We have many homosexuals and near-homosexuals among us, and often they are important and useful men. That should be our most critical concern.

When we have all understood the causes of sexual abnormality and when we have realized the dark desperation of the bedeviled ones who suffer from it, we shall have taken a big step toward curing some of the worst sores on the living body of our society, and helped many men toward happier and more useful lives.

J. K. TAUSSIG, JR.

My Crew at Pearl Harbor

"GIVE him another quarter grain of morphine, nurse."

I relaxed on my pillow and waited for the morphine to take effect. A young sailor was talking eagerly to the man in the next bed, cheering him up. I turned my head to see who was talking, and noticed that the back of his head was bleeding. I reached out and touched his back.

"Did you know that your head has been hit?"

The sailor turned around and started to reach for his neck, and stopped midway in the gesture.

"Gosh, Mr. Taussig, they got you too. That makes about four of you officers who've been brought through here."

I recognized one of our Gunners' Mates, a bluejacket named Linnartz. He had come to the hospital to see his brother, Chief Gunners' Mate Linnartz, the senior petty officer on my anti-aircraft battery. He finished his interrupted exploration of his neck and called the nurse so she could dress it.

"Aw that's nothing, sir, Pete here has caught a piece of shrapnel in his knee and a few other pieces spread around on his body. Some fight, wasn't it?"

The three of us silently agreed.

We talked over what we could remember of the day, and what we had seen. I forgot most of the conversation, as the morphine started to take effect. The next time I opened my eyes Linnartz had gone, and his brother was helping two hospital apprentices to lift me onto a cart for further transfer to the operating room. After about a twenty-minute wait at the door, I was admitted into the makeshift operating room which served nobly to save many lives. I looked around at my new surroundings with great interest. I did not know how many men had been wounded in the battle, but I knew that the casualties on my ship had been high. Four out of five anti-aircraft officers was a fairly good criterion of the enemy's effectiveness.

Nurses and doctors were moving efficiently and swiftly through the room, quietly carrying out their duties in accordance with the hospital emergency bill which they had never expected to use. I saw four operating tables in use. The doctor at my operating table looked at my wound, pried my fingers from it, cut the cloth away from the vicinity of the ripped flesh, and immediately called for a spinal. I would much rather have had ether, but I'd come this far and seen the whole show and I wasn't ready to drop the curtain yet. They might come back, and I wasn't going to miss the second performance. The corpsmen held me upright and I felt the doctor tapping on my spinal column. In a few minutes I was stretched out again and looked up at the sky light. A man was painting it over in preparation for a complete blackout, but the unpainted part disclosed a dark sky. It may have been evening approaching, but when I think back, it was probably the pall of smoke that the burning *Arizona* was belching towards the sky.

I asked the doctor to save the metal that he removed from my leg so I could have it set in my class ring. He told me to hold out my hand. Then I dozed off, only to be awakened by the necessary movement from the operating table to the cart. I looked into my hand and saw nothing but a few splinters of bone. No metal. Oh well, I could shine up a piece of bone for my ring.

I was wheeled through long halls, and seemingly longer wards full of enlisted men in various stages of disrepair. Several called greetings to me and my heart sank. Did my ship really have such a large number of casualties? I felt very sick in my stomach. In the sick officers' quarters, I was taken to a double room and introduced to my roommate-to-be.

"Lieutenant Siever, this is Mr. Taussig."

I acknowledged the introduction by becoming violently sick to my stomach. Apologizing profusely for making such a mess, I was gently lifted into bed. Of the ensuing conversation, I remember very little. Lieutenant Siever had had his right leg blown off early that morning but was in the best of spirits. He smoked incessantly and asked me what it felt like to have a pin driven through my ankle. I looked down, and there was a neat wire pin sticking out of both sides of my ankle. I hadn't noticed it before.

Suddenly, machine gun fire broke the stillness of the night. I looked out and saw tracers criss-crossing in the sky, making a spider-web of fire over the entire harbor. Had they come back? The question was too momentous for me to handle at that time. I felt myself slipping off into space. "What a horrible twenty-four hours this has been." That was my last sentence, although for accuracy's sake I might add it was embellished with many profane epithets.

And what a twenty-four hours it had been!

I had relieved the deck only twenty-four hours ago. The first watch was always easy. Plenty to do, with men going over to the Navy Yard to visit friends on other ships, men coming back from liberty in Honolulu, security watch reports, snatches of the movies seen as I moved across the deck. The movie was *The Little Foxes* and the few incidents of it I saw, I didn't like.

One of the Junior Officers, returning from the ship, stopped at my desk and told me he had seen the movie on the *Helena* with one of his classmates. That movie was entitled *Beware the Dawn*.

I was relieved by Ensign (now lieutenant) Dunlap, who next day was to distinguish himself in action by firing the ship's secondary battery at low flying planes. But that night he was just another tired ensign who had the midwatch. I wasn't very sympathetic, as I was looking forward to the forenoon watch the next day, and felt I could spare no sympathy on others.

At 07:00 on December 7th, 1941, I was awakened by the quartermaster of the watch with the time honored Navy phrase, "Mr. Taussig, you've got the next watch." I yawned, swung my feet over the side and contemplated my sad fate. The eight to twelve watch on Sunday morning was longer than the last three minutes of a football game in which your team has a one point lead and the other team the ball.

I shaved, put on my last clean uniform, ate breakfast, borrowed my room-mate's clean gloves and went up on deck. It was a pleasant morning, and I would have liked a game of tennis and a swim before church, but no, I had the eight to twelve watch.

On relieving the deck, I called the log room and told them to light off another boiler, since our steaming boiler had been on for four days. I looked around the deck. Bluejackets were lining up for the liberty party, the softball team wanted a boat to Aiea Recreation Field, my messmates wanted a boat to Ford Island— and to top it off, the garbage lighter was standing in to take our garbage! I straightened the boats out as best I could, and had the port crane manned. The garbage lighter came alongside, and in its wake came an *Arizona* motor launch with garbage for us to dump. I knew that the *Vestal* was alongside the *Arizona* so she couldn't dump, so I told the coxswain to lie off. As I looked over the side of the ship, I noticed smoke pouring from the *Helena* across the Bay and chuckled a bit to myself. One of the Executive Officers who was at the Naval Academy with me was the Executive Officer of her, and I could visualize him being reprimanded for blowing tubes while the wind was wrong. A split second later another thought flashed through my mind. *She was on fire!*

I called for the boatswain's mate, but before he could come to me I saw a torpedo plane which I casually identified as a TBD, flying towards the battle ships. She was carrying a "fish" which mildly surprised me, but I was flabbergasted when the plane dropped the torpedo! It hit a ship in the battle line and threw an immense column of water twice as high as the masts. For a moment I had the uncomfortable feeling one gets in a thrilling movie; it was incredible but it could be true. Thoughts started racing through my head.

Who is it—was it a mistake—what to do? A large hand caught me by the shoulder and Adolpho Solar, one of my leading boatswain's mates, who shortly thereafter gave his life for his ship, spun me around. "Mr. Taussig, they're bombing Ford Island."

I had heard many high-ranking officers say that we would be attacked in this manner. "General Quarters! Bugler! Boatswain's mate!" I ran for the alarm switch and as I turned it I heard Solar pass the word in a voice developed in sixteen years of service. "Man your general quarters stations on the double! This is no drill, we are being attacked by aircraft, foreign aircraft!"

Now I really had a decision to make. As officer of the deck I was responsible for the ship until properly relieved. As an anti-aircraft director officer, I had the brain needed to control my battery to fight the enemy effectively. Words spoken before a class of midshipmen three years previously by Rear Admiral Draemel flashed though my mind, as they often had previously, "Temper any decision you make by asking yourself this question, 'which is the better for the Navy?' and abide by that decision. You can't go very wrong."

Today, I have no recollection of formally reaching the decision in my mind. I don't remember leaving the deck, climbing the ladders to the boat deck; how many men were already at the guns; what preparations were being made; climbing the ladders to the futtock deck or of any congestion on those ladders. I remember pulling myself into the doorway of my director and for a fleeting second wondering whether I would be scared or not. I wasn't, but I was excited. The director swung around as I put on my phones, but no orders came over them. Then the guns started shooting. For some reason I thought it was amusing that I had no cotton in my ears, and then realized that it was merely the tension relaxing as after the kickoff in a football game. I yelled out of the door for numbers 3 and 5 guns to take director control and 1 and 7 to take local. It was my own private system, which had never been used, but for the situation I thought it highly ingenious. I watched through my checksight after we picked up a plane. I made a set up, but don't know how accurate it was. However a plane disappeared in smoke shortly afterwards, and I felt very smug. I leaned out the door to look for new planes to conquer and noticed that my director, the starboard mount, was swung over to the port side so that my guns were firing to port over the ship structure. I silently blessed the wide-awake individual who had sense enough and presence of mind to pull the firing cutouts, which as a peace time safety precaution kept us from firing over a 65 degree gun elevation. I learned later it was Linnartz.

I had no sooner bestowed my final blessing than I felt a sharp blow on my leg and bottom of my foot, as if someone had hit me with a sledge hammer. Since I was holding on to the door jamb I was not knocked down. In a storm of profanity, very inappropriate for a Sunday morning, I announced to my director crew that the so-and-so's had broken my so-and-so leg. My knee was about eight inches from my hip due to muscle contraction, and my leg simply felt as if it had gone to sleep, although the knee was bent at a grotesque angle.

Well, the war couldn't stop just because of a broken leg, so I stood on my good leg and started twisting my dials. Again a stream of non-Sabbath profanity as I found my twisting didn't change my director set up. Then the director trainer handed me his telescope sight and announced that it wasn't doing him much good. It had been blown loose. What had hit us I still don't know, but my best guess is that it was a chunk of the *Arizona*. Anyhow, the news that the telescopes and director were useless must have discouraged me, for I fell out of the director, twisting so as to break my fall on my chest. As I lay with my chest against the guard rail I noticed men crossing over the brow between the *Arizona* and the *Vestal*, but remembered that there was no smoke except from our guns which were again firing at local control targets. My men picked me up and carried me away from the gun blasts into the fire control shack and laid me on my back on the deck.

I looked around to see which officer was controlling the batteries, and saw none. I took a quick mental check of those I knew were aboard. There were three senior to me that I knew were available, but where were they? I couldn't worry them. I saw that the proper telephones were manned, although the routine reports weren't coming through. Why should they? It was very obvious to me, from the crash of the guns that the batteries were manned and very ready. The machine gun talker reported that the machine guns didn't have very much ammunition, so that word was relayed to the port battery officer. He started to ask why he was told about the machine guns and then must have figured he was the one who must send for the ammunition. We were at peace. Only about 450 rounds of machine gun ammunition were available at the guns because the weather corroded the old fashioned links, and besides we weren't going to fight anyone. Wasn't Kurusu in Washington discussing and ironing out our differences?

With the machine gun ammunition question settled, I started to see what had happened to my leg. The trousers were split from my hip to my knee and my knee was startlingly close to my hip. We ripped the trousers away from the wound and tried to put a tourniquet above the opening, but it was too high on my leg. I was bleeding freely and could only think of one thing. That pool of blood on the deck must not get much bigger or we'd be fresh out of A. A. officers. I grasped the front of my leg with my left hand. The wound looked as if someone had gashed the flesh with a knife. The length of the gash was about three inches long and an inch wide at the surface. There was considerable swelling around the wound and I thought it must be shrapnel. Then I realized that I had been hit from behind, and since there was a hole in front whatever had hit me must have gone completely through! With great reluctance I grabbed the lips of the wound and held them together. The blood oozed through my fingers, but there was no spurting.

The lookouts were reporting planes right and left, but as yet I didn't know who was attacking us. The consensus was that the Germans had lent some planes to the Japanese, because the dive-bombers looked like Stukas—but then the torpedo planes looked like our TBD's. Two facsimiles of combat planes spelled only one thing. They must be the Japs; our friends; we must not do anything to weaken our friendship to Japan; we must send them scrap metal; we can not cruise through their mandated islands, the treaty said that they would not fortify them, so why worry; the scrap we send them won't make good munitions; their Navy is too weak to fight; their planes are obsolete.

Our little yellow brothers!

The machine guns were reporting that the water lines had parted. The barrels were welding into the slides. No more urine to cool them.

Several of the lookouts were coming into the sky-control to have a look at me. I was the only one wounded on the futtock deck. Only one showed any emotion. He squatted down, put his face in his arms, and rocked back and forth.

The head lookout reported that he could see planes all over, but none were ours. I sent the lookouts to the guns. There didn't seem to be any reason to keep them up there and they could carry ammunition and replace casualties.

There were seven men left with me in the shack. Most were from my director crew, and the others were regular sky-control personnel. They were all top flight bluejackets. They told me which circuits they had manned, and two who had no job took station at the doors to give me a blow-by-blow description of the engagement.

Ensign Landreth, who had the port director, came in and saw me. I knew his director was unable to track because we had been installing new modifications. He told me he felt sort of useless and wanted to know what he could do for me. I told him that I was all right. He must have called a pharmacist's mate because in a few minutes a basket stretcher arrived and with the help of the free men I was lifted into the stretcher and had my wound looked at. There was nothing to be done because I was bleeding too freely so I stuck my hand back over the wound.

Curtis, the pharmacist's mate, had been in the Navy many years, but I believe it was the first time he had ever been top side when the guns were firing. As soon as he had done his work he became nervous. It didn't last long and in a short while he was calm as ever.

I asked one of the men for a cigarette and lit it. It sure tasted mighty good. I blew smoke rings and wondered how long this fight would last and what the results would be. Just then there was a terrific jar, although I don't remember much extra noise, and the ship lurched and listed a little to port. My port lookout didn't say anything so I decided he felt I shouldn't know what had happened. However, my cigarette was out and I knew it must have been a large bomb or a torpedo. One of the men came to me and held my head up so I could see out of the starboard door, so I figured there must also be smoke to port—and that meant fire.

Rueber, the man holding my head, relit my cigarette, and I blew some more smoke rings. I had never felt more useless in my life. When I should have been directing my battery, my director was damaged and I was wounded. All my guns were on local control, and I couldn't be on deck supervising the firing. I would like to have taken the pointer's seat on one of the guns. I had a few pet theories I wanted to work on.

My thoughts were again shattered by a new type of gunfire. My God, the secondary battery had opened up! These guns are for torpedo defense and have a very low maximum elevation. I wondered what was up. I later learned that Ensign Dunlap, whose battle station was in the foretops, and whose job it was to estimate how much our main battery salvos needed correcting in order to hit, had left his station because it was obvious that the Main Battery would not be used, and had gone down to the secondary battery guns and had them unlimber against low flying planes that were strafing boats in the water. My lookout reported shortly afterwards that the tail had been shot from one of the planes and I was amazed. My thoughts went back to the Naval Academy where we had done a little skeet and trap shooting. My goodness, there was Dunlap using a part of his Naval Academy training, which we looked upon as a purely "cultural" sport, for shooting down planes. A resounding cheer went up; he had got another plane, this time right on the nose!

My cigarette was out again. The secondary battery had stopped firing. A bomb must have landed in the casemates, but I wasn't going to let the men ease my feelings this time, so I asked how many guns in the A.A. battery were firing to port. The report was they were still all firing. So I asked where the last bomb had hit, and before thinking he answered, "Inboard, just about at number 4 casemate." From then on the lookouts told me everything that happened. My feelings were forgotten. I felt myself getting weaker and weaker. My right hand was a little greenish and the fingernails were turning blue. I asked for a cup of water and drank it greedily. So I was shocked. I didn't feel any different. The leg didn't hurt and except for the weak feeling, I was physically comfortable. Still, I knew the symptoms and asked to have the stretcher blanket put around me.

The loud speaker suddenly blared. "Lay forward the anchor detail to get underway!" My heart sank. I was the officer of the deck and should get the ship underway. I reached for the ship's service phone and called the conning tower. The talker reported that a signal was in the air for the battleships to get underway. There were no officers in con and Chief Quartermaster Sedberry had control. He wanted enough steam and he would do the rest.

I called the engine room and told them to secure the safety valves on the steaming boilers, and was informed that it was too d—— hot back there. Upon being informed that it would be a d—— sight hotter if I got down there and they weren't secured, the engineer said he would do it. I pictured myself going down the ladders, opening the necessary watertight doors, going through the airlock and raising hell with the fireroom watch. Impossible, of course, but they hadn't thought about that.

The lines were being cast off forward and we were starting to spring around on our stern lines, when Curtis handed me a piece of cotton soaked in water and said that I would need it soon. I was puzzled but accepted it.

I was not smoking when the next bomb hit, but I heard the swish and crash as it fell. Rueber's cigarette went out this time. We were low on matches and I think somewhat more worried about running out of them, than about the damage done to the ship. Bombing seems to affect men that way. Little things become very important.

Meanwhile the Nevada was swinging towards the channel. We had used no tugs, and I was frankly amazed. Our clearances were very small. Fifteen yards forward lay the *Arizona*; thirty yards aft was shoal water. That's not much room for a battleship to maneuver in but Sedberry had the old girl doing her stuff.

I soon learned the reason for the wet cotton. As we pulled alongside the *Arizona*, the heat became intolerable. We had to close the starboard doorway to keep from burning up.

As the door was being closed I saw great clouds of smoke filled with small

pieces of debris rising over the crippled *Arizona*. It was my biggest shock of
the morning. I had many friends on the *Arizona* and I felt their fate deeply.
I placed the wet cotton over my nose to keep from drawing the terrific heat
into my lungs. We must have been within thirty yards of the burning ship
and evidently we caught fire from her which augmented the flames from our
own bomb hits.

The ship had taken more list to port, and I mentally summed up my chances
for survival. I knew the depth of the harbor and the beam of my ship. If it
turned over on its side, I figured I had five feet leeway between myself and
drowning. That didn't seem like much of a chance, so I scratched myself
off the list and lit another cigarette to wait further developments. My starboard
lookout reported more dive bombers coming at us, and sure enough, shortly
afterwards my cigarette went out again.

By this time my back was beginning to get warm, and I decided we must be
on fire below on the navigation bridge. My thoughts went from drowning to
burning. I hadn't decided which I preferred, when the telephone rang and a
voice told me that we had been ordered to run aground.

I was very upset by this intelligence, because as officer of the deck I was
responsible for the ship, and in my mental condition I could only see a General
Court Martial staring me in the face for "running his ship upon a rock or shoal"
as the *Articles for the Government of the Navy* stated it. I objected strenuously,
but when I was informed that the signal was mandatory, I had to give in.

No sooner had I felt the slight jolt of grounding, than I saw the paint on the
bulkheads of the sky-control shack start to blister. I ordered the men to abandon
sky-control and got no response. They were in a huddle about what to do for
me. The small hatches up to sky-control were too small to pass a stretcher
through, so the men decided to lower me by lines tied around my chest and
legs. This seemed impractical to me, so I again ordered them to leave me and
save themselves. Again I received a silent negative.

I thought very highly of all the men with me, and especially of Owens, a
second-class boatswain's mate, with whom I had stood over 400 hours of watch
in the director. His wife had had a baby only two weeks before which he had
never seen. For this reason, I had an overwhelming desire for him to leave me.
If I were to burn I wanted him at least to go. But Owens was firm. He was the
most experienced man up in control and decided to stay and get me out.

They finally lifted the stretcher and started out of the port doorway which
was to windward and consequently had less fire near it. Then they got the foot
of the stretcher down the hatch where it stuck. My chest and shoulders were
above the deck while the rest of me was hanging below. My feet started to
get warm from the fire on the bridge. Two of the men went down the starboard
hatch, fought their way through the flames on the bridge, and pulled on the
foot of the stretcher while two others pushed on the top. In this manner the
stretcher passed through the hatch, and I was on the burning bridge. Fortunately
we were to windward and the flames were small but I did smell burning flesh

and knew that the men were suffering. However, they carried me to the side of the bridge, where I could look down on the signal bridge and on my anti-aircraft crews. Evidently the attacks were over and the men were busy bringing the fire under control and getting rid of our live ammunition. They were heroic. Despite explosions and threat of explosions from the heat around the ammunition boxes, the men were carrying the shells and throwing them over the side. Several exploded before there was a chance of getting rid of them. The officers who were available were directing the fire fighting, and one in particular, Ensign (now Lieutenant) Taylor whose eardrums had been blown out, was striving to overcome a fire near our ready boxes. I called to him, but he was stone deaf.

The men hoisted the stretcher over the bridge railing, and lowered me slowly to the boat (gun) deck. As I passed the signal bridge I saw our signal flag bags burning, giving out a dense smoke. Four men on the gun deck got the stretcher as it came down, and carried me aft to the battle dressing station. The scenes that I passed on the way there told a mute story of faithfulness to duty and devotion to country, that was so deep that to attempt to describe it is folly. We had lost 180 men in dead and wounded on a battery of 220 men. Most of these would have been saved if they had sought safety from the fire and strafing attacks, but no man left his station and consequently, the *Nevada* which started firing with all her guns and men, finished with all her guns blazing in the manner of the queen that she was. Her men had made that sacrifice for her.

As I entered the battle dressing station, I noticed many men whose skin hung from their arms like moss from a tree. They all seemed to think their buddies were much worse off and consequently should be helped. They were attempting to assist the stretcher bearers with hands from which the skin had been badly burnt.

I was shifted from the stretcher to a bunk and given a shot of morphine by the ship's doctor, who, aided by his staff and hospital corpsmen, was trying to help everyone at once. I was in a lower bunk and across from me in another tier I could see three men lying prone with terrible burns. The man on the top bunk was recognizable only because of his physique and a small shock of blond hair which hadn't burned. He was smoking a cigarette held between burned fingers through which the bone showed. He leaned over and I spoke to him. He said that he figured he was pretty badly burned, but that the fellow in the bunk under him was worse off, so he had told the doctor to treat his buddy first. I saw his buddy six months later. The man in the top bunk died without changing the position that he had struggled to, to talk to me. I watched the blood from his hands put out his cigarette.

Shortly thereafter I was shifted back to my stretcher and taken up to the fantail. There I was hoisted over the rail into a motor-whale-boat. There was an ensign in charge who was a stranger to me, so I introduced myself, asked of his ship, and of my classmate who was a shipmate of his. The ensign's name was Hollingsworth, a slow spoken southerner, who was attached to the Destroyer

Shaw. When his ship had blown up, he had picked himself up in the marine railway and manned the boat he was in. With his small crew he had made several trips to the *Oklahoma* to pick men out of the water. He had been strafed several times, but had solved the problem by throwing the stern of the boat towards the strafing plane and the bullets passed harmlessly on either side of his boat.

He had figured that the men had had enough nerve-wracking experiences for a while, so had made the short trip to the *Nevada* as a nerve cure. However, bluejackets are a very loyal body of men. These men felt that the *Oklahoma* was theirs to help, and resented having to deviate from their rescue work on that ship.

I was carried from the dock to a yard worker's car. He had made many trips that morning and his rear seat was bloody and ruined from the bleeding of his passengers. I remember taking his license number and his civilian worker button number in order to repay him for the damage done, but the morphine had started to work on me, and I promptly forgot both. I remember nothing after getting in his car until the doctor said, "Give him another quarter grain of morphine, nurse."

AUTHOR'S NOTE

This short article of my personal experiences in Pearl Harbor is not a story of the whole battle, because, believe me, no one saw the whole thing and there are still very many unanswered questions. However, it is a story of a typical young naval officer (myself) who was thrown up against a tremendous problem without warning, and I can tell you that the results were amazing.

My ship, the Nevada, was one of the oldest in service and the oldest at Pearl Harbor, but really put on the best show, having been the only battleship to be able to get under way. In the article I have touched on the heroism of my men only in instances where I actually saw it and I have used no hearsay.

The narrative is a little disjointed and I believe one must hear the swish and thud of bombs to appreciate why.

The only man mentioned (besides the author and officers) who was commended and lived to tell the tale was Curtis, the pharmacist's mate.

About myself, I was born in Newport, R. I., on May 28, 1920. My father is Vice Admiral Taussig U.S.N. (ret.) and my grandfather was Rear Admiral E. D. Taussig U.S.N. (ret.) and we have been solidly Navy since 1863, when grandfather entered Annapolis.

I graduated from the Naval Academy in 1941 and the Nevada was my first ship. Since leaving the Nevada I have been hospitalized for the broken leg, which added up to four inches of bone crushed (the doctors have been able to save all but 1½ inches of my leg) and a badly infected wound caused by my hand which held the wound together to keep me from bleeding to death. I was told that it would be a two-year tour in the hospital the day after I got hurt and naturally, I thought the doctor was crazy. However, it's been 53 weeks now and although progress is being made, the doctors no longer make estimates. I was awarded the Navy Cross for the usual etc. etc., business, but I have an understanding with my men, that I wear it for them and that it is more theirs than mine. I just happened to be the boss at the right time.

Joseph K. Taussig, Jr.
Lieutenant, U. S. Navy

U. S. Naval Hospital
Newport, R. I.
December 11, 1942

FRED C. KELLY

◀—————————————————————————————▶

Have You a Mistress?

As THE result of my own little survey, conducted largely by telephone calls to my more adventurous and informed friends, plus some meditative looking out of the window, I am ready to report at this juncture that the practice of mistress-keeping in the U. S. is on the downgrade. My conclusions may not upset Dr. Kinsey or cause any hurried changes in his forthcoming report dealing with the American female, but they seem to me sound.

A mistress, it appears, is of much interest to every man who is honest with himself—particularly if it is someone else's mistress, about whose existence he doesn't need to be secretive. I'm using the commonly accepted definition of a "mistress," that the relationship must have a semblance of permanence; a lady is not a mistress if she merely grants special favors now and then with no expectation that they are to continue.

I have no exact figures, but have been making some estimates. In doing so, I have consulted the epochal work of Dr. Kinsey on a phase of the habits of the American male. It seems that about one-half of all married men in the United States explore new pastures at one time or another. Their behavior varies according to educational level. Those who have not been to college are likely to do their roaming during the early years of marriage. The odds seem to be against any permanent alliance as a result of this experimenting. Maintaining a mistress doesn't quite pay off.

As I conceded, my report is based largely upon my own investigations. It so happens, though, that I'm an attentive listener, and both men and women have been known to confide in old Uncle Fred. From what evidence I can gather— with a little conjecture added—it appears that the man who seeks a mistress is most likely to be one getting along toward middle age, of college education, whose wife's book learning is less than his own. He is apt to be fairly successful— not tied too closely to office hours, and not obliged to use most of his earnings to meet his household budgets. The percentage of men who fulfill all these qualifications is doubtless fairly small. It is further reduced by the problem of geographical location. If a man lives on a farm or in a village, his opportunities are not too good. Mistresses are to be found mostly in a few large cities. In New York, quite suitable for anonymity, one does not need to look far to find interesting specimens. Washington, too, with its considerable semi-leisure

March, 1950

class and shifting population of well-to-do people, may be expected to have its full quota.

I know a man who happened to go to a cocktail party in Washington, where he was holding down a temporary war job, and soon afterward found himself with a mistress. He expected to return to a more routine life when the war was over; but when his job was ended, he discovered that it was not quite so simple to drop such an alliance as to start it. He received hints that if he became too forgetful perhaps his wife might hear a piece of news. He found it necessary to make fairly frequent trips to Washington, as a result, and though nothing has yet happened to break the pattern, he devotes much time to worrying.

I have said nothing about unmarried men who den-up with women out of wedlock. Since most men get married, the number of bachelors with love nests could not much affect the statistical average. My observation is, though, that bachelors have even more troubles with their mistresses than married men do. When the relationship seems too good to give up and yet not good enough to keep, it is convenient to have a marriage in the background as a deterrent to going further than one or the other wants to go. Bachelors and their mistresses seem much given to violent quarrels.

It is because the mistress plan is exceptional that it stirs our curiosity. What causes a man to lead a double life? If his wife doesn't suit him, why doesn't he get a divorce? I know one man who says getting a divorce would mean too much bother—too much red tape. Then, there's my friend Edwards. His wife is older than he, and he would be hard put to explain why he married her, except that she showed him great affection when he was a youngster working at a humble job. Since then she has given him constant devotion and lives but to serve him. He doesn't want to break her heart and, besides, they have two children. But she has aged rapidly and he feels almost as if he were living with an aunt. So once or twice a month he makes an airplane trip to Chicago, where he has a comely friend he has known since school days. She is widowed, works for an advertising agency, and is too businesslike to favor one client over another; in the office she is known as cold and aloof. Her arrangement with a man from out of town is exactly to her taste. Both like the arrangement so well that it has gone on for some time, and both try to think that the wife is not really being deprived of anything. I doubt that she would agree, if she knew all the facts, but at any rate that is the way they have chosen to rationalize a selfish situation.

Then there's the idealist—the man who is looking for something special, or thinks he is. That's why he picked the wife he did. I have in mind a man whom I shall call Jim. A long time ago, Jim fell in love with a girl he scarcely knew. Now it must be kept in mind that falling in love is by no means the same as being in love, as feeling genuine affection. Falling in love might be generally accepted as a form of insanity if it weren't so common, if it didn't occur in all walks of life to people who in other respects seem sensible enough. Well, anyhow, Jim met this girl and at once began to act the way people do. The slightest expression of her face could make him supremely happy or throw him into despair. No sinful imaginings regarding her entered his head, because he thought of her as an angel, as a creature out of this world. He had not the remotest idea why she was his ideal. Possibly, without his being conscious of it, she reminded him of his mother. They got married and then he became better acquainted with her. He found that she had been raised in so sheltered a way that she thought sex wicked. She insisted that lovemaking be limited to one night a week; and even then it was all too self-conscious and hedged-in to be beautiful.

Jim had not enjoyed wide experience with girls and supposed he had married one typical of the general run. He accepted his situation, and it was some time before he began to glance at the fruit on other trees. Then, one day, he went on business to New York, where he attended a cocktail party and met several young women willing to go look at etchings. One invited him to her apartment. Soon his horizons broadened. He now makes business trips to New York several times a year. The young woman and he like each other, but the last I heard of the affair she was growing restless, not content with these occasional meetings. I fear he's going to face complications. And to make matters worse, it looks as though Jim has a touch of delayed adolescence coming to the surface these days, since he's still afflicted with the wandering eye of the "idealist" and it probably won't be long before he'll be seeking just a little more perfection—and a little more trouble.

A main cause of a steady, though limited, demand for mistresses is the puritanical background that most of us in this country have known. From childhood, in most families, sex is hush-hush, not to be discussed openly. Sex codes and moral codes are jumbled together. For that reason, even in the privacy of many homes, nudity is frowned upon. Doctors, psychiatrists, social workers, and the Kinsey report all say that an astonishing number of husbands lack precise knowledge of how their wives would look undraped. More married women than you'd think would feel shocked even to look into a full-length mirror without the protection of at least a nightie; and they shy from love-making except in darkness. The husband, who has to depend on imagination and guesswork, may begin speculating on how entertaining he might be in the right company, or at least thinking that a change of scene might offer a nice diversion.

The husband himself may be inhibited or diffident, particularly when first associated in an intimate way with a well-bred young woman whom he has kept on a pedestal. Without quite understanding why, he may feel the need of surroundings where he could feel more at ease and more playful. Maupassant doubtless knew his psychology when he wrote a short story about the man who, on his wedding night, first visited a bagnio to get himself into the right frame of mind.

Our puritanical background often creates an interest in outside talent for a quite different reason. Since sex is taboo, it is forbidden fruit, and the pursuit of it is adventure. Where nothing is illicit—as in wedlock, with the supposedly neat combination of temptation and opportunity that G. B. Shaw has mentioned—part of the adventure is lacking. If a husband is at heart a romanticist with an inquiring mind, he may think it jolly to see what he could find in another orchard.

For most people, though, a necessity for secrecy has its disadvantages. There's not only the danger of being discovered and stirring up a ruckus; we simply do not like the idea that something questionable about us could be found out. These matters are handled in a more matter-of-fact way in Europe. In France, partly for economic reasons, it used to be fairly common practice—and I suppose still is—for a young man to join with a girl, known as his little friend, in setting up housekeeping on a modest scale, with a sharing of costs and responsibilities. Perhaps both are employed; he pays the rent and part of the grocery bill, and she does the cooking. Thus there is a money saving, and any other advantages are sort of thrown in. Usually the male of the duo felt no obligation to take his little friend about with him socially as if she were his wife. A kind of unwritten rule, however, was that she could expect him to take her to a good restaurant or give her a pleasant outing at least one night a week. When the arrangement was known to their friends, no one seemed inclined to make any fuss about it.

What is true in France is possibly because the French have achieved a uniquely sophisticated point of view on sex relations which few Americans can even understand, much less follow. One never hears of "affairs" in Milwaukee or Kansas City or Los Angeles or St. Louis in which the wife demurely puts up with another woman in her husband's life and even encourages a certain social relationship in which the jolly little trio meet for drinks or supper, as in a Noel Coward comedy. Just as apocryphal as the Design-For-Living tête-à-tête seems to be the wise and tolerant wife who understands that a little fling with a mistress will bring her John (still a boy at heart) back to her more loving and contented than ever. It doesn't often happen that way.

One man I know decided to have a bit of adventure and still not run any chances. He persuaded his wife that it would be a lark if they spent a week end at a hotel under an assumed name, pretending to be in mischief. He bought her flowers, an expensive negligee, and champagne. The affair took a turn more realistic than planned. She went out on an errand, leaving him in the room. Then she couldn't remember the name they had registered under and was not quite sure of the room number. She had to rap at three different doors before she found the right one. At one of the other rooms, the young man who came to the door tried to persuade her to tarry. So alarmed was she that when she rejoined her husband she was glad to see him. From hints he gave me, I judged that they had a pleasant time.

The most serious problem about having a mistress, I gather, is that the very things that make her desirable also make her dangerous. You cling to her because she is fond of you, genuinely interested in your welfare, always striving to chase away your worries and give you a sense of well-being. But, being fond of you, she comes to resent sharing you with a wife. She feels sure that the wife isn't doing right by you; that she doesn't even look after your home properly. I know of one mistress who said, "When I love a man as much as I do you, I'm not content to enjoy him only in my bedroom. We ought to be sharing a greater variety of interests." Little by little, she nudged him toward a divorce court. Then, after he had married her, he didn't like her nearly so well as before. As he explained to me, "The price was too high—I mean, in making another woman unhappy and all the emotional disturbances I suffered. We never like what costs too much, do we?"

Another friend told me of his problem. "It seemed ideal at first, our arrangement. What I liked best about it was that she had no interest in matrimony. She had been married once and seemed to prefer her freedom. She used to say, 'You're a wonderful friend, but you'd be a dreadful husband.' So I felt that our relations were on a high plane, with no ulterior motives on either side—just a nice exchange of courtesies. Little by little, though, I could see a sordid element coming in. She began to refer to the sad lack of permanence of our situation. Having observed that I was sober and industrious, with good earning power, she began asking herself, 'Why not a marriage certificate to hang over my bed?' She wanted me to do something I didn't want to do. That spoiled everything. She was like a drug that I hated to give up; and yet I knew I had to."

A most serious point against the whole idea of a mistress is, of course, the problem of the children at home. A man weary of his wife or simply in a frolicsome frame of mind may well think twice before exposing his children to the humiliation of learning the results of papa's roving eye; perhaps he risks losing their love, something he might consider most precious of all.

The headaches from mistresses greatly exceed the joys. But when we sum up all of the reasons why the number of mistresses is probably less than one might suspect—considering the romantic way many of the famous ones have been portrayed—we still haven't stumbled on the one true reason why this is so. Despite the divorce figures, marriage is still the most popular arrangement. Although it may sometimes seem prosaic, marriage has its points. Perhaps in France there are many mistresses because of the number of marriages of convenience; and a husband who has married for position or because all had been "arranged" may have his reasons for straying a bit. But American men as a group still seem "unsophisticated" enough to marry for love, and even with all the well-stressed failures, American women can do right well at keeping the home fires burning. With marriage there is at least the hope and expectation of permanence and emotional security. Marriage is still the best solution to a puzzling problem. As for beautiful mistresses, it will be prudent to let the other lads have them.

Memorable Fiction

IF YOU'LL EXCUSE a slight detour, and maybe it's excusable in a book of this size, we'd like to sneak up from behind on the question of *Esquire's* fiction.

Pretend that you are now holding in your hands not this book but a copy of the February 1939 issue of *Esquire*, and further pretend, if it isn't asking too much, that you're reading our editorial page . . .

. . . we've just read Cecil Beaton's *New York*, and right glad we are that we did, because we found out something about you (yes, we do mean you) that you never knew. We mean you and you can't squirm out of it, either, because you're proving it this very instant. For you read *Esquire*, you are reading it now (in flagrante, hey kid?) and here's what Cecil Beaton says about the reader of *Esquire*. Get a load of yourself:

The American expression "Rah-Rah Boy" is used to describe a certain type of college youth who watches football games in a big fur coat and a porkpie hat, with a bit of feather in the band, and shouts for his team as he waves the college pennant from a stick. The trained fan-choruses shout "Rah-Rah!" (At particularly rowdy parties the Rah-Rah Boy may shout at intervals the approving slogan, "Razzle-Dazzle!") He probably drinks heavily, drives a sports car recklessly, dances ecstatically, flirts continuously

and reads a little. Ess-quire or Esky (the magazine for men) is his bible.

Now, how do you feel, you great big beautiful fan-chorus man? If you'll stop waving that dad-blamed pennant for a minute (*Twenty-three skidoo,* you "*chicken-inspector,*" you! *Razzle-dazzle, gol ding it!*) we reckon we'll go on. Oh, sure, there's more. Look at us:

Esquire shows what we must wear to be original, giving undue importance to petty changes in men's clothes." (Editor's time-out: Can you tie that for ignorance? He don't even seem to know that Petty begins with a capital P!)

Esquire also supplies slightly risky cartoons (wife versus secretary or pretty housemaid) that recall La Vie Parisienne tricked out as something hearty and virile. The fiction seems oddly incongruous, finely written by the most interesting of younger American authors, while the best names in journalism contribute illuminating and intelligent articles on matters of current moment.

How do you like that? So our fiction's incongruous, huh? Confidentially . . . well, Cecil should just hear what some of you boys of the fan-chorus call it. Let him put *that* in his pork-pie . . .

All right, unquote. The point is simply that, from the start, many *Esquire* readers seemed to find its fiction difficult. *The Sound and the Fury* kept chanting, with a pertinacious insistence worthy of a cheering-section intoning, "We wanna touchdown," a plain song pleading with us to "Cut out the goofy endings."

This plaint of the plain reader ran to the effect that *Esquire's* stories were so dad-gummed arty or literary, realistic or highbrow or something (for any or all of which read "goofy") that the plain reader couldn't for the life of him tell, upon coming to the end of them, whether or not he had indeed come to the end. The endings were that goofy.

From January 1935 to June 1935 we argued with the readers about this, saying that we hated to fall into the old ruts that had been worn so deep by the formula-type stories that comprised the bulk of the fiction in the so-called slick-paper magazines, and pleading for their tolerance, if not their appreciation, of a better class of fiction, the truly character-integrated story where plot, or lack of plot, was an integral and inevitable outgrowth of the honest depiction of individual character. We pointed out this was the best type of story, the kind that should appeal to the mature and cultivated taste, while admitting that this is the kind of story whose ending is as inconclusive as that of life itself which ends, much more often than not, with little accomplished and nothing proved.

Still the plaints of the plain readers mounted, until in June of 1935 we finally fixed 'em by devising our own particular "end-of-joke" method of designating the terminal point of each story or article. This was accomplished by the installation of the dingus, that odd object composed of three verticals and a crossbar, with which all Esquire text features have ended ever since. This device, the approximate aesthetic equivalent of blowing a whistle, or ringing a bell, to bring the reader out of whatever trance *Esquire's* fiction may have put him in, was a great and lasting success.

To us, the endings still seemed no whit more or less goofy than before, but those readers for whose especial benefit the dingus was invented have hailed it as the most humane thing ever done for them.

ERNEST HEMINGWAY'S
"The Tradesman's Return"

WE COULDN'T THINK of a collection of writings from *Esquire's* pages without including a Hemingway story. For the magazine's first two years he was the lead-off man in our monthly batting order, crowning his efforts with the longest home run ever hit out of our park, "The Snows of Kilimanjaro," which first appeared in *Esquire* for August, 1936.

But it has also appeared in virtually every anthology published ever since, including our own 1940 *Bedside Esquire*, so we thought we'd make sure that this present collection might acquire one more claim to distinction by omitting it, and including instead another of Hemingway's contributions, "The Tradesman's Return," which first appeared as a story in *Esquire* for February 1936 and was later incorporated into the novel *To Have and Have Not*.

If you care to hear how we felt, and feel, about Ernest Hemingway's role in *Esquire*, here's what we said in our June 1937 issue:

For the magazine's first two years he was its most conscientious contributor. He had to send his copy in from all over the world and he never let us down. He more than once chartered planes to reach a point where he could dispatch his piece in time to make our monthly deadline. He began with us before the magazine even had a name, before it was even assured of a future. And for those first two years he was in there swinging every time it was his turn at bat. The worst he ever did was a neat single over the first baseman's head. Usually he hit for extra bases. And that was at that stage of the game when hits meant runs. To prolong the simile a bit, we were strictly a rookie bunch, and bush league at that, when he joined us. In the training-camp period, before our awkward squad took to the road for its first season, he took a lot of the kinks out of us, smoothed off some of our worst amateur roughnesses and saw to it that we greeted the stands with something of the semblance of pros. He was in there when we needed him and as long as we needed him. He never needed us.

He helped us. We're not sure that we helped him. But we're pretty sure he's too big to be either helped or hurt. The magazine may be the same to you without him. It isn't to us. It's bigger than ever, as you can see. And the sales, the only guide we've got, say it's better, too. That's fine. We're happy, if you're satisfied. If it's all the same to you, that's swell. But it isn't the same to us. And we think that a magazine, unlike an individual, can never be too big to be either helped or hurt. Lord knows this one has survived moves of ours that looked more hurtful than helpful, and flourishes like the proverbial green bay tree. There have been times when it has seemed to profit the largest from our most awkward mistakes. But we wander now from our point, which is that Hemingway's gone. But not forgotten.*

* After this farewell, Hemingway reappeared in *Esquire* with three more stories.

F. SCOTT FITZGERALD'S
"Pat Hobby's Christmas Wish"

WHY THE GREAT Scott Fitzgerald revival of a few years back failed to pick up the novel-length series of "Pat Hobby" stories, when publishing interest seemed to extend to everything down to and including his laundry slips, is beyond our understanding.

But here's one of them—and there were at least seventeen others. Together they would make a better book about (as well as by) Scott Fitzgerald than any of those that have appeared about him, including one that achieved best-sellerdom.

Here's what we said about the "Pat Hobby" series just after his death:

Here at Esquire he was the seven-year despair of our proofroom. Very seldom did we manage to get to press with any of his writing without receiving from one to four revised versions after the original had been set in type. And every time he wrote a new Pat Hobby story he would want the order of appearance shuffled all over again on all those awaiting publication. More than once we received revised versions of the Hobby stories either on or after the date of their actual appearance on the newsstands. Each time that happened he would act as if his whole career had been torpedoed without warning. Finally we had to send him a sort of ultimatum laying down the deadlines for revision on the various stories in the series. As this is written two of those time-limits have not yet expired.

Certainly this sequence of Pat Hobby stories adds up to something considerably short of being a masterpiece. Yet it could hardly be more fitting, as Scott's last word from his last home, for much of what he felt about Hollywood and about himself permeated these stories. Both the first and the last time he left for Hollywood he set out with a sad, proud air of resignation, like a young Russian nobleman being banished to Siberia.

Failure always fascinated him. That's why he enjoyed writing about Pat Hobby more than almost any character that came from his pen since that first far away and long ago Amory Blaine. (We are suddenly reminded of a truism with which Scott began one of his early short stories: "Start out with an individual and you find that you have created a type—

start out with a type and you find that you have created nothing.") And if your memory goes away back twenty years to This Side of Paradise, you may be interested to hear that his own favorite scene in that first book 'of his was the one where the boy holds his classmates breathless while he opens the envelope in which a pink slip will tell him that he stays in Princeton, or a blue slip that he must leave. Waving the failure slip he says, "Blue as the sky, gentlemen"—a gesture worthy of Cyrano and his plume at heaven's gate.

His last letter to this office, a matter of days before his death, spoke of his new novel, still unfinished in its first draft, as "a book I confidently expect to sell all of a thousand copies." If he had gone on from that one remark for pages more he could not possibly have given better expression to the attitude that was so typical of him, a blend of insouciance and despair.

ERNEST HEMINGWAY

The Tradesman's Return

THEY came on across in the night and it blew a big breeze from the North West. When the sun was up he sighted a tanker coming down the Gulf and she stood up so high and white with the sun on her in that cold air that it looked like tall buildings rising out of the sea and he said to the nigger, "Where the hell are we?"

The nigger raised himself up to look.

"Aint nothing like that this side of Miami."

"You know damn well we aint been carried up to no Miami," he told the nigger.

"All I say aint no buildings like that on no Florida keys."

"We've been steering for Sand Key."

"We got to see it then. It or American shoals."

Then in a little while he saw it was a tanker and not buildings and then in less than an hour he saw Sand Key light, straight, thin and brown, rising out of the sea right where it ought to be.

"You got to have confidence steering," he told the nigger.

"I got confidence," the nigger said. "But the way this trip gone I aint got confidence no more."

"How's your leg?"

"It hurts me all the time."

"It aint nothing," the man said. "You keep it clean and wrapped up and it'll heal by itself."

He was steering to the westward now to go in to lay up for the day in the mangroves by Woman Key where he would not see anybody and where the boat was to come out to meet them.

"You're going to be all right," he told the Negro.

"I don't know," the nigger said. "I hurt bad."

"I'm going to fix you up good when we get in to the place," he told him. "You aren't shot bad. Quit worrying."

"I'm shot," he said. "I aint never been shot before. Anyway I'm shot is bad."

"You're just scared."

"No sir. I'm shot. And I'm hurting bad. I've been throbbing all night."

February, 1936

89

The nigger went on grumbling like that and he could not keep from taking the bandage off to look at it.

"Leave it alone," the man who was steering told him. The nigger lay on the floor of the cockpit and there were sacks of liquor, shaped like hams, piled everywhere. He had made himself a place in them to lie down in. Every time he moved there was the noise of broken glass in the sacks and there was the odor of spilled liquor. The liquor had run all over everything. The man was steering in for Woman Key now. He could see it now plainly.

"I hurt," the nigger said. "I hurt worse all the time."

"I'm sorry, Wesley," the man said. "But I got to steer."

"You treat a man no better than a dog," the nigger said. He was getting ugly now, but the man was still sorry for him.

"I'm going to make you comfortable, Wesley," he said, "You lay quiet now."

"You don't care what happens to a man," the nigger said. "You aint hardly human."

"I'm going to fix you up good," the man said. "You just lay quiet."

"You aint going to fix me up," the nigger said. The man, whose name was Harry, said nothing then because he liked the nigger and there was nothing to do now but hit him, and he couldn't hit him. The nigger kept on talking.

"Why we didn't stop when they started shooting?"

The man did not answer.

"Aint a man's life worth more than a load of liquor?"

The man was intent on his steering.

"All we have to do is stop and let them take the liquor."

"No," the man said. "They take the liquor and the boat and you go to jail."

"I don't mind jail," the nigger said. "But I never wanted to get shot."

He was getting on the man's nerves now and the man was becoming tired of hearing him talk.

"Who the hell's shot worse?" he asked him. "You or me?"

"You're shot worse," the nigger said. "But I aint never been shot. I didn't figure to get shot. I aint paid to get shot. I don't want to be shot."

"Take it easy, Wesley," the man told him. "It don't do you any good to talk like that."

They were coming up on the Key now. They were inside the shoals and as he headed her into the channel it was hard to see with the sun on the water. The nigger was going out of his head, or becoming religious because he was hurt; anyway he was talking all the time.

"Why they run liquor now?" he said. "Prohibition's over. Why they keep up a traffic like that? Whyn't they bring the liquor in on the ferry?"

The man steering was watching the channel closely.

"Why don't people be honest and decent and make a decent honest living?"

The man saw where the water was rippling smooth off the bank even when he could not see the bank in the sun and he turned her off. He swung her around, spinning the wheel with one arm, and then the channel opened out and he took her slowly right up to the edge of the mangroves. He came astern on the engines and threw out the two clutches.

"I can put a anchor down," he said. "But I can't get no anchor up."

"I can't even move," the nigger said.

"You're certainly in a hell of a shape," the man told him.

He had a difficult time breaking out, lifting, and dropping the small anchor but he got it over, and paid out quite a lot of rope and the boat swung in against the mangroves so they came right into the cockpit. Then he went back and down into the cockpit. He thought the cockpit was a hell of a sight, all right.

All night after he had dressed the nigger's wound and the nigger had bandaged his arm he had been watching the compass, steering, and when it came daylight he had seen the nigger lying there in the sacks in the middle of the cockpit, but then he was watching the seas and the compass and looking for the Sand Key light and he had never observed carefully how things were. Things were bad.

The nigger was lying in the middle of the load of sacked liquor with his leg up. There were eight bullet holes through the cockpit splintered wide. The glass was broken in the windshield. He did not know how much stuff was smashed and wherever the nigger had not bled he himself had bled. But the worst thing, the way he felt at the moment, was the smell of booze. Everything was soaked in it. Now the boat was lying quietly against the mangroves but he could not stop feeling the motion of the big sea they had been in all night in the Gulf.

"I'm going to make some coffee," he told the nigger. "Then I'll fix you up again."

"I don't want no coffee."

"I do," the man told him. But down below he began to feel dizzy so he came out on deck again.

"I guess we won't have coffee," he said.

"I want some water."

"All right."

He gave the Negro a cup of water out of a demi-john.

"Why you want to keep on running for when they started to shoot?"

"Why they want to shoot?" the man answered.

"I want a doctor," the nigger told him.

"What's a doctor going to do that I aint done for you?"

"Doctor going to cure me."

"You'll have a doctor tonight when the boat comes out."

"I don't want to wait for no boat."

"All right," the man said. "We're going to dump this liquor now."

He started to dump it and it was hard work one handed. A sack of liquor only weighs about forty pounds but he had not dumped very many of them before he became dizzy again. He sat down in the cockpit and then he lay down.

"You going to kill yourself," the nigger said.

The man lay quietly in the cockpit with his head against one of the sacks.

The branches of the mangroves had come into the cockpit and they made a shadow over him where he lay. He could hear the wind above the mangroves and looking out at the high, cold sky see the thin blown clouds of the norther.

"Nobody going to come out with this breeze," he thought. "They won't look for us to have started with this blowing."

"You think they'll come out?" the nigger asked.

"Sure," the man said. "Why not?"

"It's blowing too hard."

"They're looking for us."

"Not with it like this. What you want to lie to me for?" The nigger was talking with his mouth almost against a sack.

"Take it easy, Wesley," the man told him.

"Take it easy, the man says," the nigger went on. "Take it easy. Take what easy? Take dyin like a dog easy? You got me here. Get me out."

"Take it easy," the man said, kindly.

"They aint coming," the nigger said. "I know they aint coming. I'm cold I tell you. I can't stand this pain and cold I tell you."

The man sat up feeling hollow and unsteady. The nigger's eyes watched him as he rose on one knee, his right arm dangling, took the hand of his right arm in his left hand and placed it between his knees and then pulled himself up by the plank nailed above the gunwale until he stood, looking down at the nigger, his right hand still held between his thighs. He was thinking that he had never really felt pain before.

"If I keep it out straight, pulled out straight, it don't hurt so bad," he said.

"Let me tie it up in a sling," the nigger said.

"I can't make a bend in the elbow," the man said. "It stiffened that way."

"What we goin to do?"

"Dump this liquor," the man told him. "Can't you put over what you can reach, Wesley?"

The nigger tried to move to reach a sack, then groaned and lay back.

"Do you hurt that bad, Wesley?"

"Oh God," the nigger said.

"You don't think once you moved it it wouldn't hurt so bad?"

"I'm shot," the nigger said. "I aint going to move. The man wants me to go to dumpin liquor when I'm shot."

"Take it easy."

"You say that once more I go crazy."

"Take it easy," the man said quietly.

The nigger made a howling noise and shuffling with his hands on the deck picked up the whetstone from under the coaming.

"I'll kill you," he said. "I'll cut your heart out."

"Not with no whetstone," the man said. "Take it easy, Wesley."

The nigger blubbered with his face against a sack. The man went on slowly lifting the sacked packages of liquor and dropping them over the side.

While he was dumping the liquor he heard the sound of a motor and looking he saw a boat headed toward them coming down the channel around the end of the key. It was a white boat with a buff painted house and a wind shield.

"Boat coming," he said. "Come on Wesley."

"I can't."

"I'm remembering from now on," the man said. "Before was different."

"Go ahead an remember," the nigger told him. "I aint forgot nothing either."

Working fast now, the sweat running down his face, not stopping to watch the boat coming slowly down the channel, the man picked up the sacked packages of liquor with his good arm and dropped them over the side.

"Roll over," he reached for the package under the nigger's head and swung it over the side. The nigger raised himself up and looked.

"Here they are," he said. The boat was almost abeam of them.

"It's Captain Willie," the nigger said. "With a party."

In the stern of the white boat two men in flannels and white cloth hats sat in fishing chairs trolling and an old man in a felt hat and a windbreaker held the tiller and steered the boat close past the mangroves where the booze boat lay.

"What you say, Harry?" the old man called as he passed. The man called Harry waved his good arm in reply. The boat went on past, the two men who were fishing looking toward the booze boat and talking to the old man. Harry could not hear what they were saying.

"He'll make a turn at the mouth and come back," Harry said to the Negro. He went below and came up with a blanket. "Let me cover you up."

"Bout time you cover me up. They couldn't help but see that liquor. What we goin to do?"

"Willie's a good skate," the man said. "He'll tell them in town we're out here. Those fellows fishing aint going to bother us. What they care about us?"

He felt very shaky now and he sat down on the steering seat and held his right arm tight between his thighs. His knees were shaking and with the shaking he could feel the ends of the bone in his upper arm grate. He opened his knees, lifted his arm out, and let it hang by his side. He was sitting there, his arm hanging, when the boat passed them coming back up the channel. The two men in the fishing chairs were talking. They had put up their rods and one of them was looking at him through a pair of glasses. They were too far out for him to hear what they were saying. It would not have helped him if he had heard it.

On board the charter boat *South Florida*, trolling down the Woman Key channel because it was too rough to go out to the reef, Captain Willie Adams was thinking, so Harry crossed last night. That boy's got *cojones*. He must have got that whole blow. She's a sea boat all right. How you suppose he smashed his windshield? Damned if I'd cross a night like last night. Damned if I'd ever run liquor from Cuba. They bring it all from Mariel now. Just go in and out. It's supposed to be wide open. "What's that you say, Cap?"

"What boat is that?" asked one of the men in the fishing chairs.

"That boat?"

"Yes, that boat."

"Oh that's a Key West boat."

"What I said was, whose boat is it?"

"I wouldn't know that, Cap."

"Is the owner a fisherman?"

"Well some say he is."

"What do you mean?"

"He does a little of everything."

"You don't know his name?"

"No sir."

"You called him Harry."

"Not me."

"I heard you call him Harry."

Captain Willie Adams took a good look at the man who was speaking to him. He saw a high cheekboned, thin-lipped, slightly pudgy face with deep set grey eyes and a contemptuous mouth looking at him from under a white canvas hat. There was no way that Captain Willie Adams could know that this man was regarded as irresistibly handsome by a great many women in Washington.

"I must have called him that by mistake," Captain Willie said.

"You can see that the man is wounded, Doctor," the other man said, handing the glasses to his companion.

"I can see that without glasses," the man addressed as Doctor said. "Who is that man?"

"I wouldn't know," said Captain Willie.

"Well you will know," the man with the contemptuous mouth said. "Write down the numbers on the bow."

"I have them, Doctor."

"We'll go over and have a look," the Doctor said.

"Are you a doctor?" Captain Willie asked.

"Not of medicine," the grey eyed man told him.

"If you're not a medical doctor I wouldn't go over there."

"Why not?"

"If he wanted us he would have signalled us. If he don't want us it's none of our business. Down here everybody aims to mind their own business."

"All right. Suppose you mind yours then. Take us over to that boat."

Captain Willie continued on his way up the channel, the two cylinder Palmer coughing steadily.

"Didn't you hear me?"

"Yes sir."

"Why don't you obey my order?"

"Who the hell you think you are?" asked Captain Willie.

"That's not the question. Do as I tell you."

"Who do you think you are?" Captain Willie asked again.

"All right. For your information I'm one of the three most important men in the United States today."

"What the hell you doing in Key West then?"

The other man leaned forward. "He's ———," he said impressively.

"I never heard of him," said Captain Willie.

"Well, you will," said the man called Doctor. "And so will everyone in this stinking jerkwater little town if I have to grub it out by the roots."

"You're a nice fellow," said Captain Willie. "How did you get so important?"

"He's the most intimate friend and closest adviser of ———," said the other man.

"Nuts," said Captain Willie. "If he's all that what's he doing in Key West?"

"He's just here for a rest," the secretary explained. "He's going to be ———."

"That's enough Harris," the man called Doctor said. "Now will you take us over to that boat," he said smiling. He had a smile which was reserved for such occasions.

"No sir."

"Listen you half-witted fisherman. I'll make life so miserable for you—"

"Yes," said Captain Willie.

"You don't know who I am."

"None of it don't mean anything to me," said Captain Willie. "And you don't know where you are."

"That man is a bootlegger isn't he?"

"What do you think?"

"There's probably a reward for him."

"I doubt that."

"He's a lawbreaker."

"He's got a family and he's got to eat and feed them. Who the hell do you eat off of with people working here in Key West for the Government for six dollars and a half a week?"

"He's wounded. That means he's been in trouble."

"Unless he shot hisself for fun."

"You can save that sarcasm. You're going over to that boat and we're going to take that man and that boat into custody."

"Into where?"

"Into Key West."

"Are you an officer?"

"I've told you who he is," the secretary said.

"All right," said Captain Willie. He pushed the tiller hard over and turned the boat, coming so close to the edge of the channel that the propeller threw up a circling cloud of marl.

He chugged down the channel toward where the other boat lay against the mangroves.

"Have you a gun aboard?" the man called the Doctor asked Captain Willie.

"No sir."

The two men in flannels were standing up now watching the booze boat.

"This is better fun than fishing, eh Doctor?" the secretary said.

"Fishing is nonsense," said the Doctor. "If you catch a sailfish what do you do with it? You can't eat it. This is really interesting. I'm glad to see this at first hand. Wounded as he is that man cannot escape. It's too rough at sea. We know his boat."

"You're really capturing him single handed," said the secretary admiringly.

"And unarmed too," said the doctor.

"With no G-men nonsense," said the secretary.

"Edgar Hoover exaggerates his publicity," said the Doctor. "I feel we've given him about enough rope." Then, "Pull alongside," he said to Captain Willie.

Captain Willie threw out his clutch and the boat drifted.

"Hey," Captain Willie called to the other boat. "Keep your heads down."

"What's that?" the Doctor said angrily.

"Shut up," said Captain Willie. "Hey," he called over to the other boat. "Listen. Get on into town and take it easy. Never mind the boat. They'll take the boat. Dump your load and get into town. I got a guy here on board some kind of a stool from Washington. Not a G-man. Just a stool. One of the heads of the alphabet. More important than the President he says. He wants to pinch you. He thinks you're a bootlegger. He's got the numbers of the boat. I aint never seen you so I don't know who you are. I couldn't identify you—"

The boats had drifted apart. Captain Willie went on shouting, "I don't know where this place is where I seen you. I wouldn't know how to get back here."

"O. K.," came a shout from the booze boat.

"I'm taking this big alphabet man fishing until dark," Captain Willie shouted.

"O. K."

"He loves to fish," Captain Willie yelled, his voice almost breaking. "But the son of a bitch claims you can't eat 'em."

"Thanks, brother," came the voice of Harry.

"That chap your brother?" asked the Doctor, his face very red but his love for information still unappeased.

"No sir," said Captain Willie. "Most everybody goes in boats calls each other brother."

"We'll go into Key West," the Doctor said; but he said it without great conviction.

"No sir," said Captain Willie. "You gentlemen chartered me for a day. I'm going to see you get your money's worth. You called me a halfwit but I'll see you get a full day's charter."

"He's an old man," said the Doctor to his secretary. "Should we rush him?"

"Don't you try it," said Captain Willie. "I'd hit you right over the head with this."

He showed them a length of iron pipe that he used for clubbing shark.

"Why don't you gentlemen just put your lines out and enjoy yourselves? You didn't come down here to get in no trouble. You come down here for a rest. You say you can't eat sailfish but you won't catch no sailfish in these channels. You'd be lucky to catch a grouper."

"What do you think?" asked the Doctor.

"Better leave him alone," the secretary eyed the iron pipe.

"Besides you made another mistake," Captain Willie went on. "Sailfish is just as good eating as kingfish. When we used to sell them to Rios for the Havana market we got ten cents a pound same as kings."

"Oh *shut* up," said the Doctor.

"I thought you'd be interested in these things as a Government man. Aint you mixed up in the prices of things that we eat or something? Aint that it? Making them more costly or something. Making the grits dearer and the grunts cheaper. Fish goin' down in price all the time."

"Oh shut up," said the Doctor.

On the booze boat Harry had the last sack over.

"Get me the fish knife," he said to the nigger.

"It's gone."

Harry pressed the self starters and started the two engines. He got the hatchet and with his left hand chopped the anchor rope through against the bit. It'll sink and they'll grapple it when they pick up the load, he thought. I'll run her up into the Garrison Bight and if they're going to take her they'll take her. I got to get to a Doctor. I don't want to lose my arm and the boat both. The load is worth as much as the boat. There wasn't too much of it smashed. A little smashed can smell plenty.

He shoved the port clutch in and swung out away from the mangroves with the tide. The engines ran smoothly. Captain Willie's boat was two miles away now headed for Boca Grande. I guess the tide's high enough to go through the lakes now, Harry thought. He shoved in his starboard clutch and the engines roared as he pushed up the throttle. He could feel her bow rise and the green mangroves coasted swiftly alongside as the boat sucked the water away from their roots. I hope they don't take her, he thought. I hope they can fix my arm. How was we to know they'd shoot at us in Mariel after we could go and come there open for six months? That's Cubans for you. Somebody didn't pay somebody so we got the shooting. That's Cubans all right.

"Hey Wesley," he said, looking back into the cockpit where the nigger lay with the blanket over him. "How you feeling, Boogie?"

"God," said Wesley. "I couldn't feel no worse."

"You'll feel worse when the old doctor probes for it," Harry told him.

"You aint human," the nigger said. "You aint got human feelings."

That old Willie is a good skate, Harry was thinking. There's a good skate that old Willie. We done better to come in than to wait. It was foolish to wait. I felt so dizzy and sicklike I lost my judgment.

Ahead now he could see the white of the La Concha hotel, the wireless masts, and the houses of town. He could see the car ferries lying at the Trumbo dock where he would go around to head up for the Garrison Bight. That old Willie, he thought. He was giving them Hell. Wonder who those buzzards was? Damn if I don't feel plenty bad right now. I feel plenty dizzy. We done right to come in. We done right not to wait.

"Mr. Harry," said the nigger. "I'm sorry I couldn't help dump that stuff."

"Hell," said Harry. "Aint no nigger any good when he's shot. You're all right nigger, Wesley."

Above the roar of the motors and the high, slapping, rush of the boat through the water he felt a strange hollow singing in his heart. He always felt this way coming home at the end of a trip. I hope they can fix that arm, he thought. I got a lot of use for that arm.

JOHN STEINBECK

The Lonesome Vigilante

THE great surge of emotion, the milling and shouting of the people fell gradually to silence in the town park. A crowd of people still stood under the elm trees, vaguely lighted by a blue street light two blocks away. A tired quiet settled on the people; some members of the mob began to sneak away into the darkness. The park lawn was cut to pieces by the feet of the crowd.

Mike knew it was all over. He could feel the let-down in himself. He was as heavily weary as though he had gone without sleep for several nights, but it was a dream-like weariness, a grey comfortable weariness. He pulled his cap down over his eyes and moved away, but before leaving the park he turned for one last look.

In the center of the mob someone had lighted a twisted newspaper and was holding it up. Mike could see how the flame curled about the feet of the grey naked body hanging from the elm tree. It seemed curious to him that Negroes turn a bluish grey when they are dead. The burning newspaper lighted the heads of the up-looking men, silent men and fixed; they didn't move their eyes from the hanged man.

Mike felt a little irritation at whoever it was who was trying to burn the body. He turned to a man who stood beside him in the near-darkness. "That don't do no good," he said.

The man moved away without replying.

The newspaper torch went out, leaving the park almost black by contrast. But immediately another twisted paper was lighted and held up against the feet. Mike moved to another watching man. "That don't do no good," he repeated. "He's dead now. They can't hurt him none."

The second man grunted but did not look away from the flaming paper. "It's a good job," he said. "This'll save the county a lot of money and no sneaky lawyers getting in."

"That's what I say," Mike agreed. "No sneaky lawyers. But it don't do no good to try to burn him."

The man continued staring toward the flame. "Well, it can't do much harm, either."

Mike filled his eyes with the scene. He felt that he was dull. He wasn't seeing enough of it. Here was a thing he would want to remember later so he

October, 1936

could tell about it, but the dull tiredness seemed to cut the sharpness off the picture. His brain told him this was a terrible and important affair, but his eyes and his feelings didn't agree. It was just ordinary. Half an hour before, when he had been howling with the mob and fighting for a chance to help pull on the rope, then his chest had been so full that he found he was crying. But now everything was dead, everything unreal; the dark mob was made up of stiff lay-figures. In the flamelight the faces were as expressionless as wood. Mike felt the stiffness, the unreality in himself, too. He turned away at last and walked out of the park.

The moment he left the outskirts of the mob a cold loneliness fell upon him. He walked quickly along the street wishing that some other man might be walking beside him. The wide street was deserted, empty, as unreal as the park had been.

The two steel lines of the car tracks stretched glimmering away down the street under the electroliers, and the dark store windows reflected the midnight globes.

A gentle pain began to make itself felt in Mike's chest. He felt with his fingers; the muscles were sore. Then he remembered. He was in the front line of the mob when it rushed the closed jail door. A driving line forty men deep had crashed Mike against the door like the head of a ram. He had hardly felt it then, and even now the pain seemed to have the dull quality of loneliness.

Two blocks ahead the burning neon word BEER hung over the sidewalk. Mike hurried toward it. He hoped there would be people there, and talk to remove this silence; and he hoped the men wouldn't have been to the lynching.

The bartender was alone in his little bar, a small, middle-aged man with a melancholy mustache and an expression like an aged mouse, wise and unkempt and fearful.

He nodded quickly as Mike came in. "You look like you been walking in your sleep," he said.

Mike regarded him with wonder. "That's just how I feel, too, like I been walking in my sleep."

"Well, I can give you a shot if you want."

Mike hesitated. "No—I'm kind of thirsty. I'll take a beer. Was you there?"

The little man nodded his mouse-like head again. "Right at the last, after he was all up and it was all over. I figured a lot of the fellas would be thirsty, so I came back and opened up. Nobody but you so far. Maybe I was wrong."

"They might be along later," said Mike. "There's a lot of them still in the park. They cooled off, though. Some of them trying to burn him with newspapers. That don't do no good."

"Not a bit of good," said the little bartender. He twitched his thin mustache.

Mike knocked a few grains of celery salt into his beer and took a long drink. "That's good," he said. "I'm kind of dragged out."

The bartender leaned close to him over the bar, his eyes were bright. "Was you there all the time—to the jail and everything?"

Mike drank again and then looked through his beer and watched the beads of bubbles rising from the grains of salt in the bottom of the glass. "Everything," he said. "I was one of the first in the jail, and I helped pull on the rope. There's times when citizens got to take the law in their own hands. Sneaky lawyer comes along and gets some fiend out of it."

The mousy head jerked up and down. "You God-dam right," he said. "Lawyers can get them out of anything. I guess the nigger was guilty all right."

"Oh, sure! Somebody said he even confessed."

The head came close over the bar again. "How did it start, mister? I was only there after it was all over, and then I only stayed a minute and then came back to open up in case any of the fellas might want a glass of beer."

Mike drained his glass and pushed it out to be filled. "Well, of course everybody knew it was going to happen. I was in a bar across from the jail. Been there all afternoon. A guy came in and says, 'What are we waiting for?' So we went across the street, and a lot more guys was there and a lot more come. We all stood there and yelled. Then the sheriff come out and made a speech, but we yelled him down. A guy with a twenty-two rifle went along the street and shot out the street lights. Well, then we rushed the jail doors and bust them. The sheriff wasn't going to do nothing. It wouldn't do him no good to shoot a lot of honest men to save a nigger fiend."

"And election coming on, too," the bartender put in.

"Well the sheriff started yelling, 'Get the right man, boys, for Christ's sake get the right man. He's in the fourth cell down.'

"It was kind of pitiful," Mike said slowly. "The other prisoners was so scared. We could see them through the bars. I never seen such faces."

The bartender excitedly poured himself a small glass of whiskey and poured it down. "Can't blame 'em much. Suppose you was in for thirty days and a lynch mob came through. You'd be scared they'd get the wrong man."

"That's what I say. It was kind of pitiful. Well, we got to the nigger's cell. He just stood stiff with his eyes closed like he was dead drunk. One of the guys slugged him down and he got up, and then somebody else socked him and he went over and hit his head on the cement floor." Mike leaned over the bar and tapped the polished wood with his forefinger. " 'Course this is only my idea but I think that killed him. Because I helped get his clothes off, and he never made a wiggle, and when we strung him up he didn't jerk around none. No, sir. I think he was dead all the time, after that second guy smacked him."

"Well, it's all the same in the end."

"No it ain't. You like to do the thing right. He had it coming to him, and he should have got it." Mike reached into his trousers pocket and brought out a piece of torn blue denim. "That's a piece of the pants he had on."

The bartender bent close and inspected the cloth. He jerked his head up at Mike. "I'll give you a buck for it."

"Oh no you won't!"

"All right. I'll give you two bucks for half of it."

Mike looked suspiciously at him. "What do you want it for?"

"Here! Give me your glass! Have a beer on me. I'll pin it up on the wall with a little card under it. The fellas that come in will like to look at it."

Mike haggled the piece of cloth in two with his pocket knife and accepted two silver dollars from the bartender.

"I know a show card writer," the little man said. "Comes in every day. He'll print me up a nice little card to go under it." He looked wary. "Think the sheriff will arrest anybody?"

"'Course not. What's he want to start any trouble for? There was a lot of votes in that crowd tonight. Soon as they all go away, the sheriff will come and cut the nigger down and clean up some."

The bartender looked toward the door. "I guess I was wrong about the fellas wanting a drink. It's getting late."

"I guess I'll get along home. I feel tired."

"If you go south, I'll close up and walk a ways with you. I live on south Eighth."

"Why, that's only two blocks from my house. I live on south Sixth. You must go right past my house. Funny I never saw you around."

The bartender washed Mike's glass and took off the long apron. He put on his hat and coat, walked to the door and switched off the red neon sign and the house lights. For a moment the two men stood on the sidewalk looking back toward the park. The city was silent. There was no sound from the park. A policeman walked along a block away, turning his flash into the store windows.

"You see?" said Mike. "Just like nothing happened."

"Well, if the fellas wanted a glass of beer they must have gone some place else."

"That's what I told you," said Mike.

They swung along the empty street and turned south, out of the business district. "My name's Welch," the bartender said. "I only been in this town about two years."

The loneliness had fallen on Mike again. "It's funny—" he said, and then, "I was born right in this town, right in the house I live in now. I got a wife but no kids. Both of us born right in this town. Everybody knows us."

They walked on for a few blocks. The stores dropped behind and the nice houses with bushy gardens and cut lawns lined the street. The tall shade trees were shadowed on the sidewalk by the street lights. Two night dogs went slowly by, smelling at each other.

Welch said softly—"I wonder what kind of a fella he was—the nigger, I mean."

Mike answered out of his loneliness. "The papers all said he was a fiend. I read all the papers. That's what they all said."

"Yes, I read them, too. But it makes you wonder about him. I've known some pretty nice niggers."

Mike turned his head and spoke protestingly. "Well, I've knew some damn fine niggers myself. I've worked right long side some niggers and they was as nice as any white man you could want to meet.—But not no fiends."

His vehemence silenced little Welch for a moment. Then he said, "You couldn't tell, I guess, what kind of a fella he was?"

"No—he just stood there stiff, with his mouth shut and his eyes tight closed and his hands right down at his sides. And then one of the guys smacked him. It's my idea he was dead when we took him out."

Welch sidled close on the walk. "Nice gardens along here. Must take a lot of money to keep them up." He walked even closer, so that his shoulder touched Mike's arm. "I never been to a lynching. How's it make you feel—afterwards?"

Mike shied away from the contact. "It don't make you feel nothing." He put down his head and increased his pace. The little bartender had nearly to trot to keep up. The street lights were fewer. It was darker and safer. Mike burst out, "Makes you feel kind of cut off and tired, but kind of satisfied, too. Like you done a good job—but tired and kind of sleepy." He slowed his steps. "Look, there's a light in the kitchen. That's where I live. My old lady's waiting up for me." He stopped in front of his little house.

Welch stood nervously beside him. "Come into my place when you want a glass of beer—or a shot. Open 'til midnight. I treat my friends right." He scampered away like an aged mouse.

Mike called "Good night."

He walked around the side of his house and went in the back door. His thin petulant wife was sitting by the open gas oven warming herself. She turned complaining eyes on Mike where he stood in the door.

Then her eyes widened and hung on his face. "You been with a woman," she said hoarsely. "What woman you been with?"

Mike laughed. "You think you're pretty slick, don't you? You're a slick one, ain't you? What makes you think I been with a woman?"

She said fiercely, "You think I can't tell by the look on your face that you been with a woman?"

"All right," said Mike. "If you're so slick and know-it-all, I won't tell you nothing. You can just wait for the morning paper."

He saw doubt come into the dissatisfied eyes. "Was it the nigger?" she asked. "Did they get the nigger? Everybody said they was going to."

"Find out for yourself if you're so slick. I ain't going to tell you nothing."

He walked through the kitchen and went into the bathroom. A little mirror hung on the wall. Mike took off his cap and looked at his face. "By God she was right," he thought. "That's just exactly how I do feel."

◄───►

Babe

I MET Babe for the first time—the first of many times—at a very chi-chi party at the French Club, in Shanghai. That was the time she stole the caviar.

She was sitting at a corner table, looking limpid-eyed at her companion over the rim of her champagne glass. Her hair was blonde, her smartly cut linen dress was exciting against the deep tan of her neck and arms, and she was drunk. Not obviously drunk, in the fashion of cheap tramps, but demurely, subtly drunk, in the fashion of very superior tramps.

Her companion was a young Englishman of the ruddy-cheek and toothbrush-mustache type. His eyebrows were a little higher on his forehead than most people's. This gave him a look of perpetual astonishment. His pongee suit was very correct, in the British style—which is to say that it was tight for him in all places.

I apologized as I borrowed one of the unused chairs at their table and prepared to move it elsewhere.

"Don't apologize, and don't take it!" she said.

"I beg your pardon?"

"I said, don't take it. Sit in it. Here."

The Englishman smiled politely. Babe gave me a long, what-kind-of-a-guy-are-you sort of stare. I made the usual silly remark about not wanting to intrude.

"You're not intruding, Cousin!" she said. "You're on an errand of mercy and you don't know it. I've done my part for Anglo-American relations for today and Captain Whoozis is just about to depart; aren't you, Captain? I'll be goddamed if I'm going to hear any more about yachting at Hendon. Even for champagne."

The Englishman stood up. It was still a smile—the thing on his tomato-red face—but it was a grim smile. His look of genteel loathing included Babe and me and possibly the entire population of the United States, including Hawaii and the Virgin Islands. "I hope you enjoy the rest of my champagne," he said.

"*Chee-lah, Tzoo-loh!*" said Babe, quite casually—which is what you say in a different tone of voice to bothersome ricksha coolies, but not to inoffensive Britons who buy champagne for you. But that was Babe, as I was to find out. We got quite friendly over the Englishman's wine, and I learned a few surface

September, 1950

facts about the attractive young woman in smart white linen who looked like a Junior Leaguer, operated like Dillinger, and had a line of dialogue that would have made Sadie Thompson seem demure.

Her name was simply "Babe."

She was originally from Nevada, but she had been in Shanghai "since Christ only knows when." She drank any kind of champagne, but preferred it when it came out of a bottle that had been paid for by someone she didn't like. ("I wouldn't let a right guy buy champagne for me. It isn't worth the dough.") And she lived in the Rue des Soeurs, in the French Concession, which made her a neighbor of mine—and that was interesting and potentially convenient.

We drank the rest of the Englishman's champagne, and I—always irresponsible after the third or fourth glass—offered to buy another. "The hell with that noise," said Babe. "We'll order another bottle and put it on the Limey's chit." Which wasn't a bad idea when you come to think of it. A man shouldn't order one bottle of champagne unless he's ready to back it up with a second.

We talked about Shanghai, which she said she hated, and the rest of the people at the party, which made for lively, baroque conversation, and about the guest of honor. My little friend was surprised to hear that the blowout had been given in honor of Chaliapin. She had thought it was for the officers of the newly arrived Lancashire Fusiliers and hadn't the faintest idea who or what Chaliapin was.

She was a glib, worldly, raffishly poised little chick in many ways, and yet naïve and uninformed in other respects; but she wasn't in the least dismayed when her shortcomings came to light. She wore her smart clothes easily and well and without seeming to be aware of them. Her little face was narrow and very demure—or it would have been demure had there not been so many four-letter words coming out of it. The lashes were long, and her blonde ringlets reminded you of one of the fantastic sirens that Nell Brinkley used to draw for the Hearst papers. Across the right side of her neck was the scar of a badly healed wound. It was a strange scar; not a clean cicatrice as from a knife, but an uneven, mottled mark like nothing I'd ever seen before.

Anyway, we had quite a yarn, she and I. The guest of honor came and departed without annoying us at all; and more champagne was charged against the poor Britisher's chit without difficulty. The Chinese in charge of the champagne apparently assumed that Babe was the man's wife. Drunk or sober, though, she was a wary little character, and she finally opined that we might just as well leave a little early. "Before that Limey gets a load of what he owes . . . not that I wouldn't enjoy staying and proving to him that he did it all of his own free will."

So we blew. And by an exit that wasn't exactly the most conspicuous egress from the club. On the way out, we came upon a white-gowned coolie who was energetically trundling a small keg into the street. The blonde asked him, in fluently guttural Shanghai dialect, where the hell he was going with the keg. Looking rather hurt that the matter had been brought up, he stood silent.

"He copped it," Babe said, rather admiringly. "What's in it?"

"Black caviar, I think. Enough for all the Tsars, back to and including Ivan the Terrible."

"Oh, goody! We'll pinch it from him. I know a Russian kid over on the Rue de Consulat who'll go nuts over this." And she turned to the coolie and informed him that I was an officer of the Settlement police. His lower jaw dropped as though someone had pulled out a cotter pin. He looked at me as if he expected me to pull a portable jail out of my pocket and slap it around him.

Taking advantage of the psychological moment, Babe told him to get back to the kitchen and forever give up caviar stealing. He wasn't good at it, she said. The poor man dropped the keg, bowed, mumbled something, and trotted quickly away.

"Pick it up, Cousin! You got a car? No? Well, no matter. We'll put it in a ricksha. Hey, *wom-bah-tsaw!*" she bawled, as we emerged on the street.

The Russian kid, who turned out to be a neat little deal in blonde braids, was delighted with the loot, when we delivered it to her. Glowing from the champagne, and pleased with herself because of the good deed and the inspired stroke of larceny, she bade me a friendly farewell.

"I like you," she told me, "if only because you aren't nosy. No questions. Just action. I hate guys who've got to know what gives. The woods are full of them."

I had never seen her before, but now I seemed to see her everywhere. Being taken to the races by young fellows from the British-American Tobacco Company, and Shanghai Power, and the other foreign companies. Dancing at the Little Club or window shopping outside Madame Greenhouse's store on upper Bubbling Well Road. Or having early breakfast down in one of the popular dives in the honky-tonk Hongkew District. She always had a wave and a hoot and a grin for me, or sometimes an acrid grimace of commentary on her escort of the moment.

But I learned nothing more of her background, her identity, or her way of getting by in a town where existence was strictly a dog-eat-dog affair.

One night, I was standing at the Number One Boy's desk at the Paramount Cabaret, waiting for my date to show, when Babe came into the place with a pink-cheeked young character who reeked of Empire. She rather spoiled the chic of her entrance—*très décolleté* and *bouffant*—by goosing me roundly and demanding to know "What's doin'?"

I jerked a thumb toward her escort, who was being very man-of-the-worldish with the Number One Boy, and asked if she had changed her mind about the British. She laughed and rubbed her fingertips against each other in the well-known cash-signifying gesture. "I love them when they're loaded, Cousin!"

When the Boy had shoved them into a ringside and returned to the portal, I tried a small-sized question. "The blonde missy; is she one of the regulars, Lum?"

Lum was usually a great man with the inside information, but he wasn't going to talk about Babe. That was for sure.

"Who is she, Lum? What's her racket?"

"No got racket." Lum wasn't liking me too well at that point.

"Don't get sore. I mean . . . how does she get by?"

I didn't get an answer until he had seated several more parties. By then my date had arrived and we had won ourselves a table. The Number One Boy had recovered his good spirits and figured out an answer. As he pushed my chair in, he murmured, "She . . . how you say? . . . make a buck here, make a buck there."

He laughed, pleased with his knowledge of Americanisms.

I learned some more about Babe from—of all people—Colonel Beauden, the commander of the Marines in Shanghai, who saw me watching her at the jai-alai one night. She was betting fat hunks of money on a big Argentine player, who was certainly justifying her faith.

"That's Babe," said Beauden. "I don't know where she gets it, but I'd rather not risk any evil-minded guesses, for she's a good-hearted wench. Made up the deficit in our fund for the orphanage—the deal we sponsor for the kids these White Russian gals are always having, with some of our men on the co-operating end. Insisted on plunking in nearly a thousand clams. Gold dollars, too. Good-hearted kid."

I thought about the reluctant philanthropy, for such causes, of the elegant lads in the throne rooms of the big American and British companies and I liked the blonde with the brown eyes and the scarred neck even more.

I didn't have a chance to talk to Babe again for many months. For one thing, I moved away from the street on which she lived, and then again, I was put on the late shift of the newspaper that paid for and often got my services, and I wasn't able to get around to the night spots so often.

Then, one night late . . . or, rather, one morning very early, I ran into Babe at the Red Rose, a White Russian dive at the juncture of Jukong Alley and North Szechuan Road, just outside the International Settlement gates.

The Red Rose was gaudy, soiled, drafty, threadbare, and very, very sad. It would have made a wonderful night club for ghosts, or for people who were considering suicide. Perhaps it was the minor-key music that the balalaika band was always plinking away at, or maybe it was the fact that the Russian lady who ran the place always wore black. She was in perpetual mourning for her husband, who had been killed in Russia by the Bolshies twenty years before. He must have been a helluva man.

This career widow from Tomsk—with her brother, a shaven-headed, beetle-browed cretin, who always looked as if he had just disposed of the body—ran the Red Rose with the assistance of probably the most variable sliding scale of prices in Shanghai. The waiters charged according to the individual patron. "Vun bottle uff vine" might cost a resident Shanghai-lander two dollars, Mex. A drunken sailor would be scraped for five bucks, while a let's-go-for-broke tourist would have to reach for a tenner, or maybe more. A White Russian would have torn the place up if asked for more than a dollar-twenty.

You entered through a long passageway, breathing gingerly as the odors of decay, cheap ylang-ylang perfume, Japanese whiskey, and ancient perspiration met your nostrils, and you remained only if you had a taste for curiosa. After a while, though, you might be glad you had stayed. Pleasantly baroque things were always happening there.

Once I heard a beautiful, if somewhat pock-marked, Korean girl sing an aria from *Madame Butterfly* in a way that would have sent the Met's best diva back to Milan for a few more lessons. Another time, a Russian lady intercepted her Portuguese gigolo there while he was entertaining another lady. She removed from his person a striped silk shirt that she had given him. Removed it stripe by stripe.

The Red Rose was very chic, in its way.

I was sitting there minding my own business and listening to the balalaika band brood over *Two Guitars* when Babe wandered in. She was beautifully dressed, as always, and wore one of the strapless, cloth-of-gold evening gowns that were then new in the Orient. She sat down at my table.

"What's doin', Cousin?"

I told her what was doing and we eventually got into one of those pseudo-philosophical, post-midnight conversations about the pointlessness of life, especially life in Shanghai, especially night life of Shanghai. A glittering tread mill was all that it was, we agreed.

"What I'd give," said Babe, "to be in San Francisco, just working for a living! At the telephone company, or at Magnin's, or maybe even dishing out waves and henna rinses in some hole-in-the-wall beauty shop. At the end of the day, I'd be clopping up Post, or Sutter, on my way to a comfortable little kitchenette apartment. I'd stop off at the corner grocery for a loaf of bread and a can of tuna, something for dinner, and a couple of packs of cigarettes. Stateside cigarettes instead of these goddam Mei Li Bah bastards. And a new magazine, fresh and clean, to read. And the afternoon papers. All about Tommy Manville's latest blonde, and the theatre in the Mission that got stuck up that morning, and that prissy schmo, Dick Tracy."

She was far away from the Red Rose, and Jukong Alley, and Shanghai, as she talked. I figured that we'd be in the tears-in-the-beer stage soon at that rate, and so I tried to take a powder on nostalgia. "Mama Russky's going to sing," I said. "Bet a buck she favors us with *Dark Eyes*."

The widow was on the small stage. The anthropoid-browed brother was lurking behind a pillar. He was a one-man claque, as it were. As soon as sister's number was through, he'd start to applaud and cheer, as if he'd been stricken with a fit. Then he'd hurl a coin onto the stage—a silver buck. The decoy dollar. This gesture was supposed to precipitate a like effusion on the part of guests. It seldom did.

As Mama Russky put her hoarse contralto through the lugubrious paces of *Dark Eyes*, Babe continued to torture herself with homesickness. "That apartment would be just right for one dame. A good radio and a record-player, and the drapes would be cretonne—I'm bugs about cretonne—and the bathroom would be in coral, with a small radio to listen to while I'm soaking myself after a hard day's work. That ain't much to ask, is it?"

"Not for a broad who's wearing emerald-cut diamonds and Paris originals, it isn't. Get a load of this, Babe! Brother Russky's going to spring with the decoy dollar!"

My companion wasn't interested. She was soaking herself in a Nob Hill kitchenette apartment, listening to the radio, and wondering about her evening's date.

"He'd be a nice kid who pumped gas for Texaco, or peddled tickets for the Southern Pacific, or something like that. No *pukka sahib* English gentleman, no Shanghai slicker with a lot of gab, a lot of angles, and too much after-midnight experience."

"Don't be too sold on the idea that the home boys aren't without angles, kid. Shanghai has no monopoly on sophistication."

"Yeah, but somehow it's more tiresome out here, Cousin. Sordid—isn't that the word? There's no contrast. The wise, smart-to-the-world attitude is so damn routine here. It would be refreshing as hell to run into a guy who thought that just a plain ordinary kiss was hot stuff.

"Like that date of mine back home who'd ring the downstairs buzzer just after I'd pressed out my blouse for work in the morning, and painted my nails, and eaten my tuna sandwich. I'd press the button to let him in and jimmy myself into a new pair of patent-leather spikes, and by the time I'd wiggled into my dress, he'd be at the door. In time to zip it up and love doing it. . . .

"Then we'd step out into the fog, and into this guy's Plymouth—he'd be about Plymouth class; last year's model but plenty shined up—and we'd go to the Bal, or the St. Francis, or maybe just to a bar for highballs. And the conversation wouldn't be clever, and there wouldn't be any sharp, double-meaning remarks, and nobody would try to impress anyone else with what they were back home—the way they do here—but there would be lots of laughs, and . . ."

". . . and eventually you'd get all you wanted of that and buy yourself a ticket back to Shanghai."

"No, you're dead wrong, Cousin. I'd stay there forever. With what I know now. I'd stay there forever. Forever."

Now she had me feeling low, too. Despite the drinks. I blamed it on the place.

"Let's go across the alley to the Venus for some chow. This trap is sure warping my *joie de vivre.*"

It was that very dark, very still hour just before dawn, as we came out on the bleak, honky-tonk gaiety of Jukong Alley. The neon lights were still gleaming coldly, but the street was all but empty. A scattering of hard-working beggars shivered in their rags, a few never-say-die ricksha pullers stood half-asleep between the shafts of their vehicles.

"About that Frisco stuff, that homesickness, Babe . . . why don't you leave Shanghai if you hate it like that?"

She wasn't at all corny or melodramatic about it. She just told me. "I can't go back home. Ever."

Shortly afterward, Johnny Morris, the UP bureau chief, mentioned Babe. Someone at the American Club—a Babbittish, Rotary Clublike place that I frequented as infrequently as possible—had told a typical sort of yarn about the girl: "Hawaiian family, a troupe of dancers, had got stuck in town, largely because of the unscrupulous machinations of their agent, a gentleman with a resounding reputation as a creep and a sonuvabitch. Babe sent them back to Honolulu. Of course, she had had to pawn a diamond bracelet in order to do it."

"Who the hell is she, this Babe?" someone asked.

"Babe is what they used to call a Coaster here in the old days," Johnny said. "A China Coaster is the term the old China hands had for it. This port is a mecca for hundreds of young Americans and Britishers who get two or three weeks off each year from the rubber plantations and tea farms and factories and godowns and branch offices of the Far East. They come surging into Shanghai with a year's pay and a year's backlog of hunger for bright lights, gaiety, booze, and broads. Sometimes they fall into the hands of the Russian women and the whores of Blood Alley and North Kiangse Road. If they're wiser, and luckier, they meet up with one of these women like Babe . . . who take their money, see them through their vacation, and send them back to their stations happy, hungover, unfrustrated, and broke. Coasters, the old-timers call them. Babe is a Coaster."

"You mean, she's a . . . well, she's a kind of high-class tramp?"

"Not at all. Some of them are more broad-minded than others, but most are just party girls who provide pleasant companionship, a knowledge of the town, and protection against the more obvious gyps. These kids have a code. They collect plenty, and give plenty . . . up to a point."

It was from Babe herself, though, that I learned how she had wandered to China and how she had become a Coaster. The telling of the story was a sequel to a really strange incident.

Babe and I had been sitting at a table in Sam Levy's Venus Café, waiting for some 4 a.m. ham and eggs. She was restless and uneasy. Rather abruptly, she excused herself and slipped away from the table, taking her bag but not troubling to pick up the mink draped over her chair.

The food came, but my companion failed to return. Levy came over, said hello, and sat down. "Where's Babe?" he asked.

I told him I didn't know. Maybe she'd taken a powder. Except that her mink was still there. Well, she didn't come back. Come daylight, Sam and I were standing at the entrance to his place, looking out into the gruesome greyness of a new Shanghai day and speculating unhopefully about possibilities. "She could be at the bottom of Soochow Creek," said Sam. He had lived in China for years, and had few illusions.

"It's probably something very reasonable and commonplace," I said, hopefully.

"Like getting hit over the head with something heavy," said Sam.

I didn't like thinking of that. I had got to like the brash little blonde. I didn't like the thought of her bobbing around in the dirty waters of the Soochow. But when nine o'clock came, it was pretty clear that Babe had gone for more than a breath of fresh air. I shouldered her coat, and took a ricksha to her apartment.

There was no one there. Her *amah* hadn't seen her. I left the coat and a message to call me and went home. If a friend of yours disappeared under such circumstances in Toledo or Seattle, you might notify the cops. In Shanghai, somehow you didn't. It might be invading someone's privacy. There were so many labyrinths and by-passes in the lives of even your closest friends. . . . You were hesitant about assuming any certainties about them. Who knows? Perhaps Babe had a lover somewhere near to whom she had gone on an impulse. I hit the hay.

I dropped by her apartment again at Tiffintime. The *amah*, who had been with her for years, was a little worried now. Missy no come home yet. Missy have hair appointment. No keep. The *amah* had spoken to the *amahs* of several of Babe's lady friends. Missy no stop alongside them. Bimeby she go American consul. I calmed her and asked if maybe Missy didn't have other friend . . . some gentleman friend, eh? The *amah* was as indignant as if her mistress were a Mother Superior. *No mastah have got!*

Casually and as if I were just looking for an item for the paper, I dropped in on the Welshman who ran things at night at the Central Police Station. Nothing. Much later I dropped in on Sam Levy. He was sure about Soochow Creek now. And then Babe walked in.

She looked a little wilted, but she was a long way from being ready for the undertaker. I got sore, in my relief. "You might at least have told me where to send the ham and eggs."

"I'm sorry, Cousin. It wasn't my fault. Take me home, will you?"

Sam was popeyed with curiosity. "You mean you ain't going to tell us where you been?"

Babe fingered her nose at him. "Go back into the woodwork, Levy. You'll have to wait and read it in my memoirs."

She didn't say a word until we arrived at her apartment. The *amah* was waiting still, bleak-eyed with worry. Her relief took the form of indignation.

"That's right; I'm a dog, Mei-Mei," said Babe. "Now go to bed and stop worrying."

I settled down in a chair and waited morosely for a drink, as if I had been much mistreated. The blonde poured one, then opened a little cabinet next to the divan that dominated the room and took out a spirit lamp, two small jars, and a long, copper, probelike needle. She lighted the spirit lamp, which was provided with a thick glass chimney. It was flattened out at the top, out of which the crest of the flame slowly licked through a small vent.

"Of course you knew I was on opium, didn't you, Cuz?" said Babe, as she opened one of the pots.

I was silent and suddenly shocked. If I had heard about it in conversation, I would perhaps have taken it more casually, but seeing her calmly manipulating the paraphernalia as she talked somehow got me down.

"I've been on it for a long time. It's father, mother, sister, brother . . . and husband and lover to me, now, Cousin." She laughed without pleasure. "I'm a hophead."

What was there to say?

"And that accounts for last night. The yen came on earlier than it usually does. I knew of a place just around the corner from Sam's place and thought that I could get off the hook with a couple of quick pills. It isn't a bad place. A kind of a hideaway in the back of the Moon Palace Hotel, and I know Leong, the guy who runs it, pretty well. I had barely got on my hip and the cook-girl was rolling the yen-pok when . . . ai-yai . . . the cops. The goddam Settlement police raided the Moon Palace."

She had the pipe out now—a handsome ivory deal with the flat Peking bowl. She dipped the somewhat spatulated end of the needle into the viscous brown stuff in one of the pots, drew it out, and held it over the flame that peeped from the top of the spirit lamp. The opium wanted to drip from the needle, but she twirled it rapidly between her fingers and the gum bubbled in the heat, sputtered a bit, then began to coagulate.

"Leong locked the door and warned us to be quiet. The entranceway is flush with the wall on the outside, and the place has been cased plenty before without anyone getting wise to it. It got by this time, too. But the cops hung around the hotel the rest of the day, looking for what they could find, and Leong wouldn't let any of us out. What's worse, he wouldn't let the cook-girl light up again for fear the odor would get to them. So there we sat, the whole goddam day, looking at the walls. Until just a little while ago, when Leong let us out."

The pill was ready now. Babe rolled it back and forth on the hot glass top of the lamp, molding it to size and shape. It was no longer viscous, the banana oil having been roasted away. It was like a pellet of fresh fudge, and suddenly she fitted it onto the pipe, just over the hole in the bowl. Then she turned the bowl so that it was just over the flame; and, placing the amber mouthpiece to her lips, she started to inhale. The room was suddenly full of sweet, sweet fumes—an unforgettable odor, subtly suggestive, somehow, of beautiful evil.

Babe continued to inhale, avidly, hungrily, noisily. With each rapid intake of breath, the pill burned brightly, the rim of fire at its top eventually consuming it entirely. Then she lay back. Her eyes were half-shuttered now. She smiled at me through the slits. "Forgive me, now?"

I finished my drink very quickly and went for the bottle. It was like watching a woman commit suicide and being able to do nothing at all about it. I wanted to tell her that she was a fool, that she had no right to louse herself up in this fashion . . . but I got drunk instead.

Before I did, and while Babe prepared and smoked many more pills, I heard more of her story. I got the rest of it when I asked her why the hell she didn't get away from China, why she didn't go home.

"You mean the kitchenette-apartment deal, and the job at Magnin's?"

"Yes. Or does that look good only when you're gassed?"

"It looks good all the time. Day and night. Only, like I said before, I can't go back. Ever."

She was nearly in the other dimension now, nearly in the dream world of the poppy-pus. She spoke slowly and clearly and without emphasis or emotion, though her eyes were closed and her hands were folded lovingly over the ivory pipe. I tilted the bottle into my glass as I listened to her tell why she couldn't go home.

"I killed a girl in San Francisco. Over something so silly that I've nearly forgotten what it was. Something about a man. I've forgotten *him* all the way. The silly bastard. Wouldn't know him if he stuck his head out from under this bed.

"We had a fight—she and I—and I slid a kitchen knife into her just below the navel. Blood enough to float the Ark, and some left over for the *Queen Mary*, and maybe the Vallejo ferryboat, too. She started to go fast. I was nearly bugs. I tried to bring her to, but she was plenty out. When I felt her pulse and got no answer, I was scared silly. I threw a coat on over my slip . . . that was all I had on . . . and charged out of the house. I didn't want to die in a roomful of gas. And I didn't want to crum out the rest of my life in jail. I wanted away.

"I knew a guy. The guy that every dame knows, that she doesn't love, but that she saves away in her mind to help her on a rainy day. And, Cuz, this was strictly a rainy day. He was the purser, or assistant purser or something like that, on a Dollar boat. Luckily, the boat was in and he was in his cabin. I sure got to know that cabin well—every inch of it. I stayed in it all the way to Shanghai.

"At first, he figured to get me off at Honolulu. But the customs people were too cagey, and the boat was only in port for one day. So my purser pal got me a dress and some toilet articles and we sailed. And one night, a couple of weeks later, after the boat dropped anchor in the Whangpoo, he sneaked me over the side into a bumboat . . . and I've been here ever since.

"Except for a trip I made. Christ, what a trip!"

Subconsciously, she fingered the scar on her neck.

"A few years back, my nightmare caught up with me. One morning, I get a call from the consulate. They'd like me to step in and see them. Well, I figure it could be nothing . . . and it could be the man with the handcuffs. Somehow, I feel it ain't just nothing. The panic is on again. I talk to Mei-Mei here, my *amah*. She's a good woman. She fixes me up with her brother, who has a freight sampan in the Yangtze River trade—a little job you wouldn't ride in for laughs.

"I packed a bag and dusted out of Shanghai like a duck who's just heard about the opening of duck season. With Mei-Mei's brother, and a crew of coolies, and not even Heaven to protect me. Cousin . . . *that was a trip!* We went upriver to parts that would make Shangri-La look suburban. We were away nearly six months. I slept on a mat and cooked rice for the coolies and even pulled on towrope with them when that damn mud scow had to be hauled through the no-wind parts of the river. That's where I got this scar on my neck—the damnedest rope burn you ever saw.

"I came back in the spring a different woman. I spoke good Chinese. I was through worrying about microbes forever. I wasn't even too worried about handcuffs any more. And I learned about opium. The world was never the same for me again."

The atmosphere of the little room was strictly minor-key now. The bottle was nearly empty and the fumes of the poppy-mud had reached me, too. The normal world of yesterday was as gone as yesterday's clouds. I was living in Babe's sad, unnatural little aura of defeat, frustration, and to-hell-with-it. She went on, with a pathetic little giggle.

"Funny thing. The summons from the consulate turned out to be only some silly thing about registration. I laughed myself into a hemorrhage."

Her voice had dwindled to a fuzzy monotone. "So that's why I can't go home. Ever."

I waited until her breathing developed into a gentle snore, and then I fumbled my way out. The cold morning air went through my nose and throat like a whiff of ammonia.

I left Shanghai shortly afterward and returned to San Francisco. I was reminded next of Babe when I received a letter from her shortly before the Japanese invasion of China. It was postmarked Nanking.

"Dear Cuz: This is to let you know that I am as fine as I hope that this finds you. Things out here are same as always, only more so now that the Nips are playing soldiers again. But it means dough for Babe (all these guys selling army supplies, and so on) so why should I kick. Why don't you come back out? There's a lot of things going on which would make work for your typewriter. (Is it still as lazy as it was? Ha Ha! Joke.) Besides, I miss you. You were always a good Joe and you were never nosy. Despite which, you learned ALL. *There must be a moral to that somewhere. Drop me a line. I have a big house here and it's gotten to be a sort of a rondayvoo for a lot of the civilians doing business with the government. Best regards.*

"Babe (Mrs. Babe Sadlir)"

It was the first time, oddly enough, that I ever heard her second name, or realized that she had been married.

Shortly afterward, I checked with the San Francisco police. Discreetly.

Yes, they had a record of the name. She had been named by a complainant as the person who had assaulted her some years ago. The victim hadn't been badly hurt, though, and the follow-up indicated that she had wanted to drop the matter. No prosecution. Babe Sadlir wasn't wanted in San Francisco.

Before I could get the information into a letter to Babe, the Japanese took Nanking. Later on, I learned that a foreign woman, named Sadlir, was among those who had overdelayed their departure from the city. She was missing. It was thought that she was dead. No word of her, no proof of how she died . . . in the words of the authorities, "No disposition whatsoever."

And now, I thought, no kitchenette apartment, no cretonne drapes, no knock at the door by that nine o'clock date. . . .

ERSKINE CALDWELL

◄───►

August Afternoon

Vᴵᴄ Gʟᴏᴠᴇʀ awoke with the noon-day heat ringing in his ears. He had been asleep for only half an hour, and he was getting ready to turn over and go back to sleep when he opened his eyes for a moment and saw Hubert's black head over the top of his bare toes. He stretched his eyelids and held them open as long as he could.

Hubert was standing in the yard, at the edge of the porch, with a pine cone in his hand.

Vic cursed him.

The colored man raked the cone over the tops of Vic's toes and stepped back out of reach.

"What do you mean by standing there tickling me with that dad-burned cone?" Vic shouted at Hubert. "Is that all you can find to do? Why don't you get out in that field and do something to those boll-weevils? They're going to eat up every pound of cotton on the place if you don't stop them."

"I surely hated to wake you up, Mr. Vic," Hubert said, "but there's a white man out here looking for something. He won't say what he wants, but he's hanging around for something."

Vic was wide awake by that time. He sat up on the quilt and pulled on his shoes without looking into the yard. The white sand in the yard beat the glare of the sun directly into his eyes and he could see nothing beyond the edge of the porch. Hubert threw the pine cone under the porch and stepped aside.

"He must be looking for trouble," Vic said. "When they come around and don't say anything, and just sit, it's trouble they're looking for."

"There he is, Mr. Vic," Hubert said, nodding his head across the yard. "There he sits up against that water oak."

Vic looked around for Willie. Willie was sitting on the top step at the other end of the porch, directly in front of the stranger. She did not look at Vic.

"You ought to have better sense than to wake me up while I'm taking a nap. This is no time of day to be up. I've got to get a little sleep every now and then."

"Boss," Hubert said, "I wouldn't wake you up at all, not at any time, but Miss Willie just sits there high up on the steps and that white man has been

Autumn, 1933

115

out there whittling on a little stick a pretty long time without saying anything. I've got scared about something happening when he whittles that little stick clear through, and it's just about whittled down to nothing now."

Vic glanced again at Willie, and from her he turned to stare at the stranger sitting under the water oak tree in his front yard.

The piece of wood had been shaved down to paper thinness.

"Boss," Hubert said, "we ain't aiming to have no trouble today, are we?"

"Which way did he come from?" Vic asked.

"I never did see him come, Mr. Vic. I just looked up, and there he was, sitting against that water oak whittling on a little stick. I reckon I must have been sleeping when he came, because when I looked up, there he was."

Vic slid down over the quilt until his legs were hanging over the edge of the porch. Perspiration began to trickle down his neck as soon as he sat up.

"Ask him what he's after, Hubert."

"We ain't aiming to have no trouble today, are we, Mr. Vic?"

"Ask him what he wants, I said."

Hubert went almost half way to the water oak tree and stopped.

"Mr. Vic says what can he do for you, white-folks."

The man said nothing. He did not even glance up.

Hubert came back to the porch, the whites of his eyes becoming larger with each step.

"What did he say?" Vic asked him.

"He ain't said nothing yet, Mr. Vic. He acts like he don't hear me at all. You'd better go talk to him, Mr. Vic. He won't give me no attention. Appears to me like he's just sitting there looking at Miss Willie on the high step. Maybe if you was to tell her to go in the house and shut the door, he might be persuaded to give some notice to what we say to him."

"Can't see any sense in sending her in the house," Vic said. "I can make him talk. Hand me that stilyerd."

"Mr. Vic, I'm trying to tell you about Miss Willie. Miss Willie's been sitting there on that high step and he's been looking up at her a right long time, Mr. Vic. If you won't object to me saying so, Mr. Vic, I reckon I'd tell Miss Willie to go sit somewhere else, if I was you. Miss Willie ain't got much on today, Mr. Vic. That's what I've been trying to tell you."

"Hand me that stilyerd, I said."

Hubert went to the end of the porch and brought the cotton steelyard to Vic. He stepped back out of the way.

"Boss," Hubert said, "we ain't aiming to have no trouble today, are we?"

Vic was getting ready to jump down into the yard when the man under the water oak reached into his pocket and pulled out another knife. It was about nine inches long, and both sides of the handle were covered with hairy cowhide. There was a spring-button on one end. The man pushed the button with his thumb, and the blade sprang open. He began playing with both knives, throwing them up in the air and catching them on the back of his hands.

Hubert moved to the other side of Vic.

"Mr. Vic," he said, "I ain't intending to mix in your business none, but it looks to me like you got yourself in for a mess of trouble when you went off and brought Miss Willie back here. It looks to me like she's got up for a city girl, more so than a country girl."

Vic cursed him.

"I'm telling you, Mr. Vic, a country girl wouldn't sit on a high step in front of a man not when she wasn't wearing nothing but that blue wrapper, anyhow."

"Shut up," Vic said, laying the steelyard down on the quilt beside him.

The man under the water oak closed the blade of the small knife and put it into his pocket. The big cowhide-covered knife he flipped into the air and caught easily on the back of his hand.

"What's your name?" he asked Willie.

"Willie."

He flipped the knife again.

"What's yours?" she asked him.

"Floyd."

"Where are you from?"

"Carolina."

He flipped it higher, catching it underhanded.

"What are you doing in Georgia?"

"Don't know," he said. "Just looking around."

Willie giggled, smiling at him.

Floyd got up and walked across the yard to the steps and sat down on the bottom one. He put his arms around his knees and looked up at Willie.

"You're not so bad-looking," he said. "I've seen lots worse looking."

"You're not so bad yourself," Willie giggled, resting her arms on her knees and looking down at him.

"How about a kiss?"

"What would it be to you?"

"Not bad. I reckon I've had lots worse."

"Well, you can't get it sitting down there."

Floyd climbed the steps on his hands and feet and sat down on the next to the top step. He leaned against Willie, putting one arm around her waist and the other over her knees. Willie slid down to the step beside him.

"Boss," Hubert said, his lips twitching, "we ain't going to have no trouble today, are we?"

Vic cursed him.

Willie and Floyd moved down a step without loosening their embrace.

"Who is that yellow-headed sap-sucker, anyhow?" Vic said. "I'll be dad-burned if he ain't got a lot of nerve—coming here and fooling with Willie."

"You wouldn't do nothing to cause trouble, would you, Mr. Vic? I surely don't want to have no trouble today, Mr. Vic."

Vic glanced at the nine-inch knife Floyd had, stuck into the step at his feet. It stood on its tip eighteen inches high, while the sun was reflected against the bright blade and made a streak of light on Floyd's pant leg.

"Go over there and take that knife away from him and bring it here," Vic said. "Don't be scared of him."

"Mr. Vic, I surely hate to disappoint you, but if you want that white-folk's knife, you'll just have to get it your own self. I don't aim to have myself all carved up with that thing. Mr. Vic, I surely can't accommodate you this time. If you want that white-folk's knife, you'll just be bound to get it yourself, Mr. Vic."

Vic cursed him.

Hubert backed away until he was at the end of the porch. He kept on looking behind him all the time, looking to be certain of the exact location of the sycamore stump that was between him and the pine grove on the other side of the cotton field.

Vic called to Hubert and told him to come back. Hubert came slowly around the corner of the porch and stood a few feet from the quilt where Vic was sitting. His lips quivered and the whites of his eyes grew larger. Vic motioned for him to come closer, but he would not come an inch farther.

"How old are you?" Floyd asked Willie.

"Fifteen."

Floyd jerked the knife out of the wood and thrust it deeper in the same place.

"How old are you?" she asked him.

"About twenty-seven."

"Are you married?"

"Not now," he said. "How long have you been?"

"About three months," Willie said.

"How do you like it?"

"Pretty good so far."

"How about another kiss?"

"You've just had one."

"I'd like another one now."

"I ought not to let you kiss me again."

"Why not?" Floyd said.

"Men don't like girls who kiss too much."

"I'm not that kind."

"What kind are you?" Willie asked him.

"I'd like to kiss you a lot."

"But after I let you do that, you'd go away."

"No, I won't. I'll stay for something else."

"What?"

"Let's go inside for a drink and I'll tell you."

"We'll have to go to the spring for fresh water."

"Where's the spring?"

"Just across the field in the grove."

"All right," Floyd said, standing up. "Let's go."

He bent down and pulled the knife out of the wood. Willie ran down the steps and across the yard. When Floyd saw that she was not going to wait for him, he ran after her, holding the knives in his pocket with one hand. She led him across the cotton field to the spring in the pine grove. Just before they got there, Floyd caught her by the arm and ran beside her the rest of the way.

"Boss," Hubert said, "we ain't aiming to have no trouble today, are we?"

Vic cursed him.

"I don't want to get messed up with a heap of trouble and maybe get my belly slit open with that big hairy knife. If you ain't got objections, I reckon I'll mosey on home now and cut a little firewood for the cook-stove."

"Come back here!" Vic said. "You stay where you are and stop making moves to go off."

"What are we aiming to do, Mr. Vic?"

Vic eased himself off the porch and walked across the yard to the water oak. He looked down at the ground where Floyd had been sitting, and then he looked at the porch steps where Willie had been. The noonday heat beat down through the thin leaves overhead and he could feel his mouth and throat burn with the hot air he breathed.

"Have you got a gun, Hubert?"

"No, sir, boss," Hubert said.

"Why haven't you?" he said. "Right when I need a gun, you haven't got it. Why don't you keep a gun?"

"Mr. Vic, I ain't got no use for a gun. I used to keep one to shoot rabbits and squirrels with, but I got to thinking one day, and I traded it off the first chance I had. I reckon it was a good thing I traded, too. If I had kept it, you'd be asking for it like you did just now."

Vic went back to the porch and picked up the steelyard and hammered the porch with it. After he had hit the porch four or five times, he dropped it and started out in the direction of the spring. He walked as far as the edge of the shade and stopped. He stood listening for a while.

Willie and Floyd could be heard down near the spring. Floyd said something to Willie, and Willie laughed loudly. There was silence for several minutes, and then Willie laughed again. Vic was getting ready to turn back to the porch when he heard her cry out. It sounded like a scream, but it was not exactly that; it sounded like a shriek, but it was not that, either; it sounded more like someone laughing and crying simultaneously in a high-pitched voice.

"Where did Miss Willie come from, Mr. Vic?" Hubert asked. "Where did you bring her from?"

"Down below here a little way," he said.

Hubert listened to the sounds that were coming from the pine grove.

"Boss," he said after a while, "it appears to me like you didn't go far enough away."

"I went far enough," Vic said. "If I had gone any farther, I'd have been in Florida."

The colored man hunched his shoulders forward several times while he smoothed the white sand with his broad-soled shoes.

"Mr. Vic, if I was you, the next time I'd surely go that far."

"What do you mean, the next time?"

"I was figuring that maybe you wouldn't be keeping her much longer than now, Mr. Vic."

Vic cursed him.

Hubert raised his head several times and attempted to see down into the pine grove over the top of the growing cotton.

"Shut up and mind your own business," Vic said. "I'm going to keep her till the cows come home. Where else do you reckon I'd find a better-looking girl than Willie?"

"Boss, I wasn't thinking of how she looks—I was thinking how she acts."

"She acts that way now because she's not old enough to do different. She won't act that way much longer. She'll get over the way she's doing pretty soon."

Hubert followed Vic across the yard. While Vic went towards the porch, Hubert stopped and leaned against the water oak where he could almost see over the cotton field into the pine grove. Vic went up on the porch and stretched out on the quilt. He took off his shoes and flung them aside.

"I surely God knowed something was going to happen when he whittled that stick down to nothing," Hubert was saying to himself. "White-folks take a long time to whittle a little piece of wood, but after they whittle it down to nothing, they're going to be up and doing."

Presently Vic sat upright on the quilt.

"Listen here, Hubert—"

"Yes, sir, boss."

"You keep your eye on that stilyerd so it will stay right where it is now, and when they come back up the path from the spring, you wake me up in a hurry. Do you hear?"

"Yes, sir, boss," Hubert said. "Are you aiming to take a little nap now?"

"Yes, I am. And if you don't wake me up when they come back, I'll break your head for you when I do wake up."

Vic lay down again on the quilt and turned over on his side to shut out the blinding glare of the early afternoon sun that was reflected upon the porch from the hard white sand in the yard.

Hubert scratched his head and sat down against the water oak facing the path from the spring. He could hear Vic snoring on the porch above the sounds that came at intervals from the pine grove across the field. He sat staring down the path, singing under his breath. It was a long time until sundown.

RAY BRADBURY

◀──▶

The Illustrated Man

"**HEY**, the Illustrated Man!"

A calliope screamed, and Mr. William Philippus Phelps stood, arms folded, high on the summer-night platform, a crowd unto himself.

He was an entire civilization. In the Main Country, his chest, the Vasties lived—nipple-eyed dragons swirling over his fleshpot, his almost feminine breasts. His navel was the mouth of a slit-eyed monster—an obscene, in-sucked mouth, toothless as a witch. And there were secret caves where Darklings lurked, his armpits, adrip with slow subterranean liquors, where the Darklings, eyes jealously ablaze, peered out through rank creeper and hanging vine.

Mr. William Philippus Phelps leered down from his freak platform with a thousand peacock eyes. Across the sawdust meadow he saw his wife, Lisabeth, far away, ripping tickets in half, staring at the silver belt buckles of passing men.

Mr. William Philippus Phelps' hands were tattooed roses. At the sight of his wife's interest, the roses shriveled, as with the passing of sunlight.

A year before, when he had led Lisabeth to the marriage bureau to watch her work her name in ink, slowly, on the form, his skin had been pure and white and clean. He glanced down at himself in sudden horror. Now he was like a great painted canvas, shaken in the night wind! How had it happened? Where had it all begun?

It had started with the arguments, and then the flesh, and then the pictures. They had fought deep into the summer nights, she like a brass trumpet forever blaring at him. And he had gone out to eat five thousand steaming hot dogs, ten million hamburgers, and a forest of green onions, and to drink vast red seas of orange juice. Peppermint candy formed his brontosaur bones, the hamburgers shaped his balloon flesh, and strawberry pop pumped in and out of his heart valves sickeningly, until he weighed three hundred pounds.

"William Philippus Phelps," Lisabeth said to him in the eleventh month of their marriage, "you're dumb and fat."

That was the day the carnival boss handed him the blue envelope. "Sorry, Phelps. You're no good to me with all that gut on you."

"Wasn't I always your best tent man, boss?"

"Once. Not any more. Now you sit, you don't get the work out."

"Let me be your Fat Man."

"I got a Fat Man. Dime a dozen." The boss eyed him up and down. "Tell you what, though. We ain't had a Tattooed Man since Gallery Smith died last year. . . ."

That had been a month ago. Four short weeks. From someone, he had learned of a tattoo artist far out in the rolling Wisconsin country, an old woman, they said, who knew her trade. If he took the dirt road and turned right at the river and then left . . .

He had walked out across a yellow meadow, which was crisp from the sun. Red flowers blew and bent in the wind as he walked, and he came to the old shack, which looked as if it had stood in a million rains.

Inside the door was a silent, bare room, and in the center of the bare room sat an ancient woman.

Her eyes were stitched with red resin-thread. Her nose was sealed with black wax-twine. Her ears were sewn, too, as if a darning-needle dragonfly had stitched all her senses shut. She sat, not moving, in the vacant room. Dust lay in a yellow flour all about, unfootprinted in many weeks; if she had moved it would have shown, but she had not moved. Her hands touched each other like thin, rusted instruments. Her feet were naked and obscene as rain rubbers, and near them sat vials of tattoo milk—red, lightning-blue, brown, cat-yellow. She was a thing sewn tight into whispers and silence.

Only her mouth moved, unsewn: "Come in. Sit down. I'm lonely here."

He did not obey.

"You came for the pictures," she said in a high voice. "I have a picture to show you, first."

She tapped a blind finger to her thrust-out palm. "See!" she cried.

It was a tattoo-portrait of William Philippus Phelps.

"Me!" he said.

Her cry stopped him at the door. "Don't run."

He held to the edges of the door, his back to her. "That's me, that's me on your hand!"

"It's been there fifty years." She stroked it like a cat, over and over.

He turned. "It's an *old* tattoo." He drew slowly nearer. He edged forward and bent to blink at it. He put out a trembling finger to brush the picture. "Old. That's impossible! You don't know *me*. I don't know *you*. Your eyes, all sewed shut."

"I've been waiting for you," she said. "And many people." She displayed her arms and legs, like the spindles of an antique chair. "I have pictures on me of people who have already come here to see me. And there are other pictures of other people who are coming to see me in the next one hundred years. And you, you have come."

"How do you know it's me? You can't see!"

"You *feel* like the lions, the elephants, and the tigers, to me. Unbutton your shirt. You need me. Don't be afraid. My needles are as clean as a doctor's fingers. When I'm finished with illustrating you, I'll wait for someone else to walk along out here and find me. And someday, a hundred summers from now, perhaps, I'll just go lie down in the forest under some white mushrooms, and in the spring you won't find anything but a small blue cornflower. . . ."

He began to unbutton his sleeves.

"I know the Deep Past and the Clear Present and the even Deeper Future," she whispered, eyes knotted into blindness, face lifted to this unseen man. "It is on my flesh. I will paint it on yours, too. You will be the only *real* Illustrated Man in the universe. I'll give you special pictures you will never forget. Pictures of the Future on your skin."

She pricked him with a needle.

He ran back to the carnival that night in a drunken terror and elation. Oh, how quickly the old dust-witch had stitched him with color and design. At the end of a long afternoon of being bitten by a silver snake, his body was alive with portraiture. He looked as if he had dropped and been crushed between the steel rollers of a print press, and come out like an incredible rotogravure. He was clothed in a garment of trolls and scarlet dinosaurs.

"Look!" he cried to Lisabeth. She glanced up from her cosmetic table as he tore his shirt away. He stood in the naked bulb-light of their car-trailer, expanding his impossible chest. Here, the Tremblies, half-maiden, half-goat, leaping when his biceps flexed. Here, the Country of Lost Souls, his chins. In so many accordion pleats of fat, numerous small scorpions, beetles, and mice were crushed, held, hid, darting into view, vanishing, as he raised or lowered his chins.

"My God," said Lisabeth. "My husband's a freak."

She ran from the trailer and he was left alone to pose before the mirror. Why had he done it? To have a job, yes, but, most of all, to cover the fat that had larded itself impossibly over his bones. To hide the fat under a layer of color and fantasy, to hide it from his wife, but most of all from himself.

He thought of the old woman's last words. She had needled him two *special* tattoos, one on his chest, another for his back, which she would not let him see. She covered each with cloth and adhesive.

"You are not to look at these two," she had said.

"Why?"

"Later, you may look. The Future is in these pictures. You can't look now or it may spoil them. They are not quite finished. I put ink on your flesh and the sweat of you forms the rest of the picture, the Future—your sweat and your thought." Her empty mouth grinned. "Next Saturday night, you may advertise! The Big Unveiling! Come see the Illustrated Man unveil his picture! You can make money in that way. You can charge admission to the Unveiling, like to an Art Gallery. Tell them you have a picture that even you never have seen, that *nobody* has seen yet. The most unusual picture ever painted. Almost alive. And it tells the Future. Roll the drums and blow the trumpets. And you can stand there and unveil at the Big Unveiling."

"That's a good idea," he said.

"But only unveil the picture on your chest," she said. "That is first. You must save the picture on your back, under the adhesive, for the following week. Understand?"

"How much do I owe you?"

"Nothing," she said. "If you walk with these pictures on you, I will be repaid with my own satisfaction. I will sit here for the next two weeks and think how clever my pictures are, for I make them to fit each man himself and what is inside him. Now, walk out of this house and never come back. Good-by."

"Hey! The Big Unveiling!"

The red signs blew in the night wind: NO ORDINARY TATTOOED MAN! THIS ONE IS "ILLUSTRATED!" GREATER THAN MICHELANGELO! TONIGHT! ADMISSION 10 CENTS!

Now the hour had come. Saturday night, the crowd stirring their animal feet in the hot sawdust.

"In one minute—" the carny boss pointed his cardboard megaphone—"in the tent immediately to my rear, we will unveil the Mysterious Portrait upon the Illustrated Man's chest! Next Saturday night, the same hour, same location, we'll unveil the Picture upon the Illustrated Man's *back!* Bring your friends!"

There was a stuttering roll of drums.

Mr. William Philippus Phelps jumped back and vanished; the crowd poured into the tent, and, once inside, found him re-established upon another platform, the band brassing out a jig-time melody.

He looked for his wife and saw her, lost in the crowd, like a stranger, come to watch a freakish thing, a look of contemptuous curiosity upon her face. For, after all, he was her husband, and this was a thing she didn't know about him herself. It gave him a feeling of great height and warmness and light to find himself the center of the jangling universe, the carnival world, for one night. Even the other freaks—the Skeleton, the Seal Boy, the Yoga, the Magician, and the Balloon—were scattered through the crowd.

"Ladies and gentlemen, the great moment!"

A trumpet flourish, a hum of drumsticks on tight cowhide.

Mr. William Philippus Phelps let his cape fall. Dinosaurs, trolls, and half-women-half-snakes writhed on his skin in the stark light.

Ah, murmured the crowd, for surely there had never been a tattooed man like this! The beast eyes seemed to take red fire and blue fire, blinking and twisting. The roses on his fingers seemed to expel a sweet pink bouquet. The tyranno-saurus-rex reared up along his leg, and the sound of the brass trumpet in the hot tent heavens was a prehistoric cry from the red monster throat. Mr. William Phillipus Phelps was a museum jolted to life. Fish swam in seas of electric-blue ink. Fountains sparkled under yellow suns. Ancient buildings stood in meadows of harvest wheat. Rockets burned across spaces of muscle and flesh. The slightest inhalation of his breath threatened to make chaos of the entire printed universe. He seemed afire, the creatures flinching from the flame, drawing back from the great heat of his pride, as he expanded under the audience's rapt contemplation.

The carny boss laid his fingers to the adhesive. The audience rushed forward silent in the oven vastness of the night tent.

"You ain't seen nothing yet!" cried the carny boss.

The adhesive ripped free.

There was an instant in which nothing happened. An instant in which the Illustrated Man thought that the Unveiling was a terrible and irrevocable failure.

But then the audience gave a low moan.

The carny boss drew back, his eyes fixed.

Far out at the edge of the crowd, a woman, after a moment, began to cry, began to sob, and did not stop.

Slowly, the Illustrated Man looked down at his naked chest and stomach.

The thing that he saw made the roses on his hands discolor and die. All of his creatures seemed to wither, turn inward, shrivel with the arctic coldness that pumped from his heart outward to freeze and destroy them. He stood trembling. His hands floated up to touch that incredible picture, which lived, moved and shivered with life. It was like gazing into a small room, seeing a thing of someone else's life, so intimate, so impossible that one could not believe and one could not long stand to watch without turning away.

It was a picture of his wife, Lizabeth, and himself.

And he was killing her.

Before the eyes of a thousand people in a dark tent in the center of a black-forested Wisconsin land, he was killing his wife.

His great flowered hands were upon her throat, and her face was turning dark and he killed her and he killed her and did not ever in the next minute stop killing her. It was real. While the crowd watched, she died, and he turned very sick. He was about to fall straight down into the crowd. The tent whirled like a monster bat wing, flapping grotesquely. The last thing he heard was a woman, sobbing, far out on the shore of the silent crowd.

And the crying woman was Lisabeth, his wife.

In the night, his bed was moist with perpiration. The carnival sounds had melted away, and his wife, in her own bed, was quiet now, too. He fumbled with his chest. The adhesive was smooth. They had made him put it back.

He had fainted. When he revived, the carny boss had yelled at him, "Why didn't you say what that picture was like?"

"I didn't know, I didn't," said the Illustrated Man.

"Good God!" said the boss. "Scare hell outa everyone. Scared hell outa Lizzie, scared hell outa me. Christ, where'd you get that damn tattoo?" He shuddered. "Apologize to Lizzie, now."

His wife stood over him.

"I'm sorry, Lisabeth," he said, weakly, his eyes closed. "I didn't know."

"You did it on purpose," she said. "To scare me."

"I'm sorry."

"Either it goes or I go," she said.

"Lisabeth."

"You heard me. That picture comes off or I quit this show."

"Yeah, Phil," said the boss. "That's how it is."

"Did you lose money? Did the crowd demand refunds?"

"It ain't the money, Phil. For that matter, once the word got around, hundreds of people wanted in. But I'm runnin' a clean show. That tattoo comes off! Was this your idea of a practical joke, Phil?"

He turned in the warm bed. No, not a joke. Not a joke at all. He had been as terrified as anyone. Not a joke. That little old dust-witch, what had she done to him and how had she done it? Had she put the picture there? No; she had said that the picture was unfinished, and that he himself, with his thoughts and his perspiration would finish it. Well, he had done the job all right.

But what, if anything, was the significance? He didn't want to kill anyone. He didn't want to kill Lisabeth. Why should such a silly picture burn here on his flesh in the dark?

He crawled his fingers softly, cautiously down to touch the quivering place where the hidden portrait lay. He pressed tight, and the temperature of that spot was enormous. He could almost feel that little evil picture killing and killing and killing all through the night.

I don't wish to kill her, he thought, insistently, looking over at her bed. And then, five minutes later, he whispered aloud: "Or *do* I?"

"What?" she cried, awake.

"Nothing," he said, after a pause. "Go to sleep."

The man bent forward, a buzzing instrument in his hand. "This costs five bucks an inch. Costs more to peel tattoos off than to put 'em on. Okay, jerk the adhesive."

The Illustrated Man obeyed.

The skin man sat back. "Christ! No wonder you want that off! That's ghastly. *I* don't even want to look at it." He flicked his machine. "Ready? This won't hurt."

The carny boss stood in the tent flap, watching. After five minutes, the skin man changed the instrument head, cursing. Ten minutes later he scraped his chair back and scratched his head. Half an hour passed and he got up, told Mr. William Phillipus Phelps to dress, and packed his kit.

"Wait a minute," said the carny boss. "You ain't done the job."

"And I ain't going to," said the skin man.

"I'm paying good money. What's wrong?"

"Nothing, except that damn picture just won't come off. Damn thing must go right down to the bone."

"You're crazy."

"Mister, I'm in business thirty years and never see a tattoo like this. An inch deep, if it's anything."

"But I've got to get it off!" cried the Illustrated Man.

The skin man shook his head. "Only one way to get rid of that."

"How?"

"Take a knife and cut off your chest. You won't live long, but the picture'll be gone."

"Come back here!"

But the skin man walked away.

They could hear the big Sunday-night crowd, waiting.

"That's a big crowd," said the Illustrated Man.

"But they ain't going to see what they came to see," said the carny boss. "You ain't going out there, except with the adhesive. Hold still now, I'm curious about this *other* picture, on your back. We might be able to give 'em an Unveiling on this one instead."

"She said it wouldn't be ready for a week or so. The old woman said it would take time to set, make a pattern."

There was a soft ripping as the carny boss pulled aside a flap of white tape on the Illustrated Man's spine.

"What do you see?" gasped Mr. Phelps, bent over.

The carny boss replaced the tape. "Buster, as a Tattooed Man, you're a washout, ain't you? Why'd you let that old dame fix you up this way?"

"I didn't know who she was."

"She sure cheated you on this one. No design to it. Nothing. No picture at all."

"It'll come clear. You wait and see."

The boss laughed. "Okay. Come on. We'll show the crowd part of you, anyway."

They walked out into an explosion of brassy music.

He stood monstrous in the middle of the night, putting out his hands like a blind man to balance himself in a world now tilted, now rushing, now threatening to spin him over and down into the mirror before which he raised his hands. Upon the flat, dimly lighted table top were peroxides, acids, silver razors, and squares of sandpaper. He took each of them in turn. He soaked the vicious tattoo upon his chest, he scraped at it. He worked steadily for an hour.

He was aware, suddenly, that someone stood in the trailer door behind him. It was three in the morning. There was a faint odor of beer. She had come home from town. He heard her slow breathing. He did not turn. "Lisabeth?" he said.

"You'd better get rid of it," she said, watching his hands move the sandpaper. She stepped into the trailer.

"I didn't want the picture this way," he said.

"You did," she said. "You planned it."

"I didn't."

"I know you," she said. "Oh, I know you hate me. Well, that's nothing. I hate you, I've hated you a long time now. Good God, when you started putting on the fat, you think anyone could love you then? I could teach you some things about hate. Why don't you ask me?"

"Leave me alone," he said.

"In front of that crowd, making a spectacle out of me!"

"I didn't know what was under the tape."

She walked around the table, hands fitted to her hips, talking to the beds, the walls, the table, talking it all out of her. And he thought: *Or did I know? Who made this picture, me or the witch? Who formed it? How? Do I really want her dead? No! And yet.* . . . He watched his wife draw nearer, nearer, he saw the ropy strings of her throat vibrate to her shouting. This and this and *this* was wrong with him! That and that and *that* was unspeakable about him! He was a liar, a schemer, a fat, lazy, ugly man, a child. Did he think he could compete with the carny boss of the tenpeggers? Did he think he was sylphine and graceful, did he think he was a framed El Greco? DaVinci, huh! Michelangelo, my eye! She brayed. She showed her teeth. "Well, you can't scare me into staying with someone I don't want touching me with their slobby paws!" she finished, triumphantly.

"Lisabeth," he said.

"Don't Lisabeth me!" she shrieked. "I know your plan. You had that picture put on to scare me. You thought I wouldn't dare leave you. Well!"

"Next Saturday night, the Second Unveiling," he said. "You'll be proud of me."

"Proud! You're silly and pitiful. God, you're like a whale. You ever see a beached whale? I saw one when I was a kid. There it was, and they came and shot it. Some lifeguards shot it. Jesus, a whale!"

"Lisabeth."

"I'm leaving, that's all, and getting a divorce."

"Don't."

"And I'm marrying a man, not a fat woman—that's what you are, so much fat on you there ain't no sex!"

"You can't leave me," he said.

"Just watch!"

"I love you," he said.

"Oh," she said. "Go look at your pictures."

He reached out.

"Keep your hands off," she said.

"Lisabeth."

"Don't come near. You turn my stomach."

"Lisabeth."

All the eyes of his body seemed to fire, all the snakes to move, all the monsters to seethe, all the mouths to widen and rage. He moved toward her—not like a man, but a crowd.

He felt the great blooded reservoir of orangeade pump through him now, the sluice of cola and rich lemon pop pulse in sickening sweet anger through his wrists, his legs, his heart. All of it, the oceans of mustard and relish and all the million drinks he had drowned himself in in the last year were aboil; his face was the color of a steamed beef. And the pink roses of his hands became those hungry, carnivorous flowers kept long years in tepid jungle and now let free to find their way on the night air before him.

He gathered her to him, like a great beast gathering in a struggling animal. It was a frantic gesture of love, quickening and demanding, which, as she struggled, hardened to another thing. She beat and clawed at the picture on his chest.

"You've got to love me, Lisabeth."

"Let go!" she screamed. She beat at the picture that burned under her fists. She slashed at it with her fingernails.

"Oh, Lisabeth," he said, his hands moving up her arms.

"I'll scream," she said, seeing his eyes.

"Lisabeth." The hands moved up to her shoulders, to her neck. "Don't go away."

"Help!" she screamed. The blood ran from the picture on his chest.

He put his fingers about her neck and squeezed.

She was a calliope cut in mid-shriek. ·

Outside, the grass rustled. There was the sound of running feet.

Mr. William Philippus Phelps opened the trailer door and stepped out.

They were waiting for him. Skeleton, Midget, Balloon, Yoga, Electra, Popeye, Seal Boy. The freaks, waiting in the middle of the night, in the dry grass.

He walked toward them. He moved with a feeling that he must get away; these people would understand nothing, they were not thinking people. And because he did not flee, because he only walked, balanced, stunned, between the tents, slowly, the freaks moved to let him pass. They watched him, because their watching guaranteed that he would not escape. He walked out across the black meadow, moths fluttering in his face. He walked steadily as long as he was visible, not knowing where he was going. They watched him go, and then they turned and all of them shuffled to the silent car-trailer together and pushed the door slowly wide. . . .

The Illustrated Man walked steadily in the dry meadows beyond the town.

"He went that way!" a faint voice cried. Flashlights bobbled over the hills. There were dim shapes, running.

Mr. William Philippus Phelps waved to them. He was tired. He wanted only to be found now. He was tired of running away. He waved again.

"There he is!" The flashlights changed direction. "Come on! We'll get the bastard!"

When it was time, the Illustrated Man ran again. He was careful to run slowly. He deliberately fell down twice. Looking back, he saw the tent stakes they held in their hands.

He ran toward a far crossroads lantern, where all the summer night seemed to gather; merry-go-rounds of fireflies whirling, crickets moving their song toward that light, everything rushing, as if by some midnight attraction, toward that one high-hung lantern—the Illustrated Man first, the others close at his heels.

As he reached the light and passed a few yards under and beyond it, he did not need to look back. On the road ahead, in silhouette, he saw the upraised tent stakes sweep violently up, up, and then *down!*

A minute passed.

In the country ravines, the crickets sang. The freaks stood over the sprawled Illustrated Man, holding their tent stakes loosely.

Finally they rolled him over on his stomach. Blood ran from his mouth.

They ripped the adhesive from his back. They stared down for a long moment at the freshly revealed picture. Someone whispered. Someone else swore, softly. The Thin Man pushed back and walked away and was sick. Another and another of the freaks stared, their mouths trembling, and moved away, leaving the Illustrated Man on the deserted road, the blood running from his mouth.

In the dim light, the unveiled Illustration was easily seen.

It showed a crowd of freaks bending over a dying fat man on a dark and lonely road, looking at a tattoo on his back which illustrated a crowd of freaks bending over a dying fat man on a . . .

WILLIAM MARCH

◄——————————————————————————————————————►

The Slate and the Sorrow

GRADY had a rash on his scalp that spring, and his mother stood at the dividing fence discussing his condition with her neighbor, Mrs. Webster. She wondered unhappily if it were worthwhile to continue sending the boy to Dr. Cromwell, the doctor who handled the company business under contract, since his condition, as anybody could see for himself, was not improved.

Mrs. Webster was of the opinion that Dr. Cromwell was capable enough at simple problems in medicine, such as cutting off a leg or probing for a bullet, but that he was entirely inadequate before the more complex ailments of man. He was particularly bad when it came to rashes and eruptions, she said positively, and that was a thing which she had always told others with the completest candor.

The screen door of the Webster cottage creaked on its hinges and slammed shut with a bang and Mrs. Webster, twisting her neck sidewise, watched her daughter Mamie lumber to the end of the back porch and empty a pan of dishwater in the weeds. Mamie Webster was a strong, clumsy girl of sixteen, and her mother regarded her now with heavy and habitual disapproval.

"Fix your stockings!" she said fretfully. "And brush that loose hair out of your eyes! How do you expect to catch a fellow for yourself when you go around looking like a tinker's slut?"

The theme of her daughter's unattractiveness was one which Mrs. Webster never quite exhausted. Mamie, as usual, pretended that she did not hear. She yawned placidly and came to the fence, the wet dishpan dripping grease and water against her legs. She stood leaning against the pickets and looked into space, saying nothing.

Mrs. Webster went on with her interrupted conversation. "No, sir," she continued heatedly. "I wouldn't even send a fice dog I thought anything of to Dr. Cromwell for tetter, ringworm or rashes of any sort." Suddenly she moved closer to Grady and examined his scalp thoroughly. "If this boy was mine," she said at length, half-closing her eyes and holding him away from her as if he were a collector's item, "I'd send him right off to Dr. Eldridge, dead wife or no dead wife, slate or no slate. Personally, I never saw anything so crazy about the doctor. It looks to me like he was only grieving more than ordinary."

November, 1944

Grady pulled away from Mrs. Webster and glanced up at his mother, waiting for her to veto the idea; but she only raised her left hand and held it flat against her cheek. "I don't know," she said doubtfully. "I don't know what's the best thing to do."

Everybody in town knew the stories that were being told about Dr. Eldridge, except, perhaps, the doctor himself. He had married in his late forties, and his devotion to his wife, who had been a school teacher when he met her, had caused the town much amusement during the three years they lived together. Then, unexpectedly, tragedy had struck, and Mrs. Eldridge drowned while bathing with friends at Crown Point. The situation was commonplace enough, and the doctor's grief at the death of his greatly loved wife was understandable. That was all natural and to be expected, as everyone agreed; it was his behavior afterwards which gave rise to the whispered stories about him.

At first he had refused to believe that she was dead and he had worked over her without rest for a long time, trying to bring breath into her body once more. At the end of the third day he collapsed and they put him to bed, his exhausted hands lying quietly on the counterpane at last. "Do what you please with her body," he said, "but I will have no part in it." Then, turning slowly on his side, he wept.

They buried her that afternoon while he was still asleep. Afterwards he refused to discuss her death with his friends, and when the Reverend Hamber called to pray with him, to counsel him to bow in humility before the stern will of God, Dr. Eldridge said: "I find you a little presumptuous, I'm afraid . . . How dare you offer me sympathy? How can you possibly know what I have lost? . . ."

These things were in the mind of Grady's mother as she stood that day listening to Mrs. Webster's advice. "I don't know," she repeated. "Anyway, I don't think Grady would go, even if I told him to."

Mamie Webster spoke for the first time. "If Grady won't go of his own free will and accord," she said, "I'll take him for you, Mrs. Dorney. I'm not scared of the doctor's wife or of his slate, either." She glanced down at the eight-year-old boy with quiet ferocity, nodding her head a couple of times. "I'll see that he gets there, all right," she said. "Don't worry about that."

"Maybe that's really the best thing to do," said Mrs. Dorney after a moment. "Nobody ever denied that Dr. Eldridge was a good doctor, even if he does hold traffic with spirits." Then, as if she had reached the end of her endurance, she gave her son an impatient shove and said, "Go see him! Go with Mamie right this minute! I'm tired of looking at that bothersome head!"

Mamie went toward her own house, saying over her shoulder: "Wait a minute till I change my clothes. I won't be gone no time at all." When she returned, she had on her Sunday dress and her new shoes. She had combed out the front section of her hair, but the back of her head remained as tangled and untidy as it had been originally. Her face was excessively powdered and she had sprinkled herself with cologne. She approached the dividing fence slowly, a little self-conscious in all her finery.

Mrs. Dorney said, "There, Mamie! Take his hand so he can't run away!"

"Come on!" said Mamie. "Come on, cry baby!"

"I'm not scared to go there," said Grady. "I'm not even thinking about that slate. I'm not thinking about ghosts, either."

"You're not scared," said Mamie. "Oh, no! I can see that!" She closed the gate behind them and gave him a jerk forward.

Later, on the road to the doctor's office, Grady abandoned his pose of contemptuous bravery. He spoke breathlessly now, half-running to keep abreast of Mamie Webster. "Is it really true that he keeps a slate under his pillow?" he asked. "Is it Mamie? Is it?"

"I wouldn't be surprised," said Mamie in an affected voice. "I wouldn't put anything silly past a man."

"Does his wife really come back from her grave and write messages on the slate like everybody says?" Grady insisted.

"Maybe she does," said Mamie. "Maybe she don't. How do I know?"

"People say that he looks at the slate every night and every morning, and if there's a message on it from his wife he always does what she tells him to without asking any questions. Do you believe it, Mamie? Do you?"

"If it's not true, then most of the folks in this town tell lies all day long," said Mamie. All at once she seemed annoyed at the boy and she jerked his arm roughly. "Talk! Talk!" she said. "Chatter! Chatter! . . . That's all boys or men, either, know how to do!"

They walked in silence after that and presently they came to the bungalow which served Dr. Eldridge both as an office and as a home. The Negro woman who kept house for him opened the door when they knocked, and they went into the reception room and sat down. To the left was the bedroom, and through the half-open door a chest of drawers, a mirror and a portion of the bed itself were visible. Grady tugged at Mamie's sleeve and pointed to the bed excitedly, but she pretended that she did not know what was in his mind.

"Sit up!" she said sternly. "Sit up on your chair; and don't give Dr. Eldridge no trouble, if you know what's good for you."

Dr. Eldridge, who had few patients these days, came out of his office a moment later. It would be difficult to imagine a less sinister figure. He was thin and not very tall. His hair was turning grey at the sides, and there was a patient, uncomprehending expression in his mild, gentle eyes. Seeing that the bedroom door had been left open, he went there first and closed it, and when he turned once more and faced his visitors he had managed somehow to bring himself back to the practical world of reality.

"Yes?" he asked, speaking to Mamie. "You came to consult me professionally?"

An astonishing change came over Mamie with the doctor's entrance, and Grady staring at her in surprise, his jaws relaxed a little, was of the opinion that she had suddenly lost the last of her wits. She giggled, scraped her foot across the floor and rolled her eyes alarmingly. "It's not me that needs treatment," she screamed. "It's Mrs. Dorney's little boy."

She continued to laugh shrilly and to roll her eyes, pressing her crushed handkerchief against her mouth as if the doctor's mistake were too witty to be endured. She lowered her lids and opened them rapidly, glancing sidewise and coquettishly at the doctor, but when she had recovered sufficiently she said: "Dr. Cromwell's been treating him, but he didn't do him no good at all, so I told Mrs. Dorney that she ought to send him to you. 'Dr. Eldridge is a perfectly wonderful man in every respect,' I said to her, 'and if he can't cure Grady's rash you might as well give up and say that *nobody* can cure it!' " She spoke more softly now, looking provocatively at the doctor through half-closed eyes.

For a moment Dr. Eldridge stared thoughtfully at the girl and then he seemed to dismiss her from his mind. He came to the boy and put his arm about him. "Come in, Grady," he said. "We'll have a look at that scalp of yours in my office." He opened the door and stood aside while the boy preceded him. "There," he said. "Sit in the chair by the window where the light is better."

All his vagueness had left him now, and he seemed very efficient. He bent above the boy and whistled softly, eager to be at work again. He patted the child reassuringly and said: "It's my guess that everybody in town except me has already prescribed for that scalp of yours. Tell me: Did your mother put on it everything the neighbors suggested?"

Suddenly Grady's fears were all gone. He looked straight into the doctor's eyes and smiled. "Yes, sir," he said, as if he and Dr. Eldridge shared the ultimate riddle of women. "Yes, sir, that's what she did, all right."

"You're suffering from too much attention," said the doctor. "Your scalp will clear up of its own accord in a few days if your mother will leave it alone that long." He turned toward his desk, saying: "Here! I'll write her a note and explain the situation." He stopped, stroked his chin and pursed out his lips humorously. "No," he went on, "I'd better prescribe something after all." He winked at the boy as if they were conspirators together, and said: "The salve I'm going to give you won't help your head in the slightest degree. Its sole purpose is to keep your mother's mind occupied. Do we understand each other, Grady?"

He came closer to the child and looked down at him affectionately. "Tell your mother that she isn't to put anything else on your head while you're using my salve—particularly no more soap and water. Tell her if she does, certain obscure chemical reactions will instantly take place, and her fine-looking young son will explode before her eyes like a cannon cracker." He laughed again and touched the boy's shoulder; and turning toward the anteroom where he compounded his own prescriptions, he added: "I'll fix the ointment for you now."

Grady waited by the desk for a time, thinking about Dr. Eldridge and staring idly out of the window; then wondering what Mamie was doing, he returned to the reception room. To his surprise, she was nowhere in sight, and he wondered if she had tired of waiting and had returned home alone; but seeing that the door to the bedroom was open once more, he approached and looked inside, and there, before his eyes, was Mamie Webster standing over the doctor's bed. She had a large, clothbound slate in her hands and when she heard the shocked, involuntary sound the boy made, she returned it quickly to its place beneath the pillow, smoothing out the sheet and counterpane. A moment later she closed the bedroom door, stuck out her heavy jaw and said: "You say one word to Dr. Eldridge or anybody else and I'll—"

She had got out of the bedroom just in time, for the doctor returned with the ointment before she could finish her sentence. He handed the jar to Mamie, saying gravely, "The directions are written on the label. They're quite simple." Inexplicably his cheerful, professional manner had deserted him, and he looked down at the floor, the lost expression once more in his eyes.

"Mrs. Dorney didn't send no money," said Mamie nervously; "but if you'll tell her what she owes you, she'll take care of it, she says."

"The money," repeated Dr. Eldridge vaguely. "Of course. I beg your pardon for forgetting." He reached absently into his pocket and put a fifty-cent piece in the boy's palm. "I'll try not to forget again," he said. "My wife usually handles these details for me but she went to Crown Point for the afternoon with some friends. If I didn't know what an expert swimmer she is, I'd be getting a little worried about her." He passed his hands over his eyes, bowed stiffly and turned away, having already forgotten Mamie Webster and the patient she had brought.

When they were on the road once more, Mamie spoke defensively: "All right, tattletale! Tell everybody in Williston what you saw! What do I care? I'll say I didn't do it, and everybody will believe me, because I'm grown up and you're not."

"He really keeps a slate under his pillow like they say," said Grady. "That part's the truth isn't it, Mamie?"

"Yes," she said. "It's the God's truth. And what's more, there's a slate pencil tied to it with a string, if you've got to know."

"That makes it easier for his wife when she writes her messages," said Grady. "It saves her the trouble of looking for the pencil every time she comes."

Suddenly he stopped in the road, caught at Mamie's hand and pulled her around so that she faced him. He stared at her a moment, an odd, intent expression in his eyes. "Was there anything written on the slate?" he asked. "Was there, Mamie?"

Mamie, her alarm at being caught red-handed having abated somewhat, decided to compromise. "Listen!" she began. "If I swear to tell the truth, will you swear never to repeat what you hear?"

"Yes," said Grady, "I swear."

"All right, then," said Mamie: "There wasn't anything written on the slate when I took it from under the pillow and looked at it."

The precise phrasing of her reply puzzled the boy. He knew she was holding something back, being so familiar with her character, but he could not decide what it was; then, remembering that she had had the pencil in her hand when he discovered her bending above the slate, he understood in a moment of intuition precisely what she had done.

"You wrote something on it *yourself!*" he said. "What was it you wrote on the slate, Mamie?"

Her eyes wavered and she glanced down. She thrust her rough, manlike hands behind her and her face and neck turned red slowly. "Let me alone," she said. "Why can't people mind their own business and let me alone?"

"What did you write on the slate?" he insisted. "You better tell me, because if you don't keep your promise, I don't have to keep mine, either. I'll tell everybody in town what I saw you do, and the first one I tell will be your mother."

She turned away in confusion and hid her face in her hands. "I can't say it right out," she said after a time. "I just couldn't! . . . I'd be too ashamed."

"Write it on the ground," said Grady. "You can rub it out as soon as I read it."

Mamie hesitated a little longer, but squatting by the roadside at last, she picked up a twig and wrote laboriously in the dust:

> When loanley or looking for
> good company
> comunercate right away with
> Miss Mamie L. Webster
> here in town.

For a time the boy and the gawky, unattractive girl knelt beside the road staring at each other; then Mamie rose upward on her heavy thighs, thrust out her foot and obliterated what she had written. "Now you know as much as I do," she said sullenly.

The boy said: "Do you think he'll do it, Mamie? Do you?"

"Why not?" she said reasonably. "Don't he always do what his wife tells him?"

At that moment Grady had a clear picture of how Mrs. Eldridge had looked in life: She had been gay and provocative and gentle, and half the men in Williston had been in love with her at the time she married the doctor. She had been soft and gracious and lovely—the very opposite of Mamie Webster in everything. It was then he knew that Mamie had revealed herself without purpose, that she had accomplished nothing, and with the detached brutality of children, he shook his head slowly and spoke:

"He won't do it, not even if he does think his wife asked him to . . . you're too big and greasy-looking."

But Mamie seized his hand more firmly, jerking him along so rapidly that he was running every few steps to keep abreast of her. "Talk! Talk!" she said bitterly. "Chatter! Chatter! It's all boys or men know how to do!"

ROBERT SWITZER

Death of a Prize Fighter

IT WAS two a.m. Billy Murdoch was at the airport, his small, sharp-chinned face pale with strain. He was catching a plane for Detroit. It was the wise thing to do because a kid named Tony Casino had died here tonight and the way people were acting you would think Billy Murdoch had killed him.

Tony Casino had been a prize fighter. Billy Murdoch had been his manager. And the kid had been hit too hard and had died of cerebral hemorrhage—and it was all Billy Murdoch's fault, of course.

Yes, Billy Murdoch thought sourly. *Oh, hell, yes.*

He slouched low on the bench in the waiting room, the collar of his camel's-hair topcoat turned up and his hat pulled down. He heard somebody say, "Hello, Billy."

He looked up and saw a fair-haired young man. *Another reporter*, he thought. *I haven't seen enough reporters tonight.*

"Hello," Billy Murdoch said.

The young man sat down. "I guess you've had a pretty tough night," he said sympathetically.

Billy Murdoch knew better than to answer that one. Nice traps these sports experts set. If he said yes, he had had a tough night, the paper would say Billy Murdoch felt sorrier for himself than he did for the dead boy. If he said he was all right, the paper would talk about the unfeeling manager. If he said something like, "It was worse for Tony," then he would be making jokes while the boy lay dead. It did not matter what you said; these guys could make you into the worst slob that ever walked.

So he said nothing. He wished he could get aboard the plane.

"Going to New York?" the reporter asked.

"Yes," Billy Murdoch said, and got up and walked across the waiting room to get away from the reporter, hoping the reporter would leave. But as he walked across the room the loud-speaker blared, "Flight 34 for Detroit," and Billy Murdoch knew that the press would be waiting for him in Detroit.

He sat to the rear of the plane. After what seemed a long time, the plane started to roll and then they were in the air. Billy Murdoch closed his eyes and thought of how it had been.

June, 1949

In the last second of the first round, Tony Casino had taken a terrific punch on his left temple, and, as the other boy was about to tear his head off, the bell rang. Tony just stood there, crouching a little, arms hanging straight down from his shoulders. Billy Murdoch and the handler brought him back to his corner. His eyes were glazed. Billy Murdoch and the handler worked on him frantically, with Billy Murdoch thinking: *He was knocked out last week, and now if he quits after one punch I'll have one sweet time matching him again.* Some expression came back into Tony's eyes.

"How you feel?" Billy Murdoch said.

"I'm all right," Tony said blurrily.

"Good. Good. Now listen. Stay away from him. Keep away from him this round. You hear?"

"Yeah," Tony said.

So the bell rang and Tony went back in and took one more punch. They tried to revive him in the ring, but could not. They carried him to the dressing room and tried to revive him, but could not. Then there was a doctor and a flock of reporters and the other fighters standing around in the dressing room they all shared and the very white body lying completely still on the rubbing table under the light bulb that dangled from the ceiling on the end of a long cord and threw a clear, brittle light on the blue-black smear of Tony's left temple. The doctor bent over the barely breathing body and without looking up said, "Call an ambulance. Quick." There was a scuffling sound on the cement floor as somebody went to telephone, but it was wasted effort because Tony died almost immediately. The doctor looked across the dry, white body at Billy Murdoch and said, "He's dead. Cerebral hemorrhage, probably."

Billy Murdoch kept his eyes on Tony Casino and felt everybody looking at him. There were a lot of men in the room and they were all watching him and waiting for him to say something.

"He was a nice boy," Billy Murdoch said. "It's a lousy thing."

For a moment nobody said anything. It was very hot in the room. Billy Murdoch could feel the sweat running down his sides.

"He was too tall for a welter," one of the fighters said.

"He should have been a middle with that height," a reporter said. "Only his bones weren't big enough."

"You got to have that bone," another fighter said. "Bone soaks it up."

Billy Murdoch wanted to leave, but there were too many people around. Somebody might get mad if he tried to leave too quickly.

"He was knocked out last week," a reporter said. "Just like tonight. He went down like he'd been shot."

The doctor said sharply, "Was he unconscious long? Last week, I mean?"

"No," Billy Murdoch said. "I've seen them out a lot longer. He was all right."

For the first time, Billy Murdoch noticed the man standing next to the doctor. A cop. Not in uniform but one hundred per cent cop. You can tell. The cop was staring at him. Billy Murdoch felt a flash of terror, and then he thought: *They can't do anything to me. I didn't kill the kid. The cop must have been at the fights and heard about this. Cops can't stay away from corpses.*

"How long was he out?" the cop said in a low voice.

"I don't know," Billy Murdoch said. "Not very long."

"About how long?"

"A few minutes, that's all."

The cop's heavy face suddenly looked heavier. "How long is a few minutes?"

"What are you trying to do?" Billy Murdoch said shrilly. "Blame me for this?"

It was very quiet in the room. Billy Murdoch felt his fingers trembling.

"I was here last week," a colored lightweight said. "Tony was out ten minutes anyway. Maybe fifteen."

"So what?" Billy Murdoch said. "I'd like to have a nickel for every boy that's been out ten minutes."

"He looked real bad when he came out of it," the lightweight said. "He was awful pale. I sat here with him for a while after Mr. Murdoch left. He was dizzy. He was sick, too, but he couldn't throw up anything. Just some of that green stuff that burns."

"Dizzy," the cop said. He looked at Billy Murdoch. "Did you ever see him dizzy?"

"No," Billy Murdoch said, thinking of the dizzy spells Tony Casino had had for the past six months. Ever since that night in Cleveland.

"I saw him fight in Cleveland," a reporter said. "About six months ago. He took one of the worst beatings I've ever seen. It was enough to finish any fighter."

"Did he lose all his fights?" the doctor asked in a puzzled voice.

"No," the reporter said. "He had a whole lot of guts. He won his share of fights. Nobody lost money on him."

Billy Murdoch heard grunts from the fighters and saw the angry eyes of the reporters and the flat eyes of the cop, and he thought: *Sure, that's what they're all thinking. I killed the kid for a few crummy bucks.*

He began to edge his way toward the foot of the rubbing table. The door was that way.

"How was he between rounds tonight?" a reporter asked. "When he came out for the second he didn't seem to know where he was going."

"I asked him how he was," Billy Murdoch said. "He said he was all right."

"They're always all right. How did he look?"

"He was hit hard. Maybe he didn't look perfect, but you can't stop a fight every time your boy gets hit."

"Where's the handler?" the cop said.

"Here," the handler said.

"How did he look?"

"He looked bad. I don't think he could see."

"Yeah," the cop said.

"Now, look," Billy Murdoch said, shrilly again. "You're all talking as if I was trying to kill the kid. That's enough of that. I don't have to take that." He started straight for the door and was faintly surprised when nobody tried to stop him.

The cop said viciously, "Murdoch!"

Billy Murdoch stopped.

"I'd like to get you bastards," the cop said in the same vicious voice. "I wish I could figure a way to get you bastards."

Billy Murdoch got out of there. A fat man followed him and caught up with him in the tunnel. He was the man who promoted the fights in this arena.

"Billy," the promoter said, "you better get out of town."

"I was leaving tomorrow, anyway. I got a couple of boys going in Detroit tomorrow night."

"Get out tonight. Don't hang around. Everybody's mad as hell. The papers will have a field day with this. I'm going to have enough trouble. It'll be better if you're not around. You know."

"Sure," Billy Murdoch said. "Tonight."

"About the kid," the promoter said. "Where'll I send him?"

"Somewhere in Brooklyn. I don't know where. The sports writers will find out for you. They'll be looking up his mother."

"I'll take care of it," the promoter said. "So long, Billy."

"So long," Billy Murdoch said, and left the arena, thinking: *Yes, you'll take care of it, you bighearted rat. You'll take care of it out of the purse you didn't pay me. You'd ship the kid C.O.D. if you could get away with it. Keep the money. I'm not stupid enough to argue about that.*

Billy Murdoch went to his hotel, threw his stuff in his bag and went out to the airport, and had to wait two hours for the fog to blow away so the plane could take off.

And now he was in the air for Detroit. The press would be waiting for him. He would have to say something to them. You can't just say, "No comment," when somebody's been killed. He would have to tell them something and it would have to be better than what he had done in the dressing room. He had handled that all wrong. Well, he had been scared. It was foolish, but he had been scared. God, he would hate to have that cop get at him. But what would he say to the reporters? He thought back again and remembered what he had said about you can't stop a fight every time somebody gets hit. He could work on that. He would have to say it right, though.

The plane came down at Detroit and four reporters jumped him. There was light in the sky now, but the sun was not up and it was chilly.

"We heard about Casino," a reporter said. "What happened?"

Nice and innocent, Billy Murdoch thought. When these guys go innocent, hang on.

"Tony was hit very hard," Billy Murdoch said. "I thought he was all right. But he was hit harder than I thought."

"Did you think of stopping the fight?"

"I thought he was all right," Billy Murdoch said again. "He was hit hard, but you can't stop a fight every time your boy gets hit. What would happen to the fight game if you stopped a fight every time somebody got hit?"

"I know what should happen to it," another reporter said. "They should take it out and bury it."

"Sure," Billy Murdoch said. "Nobody likes the fights. That's why they all go to them."

"What are you doing in Detroit?"

"Just passing through."

"To where?"

"Toronto," Billy Murdoch said. "I'm working on a main go for Danny O'Brien up there."

"How do you feel about this Casino kid?"

"How do you think I feel?"

"He was like a son to you."

"Don't be like that," Billy Murdoch said. "That's not funny."

"Forgive me," the reporter said.

Billy Murdoch got away from them, caught a cab, and checked in under a phony name at a small hotel. He slept until two in the afternoon. Then he got up, bathed, shaved, had something to eat, and felt better. He read what the papers had done about Tony Casino. It was just plain murder, the way they told it. Tony Casino had been having head trouble for months, but his manager, Billy Murdoch, had kept right on making him fight. Tony Casino should never have been a fighter, anyway. He had not been rugged enough to take the punishment. But the fight business was savage and could use kids like Tony Casino, and men like Billy Murdoch were licensed to break these kids, physically or mentally or both. The fight business was rotten from top to bottom and it was high time something was done about it.

Billy Murdoch was glad to read that last sentence. They were spreading their fire. They were shooting at the whole fight game and the target was too big and nobody would get hurt.

Billy Murdoch went to see Max Green. Green was putting on the card tonight that included Billy Murdoch's two boys. Green did not look happy at seeing him.

"I heard you were in town," Green said. "They got the finger on you good."

"I got two boys going for you tonight. Don't you remember?"

"They'll go on all right, but I don't want you out there, Billy. There might be trouble. I don't want to get mixed up in this thing. It's one of those messes and I don't want any part of it."

"All right," Billy Murdoch said. "I'll go to a movie. I'll have a time."

"I wouldn't do that, either. You should go on to New York. Dig in there for a while. A man's better off at home at a time like this."

"I'm getting tired of being run out of towns."

"So stay," Green said. "Stay and get your ears beat in. This is a small town.

They'll find you and that'll just keep them all excited. I never saw so much excitement as over this one. But New York is big. You won't stir up anything there. Is that right?"

"Sure," Billy Murdoch said. "I'll see you around."

"Good-by," Max Green said.

Billy Murdoch caught a plane for New York without being seen, and so there were no reporters waiting for him at LaGuardia Field.

He bought a paper. The Tony Casino death was splashed on page one. Billy Murdoch was surprised. He had not thought it would be played up here like this. They were really going to work on this one. Billy Murdoch could not understand it. Fighters were being killed all the time. Why did they have to knock themselves out over this one?

It was ten p.m. when Billy Murdoch stood on the corner of 58th and Sixth Avenue. There was a hotel down the street. Billy Murdoch and nine other managers kept a room in it. Most nights you could get a poker game there. Billy Murdoch went to the hotel and up to the fourteenth floor.

There were five men in the room, sitting around a table littered with chips and ash trays and glasses. They looked up casually when Billy Murdoch came in and then they all jumped to their feet and gave him a royal welcome.

"Hell," Billy Murdoch said. "I thought you might throw me out. Everybody else has."

"Yeah," Jack Latimer said. "What are you trying to do? Give us a bad name?"

"You got a tough break, Billy," Pete Torelli said. "It was too bad."

"All this hollering," Manny Gold said. "Don't let it get you, Billy. It means nothing. Every so often they got to yell. They'll yell for maybe two more days and then they'll forget it."

From across the room another man called, "What do you take in Scotch, Billy?"

"Water," Billy Murdoch said. "Just plain water."

They all went back to the table and sat down. Billy Murdoch relaxed. It was nice to be back among friends again.

WILLIAM SAROYAN

Little Miss Universe

THERE were three authorities on the horses at The Kentucky Pool Room, number One Opera Alley, in San Francisco: Mr. Levin, a fat gentleman of fifty, affectionately called *The Barrel* because he resembled one; San Jose Red, a nervous, thin person of sixty-five; and a neatly dressed young man of twenty who was known as Willie. These three gentlemen knew more about thoroughbreds than any other three people living, or for that matter, as someone had suggested, more than the horses themselves knew. Nevertheless, they were almost always broke. Each kept an accurate record of what he would have won if he had had money with which to bet, and the profit for each day was fairly amazing; for a month it was breathtaking. A month ago, for example, if Willie had had a half dollar to bet on the nose of *Panther Rock*, today he would be worth—well, to be exact (he opened a small book full of neatly written figures) —ten thousand, two hundred and eighty-six dollars and forty-five cents.

"And," said Willie, "I could use it, too."

Willie had a system. He looked up the horses in every race and chose the one with the worst record. "That horse," he explained, "has been loafing. He has been going around the track as a spectator, watching the race from a good position. But he'll win today. Even a horse has got to break the monotony. He'll win out of sheer boredom. His mother was *Ella Faultless*, and you know what she did."

"No," somebody said. "What did she do?"

"Well," said Willie, "five years ago she started twenty times and wasn't once in the money. She ran beautifully but never exerted herself. Then all of a sudden she woke up and won six races in a row."

Willie looked into the faces of his small audience with an expression of profound wisdom, as if by divine grace he alone of all mortals had been blessed with the faculty of understanding such a remarkable performance.

"Bang," he said with emotion.

"One.
Two.
Three.
Four.

December, 1934

Five . . . SIX!

In a row. Think of it." He spoke the small words distinctly, sending them from his mouth with the precision of a hen producing an egg.

"Somebody must have got the horse mad," said a young gambler named Blewett. He was a barber by profession.

Willie smiled at Blewett and whispered confidentially, "That's just it—some horse must have got her mad. We can't figure these things out because they're not in the dope sheets. But it's a cinch one horse can get another horse sore. Remember Mr. Goofus? He was a card."

"What'd he do?" asked Mr. Blewett.

"There was a horse," said Willie. He paused to catch his breath for the remarkable statement he was about to make. "There was a horse," he repeated, "that was almost human."

"Ridiculous," said D. L. Conrad, an accountant who had passed out cards to several of his pals of the pool room. "Who ever heard of such a thing? How can a horse be almost human?"

"Let me explain," said Willie with the imperial air of a duke addressing a peasant. "It is characteristic of human beings to compete, is it not? In athletics. In commerce. In life itself."

"Granted," said Mr. Conrad, the accountant. "But what has that to do with Mr. Goober, or whoever it was you mentioned?"

"Allow me," said Willie impatiently. "If you will let me proceed for a moment, you will soon know. Now then: I said Mr. Goofus was almost human. I mean just that. There was a horse that had the soul of a man. In short, he was vicious. He was a bully. Don't interrupt me. If Mr. Goofus was leading the field and another horse tried to overtake him, why, he would turn around and bite the horse. It made him mad to have another horse pass him. He didn't like it. Of course they disqualified him a couple of times, but that didn't matter. He had all the horses scared, and it wasn't often they would try to get in front of him. He had a terrible eye, they say. One look and it was all over. Mr. Goofus won a lot of races and he beat horses that were much faster than him. You've got to work on horse personalities. That is an element almost always overlooked by handicappers. Psychology. Horses have it. No use being oldfashioned. There isn't a single race horse that hasn't better breeding than the average man. You can't expect such beasts to remain uncivilized for long. They're bound to get vicious after a while."

"Nuts," said Mr. Conrad with a laugh. "A horse is a horse. Tell me who's going to win the third at Arlington and we'll have a beer together."

"I do *not* tout," said Willie with pride. "I like *Miss Universe.*"

Mr. Conrad made an ugly face. "Why," he said, "that horse has started eleven times in the past month and hasn't once been better than sixth."

"I know," said Willie. "I am aware of the facts. Nevertheless, I like her just the same."

"I'm playing *Polly's Folly,*" said Mr. Conrad. This horse was a hot favorite;

her odds were a paltry six to five to win, whereas the odds on *Miss Universe* were twenty to one. Nevertheless, Willie said:

"I hope you have luck."

Willie sat at a table and produced his note-book and a pencil. Under the classification "Tired Horses" he wrote the name *Polly's Folly*. Among other names under this classification was that of the great Equipoise. In Willie's humble estimation this horse was tired of everything; of winning, of racing, of the whole routine in general. Let it be known then that Willie, himself a superior by nature, disliked superior horses and cherished fondly those whom most bettors despised. For example, of the millions of pony-players in America he alone had hopes for the ultimate success of the two-year-old maiden *Miss Universe*. To Willie this horse was not merely another horse. She was something more subtle, more mystical. Along with the success of *Miss Universe* would date the success of Willie himself. She was his pet. He loved her passionately. He had a special alibi for each of her miserable performances, a psychological alibi. Also: the name was beautiful. It was poetry. No other horse in the history of racing had had such a glorious name. Such a horse could not fail. It would be unnatural.

Mr. Levin, called *The Barrel*, also had a system. It was externally more complicated than Willie's, but a good deal less subtle. Willie's system was centrifugal, working outward from the brain, the soul, and the personality of the horse. The hub of Mr. Levin's system was the great panorama of the earth itself. To him the horses were mere puppets, helpless and a bit foolish. His desire was to discover the dark secrets of owners, jockeys, and wise gamblers. His system took into consideration all the physical facts involved in a race: the distance, the weight and talent of the jockey, the tendencies of the owner and trainer of the horse, the weather at the track, the weather in Iowa, the number of people at the track, carload of shipments of raw products, progress of the N R A, the state of his own private stomach, and the amount of money on the person being touted.

In short, everything.

Mr. Levin was a drab realist while Willie was a mystic.

Which brings my document (for this is a document, as I shall soon show) to the case of M. San Jose Red. I have said he was a thin, nervous person of sixty-five. Do not imagine, however, that San Jose Red was an old man, for he was not. (A young man once addressed him innocently as "Pop" and was severely reprimanded for the indelicacy. "Don't call me Pop," said San Jose Red. "I don't like it. I go out of this joint every day with five hundred dollars.") This was a preposterous exaggeration, but San Jose Red apparently had the idea that if a man made money on the races he could not possibly be old. He had the slim figure of a boy, the voice of a boy, and, alas, the sense of one. He was Irish. He was angry. He puffed at his pipe with defiance. He uttered one fantastic falsehood after another, innocently, sinlessly, since he himself believed his most atrocious lies. He was never known to have a dime. Nevertheless, he maintained vigorously that he won no less than five hundred dollars per week, net. If you got him angry enough he announced, as I have already said, that he earned this sum every day. He was extravagantly careless with these sums, and threw vast figures about him with the heedlessness of the born spendthrift. Nothing definite was known about him, though from his name it is to be inferred that at one time he lived in or near the city of San Jose, sixty miles south of San Francisco, in Santa Clara Valley.

San Jose Red also had a system. It was the laughing stock of The Kentucky Pool Room, but San Jose Red believed in it implicity. After every race this fiery old codger would swiftly scribble the name of the winner on a small sheet of cardboard, and, flourishing this document, wildly, rush through the crowd, grumbling insanely, but with a beatific smile on his magnificent Irish face. "See? *Black Patricia.* I told you. Why, I picked that horse last night." And then he would go on to tell a stranger how much he cleaned up every day.

This system of course is nothing short of infallible; in fact, it is a good deal more than infallible, for there has not yet been a horse race in which at least one horse has not won. Under the circumstances, it must be designated a philosophical (and perhaps scientific) system, and San Jose Red must be identified as both a philosopher and a scientist, something in the nature of Albert Einstein with a bit of Oswald Spengler, Walter Lippmann, and the Associated Press thrown in for good measure. His philosophy accelerates on this scientific basis: one waits until a thing happens, and then declares that it happened. You can't go wrong; science, statistics, legal documents, and everything else is on your side. It is, in its way, the only system known to man worth a tinker's toot, or whatever it is. But you've got to be unimaginative to fool with it. Or else, like San Jose Red, you've got to believe in the retrogression of events. In plainer terms, you've got to confuse the outcome of an event with the state of affairs immediately preceding the outcome. Or in still simpler terms, you've got—well, you've got to be sixty-five and Irish and broke and angry and frustrated and mad at the world. You've got to give yourself all the odds, a million to one, or to use figures generally related to the age of light years (or something), sixty trillion to one.

Now, perhaps, you are beginning to see that this *is* a document, and a profound one at that; a document with stupendous implications. For the unsubtle reader, and for children, I shall hint one of the implications.

Gambling, betting on horses, among other things, is a way of life. The manner in which a man chooses to gamble indicates his character or his lack of it. In short, gambling is a game, a philosophy, just as in Spain bull fighting is these things, as Mr. Hemingway has pointed out in five hundred pages of small print and two or three dozen photographs. Of course this document would be richer if I accompanied it with photographs of San Jose Red, Mr. Levin, and Willie in various poses and at various crucial moments. I should like to have you see, for instance, an actual photographic reproduction of San Jose Red frantically flourishing the name of the latest winner, or one of Mr. Levin standing humbly behind his belly telling a boy of eighteen how to play the ponies, or yet another of Willie in his elegantly-pressed twelve-dollar suit elucidating on the subtle make-up of horse-brains; but I regret that I cannot produce these pictures. Not that these men are not real flesh-and-blood people (you can go down to number One Opera Alley any day and see for yourself that they are), but that the light in The Kentucky Pool Room is dim indeed, and furthermore that my camera lies now in hock.

My document ought, properly, to end at this point, but such an ending would be artless. Subscribers to this magazine would write letters to the editor complaining; one or two would cancel their subscriptions. "What sort of a story do you call that?" readers would be saying to themselves. "No plot, no outcome, no climax, nothing exciting."

All right then. I will proceed to a plot. I will manufacture an outcome, a climax, and produce excitement. (Mind you, nothing ever happens at The Kentucky Pool Room. Bets are made, a few lucky fellows collect, but in the long run everybody loses. These are the facts. Day in and day out Willie and Mr. Levin and San Jose Red arrive and wait for the races, but nothing ever happens, so if I make a tale, it is not my fault, but the fault of art.)

Well, Willie is sitting at a table. The next race is the third at Arlington. Mr. Levin is rolling a cigarette of borrowed paper and tobacco. While he does so he is telling the man from whom he has borrowed the tobacco that a horse named *Wacoche* is going to win the race. "He's going to win by six lengths," says Mr. Levin, feeling miserable and lonely.

San Jose Red is out of sight. He comes in after the race. No one knows where he goes between races, but he is always out of sight until the winner is announced.

Let the matter rest here for a moment. Anyone can see for himself that any number of tales are now possible. I could say, for instance, as a young man once actually said, speaking of himself, that Willie, in an idle moment, thrust his thumb and his forefinger into his upper right-hand vest pocket, an act of habit, and there felt a heavy coin, which instantly set his heart to beating and proved to be a *bona fide* American half dollar. I can go on to say that Willie rushed up to Smithy, the bookie-clerk, and bet the whole half dollar right on the nose of *Miss Universe*, and that furthermore *Miss Universe* came to life and won the race, thereby placing in Willie's neat trousers the vast sum of ten dollars. And I could continue, saying that Willie's luck, as he himself dreamed, began at this point and that from this meagre beginning in less than a week he became the possessor of four hundred and sixty-two dollars and eleven cents. I could say, for the sake of romance, that he was in love with a beautiful young stenographer who would not marry him until he earned enough money to buy a license and a cheap ring. And so on.

About Mr. Levin and San Jose Red I could say all sorts of things that would make this tale interesting and exciting, but, forgive me, I cannot. It is impossible for me to lie, even though Mr. Kipling has declared that writers can never lie, that even when they do so, they unconsciously reveal even more profound truths. But about these men I cannot make pastry. Their stories are exciting enough in themselves. Let us try to be content with the paltry romance which lies pathetically in the ugly truth.

So we return. It is Thursday. One twenty-four P.M. In about six minutes the third race at Arlington will be run.

There's the lay-out.

Now the fun begins.

I am strolling along Third Street, a melancholy-looking young writer seeking material for a tale. It is a bright day, the sun is warm, and even the forlorn men of this drab street seem to reflect the brightness of the day in their unshaved faces. I am idly eating California peaches, when suddenly I notice three men hurrying in quick succession through a narrow doorway marked "Cairo Club, Gentlemen." There is something exciting about their haste. I decide to find out where they are going and why. In less than half a minute another man passes swiftly and impatiently through the same portal. Then another. Then, yet another. This last fellow is in a terrific hurry; he is nervously jiggling two coins in his right hand. I follow him at a trot and find myself stampeding down a narrow and dark corridor, close on the heels of my guide. We make two turns, open as many doors and finally emerge into the gloom of a paved crevice between the Winchester Hotel, Rooms 35c and Up, and the Westchester Hotel, same rates.

It is Opera Alley!

I read the sign "Number 1 Opera Alley" over the swinging doors of The Kentucky Pool Room, and hasten to enter. Number One Opera Alley is a large, dark, square room containing five tables, fourteen chairs, six benches, and thirteen spittoons; not to mention sixty-three men including Mr. Levin and Willie. (San Jose Red, as I have said, is out of sight for the moment.) I am there. I myself, the writer. I see that Mr. Levin is sadly longing for someone to tout. And I see Willie seated at the table, impeccable, his face glowing with lack of character, his entire physical being a picture of graceful lack of purpose. Still, he is the neatest person in the room, so I take the chair beside him.

In precisely four minutes and twelve seconds *Miss Universe*, in company with seven other horses, will begin to scramble around the track at Arlington Park, in Chicago. There is no time to lose, but I know absolutely nothing about horses or horse racing.

Fully fifteen seconds I do not hear so much as an idle word from the lips of my contemporary. (Nine out of ten gamblers are habitual talkers-to-themselves. But not Willie.) I decide to offer him a cigarette. He replies:

"Thank you, I do not smoke."

I am astounded. What character. What discipline. Not to smoke in that atmosphere of hope and dread and spiritual fidgetiness. It is incredible.

Although I am aware of what is going on, I say to Willie in order to make conversation:

"What is going on here, anyway?"

He looks at me with eyes that are suddenly transformed. I detect in them the roar and surge of great hope. I am, bluntly, a greenhorn, and perhaps after all Willie will be able to bet on *Miss Universe*—with my money. Nevertheless, he is a subtle performer.

"I beg your pardon?" he says with elegance.

I repeat my question and Willie relates to me the entire history of horse racing, the tricks of owners, the habits of jockeys, the idiosyncrasies of horses, and the thoughtlessness of most gamblers. And while he speaks with an air of great leisure, he nevertheless imparts all this information in something less than twenty seconds flat. A thoroughbred himself.

In the meantime I have dispatched my right hand to my vest pocket where it is timidly thrilling at the feel of my last dollar, the dollar which is to keep me with food in my stomach another long week.

By this time, I have developed implicit confidence in the mystical omnipotence, etcetera, of Willie, and am itching to have him make a bet for me.

"There is one horse in this race," says Willie, "that is all but human. She hates to lose; it breaks her heart. She has been trying for all she's worth and today's her day. She is the daughter of *Lady Venus* by *The Wop*, and you know what *Lady Venus* did."

Of course I have no idea what *Lady Venus* did, and I say so.

"Everything," says Willie. "She did everything."

"Well," I say, "who is the horse?"

Willie bends to whisper into my ear, so that no one will learn the good news. "*Miss Universe*," he says passionately.

"God, what a beautiful name," I think, and the next thing I know I have given Willie my last dollar. He rushes up to Smithy, the bookie-clerk, and plasters it on the nose of *Miss Universe*—and none too soon either, for no sooner had Smithy scribbled the bet on a slip than the race began.

You see, everything worked perfectly and precisely.

Well, there I am in The Kentucky Pool Room, and about two thousand miles away, in Chicago, eight horses are running around a track, one of them *Miss Universe*. And there beside me is Willie, neat and clean, piously hopeful.

"A beautiful name," I keep thinking. "A glorious name."

The phone clerk calls: "At the quarter: *Stock Market, Dark Mist, Fiddler*." This means these horses are leading the field in the order named.

Willie is pale. I'm paler. Willie says, "She's running fourth. She starts slow but she'll come up." Then for an instant he is overcome and shouts to himself "Come on, *Miss Universe!*"

I do the same.

The phone clerk announces: "At the half: *Stock Market, Dark Mist, Fiddler*."

Willie is a little paler. I'm just a shade paler than he is.

"Her mother," Willie gasps, "lost eleven races before she got out in front. This is *Miss Universe's* eleventh race. You watch her tear loose in a minute."

The phone clerk, his voice rising (he knows everyone is excited and he wants to be sympathetic; he knows small histories are being made and unmade; he is not heartless and he can shout), shouts:

"At the three-quarters: *Stock Market,* a neck, *Fiddler,* a half-length, *Dark Mist* five lengths."

"*Cute Face* is running fourth," he declares apologetically.

Willie is visibly nervous and a bit paler than before. I resemble a well-dressed ghost.

"Come on, *Miss Universe,*" Willie whispers madly.

"Yes," I say to myself. "Come on, darling, please come on, please, please, that's all the money I have and I have a terrible appetite."

It was a prayer, I admit. All horse-bettors are religious.

The phone clerk pauses dramatically and shouts:

"The next is the winner."

Then he says:

"Number 57, *Fiddler,* wins—by a neck. 51, *Stock Market* is second—by three lengths. 53, *Dark Mist* is third."

There you have it: the story. Nothing added, nothing taken away, like pure mayonnaise.

But wait: what's this. A madman is tearing through the crowd. He is small and Irish, and he is shouting, "See. Didn't I tell you? *Fiddler. Fiddler.* Why, I had him picked last night." He is holding a slip of cardboard on which is written the name of the horse.

It is San Jose Red, but of course you knew it.

Willie is ill with disappointment. He falls exhausted into a chair.

"I'm sorry," he says. "Her father was never much to speak of."

"It's all right," I reply.

Now I am walking up Third Street with an empty pocket, and I am telling myself, "There is still half a loaf of rye bread, a quarter pound of coffee, a bit of cheese, and eleven cigarettes. *Miss Universe.* What a beautiful name. If I have one slice of bread twice a day and a cup of coffee for breakfast—well, I can make it, I suppose."

NELSON ALGREN

<———>

The Captain Is a Card

THE undersized man at the head of the first line of the evening had just been brought in off the street, and wore an oversized army overcoat dragging past his knees; its hem was frayed and caked with mud, as though he'd been sitting on a curb with the hem in the gutter. The coat's top button dangled loosely and he twisted it tenderly; feeling perhaps that the last vestige of his respectability dangled with it. If you took him seriously he looked like the original tough-luck kid, and if you didn't he looked like Amateur Night at the nearest burlesque.

What was he doing in a police lineup anyhow, the Captain wanted to know.

"Just here for protecting myself is all," the little man explained. Then he glanced uneasily toward the Captain's shadowed corner as though fearing he had, so soon in the questioning, given a wrong answer.

"Don't look over here. Tell your story to the mike."

The oversize overcoat looked into the amplifier with the face of an aging terrier searching forever, with brown-eyed weariness, a world of shadowed corners. Of padlocked poolrooms, bootleg bookies, curtained brothels, darkened sidestreets and unlit, littered alleys. He looked like he hadn't walked down an open street in daylight, nor had a friendly nod of recognition in his life. He looked lost.

"Do you ever go around looking for trouble?"

"No sir. I don't like trouble."

"Then what are you doing in front of a tavern at two in the morning with a Luger under your coat? Don't you know those things go off?"

"I'm a veteran."

"What's that got to do with it? I'm a veteran too. But I don't go prowling around taverns with artillery under my clothes."

The veteran eyed the Captain's corner furtively before he answered.

"He shoved me," was the explanation.

"Who's 'he'?"

"A fellow I never seen him before. He bought me a drink. Because I'm a veteran."

"Then what happened?"

"He told me to go home."

"Then he slugged you?"

"No sir. He just shoved me was all."

"Then what?"

"Then nothing. That's all. I went home like he told me."

"And picked up a Luger and came back to blow his head off?"

"Yes sir. Naturally." As though that had been understood all along.

"*Naturally?* Don't you realize that if the officer hadn't happened along to take that thing off you, you'd be standing there for murder now?"

Silence. "Well?"

"Yes sir. I realize."

"You're pretty cool about it."

"Yes sir. I'm a veteran."

"What the hell *has* that got to do with it?" The Captain was exasperated at last. "I saw as much over there as you did."

The little man found the Captain with his eyes at last. And snapped like a mongrel held where it cannot move.

"It wasn't you what got shoved. It was *me.*"

"Oh." The Captain lowered his eyes as though he were, suddenly, the guilty man. Then he grinned. "*Man,*" he said quizzically, half sympathy and half surprise, "I'd hate to have you get mad at me for something worth getting mad about."

The next man was half-leaning, half-crouching against the black-and-white lines of the wall. He was a blond of perhaps twenty-two.

"Stand up there!" The Captain sounded like a public-school principal on examination day.

The blond stood as best he could. The knuckles were clenched whitely; the lips were bloodless. And the tip of the nose as white as new snow. The Captain relented.

"You must be hitting it pretty hard."

The boys lips moved inaudibly toward the mike; it was hard to tell whether he was trying to speak or merely wetting his lips in preparation for saying something.

"What do you take?"

The answer could not be heard; the lips could not be read.

"Speak up, son. Do you sell it too?"

This time the answer came faintly, from somewhere in Cloudland.

"Once—upon—a—time."

"How's last Tuesday afternoon—is that once upon a time?"

The boy nodded solemnly, dreamily, with a slow-motion gravity all his own. Yes.

Any Tuesday afternoon in Cloudland was once upon a time.

The next man in line was a high yellow in his early thirties.

"What you here for?"

"Havin' whiskey in my home."

"You too? I thought they repealed that law. You don't carry a gun, do you?"

"No sir."

"Do you keep one on the premises?"

"I just keep it. I don't carry it. I leave it on the premises."

"But there was a .38 on the premises?"

"I wasn't nowhere near it."

"I didn't ask you how close you were. I asked whether it was there."

"Yes sir. That's what they claims. I'm in business. I got to have one."

"I thought you said it was your home. Now it's a business. Make up your mind, you can't beat both raps. It'll go lighter on you if you stick to the whiskey story. What you using a private home for business for anyhow? What business?"

"The True-American."

"What's *that?*"

"Social 'n Athletic club."

"With five women?"

"That's the social part."

"I see. Was afraid you'd tell me they were lady wrestlers."

The woman in the back giggled at the Captain's humor.

"No sir. A mixed club, *that's* what we got."

"I see. Good clean fun and lots of sunshine?"

"Yes sir. Meets in my home. We go on hikes."

"Now it's a home again. You're not selling whiskey there then after all?"

"Oh no sir. I give it away. They my *guests.*"

"Which one of your guests filed the numbers off that .38 for you? One of the lady wrestlers?"

"Nobody. I bought it that way."

"Now we're getting somewhere for a change. Ever been in trouble before?"

"No sir," the high yellow declared.

The Captain shook his head sadly, to indicate his resignation at human mendacity. "You know, I'll begin to think you aren't telling the whole truth to these people. You're down here for strongarm robbery on June 1, 1934. Did that happen on one of your hikes?"

"I paid a fine."

"Did you pay a fine for that no-bill for murder in 1928?"

The high yellow started almost imperceptibly. The Captain had reached him where he lived—in his courage. You could see him visibly trying to pull that courage together, like a fighter holding his guts with one hand while arranging a fixed grin for his opponent to show he isn't hurt. You can tell when they're hurt when they try to smile.

"I didn't kill her."

"You know what I mean though?"

"It's a different case."

"You know what I mean though."

The Negro's face seemed burned a rust yellow across the forehead and nose, the way a man's face is left when he is lifted out of the chair. He stared straight into the mike, deep shadows under the eyes and the eyes themselves two yellow flares.

"Yes sir," he said at last. And waited tensely for the mike to move. The yellow flares began to die down in the eyes; when they were faded to pinpoints the Captain spoke leisurely, like a man with nowhere to go and the whole night to kill.

"Tell us more about it."

Silence.

"If you don't tell it I'll read it."

The Negro's eyes were dead embers now, and his voice a dying man's voice. He spoke without emphasis, in a dead-level monotone, and—at the first moment —with the dead woman's voice:

"Us two lived t'gether 'n we sort of separated 'n got t' goin' t'gether again 'n we were drinkin' t'gether 'n I wanted t' go home 'n figures I'd bluff her, teach her a lesson, scare her so's she wouldn't run off 'n always come home with me when it was time. I pulled the gun 'n leveled it 'n she grabbed for it 'n it went off 'n shot her in the stomach 'n when I went t' see her at the hospital she took my hand 'n say, 'Honey, you shouldn't a done it,' 'n that was all she ever say."

"You're a bad man. You been going wrong fifteen years."

The mike was moved to the next man.

Next was a redheaded Irish boy of eighteen, with teeth like piano keys.

"What's your trouble, Red?"

"Left a jimmy in a gas-station door."

"At night?"

"No sir. Daytime."

"Didn't have criminal intent, did you?"

"No sir."

"You weren't going to break into that station when it got dark, were you?"

"I just had it on my mind."

"Where were you arrested?"

"I was walkin' on the rocks off 39th. The park officer called me over."

"Where were you going when he called you?"

"Home."

"Then you got it off your mind?"

The redhead grinned amiably. He had it off his mind.

While the mike was being moved the Captain turned to his audience with the deliberation of a sideshow barker at a county fair.

"I want you to look close at this next man, ladies 'n gentlemen. This, let me tell you, is a sweetheart. Folks, meet Hardrocks O'Connor. Meet the folks, O'Connor."

A flat-faced felon in his late fifties, with no bridge to his nose and a bulge for a forehead. The voice hoarse from a hundred cells. You could tell he hit the bottle hard and you could tell he'd done his time the hard way. In the hard places. And still trying to make it the hard way. It was in his posture and in his voice; in the lean set of the jaw and across his punched-in mug like a brand.

"Tell us about yourself, Morning Glory."

O'Connor's mouth split when he said:

"Take 'em west yerself."

The Captain knew when he had a prize: he took Hardrocks west for five solid pages. Danbury, Waupun, Jeff City, Wetumpka, Leavenworth, Huntsville. For a phony bunco game. For a dice game with 'missouts.' For violation of the Narcotics Act. For forgery, for the pocketbook game, for the attention racket, for using the mails to sell a pair of missouts, for bigamy, for vag, for impersonating an officer, for breach of promise, for contributing to delinquency of a minor, for defrauding an innkeeper, for indecent exposure, for tapping a gas main. And for the phony bunco game, right back where he'd started a lifetime before.

Two years, ten days, six days, six months, thirty days, a year and a day, fifty-dollar fine, given a floater out of the state in Lubbock, only to run into two years at hard labor on the pea farm at Huntsville for taking a rancher with a phony roulette wheel at a McAllen County fair.

"Why didn't you get out of the state like they gave you a chance to do at Lubbock instead of running on down to McAllen?" The Captain was merely curious.

"Had a deal on down there."

The Captain turned to his listeners.

"Five more pages, ladies 'n gentlemen—'n not one a crime of violence. He'll sell you a little dope, take a little hisself, sell you an oilwell 'r take a merry widow for a ride on her insurance money. But he won't use a gun. He'll spot a beggar paddlin' down the street when he has t' get out of town in a hurry—but he'll stop 'n try t' take the beggar." This spectacle of a man who could steal for a lifetime without once doing so by force affected the good Captain as an obscenity. "C'mon down here," he ordered. "Let the people see you so's they'll remember you. How'd you get your nose bust, Hardrocks? Trying to take the same sucker twice?"

O'Connor paused on a step from the stage to rub the place where the bridge of his nose had once been.

"Had the bone took out when I was twenty. Wanted t' be a fighter." He hesitated as though he were about to add something.

"Keep movin', Hardrocks. No speeches. All the way down front. There, that's as near as we want you. Take off that cap. That's how he looks without a cap, folks. Now put it back on. That's how he looks with it on. Walk around, Daffodil. We want to see how you look when you walk."

O'Connor began a deliberate pacing: five steps forward and five steps back. And turned heavily at an imagined door. His life was a bull-pen, and he turned within it like a gelded bull; five dogged steps forward and five dogged steps back.

"That's enough of that, O'Connor. Now stand still and turn around with your cap in your right hand."

The old man turned, the sheen of his worn brown suit showing in the glare from above like light on an aging animal's hide.

"That's how he looks with his back turned, folks. Put your cap on, Hardrocks. No, don't turn around yet. That's how he looks when he's walking away with your money. All right, O'Connor, back on the platform."

O'Connor returned slowly to his position before the mike.

"What did you say you were arrested for, Hardrocks? Stealing from a blind man?"

"I wasn't arrested. I walked into the station 'n give myself up. I can't make it no more. I want 'em t' come 'n get me, I want 'em all t' come 'n get me. Anyone who wants me, tell 'em t' come 'n get me. I can't make it no more." The woman in the back stopped tittering. The Captain cocked his head to one side in mild surprise. The young men, on either side of the hardest one of them all, looked straight out over the lights as though the old man was speaking for their futures as well as for his past.

"I been a stumblin' block, I been a obstacle to the Republic. I done it all wrong, I got hard-boiled too young. I got kicked around too soon. I was a orphan 'n got kicked around. I'm an old man, I got nobody, I can't make it no more—" Hardrocks O'Connor was crying.

The next man was a young Negro in a gabardine, heavy in the shoulders and lean in the shanks.

"What you here for, Ready-Money?"

"Don't know."

"Then you'll need a lawyer to tell you. How old was the girl?"

"She looked like sixteen."

"Yeh. But she was eleven. Are you on parole?"

"Yes sir."

"Goodbye."

The last man in the line was a dwarf with the head and torso development of a man of average height. He stood two inches short of the four-foot mark on the black-and-white diagram behind him and looked to be in his early forties. An ugly specimen.

"What's it for, Shorty?"

"Just a pickup."

"Pickup for what?"

"Don't know. Suspicion I s'pose."

"What you sit seven years in Stateville for, Shorty?"

"Suspicion."

"Isn't seven years on suspicion a little severe?"

The dwarf's voice was as shrill as a ten-year-old's.

"Yes sir. It was severe."

"Ever get boosted through a transom, Shorty?"

"Yes sir."

"Who boosted you?"

"A frien'. He's still settin'."

"How many places you rob that way, Shorty?"

"I ferget."

"You shouldn't. You're still in the business. How much time you done?"

"Year 'n a day once 'n once three years."

"You don't count Stateville?"

"You said that one."

The women tittered their enjoyment of the little man's confession. A dwarf, standing between a seven-year-long shadow and a new shadow just as long. Perhaps it was funny to be so little while transoms were so high. And shadows were so long. Perhaps they saw no shadow. Perhaps they saw no man.

Next was a middle-aged Serb, splayfooted, with the hands of a stockyards skinner. He stood with his naked forearms folded.

"What you here for this time, Rutu?"

"Neigh—bors complain."

"Again? What about?"

"Same ol' t'ing. I fight."

"Who were you fighting with this time?"

"Same ol' t'ing. Wid wife."

"Hell, that's no crime neither. Next."

"I went and let somebody use my car."

"That puts you in, too. Next."

"What's your trouble, next man?"

"I beg your pardon?"

"Don't beg my pardon," the Captain quipped. "Beg the pardon of the woman whose purse you snatched."

"I didn't snatch it."

"How'd the officers find it in your room?"

"I stole it."

"Oh, that's different. I beg your pardon. *Discharged.*"

The next man was a paunchy character with the professionally friendly aspect of a floorwalker or beauty-shop operator. His iron-grey hair had been recently marcelled.

"What you here for, Flash?"

"Just riding in a cab is all."

"What did you have in your pocket?"

"Just a toy cap pistol was all."

"What was that for—Fourth of July?"

"I was on my way to give it to my little nephew in Hammond for a Christmas present."

"How many cabs you take with that toy gun, Santa?"

"Just the one I was riding in. I don't know what come over me."

"Come off it, Coneroo. How many you hold up altogether?"

"Nine."

"I said altogether."

"Oh. Altogether. Twenty-eight."

"You know what happens to habituals in Michigan?"

"Yes sir. They get life."

"Too bad you didn't wait to get to Chicago to stick up that driver. We call that a misdemeanor here. Do you think crime pays?"

The floorwalker retired gracefully from the mike and adjusted his cravat.

The last man was a Negro of perhaps nineteen, in a torn and bloodstained shirt and with one arm in a cast. He had Mongolian features, the cheekbones set high and widely—to protect the eyes—the eyes slanted slightly and the skin like tawny parchment. The Captain explained.

"This is the sweetheart who shot Sergeant Shannon Friday night. Tell it to the people the way you told it to us, Memphis."

"Ah was out look'n fer somebody t' stick up 'n had m' gun handy 'n he come along, that's all."

"Where was this?"

"South side of 59th Street. Ah was crossin' over t' the north side when ah saw Shannon, he wasn't in uniform."

"Did he call after you?"

"Yes sir. He say, 'Hey Buddy, wait a minute,' 'n he had somethin' in his hand. It looked like a gun 'n ah pulled out m' pistol 'n stahted t' fire. He shot 'n hit me in the right ahm 'n ah ran 'n tried t' find someplace t' hide."

"You're sure you weren't out gunning for Sergeant Shannon?"

"Oh no sir."

"But you knew him from before?"

"From a lo-o-ong time."

"You know he may die?"

"That's what they tell me."

"Aren't worried much about it though, are you?"

"It was me 'r him."

"How'd they find you?"

"Ah leaned on a mail-box, ah was bleedin' pretty bad. Ah left stains on th' box 'n some of m' own people seen them 'n tol' a officer." The boy seemed more saddened by that single circumstance than by either the imminence of Shannon's death or of his own. Like a thing repeated many times in an effort to believe and accept:

"My own people."

And his voice was heavy with shame for them.

"How do you feel about getting the chair, Boy?"

"Don't care one way 'r another. Don't feel nothin', good 'r bad. Just feel a little low is all. Knew ah'd never get t' be twenty-one anyhow."

The line turned and shuffled restlessly through the door to the cells. The overhead lights went out one by one, till even the tittering women were gone. And nothing remained in the showup room but the sounds of the city, coming up from below.

The great trains howling from track to track all night. The taut and telegraphic murmur of ten thousand city wires, drawn most cruelly against a city sky. The rush of city waters, beneath the city streets.

The passionate passing of the night's last El.

CARL STEPHENSON

Leiningen Versus the Ants

"UNLESS they alter their course and there's no reason why they should, they'll reach your plantation in two days at the latest."

Leiningen sucked placidly at a cigar about the size of a corn cob and for a few seconds gazed without answering at the agitated District Commissioner. Then he took the cigar from his lips, and leaned slightly forward. With his bristling grey hair, bulky nose, and lucid eyes, he had the look of an aging and shabby eagle.

"Decent of you," he murmured, "paddling all this way just to give me the tip. But you're pulling my leg of course when you say I must do a bunk. Why, even a herd of saurians couldn't drive me from this plantation of mine."

The Brazilian official threw up lean and lanky arms and clawed the air with wildly distended fingers. "Leiningen!" he shouted. "You're insane! They're not creatures you can fight—they're an elemental—an 'act of God!' Ten miles long, two miles wide—ants, nothing but ants! And every single one of them a fiend from hell; before you can spit three times they'll eat a full-grown buffalo to the bones. I tell you if you don't clear out at once there'll be nothing left of you but a skeleton picked as clean as your plantation."

Leiningen grinned. "Act of God, my eye! Anyway, I'm not an old woman; I'm not going to run for it just because an elemental's on the way. And don't think I'm the kind of fathead who tries to fend off lightning with his fists, either. I use my intelligence, old man. With me, the brain isn't a second blindgut; I know what it's there for. When I began this model farm and plantation three years ago, I took into account all that could conceivably happen to it. And now I'm ready for anything and everything—including your ants."

The Brazilian rose heavily to his feet. "I've done my best," he gasped. "Your obstinacy endangers not only yourself, but the lives of your four hundred workers. You don't know these ants!"

Leiningen accompanied him down to the river, where the Government launch was moored. The vessel cast off. As it moved downstream, the exclamation mark neared the rail and began waving its arms frantically. Long after the launch had disappeared round the bend, Leiningen thought he could still

December, 1938

hear that dimming, imploring voice. "You don't know them, I tell you! You *don't know them!*"

But the reported enemy was by no means unfamiliar to the planter. Before he started work on his settlement, he had lived long enough in the country to see for himself the fearful devastations sometimes wrought by these ravenous insects in their campaigns for food. But since then he had planned measures of defense accordingly, and these, he was convinced, were in every way adequate to withstand the approaching peril.

Moreover, during his three years as a planter, Leiningen had met and defeated drought, flood, plague and all other "acts of God" which had come against him—unlike his fellow-settlers in the district, who had made little or no resistance. This unbroken success he attributed solely to the observance of his lifelong motto: *The human brain needs only to become fully aware of its powers to conquer even the elements.* Dullards reeled senselessly and aimlessly into the abyss; cranks, however brilliant, lost their heads when circumstances suddenly altered or accelerated and ran into stone walls, sluggards drifted with the current until they were caught in whirlpools and dragged under. But such disasters, Leiningen contended, merely strengthened his argument that intelligence, directed aright, invariably makes man the master of his fate.

Yes, Leiningen had always known how to grapple with life. Even here, in this Brazilian wilderness, his brain had triumphed over every difficulty and danger it had so far encountered. First he had vanquished primal forces by cunning and organization, then he had enlisted the resources of modern science to increase miraculously the yield of his plantation. And now he was sure he would prove more than a match for the "irresistible" ants.

That same evening, however, Leiningen assembled his workers. He had no intention of waiting till the news reached their ears from other sources. Most of them had been born in the district; the cry "The ants are coming!" was to them an imperative signal for instant, panic-stricken flight, a spring for life itself. But so great was the Indian's trust in Leiningen, in Leiningen's word, and in Leiningen's wisdom, that they received his curt tidings, and his orders for the imminent struggle, with the calmness with which they were given. They waited, unafraid, alert, as if for the beginning of a new game or hunt which he had just described to them. The ants were indeed mighty, but not so mighty as the boss. Let them come!

They came at noon the second day. Their approach was announced by the wild unrest of the horses, scarcely controllable now either in stall or under rider, scenting from afar a vapor instinct with horror.

It was announced by a stampede of animals, timid and savage, hurtling past each other; jaguars and pumas flashing by nimble stags of the pampas, bulky tapirs, no longer hunters, themselves hunted, outpacing fleet kinkajous, maddened herds of cattle, heads lowered, nostrils snorting, rushing through tribes of loping monkeys, chattering in a dementia of terror; then followed the creeping and springing denizens of bush and steppe, big and little rodents, snakes, and lizards.

Pell-mell the rabble swarmed down the hill to the plantation, scattered right and left before the barrier of the water-filled ditch, then sped onwards to the river, where, again hindered, they fled along its bank out of sight.

This water-filled ditch was one of the defense measures which Leiningen had long since prepared against the advent of the ants. It encompassed three sides of the plantation like a huge horseshoe. Twelve feet across, but not very deep, when dry it could hardly be described as an obstacle to either man or beast. But the ends of the "horseshoe" ran into the river which formed the northern boundary, and fourth side, of the plantation. And at the end nearer the house and outbuildings in the middle of the plantation, Leiningen had constructed a dam by means of which water from the river could be diverted into the ditch.

So now, by opening the dam, he was able to fling an imposing girdle of water, a huge quadrilateral with the river as its base, completely around the plantation, like the moat encircling a medieval city. Unless the ants were clever enough to build rafts, they had no hope of reaching the plantation, Leiningen concluded.

The twelve-foot water ditch seemed to afford in itself all the security needed. But while awaiting the arrival of the ants, Leiningen made a further improvement. The western section of the ditch ran along the edge of a tamarind wood, and the branches of some great trees reached over the water. Leiningen now had them lopped so that ants could not descend from them within the "moat."

The women and children, then the herds of cattle, were escorted by peons on rafts over the river, to remain on the other side in absolute safety until the plunderers had departed. Leiningen gave this instruction, not because he believed the non-combatants were in any danger, but in order to avoid hampering the efficiency of the defenders. "Critical situations first become crises," he explained to his men, "when oxen or women get excited."

Finally, he made a careful inspection of the "inner moat"—a smaller ditch lined with concrete, which extended around the hill on which stood the ranch-house, barns, stables and other buildings. Into this concrete ditch emptied the inflow pipes from three great petrol tanks. If by some miracle the ants managed to cross the water and reach the plantation, this "rampart of petrol" would be an absolutely impassable protection for the beseiged and their dwellings and stock. Such, at least, was Leiningen's opinion.

He stationed his men at irregular distances along the water ditch, the first line of defense. Then he lay down in his hammock and puffed drowsily away at his pipe until a peon came with the report that the ants had been observed far away in the South.

Leiningen mounted his horse, which at the feel of its master seemed to forget its uneasiness, and rode leisurely in the direction of the threatening offensive. The southern stretch of ditch—the upper side of the quadrilateral—was nearly three miles long; from its center one could survey the entire country-side. This was destined to be the scene of the outbreak of war between Leiningen's brain and twenty square miles of life-destroying ants.

It was a sight one could never forget. Over the range of hills, as far as eye could see, crept a darkening hem, ever longer and broader, until the shadow spread across the slope from east to west, then downwards, downwards, uncannily swift, and all the green herbage of that wide vista was being mown as if by a giant sickle, leaving only the vast moving shadow, extending, deepening, and moving rapidly nearer.

When Leiningen's men, behind their barrier of water, perceived the approach of the long-expected foe, they gave vent to their suspense in screams and imprecations. But as the distance began to lessen between the "sons of hell" and the water ditch, they relapsed into silence. Before the advance of that awe-inspiring throng, their belief in the powers of the boss began to steadily dwindle. Even Leiningen himself, who had ridden up just in time to restore their loss of heart by a display of unshakable calm, even he could not free himself from a qualm of malaise. Yonder were thousands of millions of voracious jaws bearing down upon him and only a suddenly insignificant narrow ditch lay between him and his men and being gnawed to the bones "before you can spit three times."

Hadn't his brain for once taken on more than it could manage? If the blighters decided to rush the ditch, fill it to the brim with their corpses, there'd still be more than enough to destroy every trace of that cranium of his. The planter's chin jutted; they hadn't got him yet, and he'd see to it they never would. While he could think at all, he'd flout both death and the devil.

The hostile army was approaching in perfect formation; no human battalions, however well-drilled, could ever hope to rival the precision of that advance. Along a front that moved forward as uniformly as a straight line, the ants drew nearer and nearer to the water-ditch. Then, when they learned through their scouts the nature of the obstacle, the two outlying wings of the army detached themselves from the main body and marched down the western and eastern sides of the ditch.

This surrounding maneuver took rather more than an hour to accomplish; no doubt the ants expected that at some point they would find a crossing.

During this outflanking movement by the wings, the army on the center and southern front remained still. The besieged were therefore able to contemplate at their leisure the thumb-long, reddish black, long-legged insects; some of the Indians believed they could see, too, intent on them, the brilliant, cold eyes, and the razor-edged mandibles, of this host of infinity.

It is not easy for the average person to imagine that an animal, not to mention an insect, can *think*. But now both the European brain of Leiningen and the primitive brains of the Indians began to stir with the unpleasant foreboding that inside every single one of that deluge of insects dwelt a thought. And that thought was: Ditch or no ditch, we'll get to your flesh!

Not until four o'clock did the wings reach the "horseshoe" ends of the ditch, only to find these ran into the great river. Through some kind of secret telegraphy, the report must then have flashed very swiftly indeed along the entire enemy line. And Leiningen, riding—no longer casually—along his side of the ditch, noticed by energetic and widespread movements of troops that for some unknown reason the news of the check had its greatest effect on the southern front, where the main army was massed. Perhaps the failure to find a way over the ditch was persuading the ants to withdraw from the plantation in search of spoils more easily obtainable.

An immense flood of ants, about a hundred yards in width, was pouring in a glimmering-black cataract down the far slope of the ditch. Many thousands were already drowning in the sluggish creeping flow, but they were followed by troop after troop, who clambered over their sinking comrades, and then themselves served as dying bridges to the reserves hurrying on in their rear.

Shoals of ants were being carried away by the current into the middle of the ditch, where gradually they broke asunder and then, exhausted by their struggles, vanished below the surface. Nevertheless, the wavering, floundering hundred-yard front was remorselessly if slowly advancing towards the besieged on the other bank. Leiningen had been wrong when he supposed the enemy would first have to fill the ditch with their bodies before they could cross; instead, they merely needed to act as stepping-stones, as they swam and sank, to the hordes ever pressing onwards from behind.

Near Leiningen a few mounted herdsmen awaited his orders. He sent one to the weir—the river must be dammed more strongly to increase the speed and power of the water coursing through the ditch.

A second peon was dispatched to the outhouses to bring spades and petrol sprinklers. A third rode away to summon to the zone of the offensive all the men, except the observation posts, on the near-by sections of the ditch, which were not yet actively threatened.

The ants were getting across far more quickly than Leiningen would have deemed possible. Impelled by the mighty cascade behind them, they struggled nearer and nearer to the inner bank. The momentum of the attack was so great that neither the tardy flow of the stream nor its downward pull could exert its proper force; and into the gap left by every submerging insect, hastened forward a dozen more.

When reinforcements reached Leiningen, the invaders were halfway over. The planter had to admit to himself that it was only by a stroke of luck for him that the ants were attempting the crossing on a relatively short front: had they assaulted simultaneously along the entire length of the ditch, the outlook for the defenders would have been black indeed.

Even as it was, it could hardly be described as rosy, though the planter seemed quite unaware that death in a gruesome form was drawing closer and closer. As the war between his brain and the "act of God" reached its climax, the very shadow of annihilation began to pale to Leiningen, who now felt like a champion in a new Olympic game, a gigantic and thrilling contest, from which he was determined to emerge victor. Such, indeed, was his aura of confidence that the Indians forgot their stupefied fear of the peril only a yard or two away; under the planter's supervision, they began fervidly digging up to the edge of the bank and throwing clods of earth and spadefuls of sand into the midst of the hostile fleet.

The petrol sprinklers, hitherto used to destroy pests and blights on the plantation, were also brought into action. Streams of evil-reeking oil now soared and fell over an enemy already in disorder through the bombardment of earth and sand.

The ants responded to these vigorous and successful measures of defense by further developments of their offensive. Entire clumps of huddling insects began to roll down the opposite bank into the water. At the same time, Leiningen noticed that the ants were now attacking along an ever-widening front. As the numbers both of his men and his petrol sprinklers were severely limited, this rapid extension of the line of battle was becoming an overwhelming danger.

To add to his difficulties, the very clods of earth they flung into that black floating carpet often whirled fragments towards the defenders' side, and here and there dark ribbons were already mounting the inner bank. True, wherever a man saw these they could still be driven back into the water by spadefuls of earth or jets of petrol. But the file of defenders was too sparse and scattered to hold off at all points these landing parties, and though the peons toiled like madmen, their plight became momently more perilous.

One man struck with his spade at an enemy clump, did not draw it back quickly enough from the water; in a trice the wooden haft swarmed with upward scurrying insects. With a curse, he dropped the spade into the ditch; too late, they were already on his body. They lost no time; wherever they encountered bare flesh they bit deeply; a few, bigger than the rest, carried in their hind-quarters a sting which injected a burning and paralyzing venom. Screaming, frantic with pain, the peon danced and twirled like a dervish.

Realizing that another such casualty, yes, perhaps this alone, might plunge his men into confusion and destroy their morale, Leiningen roared in a bellow louder than the yells of the victim: "Into the petrol, idiot! Douse your paws in the petrol!" The dervish ceased his pirouette as if transfixed, then tore off his shirt and plunged his arm and the ants hanging to it up to the shoulder in one of the large open tins of petrol. But even then the fierce mandibles did not slacken; another peon had to help him squash and detach each separate insect.

Distracted by the episode, some defenders had turned away from the ditch. And now cries of fury, a thudding of spades, and a wild trampling to and fro, showed that the ants had made full use of the interval, though luckily only a few had managed to get across. The men set to work again desperately with the barrage of earth and sand. Meanwhile an old Indian, who acted as medicine-man to the plantation workers, gave the bitten peon a drink he had prepared some hours before, which, he claimed, possessed the virtue of dissolving and weakening ants' venom.

Leiningen surveyed his position. A dispassionate observer would have estimated the odds against him at a thousand to one. But then such an onlooker would have reckoned only by what he saw—the advance of myriad battalions of ants against the futile efforts of a few defenders—and not by the unseen activity that can go on in a man's brain.

For Leiningen had not erred when he decided he would fight elemental with elemental. The water in the ditch was beginning to rise; the stronger damming of the river was making itself apparent.

Visibly the swiftness and power of the masses of water increased, swirling into quicker and quicker movement its living black surface, dispersing its pattern, carrying away more and more of it on the hastening current.

Victory had been snatched from the very jaws of defeat. With a hysterical shout of joy, the peons feverishly intensified their bombardment of earth clods and sand.

And now the wide cataract down the opposite bank was thinning and ceasing, as if the ants were becoming aware that they could not attain their aim. They were scurrying back up the slope to safety.

All the troops so far hurled into the ditch had been sacrificed in vain. Drowned and floundering insects eddied in thousands along the flow, while Indians running on the bank destroyed every swimmer that reached the side.

Not until the ditch curved towards the east did the scattered ranks assemble again in a coherent mass. And now, exhausted and half-numbed, they were in no condition to ascend the bank. Fusillades of clods drove them round the bend towards the mouth of the ditch and then into the river, wherein they vanished without leaving a trace.

The news ran swiftly along the entire chain of outposts, and soon a long scattered line of laughing men could be seen hastening along the ditch towards the scene of victory.

For once they seemed to have lost all their native reserve, for it was in wild abandon now they celebrated the triumph—as if there were no longer thousands of millions of merciless, cold and hungry eyes watching them from the opposite bank, watching and waiting.

The sun sank behind the rim of the tamarind wood and twilight deepened into night. It was not only hoped but expected that the ants would remain quiet until dawn. But to defeat any forlorn attempt at a crossing, the flow of water through the ditch was powerfully increased by opening the dam still further.

In spite of this impregnable barrier, Leiningen was not yet altogether convinced that the ants would not venture another surprise attack. He ordered his men to camp along the bank overnight. He also detailed parties of them to patrol the ditch in two of his motor cars and ceaselessly to illuminate the surface of the water with headlights and electric torches.

After having taken all the precautions he deemed necessary, the farmer ate his supper with considerable appetite and went to bed. His slumbers were in no wise disturbed by the memory of the waiting, live, twenty square miles.

Dawn found a thoroughly refreshed and active Leiningen riding along the edge of the ditch. The planter saw before him a motionless and unaltered throng of besiegers. He studied the wide belt of water between them and the plantation, and for a moment almost regretted that the fight had ended so soon and so simply. In the comforting, matter-of-fact light of morning, it seemed to him now that the ants hadn't the ghost of a chance to cross the ditch. Even if they plunged headlong into it on all three fronts at once, the force of the now powerful current would inevitably sweep them away. He had got quite a thrill out of the fight—a pity it was already over.

He rode along the eastern and southern sections of the ditch and found everything in order. He reached the western section, opposite the tamarind wood, and here, contrary to the other battle fronts, he found the enemy very busy indeed. The trunks and branches of the trees and the creepers of the lianas, on the far bank of the ditch, fairly swarmed with industrious insects. But instead of eating the leaves there and then, they were merely gnawing through the stalks, so that a thick green shower fell steadily to the ground.

No doubt they were victualing columns sent out to obtain provender for the rest of the army. The discovery did not surprise Leiningen. He did not need to be told that ants are intelligent, that certain species even use others as milch cows, watchdogs and slaves. He was well aware of their power of adaptation, their sense of discipline, their marvelous talent for organization.

His belief that a foray to supply the army was in progress was strengthened when he saw the leaves that fell to the ground being dragged to the troops waiting outside the wood. Then all at once he realized the aim that rain of green was intended to serve.

Each single leaf, pulled or pushed by dozens of toling insects, was borne straight to the edge of the ditch. Even as Macbeth watched the approach of Birnam Wood in the hands of his enemies, Leiningen saw the tamarind wood move nearer and nearer in the mandibles of the ants. Unlike the fey Scot, however, he did not lose his nerve; no witches had prophesied his doom, and if they had he would have slept just as soundly. All the same, he was forced to admit to himself that the situation was now far more ominous than that of the day before.

He had thought it impossible for the ants to build rafts for themselves— well, here they were, coming in thousands, more than enough to bridge the ditch. Leaves after leaves rustled down the slope into the water, where the current drew them away from the bank and carried them into midstream. And every single leaf carried several ants. This time the farmer did not trust to the alacrity of his messengers. He galloped away, leaning from his saddle and yelling orders as he rushed past outpost after outpost: "Bring petrol pumps to the southwest front! Issue spades to every man along the line facing the wood!" And arrived at the eastern and southern sections, he dispatched every man except the observation posts to the menaced west.

Then, as he rode past the stretch where the ants had failed to cross the day before, he witnessed a brief but impressive scene. Down the slope of the distant hill there came towards him a singular being, writhing rather than running, an animal-like blackened statue with a shapeless head and four quivering feet that knuckled under almost ceaselessly. When the creature reached the far bank of the ditch and collapsed opposite Leiningen, he recognized it as a pampas stag, covered over and over with ants.

It had strayed near the zone of the army. As usual, they had attacked its eyes first. Blinded, it had reeled in the madness of hideous torment straight into the ranks of its persecutors, and now the beast swayed to and fro in its death agony.

With a shot from his rifle Leiningen put it out of its misery. Then he pulled out his watch. He hadn't a second to lose, but for life itself he could not have denied his curiosity the satisfaction of knowing how long the ants would take— for personal reasons, so to speak. After six minutes the white polished bones alone remained. That's how he himself would look before you can—. Leiningen spat once, and put spurs to his horse.

The sporting zest with which the excitement of the novel contest had inspired him the day before had now vanished; in its place was a cold and violent purpose. He would send these vermin back to the hell where they belonged, somehow, anyhow. Yes, but how was indeed the question; as things stood at present it looked as if the devils would raze him and his men from the earth instead. He had underestimated the might of the enemy; he really would have to bestir himself if he hoped to outwit them.

The biggest danger now, he decided, was the point where the western section of the ditch curved southwards. And arrived there, he found his worst expectations justified. The very power of the current had huddled the leaves and their crews of ants so close together at the bend that the bridge was almost ready.

True, streams of petrol and clumps of earth still prevented a landing. But the number of floating leaves was increasing ever more swiftly. It could not be long now before a stretch of water a mile in length was decked by a green pontoon over which the ants could rush in millions.

Leiningen galloped to the weir. The damming of the river was controlled by a wheel on its bank. The planter ordered the man at the wheel first to lower the water in the ditch almost to vanishing point, next to wait a moment, then suddenly to let the river in again. This maneuver of lowering and raising the surface, of decreasing then increasing the flow of water through the ditch was to be repeated over and over again until further notice.

This tactic was at first successful. The water in the ditch sank, and with it the film of leaves. The green fleet nearly reached the bed and the troops on the far bank swarmed down the slope to it. Then a violent flow of water at the original depth raced through the ditch, overwhelming leaves and ants, and sweeping them along.

This intermittent rapid flushing prevented just in time the almost completed fording of the ditch. But it also flung here and there squads of the enemy vanguard simultaneously up the inner bank. These seemed to know their duty only too well, and lost no time accomplishing it. The air rang with the curses of bitten Indians. They had removed their shirts and pants to detect the quicker the upwards-hastening insects; when they saw one, they crushed it; and fortunately the onslaught as yet was only by skirmishers.

Again and again, the water sank and rose, carrying leaves and drowned ants away with it. It lowered once more nearly to its bed; but this time the exhausted defenders waited in vain for the flush of destruction. Leiningen sensed disaster;

something must have gone wrong with the machinery of the dam. Then a sweating peon tore up to him—

"They're over!"

While the besieged were concentrating upon the defense of the stretch opposite the wood, the seemingly unaffected line beyond the wood had become the theater of decisive action. Here the defenders' front was sparse and scattered; everyone who could be spared had hurried away to the south.

Just as the man at the weir had lowered the water almost to the bed of the ditch, the ants on a wide front began another attempt at a direct crossing like that of the preceding day. Into the emptied bed poured an irresistible throng. Rushing across the ditch, they attained the inner bank before the slow-witted Indians fully grasped the situation. Their frantic screams dumbfounded the man at the weir. Before he could direct the river anew into the safeguarding bed he saw himself surrounded by raging ants. He ran like the others, ran for his life.

When Leiningen heard this, he knew the plantation was doomed. He wasted no time bemoaning the inevitable. For as long as there was the slightest chance of success, he had stood his ground, and now any further resistance was both useless and dangerous. He fired three revolver shots into the air—the prearranged signal for his men to retreat instantly within the "inner moat." Then he rode towards the ranchhouse.

This was two miles from the point of invasion. There was therefore time enough to prepare the second line of defense against the advent of the ants. Of the three great petrol cisterns near the house, one had already been half emptied by the constant withdrawals needed for the pumps during the fight at the water ditch. The remaining petrol in it was now drawn off through underground pipes into the concrete trench which encircled the ranchhouse and its outbuildings.

And there, drifting in twos and threes, Leiningen's men reached him. Most of them were obviously trying to preserve an air of calm and indifference, belied, however, by their restless glances and knitted brows. One could see their belief in a favorable outcome of the struggle was already considerably shaken.

The planter called his peons around him.

"Well, lads," he began, "we've lost the first round. But we'll smash the beggars yet, don't you worry. Anyone who thinks otherwise can draw his pay here and now and push off. There are rafts enough and to spare on the river, and plenty of time still to reach 'em."

Not a man stirred.

Leiningen acknowledged his silent vote of confidence with a laugh that was half a grunt. "That's the stuff, lads. Too bad if you'd missed the rest of the show, eh? Well, the fun won't start till morning. Once these blighters turn tail, there'll be plenty of work for everyone and higher wages all round. And now run along and get something to eat; you've earned it all right."

In the excitement of the fight the greater part of the day had passed without the men once pausing to snatch a bite. Now that the ants were for the time being out of sight, and the "wall of petrol" gave a stronger feeling of security, hungry stomachs began to assert their claims.

The bridges over the concrete ditch were removed. Here and there solitary ants had reached the ditch; they gazed at the petrol meditatively, then scurried back again. Apparently they had little interest at the moment for what lay beyond the evil-reeking barrier; the abundant spoils of the plantation were the main attraction. Soon the trees, shrubs and beds for miles around were hulled with ants zealously gobbling the yield of long weary months of strenuous toil.

As twilight began to fall, a cordon of ants marched around the petrol trench, but as yet made no move towards its brink. Leiningen posted sentries with headlights and electric torches, then withdrew to his office, and began to reckon up his losses. He estimated these as large, but, in comparison with his bank balance, by no means unbearable. He worked out in some detail a scheme of intensive cultivation which would enable him, before very long, to more than compensate himself for the damage now being wrought to his crops. It was with a contented mind that he finally betook himself to bed where he slept deeply until dawn, undisturbed by any thought that next day little more might be left of him than a glistening skeleton.

He rose with the sun and went out on the flat roof of his house. And a scene like one from Dante lay around him; for miles in every direction there was nothing but a black, glittering multitude, a multitude of rested, sated, but none the less voracious ants: yes, look as far as one might, one could see nothing but that rustling black throng, except in the north, where the great river drew a boundary they could not hope to pass. But even the high stone breakwater, along the bank of the river, which Leiningen had built as a defense against inundations, was, like the paths, the shorn trees and shrubs, the ground itself, black with ants.

So their greed was not glutted in razing that vast plantation? Not by a long chalk; they were all the more eager now on a rich and certain booty—four hundred men, numerous horses, and bursting granaries.

At first it seemed that the petrol trench would serve its purpose. The besiegers sensed the peril of swimming it, and made no move to plunge blindly over its brink. Instead they devised a better maneuver; they began to collect shreds of bark, twigs and dried leaves and dropped these into the petrol. Everything green, which could have been similarly used, had long since been eaten. After a time, though, a long procession could be seen bringing from the west the tamarind leaves used as rafts the day before.

Since the petrol, unlike the water in the outer ditch, was perfectly still, the refuse stayed where it was thrown. It was several hours before the ants succeeded in covering an appreciable part of the surface. At length, however, they were ready to proceed to a direct attack.

Their storm troops swarmed down the concrete side, scrambled over the supporting surface of twigs and leaves, and impelled these over the few remaining streaks of open petrol until they reached the other side. Then they began to climb up this to make straight for the helpless garrison.

During the entire offensive, the planter sat peacefully, watching them with interest, but not stirring a muscle. Moreover, he had ordered his men not to disturb in any way whatever the advancing horde. So they squatted listlessly along the bank of the ditch and waited for a sign from the boss.

The petrol was now covered with ants. A few had climbed the inner concrete wall and were scurrying towards the defenders.

"Everyone back from the ditch!" roared Leiningen. The men rushed away, without the slightest idea of his plan. He stooped forward and cautiously dropped into the ditch a stone which split the floating carpet and its living freight, to reveal a gleaming patch of petrol. A match spurted, sank down to the oily surface—Leiningen sprang back; in a flash a towering rampart of fire encompassed the garrison.

This spectacular and instant repulse threw the Indians into ecstasy. They applauded, yelled and stamped, like children at a pantomime. Had it not been for the awe in which they held the boss, they would infallibly have carried him shoulder high.

It was some time before the petrol burned down to the bed of the ditch, and the wall of smoke and flame began to lower. The ants had retreated in a wide circle from the devastation, and innumerable charred fragments along the outer bank showed that the flames had spread from the holocaust in the ditch well into the ranks beyond, where they had wrought havoc far and wide.

Yet the perseverance of the ants was by no means broken; indeed, each setback seemed only to whet it. The concrete cooled, the flicker of the dying flames wavered and vanished, petrol from the second tank poured into the trench—and the ants marched forward anew to the attack.

The foregoing scene repeated itself in every detail, except that on this occasion less time was needed to bridge the ditch, for the petrol was now already filmed by a layer of ash. Once again they withdrew; once again petrol flowed into the ditch. Would the creatures never learn that their self-sacrifice was utterly senseless? It really was senseless, wasn't it? Yes, of course it was senseless—provided the defenders had an *unlimited* supply of petrol.

When Leiningen reached this stage of reasoning, he felt for the first time since the arrival of the ants that his confidence was deserting him. His skin began to creep; he loosened his collar. Once the devils were over the trench there wasn't a chance in hell for him and his men. God, what a prospect, to be eaten alive like that!

For the third time the flames immolated the attacking troops, and burned down to extinction. Yet the ants were coming on again as if nothing had happened. And meanwhile Leiningen had made a discovery that chilled him to the bone—petrol was no longer flowing into the ditch. Something must be blocking the outflow pipe of the third and last cistern—a snake or a dead rat? Whatever it was, the ants could be held off no longer, unless petrol could by some method be led from the cistern into the ditch.

Then Leiningen remembered that in an outhouse near-by were two old disused fire engines. Spry as never before in their lives, the peons dragged them out of the shed, connected their pumps to the cistern, uncoiled and laid the hose. They were just in time to aim a stream of petrol at a column of ants that had already crossed and drive them back down the incline into the ditch. Once more an oily girdle surrounded the garrison, once more it was possible to hold the position—for the moment.

It was obvious, however, that this last resource meant only the postponement of defeat and death. A few of the peons fell on their knees and began to pray; others shrieking insanely, fired their revolvers at the black, advancing masses, as if they felt their despair was pitiful enough to sway fate itself to mercy.

At length, two of the men's nerves broke: Leiningen saw a naked Indian leap over the north side of the petrol trench, quickly followed by a second. They sprinted with incredible speed towards the river. But their fleetness did not save them; long before they could attain the rafts, the enemy covered their bodies from head to foot.

In the agony of their torment, both sprang blindly into the wide river, where enemies no less sinister awaited them. Wild screams of mortal anguish informed the breathless onlookers that crocodiles and sword-toothed piranhas were no less ravenous than ants, and even nimbler in reaching their prey.

In spite of this bloody warning, more and more men showed they were making up their minds to run the blockade. Anything, even a fight midstream against alligators, seemed better than powerlessly waiting for death to come and slowly consume their living bodies.

Leiningen flogged his brain till it reeled. Was there nothing on earth could sweep this devils' spawn back into the hell from which it came?

Then out of the inferno of his bewilderment rose a terrifying inspiration. Yes, one hope remained, and one alone. It might be possible to dam the great river completely, so that its waters would fill not only the water ditch but overflow into the entire gigantic "saucer" of land in which lay the plantation.

The far bank of the river was too high for the waters to escape that way. The stone breakwater ran between the river and the plantation; its only gaps occurred where the "horseshoe" ends of the water-ditch passed into the river. So its waters would not only be forced to inundate into the plantation, they would also be held there by the breakwater until they rose to its own high level. In half an hour, perhaps even earlier, the plantation and its hostile army of occupation would be flooded.

The ranch house and outbuildings stood upon rising ground. Their foundations were higher than the breakwater, so the flood would not reach them. And any remaining ants trying to ascend the slope could be repulsed by petrol.

It was possible—yes, if one could only get to the dam! A distance of nearly two miles lay between the ranch house and the weir—two miles of ants. Those two peons had managed only a fifth of that distance at the cost of their lives. Was there an Indian daring enough after that to run the gauntlet five times as far? Hardly likely; and if there were, his prospect of getting back was almost nil.

No, there was only one thing for it, he'd have to make the attempt himself;

he might just as well be running as sitting still, anyway, when the ants finally got him. Besides, there was a bit of a chance. Perhaps the ants weren't so almighty, after all; perhaps he had allowed the mass suggestion of that evil black throng to hypnotize him, just as a snake fascinates and overpowers.

The ants were building their bridges. Leiningen got up on a chair. "Hey, lads, listen to me!" he cried. Slowly and listlessly, from all sides of the trench, the men began to shuffle towards him, the apathy of death already stamped on their faces.

"Listen, lads!" he shouted. "You're frightened of those beggars, but you're a damn sight more frightened of me, and I'm proud of you. There's still a chance to save our lives—by flooding the plantation from the river. Now one of you might manage to get as far as the weir—but he'd never come back. Well, I'm not going to let you try it; if I did I'd be worse than one of those ants. No, I called the tune, and now I'm going to pay the piper.

"The moment I'm over the ditch, set fire to the petrol. That'll allow time for the flood to do the trick. Then all you have to do is to wait here all snug and quiet till I'm back. Yes, I'm coming back, trust me"—he grinned—"when I've finished my slimming-cure."

He pulled on high leather boots, drew heavy gauntlets over his hands, and stuffed the spaces between breeches and boots, gauntlets and arms, shirt and neck, with rags soaked in petrol. With close-fitting mosquito goggles he shielded his eyes, knowing too well the ants' dodge of first robbing their victim of sight. Finally, he plugged his nostrils and ears with cottonwool, and let the peons drench his clothes with petrol.

He was about to set off, when the old Indian medicine man came up to him; he had a wondrous salve, he said, prepared from a species of chafer whose odor was intolerable to ants. Yes, this odor protected these chafers from the attacks of even the most murderous ants. The Indian smeared the boss' boots, his gauntlets, and his face over and over with the extract.

Leiningen then remembered the paralyzing effect of ants' venom, and the Indian gave him a gourd full of the medicine he had administered to the bitten peon at the water ditch. The planter drank it down without noticing its bitter taste; his mind was already at the weir.

He started off towards the northwest corner of the trench. With a bound he was over—and among the ants.

The beleaguered garrison had no opportunity to watch Leiningen's race against death. The ants were climbing the inner bank again—the lurid ring of petrol blazed aloft. For the fourth time that day the reflection from the fire shone on the sweating faces of the imprisoned men, and on the reddish-black cuirasses of their oppressors. The red and blue, dark-edged flames leaped vividly now, celebrating what? The funeral pyre of the four hundred, or of the hosts of destruction?

Leiningen ran. He ran in long equal strides, with only one thought, one sensation, in his being—he must get through. He dodged all trees and shrubs; except for the split seconds his soles touched the ground the ants should have no opportunity to alight on him. That they would get to him soon, despite the salve on his boots, the petrol in his clothes, he realized only too well, but he knew even more surely that he must, and that he would, get to the weir.

Apparently the salve was some use after all; not until he had reached half-way did he feel ants under his clothes, and a few on his face. Mechanically, in his stride, he struck at them, scarcely conscious of their bites. He saw he was drawing appreciably nearer the weir—the distance grew less and less—sank to five hundred—three—two—one hundred yards.

Then he was at the weir and gripping the ant-hulled wheel. Hardly had he seized it when a horde of infuriated ants flowed over his hands, arms and shoulders. He started the wheel—before it turned once on its axis the swarm covered his face. Leiningen strained like a madman, his lips pressed tight; if he opened them to draw breath . . .

He turned and turned; slowly the dam lowered until it reached the bed of the river. Already the water was overflowing the ditch. Another minute, and the river was pouring through the near-by gap in the breakwater. The flooding of the plantation had begun.

Leiningen let go the wheel. Now, for the first time, he realized he was coated from head to foot with a layer of ants. In spite of the petrol, his clothes were full of them, several had got to his body or were clinging to his face. Now that he had completed his task, he felt the smart raging over his flesh from the bites of sawing and piercing insects.

Frantic with pain, he almost plunged into the river. To be ripped and slashed to shreds by piranhas? Already he was running the return journey, knocking ants from his gloves and jacket, brushing them from his bloodied face, squashing them to death under his clothes.

One of the creatures bit him just below the rim of his goggles; he managed to tear it away, but the agony of the bite and its etching acid drilled into the eye nerves; he saw now through circles of fire into a milky mist, then he ran for a time almost blinded, knowing that if he once tripped and fell . . . The old Indian's brew didn't seem much good; it weakened the poison a bit, but didn't get rid of it. His heart pounded as if it would burst; blood roared in his ears; a giant's fist battered his lungs.

Then he could see again, but the burning girdle of petrol appeared infinitely far away; he could not last half that distance. Swift-changing pictures flashed through his head, episodes in his life, while in another part of his brain a cool and impartial onlooker informed this ant-blurred, gasping, exhausted bundle named Leiningen that such a rushing panorama of scenes from one's past is seen only in the moment before death.

A stone in the path . . . too weak to avoid it . . . the planter stumbled and collapsed. He tried to rise . . . he must be pinned under a rock . . . it was impossible . . . the slightest movement was impossible . . .

Then all at once he saw, starkly clear and huge, and, right before his eyes, furred with ants, towering and swaying in its death agony, the pampas stag. In six minutes—gnawed to the bones. God, he *couldn't* die like that! And something outside him seemed to drag him to his feet. He tottered. He began to stagger forward again.

Through the blazing ring hurtled an apparition which, as soon as it reached the ground on the inner side, fell full length and did not move. Leiningen, at the moment he made that leap through the flames, lost consciousness for the first time in his life. As he lay there, with glazing eyes and lacerated face, he appeared a man returned from the grave. The peons rushed to him, stripped off his clothes, tore away the ants from a body that seemed almost one open wound; in some places the bones were showing. They carried him into the ranch house.

As the curtain of flames lowered, one could see in place of the illimitable host of ants an extensive vista of water. The thwarted river had swept over the plantation, carrying with it the entire army. The water had collected and mounted in the great "saucer," while the ants had in vain attempted to reach the hill on which stood the ranch house. The girdle of flames held them back.

And so imprisoned between water and fire, they had been delivered into the annihilation that was their god. And near the farther mouth of the water-ditch, where the stone mole had its second gap, the ocean swept the lost battalions into the river, to vanish forever.

The ring of fire dwindled as the water mounted to the petrol trench, and quenched the dimming flames. The inundation rose higher and higher: because its outflow was impeded by the timber and underbrush it had carried along with it, its surface required some time to reach the top of the high stone breakwater and discharge over it the rest of the shattered army.

It swelled over ant-stippled shrubs and bushes, until it washed against the foot of the knoll whereon the besieged had taken refuge. For a while an alluvial of ants tried again and again to attain this dry land, only to be repulsed by streams of petrol back into the merciless flood.

Leiningen lay on his bed, his body swathed from head to foot in bandages. With fomentations and salves, they had managed to stop the bleeding, and had dressed his many wounds. Now they thronged around him, one question in every face. Would he recover? "He won't die," said the old man who had bandaged him, "if he doesn't want to."

The planter opened his eyes. "Everything in order?" he asked.

"They're gone," said his nurse. "To hell." He held out to his master a gourd full of a powerful sleeping draught. Leiningen gulped it down.

"I told you I'd come back," he murmured, "even if I am a bit streamlined." He grinned and shut his eyes. He slept.

IRWIN SHAW

The Eighty-Yard Run

THE pass was high and wide and he jumped for it, feeling it slap flatly against his hands, as he shook his hips to throw off the halfback who was diving at him. The center floated by, his hands desperately brushing Darling's knee as Darling picked his feet up high and delicately ran over a blocker and an opposing linesman in a jumble on the ground near the scrimmage line. He had ten yards in the clear and picked up speed, breathing easily, feeling his thigh pads rising and falling against his legs, listening to the sound of cleats behind him, pulling away from them, watching the other backs heading him off toward the sideline, the whole picture, the men closing in on him, the blockers fighting for position, the ground he had to cross, all suddenly clear in his head, for the first time in his life not a meaningless confusion of men, sounds, speed. He smiled a little to himself as he ran, holding the ball lightly in front of him with his two hands, his knees pumping high, his hips twisting in the almost-girlish run of a back in a broken field. The first halfback came at him and he fed him his leg, then swung at the last moment, took the shock of the man's shoulder without breaking stride, ran right through him, his cleats biting securely into the turf. There was only the safety man now, coming warily at him, his arms crooked, hands spread. Darling tucked the ball in, spurted at him, driving hard, hurling himself along, his legs pounding, knees high, all two hundred pounds bunched into controlled attack. He was sure he was going to get past the safety man. Without thought, his arms and legs working beautifully together, he headed right for the safety man, stiff-armed him, feeling blood spurt instantaneously from the man's nose onto his hand, seeing his face go awry, head turned, mouth pulled to one side. He pivoted away, keeping the arm locked, dropping the safety man as he ran easily toward the goal line, with the drumming of cleats diminishing behind him.

How long ago? It was autumn then and the ground was getting hard because the nights were cold and leaves from the maples around the stadium blew across the practice fields in gusts of wind and the girls were beginning to put polo coats over their sweaters when they came to watch practice in the afternoons . . . Fifteen years. Darling walked slowly over the same ground in the spring twilight, in his neat shoes, a man of thirty-five dressed in a double-breasted suit, ten pounds heavier in the fifteen years, but not fat, with the years between 1925 and 1940 showing in his face.

The coach was smiling quietly to himself and the assistant coaches were looking at each other with pleasure the way they always did when one of the second stringers suddenly did something fine, bringing credit to them, making their $2,000 a year a tiny bit more secure.

Darling trotted back, smiling, breathing deeply but easily, feeling wonderful, not tired, though this was the tail end of practice and he'd run eighty yards. The sweat poured off his face and soaked his jersey and he liked the feeling, the warm moistness lubricating his skin like oil. Off in a corner of the field some players were punting and the smack of leather against the ball came pleasantly through the afternoon air. The freshmen were running signals on the next field and the quarterback's sharp voice, the pound of the eleven pairs of cleats, the "Dig, now, *dig!*" of the coaches, the laughter of the players all somehow made him feel happy as he trotted back to midfield, listening to the applause and shouts of the students along the sidelines, knowing that after that run the coach would have to start him Saturday against Illinois.

Fifteen years, Darling thought, remembering the shower after the workout, the hot water steaming off his skin and the deep soapsuds and all the young voices singing with the water streaming down and towels going and managers running in and out and the sharp sweet smell of oil of wintergreen and everybody clapping him on the back as he dressed and Packard, the captain, who took being captain very seriously, coming over to him and shaking his hand and saying, "Darling, you're going to go places in the next two years."

The assistant manager fussed over him, wiping a cut on his leg with alcohol and iodine, the little sting making him realize suddenly how fresh and whole and solid his body felt. The manager slapped a piece of adhesive tape over the cut and Darling noticed the sharp clean white of the tape against the ruddiness of the skin, fresh from the shower.

He dressed slowly, the softness of his shirt and the soft warmth of his wool socks and his flannel trousers a reward against his skin after the harsh pressure of the shoulder harness and thigh and hip pads. He drank three glasses of cold water, the liquid reaching down coldly inside of him, soothing the harsh dry places in his throat and belly left by the sweat and running and shouting of practice.

Fifteen years.

The sun had gone down and the sky was green behind the stadium and he laughed quietly to himself as he looked at the stadium, rearing above the trees, and knew that on Saturday when the 70,000 voices roared as the team came running out onto the field, part of that enormous salute would be for him. He walked slowly, listening to the gravel crunch satisfactorily under his shoes in the still twilight, feeling his clothes swing lightly against his skin, breathing the thin evening air, feeling the wind move softly in his damp hair, wonderfully cool behind his ears and at the nape of his neck.

Louise was waiting for him at the road, in her car. The top was down and he noticed all over again, as he always did when he saw her, how pretty she was, the rough blonde hair and the large, inquiring eyes and the bright mouth, smiling now.

She threw the door open. "Were you good today?" she asked.

"Pretty good," he said. He climbed in, sank luxuriously into the soft leather, stretched his legs far out. He smiled, thinking of the eighty yards. "Pretty damn good."

She looked at him seriously for a moment, then scrambled around like a little girl, kneeling on the seat next to him, grabbed him, her hands along his ears, and kissed him as he sprawled, head back, on the seat cushion. She let go of him, but kept her head close to his, over his. Darling reached up slowly and rubbed the back of his hand against her cheek, lit softly by a streetlamp a hundred feet away. They looked at each other, smiling.

Louise drove down to the lake and they sat there silently, watching the moon rise behind the hills on the other side. Finally he reached over, pulled her gently to him, kissed her. Her lips grew soft, her body sank into his, tears formed slowly in her eyes. He knew, for the first time, that he could do whatever he wanted with her.

"Tonight," he said. "I'll call for you at seven-thirty. Can you get out?"

She looked at him. She was smiling, but the tears were still full in her eyes. "All right," she said. "I'll get out. How about you? Won't the coach raise hell?"

Darling grinned. "I got the coach in the palm of my hand," he said. "Can you wait till seven-thirty?"

She grinned back at him. "No," she said.

They kissed and she started the car and they went back to town for dinner. He sang on the way home.

Christian Darling, thirty-five years old, sat on the frail spring grass, greener now than it ever would be again on the practice field, looked thoughtfully up at the stadium, a deserted ruin in the twilight. He had started on the first team that Saturday and every Saturday after that for the next two years, but it had never been as satisfactory as it should have been. He never had broken away, the longest run he'd ever made was thirty-five yards, and that in a game that was already won, and then that kid had come up from the third team, Diederich, a blank-faced German kid from Wisconsin, who ran like a bull, ripping lines to pieces Saturday after Saturday, plowing through, never getting hurt, never changing his expression, scoring more points, gaining more ground than all the rest of the team put together, making everybody's All-American, carrying the ball three times out of four, keeping everybody else out of the headlines. Darling was a good blocker and he spent his Saturday afternoons working on the big Swedes and Polacks who played tackle and end for Michigan, Illinois, Purdue, hurling into huge pile-ups, bobbing his head wildly to elude the great raw hands swinging like meat-cleavers at him as he went charging in to open up holes for Diederich coming through like a locomotive behind him.

Still, it wasn't so bad. Everybody liked him and he did his job and he was pointed out on the campus and boys always felt important when they introduced their girls to him at their proms, and Louise loved him and watched him faithfully in the games, even in the mud, when your own mother wouldn't know you, and drove him around in her car keeping the top down because she was proud of him and wanted to show everybody that she was Christian Darling's girl. She bought him crazy presents because her father was rich, watches, pipes, humidors, an icebox for beer for his room, curtains, wallets, a fifty-dollar dictionary.

"You'll spend every cent your old man owns," Darling protested once when she showed up at his rooms with seven different packages in her arms and tossed them onto the couch.

"Kiss me," Louise said, "and shut up."

"Do you want to break your poor old man?"

"I don't mind. I want to buy you presents."

"Why?"

"It makes me feel good. Kiss me. I don't know why. Did you know that you're an important figure?"

"Yes," Darling said gravely.

"When I was waiting for you at the library yesterday two girls saw you coming and one of them said to the other, 'That's Christian Darling. He's an important figure.'"

"You're a liar."

"I'm in love with an important figure."

"Still, why the hell did you have to give me a forty-pound dictionary?"

"I wanted to make sure," Louise said, "that you had a token of my esteem. I want to smother you in tokens of my esteem."

Fifteen years ago.

They'd married when they got out of college. There'd been other women for him, but all casual and secret, more for curiosity's sake, and vanity, women who'd thrown themselves at him and flattered him, a pretty mother at a summer camp for boys, an old girl from his home town who'd suddenly blossomed into a coquette, a friend of Louise's who had dogged him grimly for six months and had taken advantage of the two weeks when Louise went home when her mother died. Perhaps Louise had known, but she'd kept quiet, loving him completely, filling his rooms with presents, religiously watching him battling with the big Swedes and Polacks on the line of scrimmage on Saturday afternoons, making plans for marrying him and living with him in New York and going with him there to the nightclubs, the theatres, the good restaurants, being proud of him in advance, tall, white-teethed, smiling, large, yet moving lightly, with an athlete's grace, dressed in evening clothes, approvingly eyed by magnificently dressed and famous women in theatre lobbies, with Louise adoringly at his side.

Her father, who manufactured inks, set up a New York office for Darling to manage and presented him with three hundred accounts and they lived on Beekman Place with a view of the river with fifteen thousand dollars a year between them, because everybody was buying everything in those days, including ink. They saw all the shows and went to all the speakeasies and spent their fifteen thousand dollars a year and in the afternoons Louise went to the art galleries and the matinees of the more serious plays that Darling didn't like to sit through and Darling slept with a girl who danced in the chorus of *Rosalie* and with the wife of a man who owned three copper mines. Darling played squash three times a week and remained as solid as a stone barn and Louise never took her eyes off him when they were in the same room together, watching him with a secret, miser's smile, with a trick of coming over to him in the middle of a crowded room and saying gravely, in a low voice, "You're the handsomest man I've ever seen in my whole life. Want a drink?"

Nineteen twenty-nine came to Darling and to his wife and father-in-law, the maker of inks, just as it came to everyone else. The father-in-law waited until 1933 and then blew his brains out and when Darling went to Chicago to see what the books of the firm looked like he found out all that was left were debts and three or four gallons of unbought ink.

"Please, Christian," Louise said, sitting in their neat Beekman Place apartment, with a view of the river and prints of paintings by Dufy and Braque and Picasso on the wall, "please, why do you want to start drinking at two o'clock in the afternoon?"

"I have nothing else to do," Darling said, putting down his glass, emptied of its fourth drink. "Please pass the whiskey."

Louise filled his glass. "Come take a walk with me," she said. "We'll walk along the river."

"I don't want to walk along the river," Darling said, squinting intensely at the prints of paintings by Dufy, Braque and Picasso.

"We'll walk along Fifth Avenue."

"I don't want to walk along Fifth Avenue."

"Maybe," Louise said gently, "you'd like to come with me to some art galleries. There's an exhibition by a man named Klee—"

"I don't want to go to any art galleries. I want to sit here and drink Scotch whiskey," Darling said. "Who the hell hung those goddam pictures up on the wall?"

"I did," Louise said.

"I hate them."

"I'll take them down," Louise said.

"Leave them there. It gives me something to do in the afternoon. I can hate them." Darling took a long swallow. "Is that the way people paint these days?"

"Yes, Christian. Please don't drink any more."

"Do you like painting like that?"

"Yes, dear."

"Really?"

"Really."

Darling looked carefully at the prints once more. "Little Louise Tucker. The middle-western beauty. I like pictures with horses in them. Why should you like pictures like that?"

"I just happen to have gone to a lot of galleries in the last few years. . . ."

"Is that what you do in the afternoon?"

"That's what I do in the afternoon," Louise said.

"I drink in the afternoon."

Louise kissed him lightly on the top of his head as he sat there squinting at the pictures on the wall, the glass of whiskey held firmly in his hand. She put on her coat and went out without saying another word. When she came back in the early evening, she had a job on a woman's fashion magazine.

They moved downtown and Louise went out to work every morning and Darling sat home and drank and Louise paid the bills as they came up. She made believe she was going to quit work as soon as Darling found a job, even though she was taking over more responsibility day by day at the magazine, interviewing authors, picking painters for the illustrations and covers, getting actresses to pose for pictures, going out for drinks with the right people, making a thousand new friends whom she loyally introduced to Darling.

"I don't like your hat," Darling said, once, when she came in in the evening and kissed him, her breath rich with Martinis.

"What's the matter with my hat, Baby?" she asked, running her fingers through his hair. "Everybody says it's very smart."

"It's too damned smart," he said. "It's not for you. It's for a rich, sophisticated woman of thirty-five with admirers."

Louise laughed. "I'm practicing to be a rich, sophisticated woman of thirty-five with admirers," she said. He stared soberly at her. "Now, don't look so grim, Baby. It's still the same simple little wife under the hat." She took the hat off, threw it into a corner, sat on his lap. "See? Homebody Number One."

"Your breath could run a train," Darling said, not wanting to be mean, but talking out of boredom, and sudden shock at seeing his wife curiously a stranger in a new hat, with a new expression in her eyes under the little brim, secret, confident, knowing.

Louise tucked her head under his chin so he couldn't smell her breath. "I had to take an author out for cocktails," she said. "He's a boy from the Ozark mountains and he drinks like a fish. He's a Communist."

"What the hell is a Communist from the Ozarks doing writing for a woman's fashion magazine?"

Louise chuckled. "The magazine business is getting all mixed up these days. The publishers want to have a foot in every camp. And anyway, you can't find an author under seventy these days who isn't a Communist."

"I don't think I like you to associate with all those people, Louise," Darling said. "Drinking with them."

"He's a very nice, gentle boy," Louise said. "He reads Ernest Dobson."

"Who's Ernest Dobson?"

Louise patted his arm, stood up, fixed her hair. "He's an English poet."

Darling felt that somehow he had disappointed her. "Am I supposed to know who Ernest Dobson is?"

"No, dear. I'd better go in and take a bath."

After she had gone, Darling went over to the corner where the hat was lying and picked it up. It was nothing, a scrap of straw, a red flower, a veil, meaningless on his big hand, but on his wife's head a signal of something . . . big city, smart and knowing women drinking and dining with men other than their husbands, conversation about things a normal man wouldn't know much about, Frenchmen who painted as though they used their elbows instead of brushes, composers who wrote whole symphonies without a single melody in them, writers who knew all about politics and women who knew all about writers, the movement of the proletariat, Marx, somehow mixed up with five-dollar dinners and the best looking women in America and fairies who made them laugh and half-sentences immediately understood and secretly hilarious and wives who called their husbands, "Baby." He put the hat down, a scrap of straw and a red flower, and a little veil. He drank some whiskey straight and went into the bathroom where his wife was lying deep in her bath, singing to herself and smiling from time to time like a little girl, paddling the water gently with her hands, sending up a slight spicy fragrance from the bath-salts she used.

He stood over her, looking down at her. She smiled up at him, her eyes half closed, her body pink and shimmering in the warm, scented water. All over again, with all the old suddenness, he was hit deep inside him with the knowledge of how beautiful she was, how much he needed her.

"I came in here," he said, "to tell you I wish you wouldn't call me 'Baby.'"

She looked up at him from the bath, her eyes quickly full of sorrow, half-understanding what he meant. He knelt and put his arms around her, his sleeves plunged heedlessly in the water, his shirt and jacket soaking wet as he clutched her wordlessly, holding her crazily tight, crushing her breath from her, kissing her desperately, searchingly, regretfully.

He got jobs after that, selling real estate and automobiles, but somehow, although he had a desk with his name on a wooden wedge on it, and he went to the office religiously at nine each morning, he never managed to sell anything and he never made any money.

Louise was made the assistant editor and the house was always full of strange men and women who talked fast and got angry on abstract subjects like mural painting, novelists, labor unions. Negro short-story writers drank Louise's liquor, and a lot of Jews, and big solemn men with scarred faces and knotted hands who talked slowly but clearly about picket lines and battles with guns and lead-pipe at mine-shaft-heads and in front of factory gates. And Louise moved among them all, confidently, knowing what they were talking about, with opinions that they listened to and argued about just as though she were a man. She knew everybody, condescended to no one, devoured books that Darling had never heard of, walked along the streets of the city, excited, at home, soaking in all the million tides of New York without fear, with constant wonder.

Her friends liked Darling and sometimes he found a man who wanted to get off in the corner and talk about the new boy who played fullback for Princeton, and the decline of the double wing-back, or even the state of the stock market, but for the most part he sat on the edge of things, solid and quiet in the high storm of words. "The dialectics of the situation . . . the theatre has been given over to expert jugglers . . . Picasso? What man has a right to paint old bones and collect ten thousand dollars for them? . . . I stand firmly behind Trotsky . . . Poe was the last American critic. When he died they put lilies on the grave of American criticism. I don't say this because they panned my last book, but . . ."

Once in a while he caught Louise looking soberly and consideringly at him through the cigarette smoke and the noise and he avoided her eyes and found an excuse to get up and go into the kitchen for more ice or to open another bottle.

"Come on," Cathal Flaherty was saying, standing at the door with a girl, "you've got to come down and see this. It's down on Fourteenth Street, in the old Civic Repertory, and you can only see it on Sunday nights and I guarantee you'll come out of the theater singing." Flaherty was a big young Irishman with a broken nose who was the lawyer for a longshoreman's union, and he had been hanging around the house for six months on and off, roaring and shutting everybody else up when he got in an argument. "It's a new play, *Waiting for Lefty*, it's about taxi-drivers."

"Odets," the girl with Flaherty said. "It's by a guy named Odets."

"I never heard of him," Darling said.

"He's a new one," the girl said.

"It's like watching a bombardment," Flaherty said. "I saw it last Sunday night. You've got to see it."

"Come on, Baby," Louise said to Darling, excitement in her eyes already. "We've been sitting in the Sunday *Times* all day, this'll be a great change."

"I see enough taxi-drivers all day," Darling said, not because he meant that, but because he didn't like to be around Flaherty, who said things that made Louise laugh a lot and whose judgment she accepted on almost every subject. "Let's go to the movies."

"You've never seen anything like this before," Flaherty said. "He wrote this play with a baseball bat."

"Come on," Louise coaxed, "I bet it's wonderful."

"He has long hair," the girl with Flaherty said. "Odets. I met him at a party. He's an actor. He didn't say a goddam thing all night."

"I don't feel like going down to Fourteenth Street," Darling said, wishing Flaherty and his girl would get out. "It's gloomy."

"Oh, hell!" Louise said loudly. She looked coolly at Darling, as though she'd just been introduced to him and was making up her mind about him, and not very favorably. He saw her looking at him, knowing there was something new and dangerous in her face and he wanted to say something, but Flaherty was there and his damned girl, and anyway, he didn't know what to say.

"I'm going," Louise said, getting her coat. "I don't think Fourteenth Street is gloomy."

"I'm telling you," Flaherty was saying, helping her on with her coat, "it's the Battle of Gettysburg, in Brooklynese."

"Nobody could get a word out of him," Flaherty's girl was saying as they went through the door. "He just sat there all night."

The door closed. Louise hadn't said good-night to him. Darling walked around the room four times, then sprawled out on the sofa, on top of the Sunday *Times*.

He lay there for five minutes looking at the ceiling, thinking of Flaherty walking down the street talking in that booming voice, between the girls, holding their arms.

Louise had looked wonderful. She'd washed her hair in the afternoon and it had been very soft and light and clung close to her head as she stood there angrily putting her coat on. Louise was getting prettier every year, partly because she knew by now how pretty she was, and made the most of it.

"Nuts," Darling said, standing up. "Oh, nuts."

He put on his coat and went down to the nearest bar and had five drinks off by himself in a corner before his money ran out.

The years since then had been foggy and downhill. Louise had been nice to him, and in a way, loving and kind, and they'd fought only once, when he said he was going to vote for Landon. ("Oh, Christ," she'd said, "doesn't anything happen inside your head? Don't you read the papers? The penniless Republican!") She'd been sorry later and apologized for hurting him, but apologized as she might to a child. He'd tried hard, had gone grimly to the art galleries, the concert halls, the bookshops, trying to gain on the trail of his wife, but it was no use. He was bored, and none of what he saw or heard or dutifully read made much sense to him and finally he gave it up. He had thought, many nights as he ate dinner alone, knowing that Louise would come home late and drop silently into bed without explanation, of getting a divorce, but he knew the loneliness, the hopelessness, of not seeing her again would be too much to take. So he was good, completely devoted, ready at all times to go any place with her, do anything she wanted. He even got a small job, in a broker's office and paid his own way, bought his own liquor.

Then he'd been offered the job of going from college to college as a tailor's representative. "We want a man," Mr. Rosenberg had said, "who as soon as you look at him, you say 'There's a university man.'" Rosenberg had looked approvingly at Darling's broad shoulders and well-kept waist, at his carefully brushed hair and his honest, wrinkle-less face. "Frankly, Mr. Darling, I am willing to make you a proposition. I have inquired about you, you are favorably known on your old campus, I understand you were in the backfield with Alfred Diederich."

Darling nodded. "Whatever happened to him?"

"He is walking around in a cast for seven years now. An iron brace. He played professional football and they broke his neck for him."

Darling smiled. That, at least, had turned out well.

"Our suits are an easy product to sell, Mr. Darling," Rosenberg said. "We have a handsome, custom-made garment. What has Brooks Brothers got that we haven't got? A name. No more."

"I can make fifty, sixty dollars a week," Darling said to Louise that night. "And expenses. I can save some money and then come back to New York and really get started here."

"Yes, Baby," Louise said.

"As it is," Darling said carefully, "I can make it back here once a month, and holidays and the summer. We can see each other often."

"Yes, Baby." He looked at her face, lovelier now at thirty-five than it had ever been before, but fogged over now as it had been for five years with a kind of patient, kindly, remote boredom.

"What do you say?" he asked. "Should I take it?" Deep within him he hoped fiercely, longingly, for her to say, "No, Baby, you stay right here," but she said, as he knew she'd say, "I think you'd better take it."

He nodded. He had to get up and stand with his back to her, looking out the window, because there were things plain on his face that she had never seen in the fifteen years she'd known him. "Fifty dollars is a lot of money," he said. "I never thought I'd ever see fifty dollars again." He laughed. Louise laughed, too.

Christian Darling sat on the frail green grass of the practice field. The shadow of the stadium had reached out and covered him. In the distance the lights of the university shone a little mistily in the light haze of evening. Fifteen years. Flaherty even now was calling for his wife, buying her a drink, filling whatever bar they were in with that voice of his and that easy laugh. Darling half-closed his eyes, almost saw the boy fifteen years ago reach for the pass, slip the halfback, go skittering lightly down the field, his knees high and fast and graceful, smiling to himself because he knew he was going to get past the safety man. That was the high point, Darling thought, fifteen years ago, on an autumn afternoon, twenty years old and far from death, with the air coming easily into his lungs, and a deep feeling inside him that he could do anything, knock over anybody, outrun whatever had to be outrun. And the shower after and the three glasses of water and the cool night air on his damp head and Louise sitting hatless in the open car with a smile and the first kiss she ever really meant. The high point, an eighty-yard run in the practice, and a girl's kiss and everything after that a decline. Darling laughed. He had practiced the wrong thing, perhaps. He hadn't practiced for 1929 and New York City and a girl who would turn into a woman. Somewhere, he thought, there must have been a point where she moved up to me, was even with me for a moment, when I could have held her hand, if I'd known, held tight, gone with her. Well, he'd never known. Here he was on a playing field that was fifteen years away and his wife was in another city having dinner with another and better man, speaking with him a different, new language, a language nobody had ever taught him.

Darling stood up, smiled a little, because if he didn't smile he knew the tears would come. He looked around him. This was the spot. O'Connor's pass had come sliding out just to here . . . the high point. Darling put up his hands, felt all over again the flat slap of the ball. He shook his hips to throw off the halfback, cut back inside the center, picked his knees high as he ran gracefully over two men jumbled on the ground at the line of scrimmage, ran easily, gaining speed, for ten yards, holding the ball lightly in his two hands, swung away from the halfback diving at him, ran, swinging his hips in the almost girlish manner of a back in a broken field, tore into the safety man, his shoes drumming heavily on the turf, stiff-armed, elbow locked, pivoted, raced lightly and exultantly for the goal line.

It was only after he had sped over the goal line and slowed to a trot that he saw the boy and girl sitting together on the turf, looking at him wonderingly.

He stopped short, dropping his arms. "I . . ." he said, gasping a little though his condition was fine and the run hadn't winded him, "I . . . Once I played here."

The boy and the girl said nothing. Darling laughed embarrassedly, looked hard at them sitting there, close to each other, shrugged, turned and went toward his hotel, the sweat breaking out on his face and running down into his collar.

F. SCOTT FITZGERALD

Pat Hobby's Christmas Wish

IT WAS Christmas Eve in the studio. By eleven o'clock in the morning, Santa Claus had called on most of the huge population according to each one's deserts.

Sumptuous gifts from producers to stars, and from agents to producers arrived at offices and studio bungalows; on every stage one heard of the roguish gifts of casts to directors or directors to casts; champagne had gone out from publicity office to the press. And tips of fifties, tens and fives from producers, directors and writers fell like manna upon the white collar class.

In this sort of transaction there were exceptions. Pat Hobby, for example, who knew the game from twenty year's experience, had had the idea of getting rid of his secretary the day before. They were sending over a new one any minute—but she would scarcely expect a present the first day.

Waiting for her, he walked the corridor, glancing into open offices for signs of life. He stopped to chat with Joe Hopper from the scenario department.

"Not like the old days," he mourned. "Then there was a bottle on every desk."

"There're a few around."

"Not many," Pat sighed. "And afterwards we'd run a picture—made up out of cutting-room scraps."

"I've heard. All the suppressed stuff," said Hopper.

Pat nodded, his eyes glistening.

"Oh, it was juicy. You darned near ripped your guts laughing—"

He broke off as the sight of a woman, pad in hand, entering his office down the hall recalled him to the sorry present.

"Gooddorf has me working over the holiday," he complained bitterly.

"I wouldn't do it."

"I wouldn't either except my four weeks are up next Friday, and if I bucked him he wouldn't extend me."

As he turned away Hopper knew that Pat was not being extended anyhow. He had been hired to script an old-fashioned horse-opera and the boys who were "writing behind him"—that is working over his stuff—said that all of it was old and some didn't make sense.

"I'm Miss Kagle," said Pat's new secretary.

She was about thirty-six, handsome, faded, tired, efficient. She went to the typewriter, examined it, sat down and burst into sobs.

January, 1940

187

Pat started. Self-control, from below anyhow, was the rule around here. Wasn't it bad enough to be working on Christmas Eve? Well—less bad than not working at all. He walked over and shut the door—someone might suspect him of insulting the girl.

"Cheer up," he advised her. "This is Christmas."

Her burst of emotion had died away. She sat upright now, choking and wiping her eyes.

"Nothing's as bad as it seems," he assured her unconvincingly. "What's it, anyhow? They going to lay you off?"

She shook her head, did a sniffle to end sniffles, and opened her notebook.

"Who you been working for?"

She answered between suddenly gritted teeth.

"Mr. Harry Gooddorf."

Pat widened his permanently bloodshot eyes. Now he remembered he had seen her in Harry's outer office.

"Since 1921. Eighteeen years. And yesterday he sent me back to the department. He said I depressed him—I reminded him he was getting on." Her face was grim. "That isn't the way he talked after hours eighteen years ago."

"Yeah, he was a skirt chaser then," said Pat.

"I should have done something then when I had the chance."

Pat felt righteous stirrings.

"Breach of promise? That's no angle!"

"But I had something to clinch it. Something bigger than breach of promise. I still have too. But then, you see, I thought I was in love with him." She brooded for a moment. "Do you want to dictate something now?"

Pat remembered his job and opened a script.

"It's an insert," he began. "Scene 114 A."

Pat paced the office.

"Ext. Long Shot of the Plains," he decreed, "Buck and Mexicans approaching the hyacenda."

"The what?"

"The hyacenda—the ranch house." He looked at her reproachfully. "114 B. Two Shot: Buck and Pedro. Buck: 'The dirty son-of-a-bitch. I'll tear his guts out!' "

Miss Kagle looked up, startled.

"You want me to write that down?"

"Sure."

"It won't get by."

"I'm writing this. Of course, it won't get by. But if I put 'you rat' the scene won't have any force."

"But won't somebody have to change it to 'you rat'?"

He glared at her—he didn't want to change secretaries every day.

"Harry Gooddorf can worry about that."

"Are you working for Mr. Gooddorf?" Miss Kagle asked in alarm.

"Until he throws me out."

"I shouldn't have said—"

"Don't worry," he assured her. "He's no pal of mine any more. Not at three-fifty a week, when I used to get two thousand ... Where was I?"

He paced the floor again, repeating his last line aloud with relish. But now it seemed to apply not to a personage of the story but to Harry Gooddorf. Suddenly he stood still, lost in thought. "Say, what is it you got on him? You know where the body is buried?"

"That's too true to be funny."

"He knock somebody off?"

"Mr. Hobby, I'm sorry I ever opened my mouth."

"Just call me Pat. What's your first name?"

"Helen."

"Married?"

"Not now."

"Well, listen Helen: What do you say we have dinner?"

II

On the afternoon of Christmas Day he was still trying to get the secret out of her. They had the studio almost to themselves—only a skeleton staff of technical men dotted the walks and the commissary. They had exchanged Christmas presents. Pat gave her a five dollar bill, Helen bought him a white linen handkerchief. Very well he could remember the day when many dozen such handkerchiefs had been his Christmas harvest.

The script was progressing at a snail's pace but their friendship had considerably ripened. Her secret, he considered, was a very valuable asset, and he wondered how many careers had turned on just such an asset. Some, he felt sure, had been thus raised to affluence. Why, it was almost as good as being in the family, and he pictured an imaginary conversation with Harry Gooddorf.

"Harry, it's this way. I don't think my experience is being made use of. It's the young squirts who ought to do the writing—I ought to do more supervising."

"Or—?"

"Or else," said Pat firmly.

He was in the midst of his daydream when Harry Gooddorf unexpectedly walked in.

"Merry Christmas, Pat," he said jovially. His smile was less robust when he saw Helen. "Oh, hello Helen—didn't know you and Pat had got together. I sent you a remembrance over to the script department."

"You shouldn't have done that."

Harry turned swiftly to Pat.

"The boss is on my neck," he said. "I've got to have a finished script Thursday."

"Well, here I am," said Pat. "You'll have it. Did I ever fail you?"

"Usually," said Harry. "Usually."

He seemed about to add more when a call boy entered with an envelope and handed it to Helen Kagle—whereupon Harry turned and hurried out.

"He'd better get out!" burst forth Miss Kagle, after opening the envelope. "Ten bucks—just *ten bucks*—from an executive—after eighteen years."

It was Pat's chance. Sitting on his desk he told her his plan.

"It's soft jobs for you and me," he said. "You the head of a script department, me an associate producer. We're on the gravy train for life—no more writing—no more pounding the keys. We might even—we might even—if things go good we could get married."

She hesitated a long time. When she put a fresh sheet in the typewriter Pat feared he had lost.

"I can write it from memory," she said. "This was a letter he typed *himself* on February 3rd, 1921. He sealed it and gave it to me to mail—but there was a blonde he was interested in, and I wondered why he should be so secret about a letter."

Helen had been typing as she talked, and now she handed Pat a note.

To Will Bronson
First National Studios
    Personal
Dear Bill:

We killed Taylor. We should have cracked down on him sooner. So why not shut up.

                                                        Yours, Harry

Pat stared at it stunned.

"Get it?" Helen said. "On February 1st, 1921, somebody knocked off William Desmond Taylor, the director. And they've never found out who."

III

For eighteen years she had kept the original note, envelope and all. She had sent only a copy to Bronson, tracing Harry Gooddorf's signature.

"Baby, were set!" said Pat. "I always thought it was a *girl* got Taylor."

He was so elated that he opened a drawer and brought forth a half-pint of whiskey. Then, with an afterthought, he demanded:

"Is it in a safe place?"

"You bet it is. He'd never guess where."

"Baby, we've got him!"

Cash, cars, girls, swimming pools swam in a glittering montage before Pat's eye.

He folded the note, put it in his pocket, took another drink and reached for his hat.

"You going to see him now?" Helen demanded in some alarm. "Hey, wait till I get off the lot. *I* don't want to get murdered."

"Don't worry! Listen, I'll meet you in 'The Muncherie' at Fifth and La Brea— in one hour."

As he walked to Gooddorf's office he decided to mention no facts or names within the walls of the studio. Back in the brief period when he had headed a scenario department Pat had conceived a plan to put a dictaphone in every writer's office. Thus their loyalty to the studio executives could be checked several times a day.

The idea had been laughed at. But later, when he had been "reduced back to a writer," he often wondered if his plan was secretly followed. Perhaps some indiscreet remark of his own was responsible for the doghouse where he had been interred for the past decade. So it was with the idea of concealed dictaphones in mind, dictaphones which could be turned on by the pressure of a toe, that he entered Harry Gooddorf's office.

"Harry—" He chose his words carefully, "do you remember the night of February 1st, 1921?"

Somewhat flabbergasted, Gooddorf leaned back in his swivel chair.

"What?"

"Try and think. It's something very important to you."

Pat's expression as he watched his friend was that of an anxious undertaker.

"February 1st, 1921." Gooddorf mused. "No. How could I remember? You think I keep a diary? I don't even know where I was then."

"You were right here in Hollywood."

"Probably. If you know, tell me."

"You'll remember."

"Let's see. I came out to the coast in sixteen. I was with Biograph till 1920. Was I making some comedies? That's it. I was making a piece called *Knuckle-duster*—on location."

"You weren't always on location. You were in town February 1st."

"What is this?" Gooddorf demanded. "The third degree?"

"No—but I've got some information about your doings on that date."

Gooddorf's face reddened; for a moment it looked as if he were going to throw Pat out of the room—then suddenly he gasped, licked his lips and stared at his desk.

"Oh," he said, and after a minute: "But I don't see what business it is of yours."

"It's the business of every decent man."

"Since when have you been decent?"

"All my life," said Pat. "And, even if I haven't, I never did anything like that."

"My foot!" said Harry contemptuously. "You showing up here with a halo! Anyhow, what's the evidence? You'd think you had a written confession. It's all forgotten long ago."

"Not in the memory of decent men," said Pat. "And as for a written confession—I've got it."

"I doubt you. And I doubt if it would stand in any court. You've been taken in."

"I've seen it," said Pat with growing confidence, "and it's enough to hang you."

"Well, by God, if there's any publicity I'll run you out of town."

"You'll run *me* out of town."

"I don't want any publicity."

"Then I think you'd better come along with me. Without talking to anybody."

"Where are we going?"

"I know a bar where we can be alone."

The Muncherie was in fact deserted, save for the bartender and Helen Kagle who sat at a table, jumpy with alarm. Seeing her, Gooddorf's expression changed to one of infinite reproach.

"This is a hell of a Christmas," he said, "with my family expecting me home an hour ago. I want to know the idea. You say you've got something in my writing."

Pat took the paper from his pocket and read the date aloud. Then he looked up hastily:

"This is just a copy, so don't try and snatch it."

He knew the technique of such scenes as this. When the vogue for Westerns had temporarily subsided he had sweated over many an orgy of crime.

"To William Bronson, Dear Bill: We killed Taylor. We should have cracked down on him sooner. So why not shut up. Yours, Harry."

Pat paused, "You wrote this on February 3rd, 1921."

Silence. Gooddorf turned to Helen Kagle.

"Did you do this? Did I dictate that to you?"

"No," she admitted in an awed voice. "You wrote it yourself. I opened the letter."

"I see. Well, what do you want?"

"Plenty," said Pat, and found himself pleased with the sound of the word.

"What exactly?"

Pat launched into the description of a career suitable to a man of forty-nine. A glowing career. It expanded rapidly in beauty and power during the time it took him to drink three large whiskeys. But one demand he returned to again and again.

He wanted to be made a producer tomorrow.

"Why tomorrow?" demanded Gooddorf. "Can't it wait?"

There were sudden tears in Pat's eyes—real tears.

"This is Christmas," he said. "It's my Christmas wish. I've had a hell of a time. I've waited so long."

Gooddorf got to his feet suddenly.

"Nope," he said. "I won't make you a producer. I couldn't do it in fairness to the company. I'd rather stand trial."

Pat's mouth fell open.

"What? You won't?"

"Not a chance. I'd rather swing."

He turned away, his face set, and started toward the door.

"All right!" Pat called after him. "It's your last chance."

Suddenly he was amazed to see Helen Kagle spring up and run after Good-dorf—try to throw her arms around him.

"Don't worry!" she cried. "I'll tear it up, Harry! It was a joke Harry—"

Her voice trailed off rather abruptly. She had discovered that Gooddorf was shaking with laughter.

"What's the joke?" she demanded, growing angry again. "Do you think I haven't got it?"

"Oh, you've got it all right," Gooddorf howled. "You've got it—but it isn't what you think it is."

He came back to the table, sat down and addressed Pat.

"Do you know what I thought that date meant? I thought maybe it was the date Helen and I first fell for each other. That's what I thought. And I thought she was going to raise Cain about it. I thought she was nuts. She's been married twice since then, and so have I."

"That doesn't explain the note," said Pat sternly but with a sinky feeling. "You admit you killed Taylor."

Gooddorf nodded.

"I still think a lot of us did," he said. "We were a wild crowd—Taylor and Bronson and me and half the boys in the big money. So a bunch of us got together in an agreement to go slow. The country was waiting for somebody to hang. We tried to get Taylor to watch his step but he wouldn't. So instead of cracking down on him, we let him 'go the pace.' And some rat shot him—who did it I don't know."

He stood up.

"Like somebody should have cracked down on you, Pat. But you were an amusing guy in those days, and besides we were all too busy."

Pat sniffed suddenly.

"I've been cracked down on," he said. "Plenty."

"But too late," said Gooddorf, and added, "You've probably got a new Christmas wish by now, and I'll grant it to you. I won't say anything about this afternoon."

When he had gone, Pat and Helen sat in silence. Presently Pat took out the note again and looked it over.

" 'So why not shut up?' " he read aloud. "He didn't explain that."

"Why *not* shut up?" Helen said.

MARTHA GELLHORN

About Shorty

I DO NOT remember her name. She had a pug-dog face and she was twenty-five years old. A pug-dog face is not necessarily unattractive. She was sunburned and had small square teeth; when she smiled, her gums showed. She smiled, she laughed, she giggled. And her gums showed, and her snub nose wrinkled and her round blue eyes, with the light eyelashes, looked confidingly upon the world. Her hair was very blonde and cut short; the job seemed to have been done with a nail scissors. The hair was not thick—ragged, but fluffy. She was of what they call medium height and she had a good body. Men would notice this; but women, deceived by the unpainted face, would not consider it.

What can her name have been? Trudi perhaps, only it wasn't Trudi. It was a German nickname, ending in "i," the kind of nickname that made you think of "Shorty." I have to call her something. She now becomes Shorty.

They brought her to my hotel room, in Madrid, one late afternoon in the Winter of 1937. I was feeling sorry for myself as I had flu and had been abandoned while everyone went out to look at the war. The men were far too merry for my taste; they had found Shorty somewhere and were enjoying themselves. She giggled at their jokes and she listened in awe to their knowledgeable war prophecies; they had observed her shape with satisfaction. There was little amusement in Madrid that winter and less food, and all we ever had for entertainment was each other and anyone else we could dig up. Women were scarce too, foreign women who understood English especially. I thought I was prettier than Shorty, but not as successful. I would not have been able to giggle so enthusiastically at such mediocre jokes. The men were showing off. I disliked Shorty, for a lot of instant virtuous reasons, because I was jealous.

After a while, they all went away, looking for a room that had liquor in it and a more welcoming host. Later that night, Jim Russell came back and told me about Shorty. She was, it seemed, a good girl. She was a German, as "Aryan" as can be, married to another German who was a Jew. Her husband was a doctor in one of the International Brigades. We all knew him. We thought he was the finest man in Spain. We could not have said why, except that he was not dramatic; he was funny; he never talked about the Cause; he did not spare himself, slaving with less than the minimum of equipment to help the wounded, who were numerous enough. His name was Otto—I remember that. Shorty had been working near Valencia in a home for the newly created orphans of Madrid. Shorty and Otto were an admirable couple, unlike the rest of us, who had passports and salaries and were attending this war in the rare modern capacity of press tourists. In Spain, in those days, you felt like a profiteer and a monster if you had cigarettes, let alone a passport and any other place to go when you got sick of this.

Someone gave or bought Shorty a dress. She had been more alluring really, in a sort of Elizabeth Bergner way, when she arrived in blue dungarees and the ragged boy's haircut. Her hair grew and she curled it; she used lipstick and presently mascara. She turned very womanly. She should have stayed in Valencia where she knew what she was about. Otto was nearly always at the front. And Shorty liked to have a good time; she was obliging, grateful, humble, and not weighed down with intelligence.

When we first heard or saw or guessed that Shorty had become the mistress of a Russian journalist, my gentlemen war-correspondent friends were surprisingly angry. It appeared they had all been honorable and undemanding because of Otto, because they loved Otto, and now this lousy little tart was cheating on him and he would certainly find out and it would break his heart. The men did not blame the Russian, of course; he was only doing what anyone would do, if you didn't happen to know Otto.

I was exceedingly noble about this. I told Jim Russell and Owen James, one night in my room, that they were grotesque; probably Otto had a girl too, and why not? War was long and life was not guaranteed here to stay; poor Shorty had had a tough time and if she wanted a little pleasure, she had a right to it. They howled me down. Now that Shorty had displeased them, I was again the apple of their eyes, by default, due to the lack of competition. I could afford to be noble. Besides, in a general way, I found this free use of the Scarlet Letter tiresome and dishonest. Gradually I became Shorty's champion, and her friend. That is to say, I was as much her friend as I could be. Our pasts and presents and futures were too different; my follies were not hers; I have always thought there is a secret basis of pity in the friendship of most women, and that is a crumbling rock to build on. Shorty pitied me, I think, because I was so pompously determined to do my job like a real newspaperman (an idiot job of watching other people do theirs). I pitied her because apparently she could not learn by experience and she was unable to form and enunciate the word "No." So we were friends.

The Russian pulled out, with predictable speed. I imagine Shorty adored a man into the ground. Shorty looked bewildered for a while, like a puppy who has licked your hand and been slapped for its pains. She stayed in her room, waiting in the classical manner for the telephone that does not ring. Then her native jollity reappeared and she was back at Chicote's bar and in the hotel lobbies and the cluttered dirty bedrooms we called home; and a Frenchman, convalescing from a leg wound, replaced the Russian. The Frenchman returned to his brigade, and a Canadian, who was working for the Quakers, took over.

By now, Shorty was classed as one of what Jim Russell named the whores de combat. These few ladies were distinguished from the large professional body because they did not receive money for their services. As I grew to know Shorty, I realized that she loved all these passing men and continued to love Otto. This operation was possible, due to a cloudy, romantic German turn of mind which was very boring to listen to, and very pathetic.

We were out of Madrid a good deal, driving to the various fronts in whatever transport we could buy or borrow or talk away from its rightful owner. The men had become casual about Shorty, saying, simply, hello kid, whenever they saw her, and acting as if she weren't there. She was doing no work for the war, so she had nothing to say that would interest them; and the taboo, established for Otto's sake, prevailed. Shorty lived in another hotel but she visited us, occasionally, to beg. There were few enough gifts to give—extra cigarettes, an envelope full of sugar, a partially used cake of soap. The men gave Shorty what she asked for, if they had it, with affable contempt. And when any of us happened to stop at Otto's brigade headquarters and he wanted news of Shorty, the men were vague. She's doing okay, they'd say, seems in okay health, looks okay. It was amazing, in such a small war, where everyone appeared to know everyone else, that Otto hadn't heard.

The spring that year was more beautiful than it had ever been anywhere before, probably because of the long ugly winter that preceded it. We loved Spain, we the voluntarily uprooted, and we took a personal pride in the spring and in the grace it laid upon this land that we felt to be ours. We had watched many brave people pull Spain through the winter, and though we had done nothing but accomplish an act of presence, still we owned the country too, in a small but devoted way. The spring healed us. Quarrels had grown up during the winter, based on propinquity, dirt, lack of food and heat, the harassing daily German artillery fire, the fact that no one, notably our editors, was interested in what we wrote and apparently no one believed us. Now, in this new sun and this new greenness, we became friends again; and, due to the weather, we decided we were going to win the war.

The spring did something for Shorty too. She became haggard and pale under the orange rouge she used, and her blue eyes, no longer full of gayety, looked stupid and hurt and alarmed and wary. Suddenly she put on her dungarees and left for the front, near Teruel as I remember, to be a nurse. In that war anyone could do anything, what with the widespread lack of specialized training and the labor shortage. The men were friendly to her just before she left. She seemed to be the original Shorty again—her face washed, her hair ragged and uncurled, going forth like a good girl to do her part. It was there, wherever she was, that Shorty met the Spanish colonel whom we called Juanito.

We knew Juanito too and had decided he was very likely the second finest man in Spain. I had always found Otto handsome, but this was a question of taste.

Otto had a lean, swarthy, brilliant face, with a bony nose and lively eyes; he was not very tall, stooped and shabby, and he had beautiful hands. I liked his mouth particularly, and his voice. Perhaps he wasn't handsome. But there could be no argument about Juanito: he was a beauty. And he was much more—he was a man who had never heard of defeat, any kind of defeat. Otto was brave in a way that does not show and also never ends; Juanito was brave in the superb, heart-lifting way that ends you up dead.

Shorty fell in love with Juanito, and since she did not understand Spanish very well she must have interpreted Juanito's conversation eagerly, to suit herself. I am certain Juanito would not make a woman believe that he loved her with a true undying passion and wished to have her as his wife, if he had no such idea. I do not think Juanito loved anything truly and undyingly except Spain, and I think he was far too busy with the war to want a woman except for whatever brief delight she could offer. Shorty wrote two letters, from the shelled farmhouse where she was working. One was to me and the other was to Otto. I know about Otto's because she told me. She said that at last she had found the one love of her life, there was no turning back, she had explained to Otto and though she would always love him too in a different way, she could no longer be his wife, *etcetera* and *etcetera*. I showed my letter to the men, since we all saw Otto from time to time and we had to know how to treat him. Jim Russell opined that it would have been a good thing if the shell that landed down the hall from Shorty, last winter, had landed in her room. Shorty, they agreed, was on Franco's side, distracting Juanito from his work and destroying Otto.

Destroy Otto she did, as far as anyone can tell about anyone else simply by looking. His brigade was making an attack in the north, and Owen James and Jim Russell and I had to go up there to write about it, and we could not avoid Otto. Otto must have been thirty-three or -four, that spring, but he wasn't a young man any more. The brilliance had left his face and his skin was stone-colored and heavy; his eyes seemed to hurt him and the fine things that had always been in them, wisdom and compassion and hope, were gone. He did not speak of Shorty nor of anything else. He ordered us out of the terrible two rooms where he was working, with the wounded spread on the floor like a stinking human quilt; he said he had too much to do to bother with journalists; why didn't we pick up guns and be useful? Even writers ought to be able to see the attack was going badly.

Ten days later, when we were back in Madrid, Otto was killed. Someone reported he had been working in the trenches; it was a direct mortar hit. We checked; he was dead. Jim Russell and Owen James got drunk that night, in a somber untalking way, and suddenly Jim Russell said that if he ever ran into Shorty he would break her neck; even, if he had time, he would look her up, for this purpose. Not that Shorty had anything to do with the mortar shell; no one was dumb enough to think that; people got killed or they didn't, that was how it was; but you didn't have to kill them twice—not if they were Otto.

I do not know how Juanito disembarrassed himself of Shorty. It isn't anything I want to imagine. But he did it, and the Canadian who worked for the Quakers came to Madrid in the early summer and said he'd seen Shorty in Barcelona. What is she doing, I said, what does she always do, he said. We did not see Shorty again. She was crossed off as a war casualty, and forgotten.

We got out of Spain all right, at the end. We had passports and money. But that defeat was ours; we carried it with us in our hearts, in our brains, where it mattered. I daresay we all became more competent press tourists because of it, since we never again cared so much. You can only love one war; afterwards, I suppose you do your duty, use up your life in your own way, think as elevated thoughts as you can manage. Our little group split up, taking all those airplanes that go to all those places. We had, it seemed, picked a fine trade and could be busily employed from then on.

I was in Paris in the Summer of 1939, returning from China. The idea was to hang around and be handy for the oncoming European war. Some French colleague, who was hard up for copy, interviewed me; I said a few inspiring things about the gallant Chinese—who, in fact, seemed to me as unlucky, badly led, and doomed as anyone then extant—and the colleague, in that droll Frenchy way, wrote not only my dreary remarks, but a description of my clothes and my allegedly flower-filled room at the Plaza Athénée. The next morning Shorty telephoned me. An hour later she arrived.

I had unthinkingly decided Shorty was dead. This is a bad habit you acquire from attending wars; so many people actually are dead that if anyone disappears for a while you jump to conclusions. Shorty was wonderfully, unrecognizably, adorably alive.

The pug-dog face shone, not with its usual or former mindless merriment, but with something so seldom seen that I could not at once place it. It turned out to be peace. They say women acquire a Madonna-like expression when they are pregnant, and I doubt the truth of this; there can be no universal biological rule. But Shorty had it. Shorty looked smoothed out, certain, serene, and happy in a way that made you think sentimentally of rivers, clouds, and wide fields quiet under the sun. She bulged in the unbecoming, accepted manner, and she announced in a voice of joy that she threw up all the time. Her baby was coming in two months. It would be a girl. Why? Because it must not be killed in a war. I did not argue this. She had forgotten the sexually impartial effectiveness of aerial and artillery bombardment. She was married. I did not point out that this was still a stylish habit for women in her condition. Her husband was named Louis Lefèvre, and he ran the luggage section of a Paris department store. She did not tell me where or how she had met him, nor how she had left Spain. Her husband, she said proudly, had no political ideas at all and, due to a weak heart, wasn't even in the army. Good, said I. They lived in the suburbs in their own house; it was entirely paid for. She was going to get real papers, just like anyone else, real citizenship papers; she was going to have a passport. Splendid I said.

Then I inquired if there was anything she needed and Shorty was very grand about her husband's salary, their furniture, their house again, and her husband's father who was retired and lived in another house, which he also owned himself, near the Loire.

Did I think there was going to be a war, Shorty asked, suddenly anxious. She was easy to lie to; anyone happy has a way of staying happy as long as possible. She gave me her address. I must look her up the next time I was in Paris; she wanted me to meet her husband. She would have the baby ready to show me. It is all I ever wanted, Shorty said, just one baby—if I could only get one, that was all I wanted. But we never had time, you know, since 1933, and no place to live and no papers and war. I'm glad you've got it, I said. I would like to name her after you, Shorty said, because you are my friend. I am sorry I cannot. But I have alway known what I was going to call my baby and I have waited a long time so I have to do it. What is it, I said. Myrtle, she said, pronouncing it as a French word, with a German accent. *Oh well, I thought, the child can probably invent some nickname for herself later, to get over that horrid handicap.*

I was busy writing a lot of nonsense about would-there-be-war-wouldn't-there-be-war—and then it came, as it had to by then. I was sent to Poland and after that to Finland, and though I meant to write Shorty saying I hoped the baby was fine and that she and her husband were fine (as if anyone in Europe could be), I did not. But I got a rest at Christmas and came back to Paris with the notion that I had to see it once more before it was broken into rubble. Paris was as beautiful as you could hope, if you were looking at it for what you believed to be the last time. It was soft with snow, and quiet, and I walked around having a final heartsick love affair with the city. I decided that, these days, people would be well advised to love nothing; and this reminded me of Shorty and her baby and it was Christmas and a present was in order. I telephoned her. Her voice sounded the way she had looked in the summer; it was fantastic for any voice, here and now, to sing and exult in this way. But I would not go to her house; I said I had too much work. I imagined her house must be a glorious place, from her voice, and I did not want to take my despair into it.

She came to see me, and the peace had not left her face. I could hardly believe how she looked. She seemed to have arranged in her mind that the war was not coming here, it would be fought neatly in the north along the Maginot Line where it belonged. No harm could strike this city; no evil could befall. She had Myrtle, and such happiness, given only by God, would obviously be protected by Him. She spoke of Myrtle as if she were already twice as beautiful as Helen of Troy; she spoke of the pink-and-white room she had fixed for Myrtle. I did not ask if she needed anything. The only thing she needed was a world forever at peace. Presently I went back to Finland, which was cold and certain to be defeated.

I could not get Shorty on the telephone the next time I was in Paris and I wasn't there long. I left, together with a good proportion of the citizenry. Shorty and Myrtle and the husband with the weak heart must already have gone to the retired father, to the house near the Loire that was still, and one passionately hoped would remain, safe. After that there was only the war, all the years of it, and Shorty in Occupied France where I could not have reached her had I thought about her, which I didn't.

The Peace Conference was well attended by many of the former Spanish War correspondents. I do not know about the others, but I felt that I had lived longer than was decent, and judging by the appearance of my friends, who had also been wandering around the wars, we all looked that way. One afternoon, limp with boredom and prickly with contempt, I was taking my ease in the Luxembourg Palace press bar when Owen James came in. I had seen him once in Italy, during the Cassino winter, but our real bond was Spain. We fell upon each other with suitable rejoicing. We settled the affairs of the world. We told each other how this Peace Conference ought to be and wasn't. And then, for no reason at all, he mentioned Shorty.

Do you remember Jean Roche, he said (Jean Roche was a French correspondent in Madrid, who wore the largest horn-rimmed spectacles I have ever seen on anyone). Sure, I said. Well, he kind of kept up with Shorty in Paris after the war. (The war, for us old boys, was always Spain.) He met her husband. I had dinner with Jean last week. He told me about Shorty. It seems she and her baby and her husband moved down somewhere in the country with her father-in-law. Then the krauts took over. It was okay for a while; you know, nothing gets organized too fast. But the krauts started settling in and checking up on everybody and seeing everything was on the level. Shorty didn't have any papers; there wasn't enough time for the red tape between her being married and the war declared. And she was a German anti-Fascist—which, as you know—is what the krauts would not take—and had been in Spain, which was really bad, and her first husband was a Jew—and that's the kiss of death. So it seems Shorty sat around there thinking about all this. Jean Roche got the story from her husband. And then one day she walked out the front door and disappeared.

But why, I said, why? Well, Owen James said, she left a note, so her husband told Jean Roche. She said she didn't want to bring danger to her baby. He was to look after the baby, that was all; and she didn't want to cause trouble for the kid.

I said nothing, and we had two more brandies. But now, I said, but now that it's over, hasn't anything happened? No, Owen James said, she's gone; I guess you have to assume she's dead. How dreadful, I said (and the word sounded insulting to me—tiny, feeble, a caricature). How perfectly awful. I remembered Shorty in her happiness. Owen James wouldn't have known what she had; Owen James wouldn't know about the peace on her face. Then somebody bounced into the bar and said that the whole Jugoslav Delegation was boycotting the session, and everyone rushed for the press galleries. I did too. I have not thought about Shorty since.

This week, I am in New York, that mammoth stone ant heap, buying unseasonal summer clothes. The sky sparkles in these parts, and those who can go about wrapped in furs. I am buying silks and cottons, as I am leaving for South

America on a long insignificant assignment about something or other. It seems that the calendar is confused for South America, and they have summer while other folks have winter. I do not know why, in the middle of inspecting without interest a pale green flowered print for wear during the cocktail hour, I should have remembered Shorty. I do not know why at all. I only know that she is here. It occurs to me that, if you live long enough, there are more people you would like to forget than people you would like to remember. I would like, for instance, to forget Shorty as I have forgotten her name.

The Corbina

MY LITTLE SON, who is five years old, had for three days refused to do anything I told him to do. Worse, he had refused to stop doing anything I told him to stop doing. Since he is naturally of a grave and courteous disposition, I could not think what had got into him to make him so unhappy. But, having tried every imaginable form of patience and impatience, I finally told him that now I would not take him fishing with me on Saturday.

For my own part I had looked forward to this expedition with an eagerness which I felt obliged to cover up in an assumed and probably stupid gruffness. We had planned it for over a year while he had simply tagged along of a Saturday, serving his apprenticeship. He had been a good companion and stayed clear of my rod, handing me bait when I wanted it, and following all I did with sober attention. At last I had bought him a rod of his own, and we were to have gone fishing as equals.

When I delivered my sentence I felt he had expected it, and for some obscure reason had even provoked it deliberately. Yet at the same time I saw that he was not quite able to believe I meant it and would ever really go without him. Even when I backed the car out of the driveway on Saturday morning he could not quite believe it. He stood at the back door, a little paler than usual, and watched me. I was aware that his new rod was just inside where he could snatch it and come running with it when I relented at the last moment. But I did not relent. And the last I saw of him in the rear-view mirror, he had come out into the driveway. The rod was in his hand now, and he stood there with it, looking after me.

Driving to town I almost crashed a truck marked "inflammables." I bought two dozen sand crabs from the bait man on the pier, and went down the coast to a spot which I had previously looked over. Here on the flood tide two almost imperceptible eddies worked against each other like a pair of cogwheels. They had built up a submerged sandspit off the beach, and I had felt that there if anywhere the boy would hook and land his first corbina. I parked the car on the bluff; and when I looked down, the tide was flooding strong and quiet and the twin slicks of the eddies were already rotating together just beyond the surf.

I tobogganed down the bluff with my equipment, rigged up, baited, and cast. When I felt the sinker hold, I set the rod up on the spike, reeled in the slack,

July, 1949

and lighted a cigarette. I tried to keep my mind on watching the shore birds, or now and then a cormorant or a line of pelicans out over the ocean. After a few minutes I saw the tip of my rod vibrate sharply. I let it happen twice more to make sure of him, and then brought him in carefully, remembering the corbina's delicate tubular mouth. Corbina fishing is actually less a sport than a minor art.

It was a nice fifteen-incher, but as I dropped it flapping into the sack I thought how the boy would have exulted with me. I even thought I would rather have lost the fish altogether if only he had been there to be tactful about it afterwards.

I shook my head like a fish trying to get rid of a hook. I told myself angrily that I was going to enjoy this Saturday just as I had always enjoyed them before my wife had borne him in such pain and trouble five years ago. I baited again, and spat on the bait, and announced aloud that now I would get the big one. This time I cast right into the meshed watery gears of the eddies, and when I had set the rod up I even forced myself to be superstitious about watching it only out of the corners of my eyes, so that the fish or fate or something might not suspect how eager I was. But secretly I knew that now neither my wife nor I would ever again do anything or want to do anything quite as we had done it five years ago. Because now he was with us, and we loved him.

I had just flipped the butt of a second cigarette into the surf when something kicked up a little jet of sand a few feet from where I stood. Then it happened again on the other side. I turned all around, trying to account for it. It happened a third time, and then I saw him up on the bluff just in the act of throwing still another rock at me. My first thought was, "What a wing!" And then I wondered how he had caught up with me so fast—and I visualized a white-faced little boy standing at the side of the road, overcoming his usual shyness of strangers and furiously thumbing rides.

When he saw I had spotted him he dropped the rock he was getting ready to throw next, and stood looking down, silhouetted against the sky with his hair blowing. I reflected that it was outrageous to throw rocks at one's father for any reason. But I thought that by the time I had scrambled up the bluff I would be winded, and if he ran I would probably not be able to catch him. And if he did not run I did not at all know now how I would cope with this thing which suddenly had become so enormous to both of us.

We stared at each other while I thought about it, and finally with a calm disdain which I was far from feeling I waved at him to go away. This stung him to a frenzy which really frightened me. He began dancing at the very edge of the bluff and shouting at me. Against the sea breeze, and over the sound of the surf, I could not make out most of the things he called me, but I certainly distinguished at least one appalling reference to his grandmother. With what I hoped was an air of majestic indifference I hastily turned my back.

But as I stared out over the ocean my heart was banging my breastbone. I was thinking that our good intentions had not after all been enough, and somehow my wife and I had failed the boy, and now he was damaged for good and would have to be turned over to some psychiatrist. I thought how it would be when he was brought into juvenile court later on, to be committed to some hellish reformatory. I had even begun picturing his mother's despair in Technicolor, when a sense of some sudden violence close behind me made me turn.

He had just arrived at the foot of the bluff, head-over-heels in a landslide of pebbles and sand. I thought his back must be broken, but he bounced up with only a skinned place on his forehead and came rushing toward me so wild-looking that I thought he meant to attack me physically. But he dashed on to the rod, hopping around it, and waving his arms and legs. "You big fool!" he screamed in the last extremity of excitement. "You got one!"

I looked, and the rod was whipping and springing as I had never seen it do. I was there in two jumps and caught it just as it came down with the loosened spike. I reeled madly, for suddenly everything was slack. But just as I had experienced the full extent of that bitterness which is known only to a fisherman who has lost a big one through his own fault, the line jerked unexpectedly taut again and I felt the angry weight of the fish still on it. It was very big. I thought it must be a skate or some confounded sea lion. But if it was a corbina it was one of those fabulous corbinas which are reported to stray up the California coast every once in a while out of their Mexican waters.

Whatever it was, I played it as if it were a million dollars, praying for the off-chance that my impossible little hook had somehow set itself in bone. I would coax him in a bit with each wave, but each time I brought him up to the surf I kept having to let him off again, not daring to hold him in the full power of the outwash. Now the boy was in his usual place again, behind me and a little to the left, and I seemed to feel great silent pulses of his uncritical confidence warming all that shoulder and side. But each time I felt the weight of the outwash added to the weight of the fish, I was glad after all that he had not brought his own rod today and hooked this one as his first one only to lose it. Now and then we would have an astonishing glimpse of the fish as the sand settled in the outsliding shallow water between the breakers. But I did not see how I would ever get him through the surf unless somebody came along unexpectedly and handed me a harpoon.

Just about that unexpectedly I got smart. I walked the fish down the beach and led him back into the eddies, and from one to the other until I could feel him grounding on the submerged ridge between them. I watched for the big wave, and it rolled up and broke, and just as it started sliding out again I risked everything and held. The tip of the rod went over and down, and stayed there, and we watched the run-off divide over so slightly on the ridge, and I think the tackle held by its last thread. And suddenly there he was, beating himself on the wet sand, gleaming and huge—huge for a corbina anyway. And at that moment I felt the rod dead in my hands and saw that he had finally shaken the hook, and I'd lost him.

It was beyond cursing or crying over. I just stood there and watched for the next wave to sweep him back where he'd come from. But something shot past me—a scrambling blur like a terrier after a cat—and the boy flung himself on the corbina just as the wave got there. It broke, and tumbled them together, and then both of them disappeared into the froth.

I dropped the rod with its fine reel in the sand and ran over, because he is not much of a swimmer yet. But just as the wave started drawing back to deep water, he heaved up out of it like a Triton, or (but for his sagging clothes) like the figure of a boy on a Renaissance fountain. He still had the fish round its middle in a death grip, and for just a moment I had an extraordinary view of their four eyes bulging up at me. He staggered right back across the beach with it, stumbling over the beating tail. And when he had carried it a full twenty yards above the high-tide mark, he fell down on it, and I could hardly pry him off.

I must pay this tribute to his mother's greatness as a woman, that when I got him home twenty minutes later, sodden and shivering, his clothes sifted as full of sea sand as a breakfast bun with cinnamon, spangled over with fish scales, and smelling to heaven of corbina, and when he bore in our prize and laid it reverently on her living-room carpet where it flapped its last and expired—she admired the creature convincingly for a full minute.

At nine that night I went in to say good night to the boy. His head was a tousled round shadow on the pillow, and I could just discern the rest of him outlined in the cot to which he had but recently graduated from the crib of his infancy. He looked so unexpectedly little that for a moment I was glad the darkness kept him from seeing my face.

"Good night, old man," I said after a moment.

"Good night. We sure fixed that crowbina!" he said. "We sure caught him all right!"

"We sure did."

Then I lingered in the doorway. "What was it, old man?" I said. "What made you act that way this week?"

"Which way?"

"You know which way."

"It wasn't a whole week anyway," he said.

"Three days then."

"Well," he said. "I thought you didn't really want to take me fishing."

BUDD SCHULBERG

The Real Viennese Schmalz

Harold Edson Brown's indignation could be heard throughout the entire studio. The only thing that was louder than his voice was the sport coat on which a couple of gag men had once played a game of checkers.

It was an outrage. Here he was, Harold Edson Brown, the highest paid writer on the lot, the only Pulitzer Prize winner on contract (though that winning play had been written twenty years ago with an enthusiasm and intensity which had sickened and died before he ever reached Hollywood), the man who had juggled such themes as mother love, comradery and sex for over ten years without ever dropping a script, being denied the fattest assignment of the year.

"What d'ya mean I can't write it?" Brown demanded in that golden voice that had gilded some of the most wilted Hollywood lilies of the past decade. "I didn't do so bad with *Mardi Gras. At the Pole* ain't exactly a stinker either. I got range."

(Actually Harold Edson Brown was one of the town's better educated writers. Bad grammar was a luxury he took childish delight in indulging because he knew everybody else knew he knew better.)

"But you don't know Vienna," the producer repeated. "I'm going to throw a million dollars into *The Blue Danube*. I've got to have the real Vienna—the old Viennese *schmalz*."

"The real Vienna—that's right down my alley. Don't you think I've ever been to Vienna?"

"Sure. For two days. The only time you left your hotel room was when you chased that dame into the lobby. I happen to know. I was with you."

"But I'm an expert on Vienna. I didn't spend seventeen months on *The First Waltz* for nothing."

"I should say not! Not at two grand a week. But *The Blue Danube* has to make *First Waltz* look like a quickie! I want the whole picture to sway like a beautiful waltz from start to finish. It's got to be absolutely lousy with the real Viennese *schmalz*."

"And just who is going to supply this R.V.S.?" Brown asked irritably.

The producer spoke the name with the proper air of mystery. "Hannes Dreher."

"Hannes Dreher! Never even heard of him. What are his credits?"

September, 1941

"Myron Selznick sold him to me. He's come straight from Europe. He's written Vienna's favorite operettas for years. This picture has got to be authentic. So it's going to be written by a one hundred per cent genuine Viennese."

II

Harold Edson Brown sat at the head of the writer's table in the commissary dishing out the latest inside dope like the man-about-studio he was, when a funny little stranger edged himself into the room.

"Who's that penguin with a hat on?" asked a gag man.

Harold Edson Brown prided himself on being a one-man studio bulletin. He always knew who had just been hired and who was about to be fired. He was supposed to have an *in* with the producers. "That must be Hannes Dreher," he announced. "He's the Austrian genius they imported for *The Blue Danube.* I'll get him over."

The lunch hour was at its height and the commissary vibrated with rapid talk punctuated by the grating clatter of many plates. Hannes Dreher was still standing close to the door, like a bewildered child arriving at boarding school for the first time. His coat looked as if it had started out to be a cutaway and changed its mind, and beneath it he wore the old-fashioned white vest which gave him the penguin look. His heavy grey fedora was balanced on his head like a book. The eyes were a gentle, light watery blue, and the only weapon he had developed throughout his half century on this earth was the vagueness which drew a screen of gauze between him and the brashness of life.

As Harold Edson Brown strode toward him with his two-thousand-dollar-a-week smile and his hand outstretched in the manner that had earned him the nickname Ward-Boss of Writer's Row, Dreher shied like a horse that had been whipped.

"You must be Hannes Dreher. Glad to meetcha, boy. I'm Harold Edson Brown."

Dreher smiled at him gratefully, bringing his heels together so gently that they produced no *click.* Because he always tried to be kind, he did his best to act as if he had heard Brown's name before.

"The same gang put on the feed bag here together every day. Make yourself at home."

Dreher bowed timidly. "Dankeschön, Herr Brown, you are very nice."

As Dreher ate, Brown nudged him familiarly. "Well, kid, you're running into plenty of luck. Just between you and me and Louella O. Parsons, the boss is throwing Jeanette MacDonald and Nelson Eddy into *The Blue Danube.* Which means you grab yourself an A credit right off the bat."

"*The Blue Danube,*" Dreher reflected. "Der schöne, blaue Donau." He looked out, through the window, and Brown's eyes followed, but there was nothing out there to see.

"You're in a great spot, baby," Brown continued. "We've had plenty of these Viennese horse-operas but they've always been strictly phonies. The boss tells me you're going to give it the real Viennese *schmalz.*"

"The real Viennese *schmalz*," Dreher repeated with a slow smile his eyes did not reflect. "Ach, that is very hard to give, ja?"

"You sure you wouldn't kid me, Mr. Strauss?" Brown laughed. "I'll bet you do your typing in three-quarter time."

III

Brown looked in on Dreher on his way to lunch next day. "Well, how's the Beautiful Blue Danube?" he asked. "Rolling along?"

Dreher looked up from his desk wearily. He hadn't written a line all morning and there were tight lines of worry around his eyes. "Nein, nein, she moves very slow," he answered.

"Oh, you'll hit it," Brown said. "How about ducking out for a little lunchee?" As the self-appointed good-will ambassador of the writers, he had to make the screwy little foreigner feel at home. And of course it wouldn't do him any harm to be chummy with Dreher, just in case he got a sole credit on *Danube* and became a big shot.

"Dankeschön, Herr Brown," Dreher said. "But when I write I am never hungry. See, I have brought a sandwich with me."

From that moment on Brown had Dreher pegged as an all day sucker. He couldn't figure him at all. In his ten years in the business he had seen hundreds of writers come and go, but he had never seen one take a job so hard. Believe you me, he would tell his pals, the little Austrian sausage is doing it the hard way, strictly from torture.

Brown himself was the town's champion horizontal writer. He was one of the last holdouts against the Screen Writers' Guild because he didn't believe a writer should have ethics. He had a well developed memory and a great gift for other writers' phrases. All he ever did was stretch out on a divan between the hours of ten and five and dictate last year's story with a new twisteroo. So you could have knocked him over with a paper-clip when he found out that Dreher was checking in at eight-thirty every morning and pounding away until seven or eight at night. And he was even more flabbergasted when he got news straight from Leah of the stenographic department that Dreher hadn't turned in a single page. Since the new efficiency move was a minimum of five pages a day, this sounded like professional hara-kiri.

Next time Brown saw the producer he couldn't resist giving Dreher a stab in the back, just a little one for luck.

"What's Dreher been doing?—Dozing on the banks of the Danube?"

But the producer only nodded like Solomon. "Give him time. A man who loves Vienna like him! For the real Viennese *schmalz*—I'm willing to wait."

IV

When Brown had to stop back at his office late one night to pick up a script, he was amazed to find Dreher still plugging away, his office full of smoke, an atmosphere of desperation, his hand pushing and pulling a cigarette into his mouth in a series of twitching gestures. The floor around his typewriter was cluttered with pages he had rolled up into nervous little balls and thrown away.

"How's she coming, pal?" Brown asked.

Dreher put out the cigarette he had just lit and tried to smile the way he had heard you should in a studio, but the attempt was pretty sad. "This is the . . . how you say . . . toughest . . . story I ever wrote," he said.

"I don't get it," Brown said. "A real Viennese like you. It oughta be a cake-walk. Old Vienna in the Springtime! Waltzing in the streets! Love on the banks of the Danube! You oughta be able to write it with your eyes closed!"

Dreher closed his eyes slowly. "Ja, the Blue Danube," he sighed. "The lovely streets of Vienna—and the waltzes." He stopped short; his fingers stiffened. After too long he said, "Ach, no, it is no . . . cakewalk."

Brown perched on the edge of his desk and waved his cigar around. "How's this for an angle? I'm just thinking out loud, see, but suppose we've got a charming young Viennese student. Nelson Eddy. You know, like the *Student Prince?* Well, Nelson's in love with the barmaid, Jeanette MacDonald, only he can't marry her because he's engaged to some princess he's never seen. But Jeanette's really the princess who ran away from the castle to find *life,* only she don't want to tell Nelson because she wants to be sure he loves her—for herself, see?

"So . . . well anyway, you can pick it up from there—and how do you like this for the topper at the finish—Nelson and Jeanette doing a duet alone in a little sail boat floating down the Blue Danube, and suddenly their song is echoed by thousands of voices, and you're into a terrific number with all the lords and ladies paired off in little boats singing the Blue Danube like it's never been sung before?"

Brown built his climax at the top of his voice, emphasizing its power by thumping Dreher's chest. Dreher had tried to listen attentively. Even though he recognized Brown's angle all too well. He looked from Brown's confident face to the labored, tediously crossed-out manuscript beside his typewriter. It was bad enough for Brown to appropriate a famous old plot. But when a man begins to plagiarize his own work! For Dreher couldn't fool himself any longer. Brown's enthusiasm-coated clichés had jolted him into realizing that the story he was working on was nothing more than a feeble carbon copy of his first operetta.

"Dankeschön," he said miserably. "You are very . . . helpful."

"Aw, don't mention it, Hans. Just let the plot take care of itself." And from the door: "Just give it that real Viennese *schmalz.*"

Dreher stared after him for a moment, absently shredding the cigarette he was about to light. Then he was grabbing everything he had written these last two weeks, viciously tearing it in two, flinging it in the wastebasket, and crazily twirling another blank sheet into his typewriter.

He began again, slowly, tentatively, as if every word were being wrung from it—peck, peck-peck, pause, peck-peck. The typing faltered and stopped. As he pressed his small trembling fists against his forehead, he could still hear Brown walking down the hall whistling *Blue Danube*. Then his keys beat another slow-motion staccato, until finally page after page was being torn from the roller and thrown among the heap that lay crushed on the floor.

V

Harold Edson Brown stopped looking in on Dreher after that, because he had seen the handwriting on the producer's desk. The finger was on Hannes Dreher.

"One month and I haven't seen a page," the producer grumbled to Brown. "I think he's a fake. For my money he's never even seen Vienna."

Impulsively the producer got Dreher on the phone. "I don't want any more stalling, Dreher. If you got something I can read, get it up here. If you haven't, get out. I'll give you twenty-four hours."

Next morning Dreher knocked shyly on the door and presented the producer with a manuscript the size of a telephone book. His hand trembled with strain and fatigue as he laid it on the desk. For the last twenty-four hours he hadn't even left his office. He had written faster and faster, pounding feverishly into his typewriter the words that came rushing, the most furious labor of his career, attacking his story the way Van Gogh slashed color at his canvases.

The producer fingered through Dreher's script dubiously, and only said, "I'll call you back in an hour."

An hour later when the producer told his secretary to call Mr. Dreher down again, Dreher was still sitting anxiously in his reception room.

The producer had impressed him with his club-room informality at their first meeting. Now he was barely polite, and his voice sounded crisp and anxious to get it over. "Dreher, I only had to read the first fifty pages to know it was all wrong. It's not what I wanted at all. It's got no life, no charm, it reads like a horror story. It doesn't sound as if you've ever been to Vienna. I'm afraid we'll have to close you out as of today."

By the time they were shaking hands, the producer was already getting Brown on the phone.

At the threshold Dreher's only response was to smile with amusement but no joy, and to bring his heels together in a weary *click*, as he said goodbye in a soft, sad voice.

On his way out of the studio, Dreher had to pass the projection room, where they were testing sound tracks of Jeannette MacDonald singing *The Blue Danube*. The lilting rhythm almost seemed to make his head sway, but the movement was mostly in his mind.

That lovely spring afternoon in Vienna. He had just finished his new play and was celebrating with friends at a sidewalk café. Over the radio had come the strains of *The Blue Danube*, and just as it seemed as if the entire place was beginning to sway, the waltz was harshly cut off. Suddenly, in a nightmare, they are listening to the trembling voice of Chancellor Schuschnigg.

*This day has placed us in a tragic and decisive situation . . . the German
Government . . . ultimatum . . . we have yielded to force . . . God protect
Austria!*

That had been the signal for the explosion . . . *the thunder of Nazi throats
and Nazi boots along the cobblestones . . . the last night . . . full of hoarse
screams futile cries the death rattle of old Vienna . . . and there was Lothar,
Lothar my only son just turned twenty-one a scholarship student at the
University still wearing the red-and-white ribbon of the Republic . . . my
Lothar tying some clothes and books into a hasty bundle whispering: They
are hunting every leader of our Fatherland Front . . . I must get out. Remembering. The mad rush to the station . . . the fear-crazed crowd fighting for
places on the train . . . and the new conquerors of Vienna dragging them
off . . . Then the last hope of freedom, the steamer anchored in the Danube
ready to sail for Prague . . . Remembering: the small boat the muffled oars
the friendly Danube the beautiful blue Danube where Lothar learned to
swim . . . then the angry put-put-put-put of the motor-boat full of the cruel
young faces of Lothar's classmates and Lothar slipping over into the dark
water diving down to leave behind the ghastly path of their searchlight . . .
and the beam always flashing across the darkness to pick him out again . . .
the sound of steel winging along the surface like ducks . . . the grotesque
pizzicato of the bullets plunk-plunk-plunking into the river . . .*

VI

Harold Edson Brown was reading Dreher's script. "You don't have to read
it," the producer had told him. "Unless you want an idea of what I don't want."
Brown had looked at the title *Last Waltz in Vienna* and had only meant
to skim through the first couple of pages, but here he was on one-hundred-
and-two, feeling every second of Dreher's last night in Vienna. For a moment
the power of Dreher's script drove so deep it reached the evaporating pool
of integrity buried within him. He still knew real writing when he saw it. He
was going to rush up to the producer, slam this script on his desk and shout
the truth. "The climax where the old musician is playing a Strauss waltz in
a Viennese beer garden as the tramp of Nazi troops and the sound of their
drums begins to drown him out—the old Viennese playing louder and
louder as if trying to make the voice of old Vienna heard above the tumult—
until finally nothing but brown shirts and the roar of their feet, voices and
martial music fills the screen and sound track—that will be one of the most
terrific moments in the history of pictures!"

But when Brown finished reading he shoved the manuscript under a
bunch of loose papers in his bottom drawer, violently pushing it out of his
mind. He wondered if he was going to let it lie buried there forever. One
of these days (maybe), when he couldn't look his fat check in the face any
more, he was going to pull it out and fight for it and watch it blast his
piddling little comedies off the screen.

He tilted his chair back, sprawled his feet across the desk and pulled out a bottle of whiskey. What's the matter with me today? I'm getting soft, I'm sitting around mooning like a goddamed sophomore, he lashed himself as he washed ideas out of his head with a healthy slug.

At the same moment Hannes Dreher was slowly climbing off a bus in Hollywood, wondering how to tell his family that the money they were waiting for to buy their way out of Vienna might not be coming for a long, long time.

VII

Harold Edson Brown took his customary place at the writer's table. He was completely recovered. He wore a smile the way a winning race horse wears a wreath.

"What's the big grin for?" the gag man asked him. "You look like the cat who just swallowed a producer."

"Better than that," Brown laughed. "Just got a new assignment. And I'm tickled to death. *The Blue Danube.*"

Don't forget to change the names of the characters from *First Waltz,*" the gag man said, "so the audience won't know it's a rehash."

"Rehash hell!" Brown said. "Wait'll you hear the new angle I got on it— a twist on the *Student Prince.* I'm going to give it that real Viennese *schmalz!*"

WILLIAM LINDSAY GRESHAM

Load of Respect

IN THE Neighborhood you've got to have Respect. If you don't have it you might just as well move out of the Neighborhood. And the guy who's got more respect than anybody else is Angie.

Angie is the boss in this territory and he is papa and he is *padrone* and in fact he *is* the territory. He has one finger in the territory and one in the Power House, that's how big he is. And at election time don't think that the Power House ever forgets Angie and the boys.

The only reason in the world why Angie can get this Neighborhood organized right down to the penny-ante games on the front stoops is because he carries such a load of respect and it all comes from the time, years ago, when he stands up to John the Dancer. Because Angie stands up to John the Dancer in the biggest way there is.

You know that service flag that hangs across the street just off the Avenue—the one that says "We Are Proud of Our Boys" and has the picture of the soldier, the sailor, and the marine and all the stars? Well, Angie donated that to the block.

Every Fourth of July one of his boys goes around to the candy stores with a pocketful of dough and makes a "drop" at each store. When a kid comes in and buys a nickel's worth of firecrackers he gets two packs of four-inch salutes free. And he knows that they come from Angie.

Since Angie is the boss the Neighborhood has run as smoothly as one of these Flying Fortress engines. All the handbookies are organized, and the brass men— the bail bondsmen. Angie cuts into every racket there is and everything runs peaceful and quiet.

You take the crap game in the garage down the street. Just after it starts you'll see a crippled kid called Gimpy step up and say, "I'm cutting." They all know he's there to cut it and he cuts it. He turns in the dough, getting his own cut, and the rest goes on up and up until it gets to Angie and then he cuts it and the Power House is the end of the line—where it goes from there is anybody's answer.

Angie has the numbers racket running smooth, and likewise the window-smashing racket—it only costs you half a bob a week, if you've got a store, to keep from getting your windows busted, and it's worth it. Same way with the laundry racket and all the other rackets that came out after Prosperity was repealed. Angie's got them all tied together in one knot and he holds on to the knot. But he couldn't hold it for a count of ten if he didn't have respect.

Just to show you how much he's got, you take what happened the other night over at Nick's Friendly Hour Tavern. Nick is Angie's brother. The two of them ran the place as a speak back during Prosperity and then when repeal came they put in all modern fixtures and got a neon sign.

Well, this evening everybody is out except Bob, who is Nick's boy. Bob is behind the bar, listening to the drummer in a hot band on the radio, when in comes a "cowboy" from over at the edge of the Neighborhood. This cowboy is a punk who's got no respect at all. He travels with a mob of other cowboys and they have maybe one rod in six or eight of them. One carries it one night and another the next night. The punk that carries the rod gets respect— but only inside the gang and only for the night he's got the hot stuff on him. Any other night he's got no respect at all.

The cowboy hollers for a double rye and Bob, the kid, draws him a small beer and slides it along the bar to him and never leaves the radio. Bob can do this because he's got some respect from being Nick's son and Angie's nephew.

The cowboy starts making with the Big Mouth and soon in come half a dozen other cowboys and they help the Big Mouth in making noise. They're talking about a stickup they just pulled and to show you what crumbs they are, where do they pick to pull this heist but right in the Neighborhood—a delicatessen off the Avenue, about six blocks up.

Bob, the kid, hasn't got enough respect to throw the whole mob out, especially since he hears an offbeat and he's afraid his favorite drummer is slipping. But it isn't the radio, it's a rod knocking the bar and the rod is stuffed down in the pants of the Big Mouth.

Bob is wondering what to do but he doesn't have to wonder long because all of a sudden the noise fades out and everybody stops yapping except the Big Mouth and he is getting smaller all the time. For who is standing there but Nick, and Angie is right in back of him.

Nick goes over and grabs the cowboy by the front of the shirt and then he feels a tap on his shoulder and it's Angie. Angie says, "No, Nick—let me handle it."

Angie throws the punk's coat open and jerks out the rod. It's a .22 and anywhere but in this yellow-gut mob it carries no respect at all, a little gun like that. Angie throws it on the floor and then he gives the punk the open hand right in the face, back and forth. He goes down the line and he gives every one of those kids the open hand. He finds another little rod on one of the others, but the punk didn't have heart enough to pull it on account of the load of respect Angie carries. After that the cowboys are glad to move out of there.

Angie and Nick have got so much respect the right guys ask them before they do anything that might give the Neighborhood a bad name. Take an example:

There's a kid at a party and his girl is there and she's getting noisy. Well, the kid calls up Nick at the tavern and asks him is it all right to boff her a couple of times. Nick wants to know what kind of people they are at the party and the kid says they are a very legit crowd and that one is a dentist. So Nick tells the kid, "Take her out in the hall and boff her and then bring her back." You see what I mean—this kind of advice gives the Neighborhood class.

Or take this one: there's a kid named Joey Ricks, one of old man Ricciardi's kids. He calls up Nick all in a hessy because he and his girl have had words and he gives her a couple of light ones in the puss. She wasn't marked up any, but she was burning plenty and Joey breaks out in a sweat on account of her brother finding out about it.

This brother is a real shiv man. His tick stopper has a blade seven inches long that jumps out of the handle when you press a button. I saw him take a swipe at a guy once—just kidding around—and he cuts through the guy's coat, his vest, his shirt and his undershirt and never leaves a mark on his skin. That's a real shiv man.

Now the kid, Joey, doesn't want to lose any respect and yet he knows the girl will tell her brother. And here's where you can see how Nick rates as a Brain Guy.

Nick says to the kid, "You've got to call him in spades." Then he tells the kid, Joey, about a pigeon loft at a certain address on the block where there is a panel at one end of the flat where the pigeons live. Inside this panel is where they keep a lot of the hot stuff. If anybody ever finds it, the folks downstairs don't know who keeps the pigeons and that's that.

Nick tells the kid to go up there and get a .38 and stick it in the waistband of his pants. Now, naturally a .38 carries a lot of respect. Nick tells the kid to get the Betsy and then to call up the girl and apologize and ask her to meet him downstairs for a couple of minutes. She does, and the kid, Joey, tells her he is sorry he boffed her. Only he isn't sorry—if you ask me that particular girl has had a good boffing coming to her a long time, only every other guy she ever went out with was afraid to boff her on account of the respect her brother has.

All right, Joey apologizes to the girl and kisses her goodnight the way kids like to do. Only when he kisses her she feels that .38 under his coat. Joey knows she will tell this to the brother. So Joey has "seen" the brother and raised him a stack; if the brother means to do any business, then he's got to get himself That Thing—his shiv's no good. Everybody knows that if a guy calls you, you've got to meet him with the same thing he calls you with. So Joey takes care of the brother without really having to lay it on the line. And in doing this he gets some respect because he does it with a .38 and also because he gets the tip from Nick and Nick is Angie's brother.

But it all goes back to John the Dancer. He started out working vaudeville and cabarets, doing adagio numbers and other kinds of work where you've got to be light on your feet but with plenty of muscle under the boiled shirt so you can boost the tomato up on your shoulders and let her down slow and easy and all the rest of it.

But being a dancer didn't get him any respect at all in the Neighborhood and what Johnny wanted more than anything was respect.

It's not long before he gets himself a Roscoe and with this Roscoe—which is a short-barreled .45 and hotter than the hinges of hell because it once cooled off a detective from the Loft Squad—with it he pulls a solo heist.

As everybody knows, a solo heist gets a guy more respect than anything else except One Thing.

Not only does Johnny work it solo but he picks his spot. The guy who gets heisted is a guy Johnny knows about from working the night clubs—he always carries at least a grand on him and once a week he visits a dame that he's bought plenty of jewelry for. Okay: one morning about four o'clock the guy gets through visiting and starts home to the wife, when who is waiting for him in the hallway but John the Dancer. All Johnny has to say is, "Give me the dough," and the guy gives it to him. He doesn't dare beef to the cops because they will ask him, "Where were you when you got heisted and what were you doing there?" and this guy is married.

The first thing the Dancer does with the dough is to make a drop at the candy stores. This drop buys lots of candy for the kids of the Neighborhood and they all know it comes from the Dancer. This gets the Dancer more respect. Next thing, he makes a drop at the speak-easy where the boys hang out—he sends out for a big spread and everybody has all they can eat and drink and the Dancer's drop covers the check and he has about all the respect there is.

He has about six hundred skins out of the grand and with this he goes into business, lending it out at six-for-five. You borrow five Saturday and the next Saturday you pay him back six. In this way the six yards bring him in a hundred and twenty a week and he always gets paid back on time because of the load of respect he carries from the solo heist.

Things go along pretty good for John the Dancer and before you know it he buys into a night club where he once danced for peanuts.

About this time there was a big difference of opinion on who was going to run the alky business in the territory—this was back during Prosperity, of course.

Nick and Angie were working in the alky business. They had plenty of headaches but their sister Carlotta gave them as many as the alky business.

Carlotta had respect because she had been to college. But she picked up a lot of ideas in college that didn't fit into the Neighborhood which worried Nick and Angie.

One evening Angie comes into the parlor of the flat and he is in a hurry—he needs a sub-machine gun which he had hid for safekeeping up the chimney. His mind is only on getting the chopper but he happens to see

Carlotta on the couch in a deep clinch with some fellow who when they break apart he sees is John the Dancer.

When he has time to think about it he is pleased at this because with Carlotta married it won't matter what kind of ideas she has. A couple of days later he asks Carlotta when she is going to announce the engagement and that is when the trouble starts. Carlotta says, "Johnny is a sweet lad but I don't think he's a stable personality. After all it is one thing to go around with a boy and another thing to get yourself married to him." You can see now what sort of ideas she had that worried Angie.

Angie can't quite make this out but he says, "You are going to marry Johnny. You tell him to get up his half of the ring and I'll get up your half. Tell him."

Well, the Dancer liked the idea at first because Carlotta is classy-looking and he wants to put up the whole works for the ring but Angie tells him not to talk foolish—what will people think if Angie's sister doesn't have her half for the ring—so they compromise.

Carlotta was going around wearing a long face at this point and Johnny takes her out to night clubs and introduces her to all the best people but she still wears a long face. Then John the Dancer blows up the works.

It seems that in this night club he now owns he does some dancing just to keep his hand in and for flash—the dancing gets him even more respect since he is already a solo-heister, a moneylender and a night-club owner. But the dame he uses for a dancing partner is not just pretty like Carlotta, she is one of the most beautiful tomatoes in town and educated in the muscles if not in the head.

One day John the Dancer is bringing Carlotta home from somewhere and he says, "Carlotta—I think your first idea was right—we don't love each other and we have a right to marry people of our own choice. You keep the ring and we'll call it square."

At this Carlotta begins to laugh. She pulls off the ring and drops it into the blind beggar's cup and she never sees John the Dancer again. But the next day she calls up a guy who was one of her teachers in the college and inside of two weeks they get married—the drop all the boys make furnishes their house up in New Rochelle.

This gives Carlotta's family quite a load of respect, except for Angie because the Neighborhood is waiting for Angie to send the Dancer an eel.

Now, in the Neighborhood when a guy opens a bundle and finds an eel in it he knows that somebody is not wishing him any long life and he had better stand up to the guy or take a trip for his health.

But Angie doesn't send the Dancer the eel. A week goes by and the territory is holding its breath, waiting for the eel, but it never comes. Two weeks and then three weeks and nobody can figure it because Angie has got plenty of respect in the alky business and nobody figures there is any yellow-gut about him.

Then everybody is talking about a new angle—they've got it figured that

Angie is waiting for June Fifteenth, which was the day John the Dancer was supposed to have married Carlotta.

Well, after a lot of time has gone by, the fifteenth of June arrives and in the Neighborhood all the kids are playing close to their own stoops and their mothers are looking out the window.

The wedding would have been set for noon and the closer it gets to noon the quieter the Neighborhood gets. And it seems that this wait has also been working on John the Dancer.

Just at noon a guy turns the corner off the Avenue and into the street where Angie lives. It's Johnny and he is all by himself. And what's more, he has the whole street to himself, there isn't a kid in sight and nobody looking out of windows.

He walks on down toward Angie's house and then he leaves the sidewalk and steps into the middle of the street and keeps walking, whistling something out of *Rigoletto*. He has his hands in his pockets and he is watching both sides of the street and in front of him and in back of him, but John the Dancer has respect. And he hasn't brought any of his own friends with him.

All this while Angie is sitting in a *pizzeria* on the ground floor of the house where he lives. He's had his dinner and he's gone down to the *pizzeria* to get a *pizza* with anchovies. He is facing the door, digging into the pie when he sees John the Dancer outside

Angie looks up at him and says, "Hello, John," and that's all he says because he takes a big bite of *pizza* and you can't talk around the cheese and anchovies.

Johnny stands looking at him and then he says, "Hello, Angelo," and walks on. He makes it to the end of the block and then he turns a corner and gets into his car where he has four or five guys waiting for him and they drive off.

Well, when Angie finishes his *pizza* he calls over the old guy that runs the place to pay him and the old guy says, "What *pizza?* You didn't have no *pizza*. You never been here before."

Now, Angie has been in and out of there for twenty years. But the old guy won't take his money on account of Angie has dropped every bit of respect he ever had.

Angie puts on his hat and then he goes over and sticks a folded-up dollar in the old guy's apron pocket and the old guy watches him walk out, shaking his head, because Angie is from the Neighborhood and now everybody will hear it, all the way to Brooklyn.

Well, you can see from this how tough it gets for Angie to keep living in the Neighborhood. But he stays and everybody is wishing he would move out because nobody quite gets up the heart to throw it at him that he let a guy run out on his sister.

People are trying to forget Angie and the whole business and John the

Dancer has got all the respect there is because of the way he walks down the street that day.

It is now nearly two months since Carlotta's engagement is broken off and Angie's brother Nick has lost respect because he is the next brother and he hasn't sent John the Dancer the eel.

And then one day Angie shows up home and he is in pretty bad shape. He has three bullet holes in him and he is bleeding out of all three of them. But John the Dancer is in even worse shape.

This night club he owns has an entrance down a flight of steps into a basement and at the bottom of these steps John the Dancer is lying. He only has one bullet-hole but it is through the heart.

That is when Angie gets all the respect in the world. He has called the Dancer and not only that but he gets away, and nobody on the block where the blasting was going on tumbles to anything—it's an hour before anybody finds the Dancer's body.

Now, you can't go blasting away in the middle of a block, even during Prosperity, without people getting curious and looking out of windows and maybe seeing the guy who's been doing the blasting making his getaway. But there is where Angie not only shows that he has the heart but also that he is a brain guy. What Angie has been waiting three months for is nothing but the Fourth of July.

Two Legs for the Two of Us

"**No**" said the big man in the dark blue suit, and his voice was hoarse with drunkenness. "I cant stay. I've got some friends out in the car."

"Well, why didn't you bring them in with you, George?" the woman said in mock disgust. "Don't let them sit out in the cold."

George grinned fuzzily. "To hell with them. I just stopped by for a minute. You wouldnt like them anyway."

"Why, of course I'd like them, if they're your friends. Go on and call them."

"No. You wouldnt like them. Let the bastards sit. I just wanted to talk to you, Sandy." George looked vaguely around the gayness of the kitchen with its red and white checkered motif. "Jesus, I love this place. We done a good job on it, Sandy, you know it? I used to think about it a lot. I still do."

But the woman was already at the kitchen door and she did not hear. "Hey out there!" she called. "Come on in and have a drink."

There was a murmur of words from the car she could not understand and she opened the screen door and went outside to the car in the steaming cold winter night. A man and woman were in the front seat, the man behind the wheel. Another woman was in the back seat by herself. She was smoothing her skirt.

Sandy put her head up to the car window. "George is drunk," she said. "Why dont you go on home and leave him here and let me take care of him?"

"No," the man said.

"He's been here before."

"No," the man said sharply. "He's with us."

Sandy put her hand on the door handle. "He shouldnt be drinking," she said. "In his condition."

The man laughed. "Liquor never bothers me," he said.

"Poor George. I feel so sorry for him I could cry."

"No, you couldnt," the man said contemptuously. "I know you. Besides, it aint your sympathy he wants." He thumped the thigh of his left leg with his fist. It made a sound like a gloved fist striking a heavy bag. "I pawned one myself," he said.

September, 1951

Sandy moved as if he had struck her. She stepped back, putting her hand to her mouth, then turned back toward the house.

George was standing in the door. "Tom's an old buddy of mine," he grinned. "He was in the hospital with me for ten months out in Utah." He opened the screen.

Sandy stepped inside with slumped shoulders. "Why didnt you tell me? I said something terrible. Please tell him to come in, George, he wont come now unless you tell him."

"No. Let them sit. We got a couple of pigs from Greencastle with us." He grinned down at her belligerently through the dark circles and loose lips of an extended bat.

"Ask them all in, for a drink. I'm no Carrie Nation, George. Tell them to come in. Please, George. Tell them."

"All right. By god I will. I wasnt going to, but I will. I just wanted to see you, Sandy."

"Why dont you stay here tonight, George?" Sandy said. "Let them go on and I'll put you to bed."

George searched her face incredulously. "You really want me to stay?"

"Yes. You need to sober up, George."

"Oh." George laughed suddenly. "Liquor never bothers me. No sir by god. I aint runnin out on Tom. Tom's my buddy." He stepped back to the door. "Hey, you bastards!" he bellered. "You comin in here an have a drink? or I got to come out and drag you in?" Sandy stood behind him, watching him the big bulk of shoulder, the hair growing softly on the back of his neck. There was a laugh from the car and the door slammed. The tall curly-haired Tom came in, swinging his left side in a peculiar rhythm. After him came the two women, one tall and blonde, the other short and dark. They both smiled shyly as they entered. They both were young.

"Oh," said the short one. "This is pretty."

"Its awful pretty," the blonde one said, looking around.

"You goddam right its pretty," George said belligerently. "And its built for utility. Look at them cupboards."

George introduced the girls by their first names, like a barker in a sideshow naming the attractions. "An this heres Tom Hornney," he said, "and when I say Hornney, I mean Hornney." George laughed and Tom grinned and the two girls tittered nervously.

"I want you all to meet Miss Sandy Thomas," George said, as if daring them.

"Sure," Tom said. "I know all about you. I use to read your letters out in Utah."

George looked at Sandy sheepishly. "A man gets so he cant believe it himself. He gets so he's got to show it to somebody. Thats the way it is in the army."

Sandy smiled at him stiffly, her eyes seeming not to see. "How do you want your drinks? Soda or Coke?"

"They want Coke with theirs," Tom pointed to the girls. "They dont know how to drink."

"This is really a beautiful place," the blonde one said.

"Oh my yes," the short one said. "I wish I ever had a place like this here." Sandy looked up from the drinks and smiled, warmly. "Thank you."

"I really love your place," the blonde one said. "Where did you get those funny spotted glasses? I seen some like them in a Woolworth's once."

George, laughing over something with Tom, turned to the blonde one. "Shut up, for god sake. You talk too much. You're supposed to be seen."

"Or felt," Tom said.

"I was only being polite," the blonde one said.

"Well dont," George said. "You dont know how."

"Well," said the blonde one. "I like that."

"Those are antiques, dear," Sandy said to her. "I bought them off an old woman down in the country. Woolworth has reproductions of them now."

"You mean them are *genuine* antiques?" the short one said.

Sandy nodded, handing around the drinks.

"For god sake, shut up," George said. "Them's genuine antiques and they cost ten bucks apiece, so shut up. Talk about something interesting."

The short one made a little face at George. She turned to Sandy and whispered delicately.

"Surely," Sandy said. "I'll show you."

"See what I mean?" Tom laughed. "I said they couldnt hold their liquor."

Sandy led the girls out of the kitchen. From the next room their voices came back, exclaiming delicately over the furnishings.

"How long were you in the army?" Sandy asked when they came back.

"Five years," Tom said, grinning and shaking his curly head. "My first wife left me three months after I got drafted."

"Oh?" Sandy said.

"Yeah. I guess she couldnt take the idea of not getting any for so long. It looked like a long war."

"War is hard on the women too," Sandy said.

"Sure," Tom said. "I dont see how they stand it. I'm glad I was a man in this war."

"Take it easy," George growled.

Tom grinned at him and turned back to Sandy. "I been married four times in five years. My last wife left me day before yesterday. She told me she was leaving and I said, Okay, baby. Thats fine. Only remember there wont be nobody here when you come back. If I wanted, I could call her up right now and tell her and she'd start back tonight."

"Why dont you?" Sandy said. "Ive got a phone."

Tom laughed. "What the hell. I'm doin all right. Come here, baby," he said to the blonde one, and patted his right leg. She came over, smiling, on his left side and started to sit on his lap.

"No," Tom said. "Go around to the other side. You cant sit on that one."

The blonde one obeyed and walked around his chair. She sat down smiling on his right thigh and Tom put his arm clear around her waist. "I'm doin all right, baby, aint I? Who wants to get married?"

George was watching him, and now he laughed. "I been married myself," he said, not looking at Sandy.

"Sure," Tom grinned. "Dont tell me. I was out in Utah when you got the rings back, remember? Ha!" he turned his liquorbright eyes on Sandy. "It was just like Robert Taylor in the movies. He took them out in the snow and threw them away with a curse. Went right out the ward door and into the snowing night.

"One ring, engagement, platinum, two carat diamond," Tom said, as if giving the nomenclature of a new weapon. "One ring, wedding, platinum, diamond circlet.—I told him he should of hocked them."

"No," Sandy said. "He should have kept them, then he could have used them over and over, every other night."

"I'll say," Tom said. "I'll never forget the first time me and George went on pass in Salt Lake City. He sure could of used them then."

"Aint you drinkin, Sandy?" George said.

"You know I dont drink."

"You used to. Some."

"That was only on special occasions," Sandy said, looking at him. "That was a long time ago. I've quit that now," she said.

George looked away, at Tom, who had his hand up under the blonde one's armpit, snuggled in. "Now this heres a very fine thing," Tom said, nodding at her. "She's not persnickity like the broads in Salt Lake."

"I didnt really like it then," Sandy said.

"I know," George said.

"George picked him up a gal in a bar in Salt Lake that first night," Tom said. "She looked a lot like you, honey," he said to the blonde one. The blonde one tittered and put her hand beneath his ear.

"This gal," Tom continued, "she thought George was wonderful; he was wearing his ribbons. She asked him all about the limp and how he got wounded. She thought he was the nuts till she found out what it was made him limp." Tom paused to laugh.

"Then she got dressed and took off; we seen her later with a marine." He looked at George and they both laughed. George went around the table and sat down beside the short one.

"You ought to have a drink with us, Sandy," George said. "You're the host."

"I dont feel much like being formal," Sandy said.

Tom laughed. "Me neither."

"Do you want something to eat?" Sandy asked him. "I might eat something."

"Sure," Tom said. "I'll eat anything. I'm an old eater from way back. I really eat it. You got any cheese and crackers?"

Sandy went to one of the cupboards. "You fix another drink, George."

"That's it," Tom said. "Eat and drink. There's only one thing can turn my stommick," he said to the blonde one. "You know whats the only thing can turn my stommick?"

"Yes," said the blonde one apprehensively, glancing at Sandy. "I know."

"I'll tell you the only thing can turn my stommick."

"Now, honey," the blonde one said.

George turned around from the bottles on the countertop, pausing dramatically like an orator.

"Same thing that can turn my stommick."

He and Tom laughed uproariously, and he passed the drinks and sat down. The blonde one and the short one tittered and glanced nervously at Sandy.

Tom thumped George's right leg with his fist and the sound it made was solid, heavy, the sound his own had made out in the car.

"You goddam old cripple, you."

"Thats all right," George said. "You cant run so goddam fast yourself."

"The hell I cant." Tom reached for his drink and misjudged it, spilling some on the tablecloth and on the blonde girl's skirt.

"Now see what you did?" she said. "Damn it."

Tom laughed. "Take it easy, baby. If you never get nothing worse than whiskey spilled on your skirt, you'll be all right. Whiskey'll wash out."

George watched dully as the spot spread on the red and white checked tablecloth, then he lurched to his feet toward the sink where the dishrag always was.

Sandy pushed him back into his chair. "Its all right, George. I'll change it tomorrow."

George breathed heavily. "Watch yourself, you," he said to Tom. "Goddam you, be careful."

"What the hell. I dint do it on purpose."

"Thats all right, just watch yourself."

"Okay, Sergeant," Tom said. "Okay, halfchick."

George laughed suddenly, munching a slab of cheese between two crackers, spraying crumbs. "Dont call me none of your family names."

"We really use to have some times," he said to Sandy. "You know what this crazy bastard use to do? After we got our leather, we use to stand out in the corridor and watch the guys with a leg off going down the hall on crutches. Tom would look at them and say to me, Pore feller. He's lost a leg. And I'd say, Why thats turrible, aint it?"

Sandy was looking at him, watching him, her sandwich untouched in her hand. Under her gaze George's eyebrows suddenly went up, bent in the middle.

"We use to go to town," he said, grinning at her. "We really had some times. You ought to seen their faces when we'd go up to the room from the bar. You ought to see them when we'd take our pants off." He laughed viciously. "One broad even fainted on me. They didnt like it." His gaze wavered, then fell to his drink. "I guess you cant blame them though."

"Why?" Sandy said. "Why did you do it, George?"

"Hell," he said, looking up. "Why? Don't you know why?"

Sandy shook her head slowly, her eyes unmoving on his face. "No," she said. I dont know why. I guess I never will know why," she said.

Tom was pinching the blonde one's bottom. "That tickles mine," he said. "You know what tickles mine?"

"No," she said, "what?"

Tom whispered in her ear and she giggled and slapped him lightly.

"No," George said. "I guess you wont. You aint never been in the army, have you?"

"No," Sandy said. "I havent."

"You ought to try it," George said. "Fix us one more drink and we'll be goin."

"All right, George. But I wish you'd stay."

George spread his hands and looked down at himself. "Who?" he said. "Me?"

"Yes," Sandy said. "You really do need to sober up."

"Oh," George said. "Sober up. Liquor never bothers me. Listen, Sandy. I wanted to talk to you, Sandy."

Under the red and white checked tablecloth George put his hand on Sandy's bare knee below her skirt. His hand cupped it awkwardly, but softly, very softly.

"I'll get your drink," Sandy said, pushing back her chair. George watched her get up and go to the countertop where the bottles were.

"Come here, you," George said to the short dark one. He jerked her toward him so roughly her head snapped back. He kissed her heavily, his left hand behind her head holding her neck rigid, his right hand on her upper arm, stroking heavily, pinching slightly.

Sandy set the drink in front of him. "Here's your drink you wanted, George," she said, still holding the tabled glass. "George, here's your drink."

"Okay," George said. "Drink up, you all, and lets get out of this."

The short one was rubbing her neck with her hand, her face twisted breath-lessly. She smiled apologetically at Sandy. "You got a wonderful home here, Miss Thomas," she said.

George lurched to his feet. "All right. All right. Outside." He shooed them out the door, Tom grinning, his hand hidden under the blonde one's arm. Then he stood in the doorway looking back.

"Well, so long. And thanks for the liquor."

"All right, George. Why dont you stop drinking, George?"

"Why?" George said. "You ask me why."

"I hate to see you ruin yourself."

George laughed. "Well now thanks. That sure is nice of you, Sandy girl. But liquor never bothers me." He looked around the gayness of the kitchen. "Listen. I'm sorry about the tablecloth. Sorry. I shouldnt of done it, I guess. I shouldnt of come here with them."

"No, George. You shouldnt."

"You know what I love about you, Sandy girl? You're always so goddam stinking right."

"I just do what I have to," Sandy said.

"Sandy," George said. "You dont know what it was like, Sandy."

"No," she said. "I guess I dont."

"You goddam right you dont. And you never will. You'll never be . . ."

"I cant help the way I'm made."

"Yes? Well I cant neither. The only thing for us to do is turn it over to the United Nations. Its their job, let them figure it out."

Tom Hornney came back to the door. "Come on, for Christ sake. Are you comin or aint you?"

"Yes goddam it I'm comin. I'm comin and I'm goin." George limped swingingly over to the countertop and grabbed a bottle.

Tom stepped inside the door. "Listen, lady," he said. "What the hells a leg? The thing a man wants you dames will never give him. We're just on a little vacation now. I got a trucking business in Terre Haute. Had it before the war. There's good money in long-distance hauling, and me and George is goin to get our share. We got six trucks and three more spotted, and I know this racket, see? I know how to get the contracks, all the ways. An I got the pull. And me and George is full-time partners. What the hells a leg?"

George set down the bottle and came back, his right leg hitting the floor heavy and without resilience. "Tom and me is buddies, and right or wrong what we do we do together."

"I think thats fine, George," she said.

"Yeah? Well then, its all all right then, aint it?"

"Listen, lady," Tom said. "Someday he'll build another house'll make this place look sick, see? To hell with the respectability if you got the money. So what the hells a leg?"

"Shut up," George said. "Lets go. Shut up. Shut up, or I'll mash you down."

"Yeah?" Tom grinned. "I'll take your leg off and beat you to death with it, Mack."

George threw back his head, laughing. "Fall in, you bum. Lets go."

"George," Sandy said. She went to the countertop and came back with a nearly full bottle. "Take it with you."

"Not me. I got mine in the car. And I got the money to buy more. Whiskey never bothers me. Fall in, Tom, goddam you."

Tom slapped him on the back. "Right," he said. And he started to sing.

They went out of the house into the steaming chill of February night. They went arm in arm and limping. And they were singing.

> Si-n-n-g glorious, glorious,
> One keg of beer for the four of us,
> Glory be to God there's no more of us,
> 'Cause . . ."

Their voices faded and died as the motor started. Tom honked the horn once, derisively.

Sandy Thomas stood in the door, watching the headlights move away, feeling the need inside, holding the bottle in her hand, moisture overflowing her eyes unnoticed, looking backward into a past the world had not seen fit to let alone. Tomorrow she would change the tablecloth, the red and white checkered tablecloth.

JAMES A. MICHENER

◀──────────────────────────────────────▶

The Precious Drop

"Even so distinguished a scholar as Sir Peter Buck was not allowed to become an American citizen. He could not prove that he had 51 per cent white blood."

IN THE Kingdom of Tonga, on the island of Tongatabu, not far from the capital of Nukualofa, in the village of Kolovai live the sacred bats. On trees lining the public malae these flying foxes sleep upside down all day. No one may touch them, for they represent the spirits of departed souls.

At dusk the bats leave the village of Kolovai and wing low across the entire island, eating fruit and night insects. If you are abroad in Tonga you may hear a swish about your ears, a chirping sound like a small dog barking, and then silence as the bats fly back to their village.

White people have never believed that the flying foxes were sacred, and it has always been a popular sport for men to station themselves some miles from Kolovai and shoot the animals as they flew out of the dusk. Natives from the bush liked the musk-flavored foxes, and it was great fun to watch brown savages dig about the grass for bats which the white men had shot.

In the middle years of the last century, Ross Lewin, one of the worst pirates ever to sail the Pacific, was stormbound in Tonga. He took his riotous crew inland to shoot the sacred flying foxes, and that night the animals came over in great number. A score of natives joined the murderous pirates to collect free meat for their feasts.

The people of Kolovai did not sanction such slaughter of their gods, and they sent a deputation to Lewin, asking him to stop shooting the bats. One of these envoys was Tuni, a man of thirty, and trailing some distance behind him was his wife Talota. When the villagers came to where Lewin was shooting the foxes, there was a brief argument; then the pirates lowered their guns and massacred the messengers.

At this outrage Talota became demented and started to claw at the murderers. One of the gang raised his gun to shoot her, but Ross Lewin, seeing that she was a handsome brown wench, ordered two of his men to grab her. They dragged her into the bush where the dead bats had fallen, and Lewin ravished her three times.

December, 1951

That was the beginning of the white blood that moved in the descendants of Talota, who lived by the malae in Kolovai. In time she forgot Tuni and married again, a good man named Niufa. But her great pride was in the daughter who sprang from that terrible night in the bush.

Lucy, as the girl was named by the missionaries, was fair and happy. She was a delightful baby, much spoiled by the missionary's wife, who had no children of her own. Lucy learned to read, to do figures, and to sew. It was a great joy to both Talota and her husband Niufa to watch Lucy adopt European ways.

At fifteen, Lucy was a charming girl and the missionaries wept when they gave her their Bible and said good-by on the wharf at Nukualofa. They left a letter at the mission instructing their successors that "Lucy, the Christian daughter of Talota, is to be taught such subjects as she can absorb."

The new missionary was a man of thirty-eight, from Bristol. He had three children, all girls, and all younger than Lucy. He taught Lucy mathematics and history, for which she served as nursemaid to his children.

The mission lay east of the malae and each day, as Lucy walked barefoot to work along the dusty roads, she studied the sleeping bats that hung upside down in great profusion. It became apparent to her that if Jesus Christ were actually the Son of God there was little need of bat gods, too. This thought challenged her, for she had heard from gossips that her skin was fair because her father had gone out one night to protest against the killing of these tribal gods.

At the mission Lucy worked faithfully and did her best to avoid the missionary's wife, who was always complaining. In the evening, when Lucy walked home, scuffing her feet in the dust, she was often joined at the halfway mark by a good-looking Tonga boy, who twice prevailed upon her to spend most of the night in the bush beside the road.

This infuriated her mother, old Talota, who took her aside one day and said, "It's good for other girls to carry on in the bush, but not you. Your blood is white!"

"But the girls have a good time with the boys," Lucy protested.

"Forget that!" Talota commanded. "Work hard. Earn a pair of shoes. Become a European. And because you are very beautiful, some white man will marry you."

So Lucy usually said no when the Tonga boys tried to get her to sleep in the bush with them. And on the occasions when she did agree, she left early and hurried home as if nothing had happened. Then, on a most important day, she went in to Nukualofa and paid a Chinaman two shillings for a pair of old shoes, and she wore them along the streets of that town.

No white man accosted her, as she hoped might happen, but she noticed that when she stepped into the breeze her linen dress blew against her legs and the white men stopped talking for a moment. That night the missionary met her along the road. She was carrying her shoes and excused herself while she put them on, and when she straightened up his arms were about her and he professed his love for her. She had never thought much of Mr. Taylor. He was not a big man like the white men in Nukualofa, and he cried when he preached. He cried that night, too, when Lucy showed him a kind of nest deep in the bush. And Lucy was perplexed.

During the next months Mr. Taylor met Lucy whenever they could sneak away somewhere, and when she told her mother the old woman frowned and said, "That's no good. You didn't buy shoes to catch a missionary. But we wait and see what happens."

The happenings were dramatic. Mr. Taylor could not keep his hands off the golden girl and one night insisted that she stay right in his room, and, as he said, "Bother Mrs. Taylor." But Mrs. Taylor found out and next afternoon they found her dead from swallowing poison.

Mr. Taylor left his three daughters at the mission and ran away to Nukualofa. A white storekeeper gave him a horsewhipping and he disappeared on a little schooner headed for Australia.

In three months Lucy got a letter from him, and she left the island on a large white boat. Mr. Taylor met her in Sydney and married her, properly.

For eighteen years they worked a sugar plantation in Queensland. Some of the white women would associate with Lucy; some would not. She read many books, learned to sing English songs, and had four children. When Mr. Taylor died in the Solomons while trying to get labor for his sugar fields, three of Lucy's children decided to remain in Queensland and run the sugar plantation, which was now sizable. But Lucy took her youngest daughter back to Tonga and the village of Kolovai.

Lucy brought with her a thousand pounds and left behind a written deed relinquishing all interest in the plantation. Her three children kissed her good-by and she never heard of them again.

On Tonga, Lucy found her old mother still living, and the ancient one's greatest joy was in seeing Lucy's girl Rose playing in the sand as Lucy had done years before. "She's a white girl!" the old woman said again and again before she died.

But Rose, three-fourths white, was a disappointment to her mother. At fifteen she started to sleep in those very bushes where her mother had explored the ways of Tongan life, and at sixteen she took up with a half-caste trader who drank heavily and who sometimes deserted her for years on end. This Marjoram, as he was called, had a couple of wives across the world, but Rose finally grew tired of his coming and going; so she made him marry her, too. Then she moved everything she owned aboard the tramp schooner, *Bird of Passage*, and from then on she was his mate.

The little boat became famous in the islands. It weathered many a hurricane, made a profit on everything it handled, and could be engaged for any dirty business afloat. Marjoram and Rose ran slaves and, after that trade was ended, picked up one of the last cargoes of sandalwood ever to be gathered in the islands, and—it was rumored—shanghaied and murdered several beachcombers with odds and ends of property.

Rose and her man became a famous pair and would sometimes blow into Nukualofa and hire a hansom cab for the trip to Kolovai. They would beat the horse cruelly and be drunk and dusty when they arrived. There, beneath the trees where the sacred foxes still hung, Rose and Marjoram would tell Lucy of their experiences.

"Why don't you have children?" Lucy interrupted.

This question made Marjoram furious, for he knew that word had gone through Tonga that he could have no children. "I've got sixteen kids in Samoa. Why bother with more?" he asked.

"But why not children here in Tonga?" Lucy persisted.

Marjoram dragged Rose back into the carriage and beat the horse all the way into Nukualofa. That was when a strong young Tongan boy began to cuckold Marjoram. The captain suspected this and laid a trap for his wife. He anchored the schooner in the roads, let down the dinghy, and rowed ashore. Then he swam back and Rose met him with a fish spear.

"You damned fool!" she cried, poking his head under as he tried to clamber aboard. Finally she relented and made him swim back to the beach and get the dinghy.

But on the next trip the young Tongan came boldly aboard the *Bird of Passage* and said that, since Rose was pregnant, she must live ashore with him.

"What do you say?" Marjoram bellowed, grabbing at a reaving pin. The Tongan saw him coming and, with a quick side-step brought a bowl of fruit down on the captain's head.

Marjoram crashed to the deck and, as he lay stunned, he heard Rose whisper to the Tongan, "Well, if you're going to kill him, do it now."

So Marjoram drew his knees up and kicked with all his might at the Tongan boy. When the native fell backwards, Marjoram leaped upon him and stabbed him some forty times with the pin.

Then, with a board, he beat Rose for half an hour. "I'll kill you!" he screamed. "And I'll kill the bastard you're carrying."

It was a miracle the baby was ever born. A native midwife on Tutuila delivered the girl, who was quite dark. At first Marjoram was disposed to kill it at sea, but as the years went by he became accustomed to the child and introduced her everywhere as his daughter.

Now the three of them traded about the islands and in due course settled in Tongareva, where Marjoram traded for pearls. In time he became wealthy, when to his disgust he found that his daughter Camilla was spending her nights on a reef islet with a native boy. Marjoram whipped his girl and forbade her to see the boy again, but in those days the customs on Tongareva were so loose that any girl without a lover was almost an outcast.

So one night, after Marjoram had locked Camilla in her room, he heard a noise and found that she had opened the window and fled to the islet. Marjoram tried to follow them, but got lost. He returned home and hid behind the crotons in his garden. Then, as the lovers walked dreamily home toward morning, he leaped out and beat the boy's head in.

"Well," Rose said as she studied the body which had been dragged into the kitchen. "You've done it again."

Camilla started to cry, but her mother walloped her heavily on the side of the head. "We'll have to tell them this boy attacked us," Rose said wearily. She looked with great disgust at her husband.

The three Marjorams stuck together on the story about a burglar. It was pretty well understood on Tongareva that the captain had murdered the native boy but Marjoram passed as a white man there and his story was not attacked.

It was an odd case because, as soon as the captain was acquitted, his daughter Camilla took up with another native boy. That was enough for Marjoram. "We're all going back to Tonga," he said.

"It's about time," Rose agreed.

They sold their sacks of pearls and kept a dozen of the biggest as a nest egg. They returned to Tonga in style and opened a store in the village of Kolovai, where Marjoram outraged the natives by being the first inhabitant of that village to shoot a sacred fox.

"They're a damned nuisance," he declared, and this sacrilege was believed to be the cause of his misfortunes, for his wife Rose died, his daughter Camilla took up with a native boy and disappeared into the bush, and his last bag of pearls was stolen from him.

He heard a rumor that his own daughter had engineered the steal, having told her native lover where the jewels were kept. Marjoram, therefore, organized a vendetta party and would have committed another murder had not his daughter met him halfway to the bush village and boxed his ears.

"Go on home!" she said. "Sail your boat away from here. You're not my father."

Marjoram was so humiliated that he could not appear in public for some time. When he did, he discovered that all Tonga knew he had been unable to have children, so he got into his schooner and sailed beyond the reef. Years later it was reported that he was trading on the north coast of New Guinea.

His daughter Camilla was a bad sort. She lived in the bush like a native and did many things that shamed both the Tongans and the whites. She sold her pearls one by one and spent some time in jail for bamboozling a Chinaman out of three hundred pounds.

Suddenly she astonished everyone by turning violent Christian. She sang uproariously in church, dug up all the money she had stolen from the Chinaman and turned it in to help build a new church. Then she married a half-caste trader and surprised everyone again by having a daughter.

No one could say how much white blood this daughter Rachel had, but she turned into one of those crystalline beauties who, from time to time, have enhanced the islands. Robert Louis Stevenson knew her as a fair baby. Rupert Brooke stared breathlessly at her when at twenty, she sang in the choir, and the

French poet Leguois, on his way to Tahiti, stayed many months on Tonga, actually worshiping her.

Rachel's mother was no fool. Camilla knew she had a prize in this girl. She reared Rachel as a devout Christian, kept her away from native boys, and coached her constantly on how to win a white husband. Leguois seemed a likely prospect, but he had a wife in Paris, and that was that.

"You cannot marry him," Camilla explained to her daughter, "so tell him to go away."

But Leguois would not go. On this remote island he had met a princess, and his poet's heart simply refused to obey any other command. This Rachel MacDonald was about as close to a goddess as we ever see on earth. She was tall, slender, wide-eyed, large-lipped. She moved liquidly and wore her dark hair long. She wore silky white dresses imported from Sydney, and sometimes she plaited her hair into two strands, fastening each with a bow of satin that Leguois had bought from a passing ship. She was beautiful, and I can still hear my mother saying, "A girl as pretty as that carries her own punishment."

For the present, her punishment seemed easy to bear. Leguois would not let her go anywhere without following her. He was an odd man, this Frenchman. He was a shade shorter than Rachel, but there was something about him that we had not seen on Tonga before. He had no shell around him, as if he were God in man, standing free. He was in love with an island girl, and he did not care who knew. When he looked at Rachel, either in church or at the picnics which were so common in those days, he did not mask his feelings. He had stumbled upon perfection, and he would stay within its shadow as long as he should live. He wrote letters to Tahiti, others to Paris, and then he set up a small trading outfit in the village of Kolovai.

There was eager discussion as to what Rachel should do. It flattered her to have so distinguished a man insane for her, but Camilla kept telling her that any man in Nukualofa—white men, too—would consider marrying her, if they could get her in no other way.

She walked the island very simply in those days, and we all knew she was trying to make up her mind what to do. She was not helped by her mother, who was a widow now, and who had taken to drink. Camilla sang vehemently in church each Sunday and Wednesday, but was drunk most of the other days. She shocked the community by announcing that Rachel was going to become a nun, which was preposterous because Camilla was a Methodist. Then she wept in the streets of Nukualofa, bawling out to everyone that her daughter was going to a hospital in Australia to become a nursing sister. Things became ridiculous when she started the rumor Leguois had leprosy. The medical authorities insisted on an examination and the young doctor from Fiji looked up with terror, Leguois *had* leprosy!

They weren't sure at first—the young doctor kept everything hushed up and cabled for an older man to come down from one of the northern islands—but Leguois was certain, and he made plans to close his shop.

But as he started the doleful job of casting up his debts, he heard a step behind him, and it was Rachel. I was only a child that day, but I can remember how she looked as she crossed the malae, where the bats were sleeping. She wore a flowing white dress, and the golden color of her skin reflected the dusty sunlight of our village square. Her hair was not braided. It was very long and straight and its blackness matched her eyes, which were filled with tears.

She entered Leguois' shop and said, "Will you have to go away?"

He could not look at her, but kept adding columns of figures. "I've known for some time," he said. "I came here to die." Then a shiver possessed him and he cried, "My God! If I were clean do you suppose that I would have kept my distance, staring at you?"

"Your wife?" Rachel asked.

Leguois leaped up. "What of her? How could she have stopped us?" Violently he caught Rachel by the shoulders and gave her his first kiss. She trembled for a moment and then flung her arms about him.

They hurried from the shop and rented a horse cab. They rode desperately across the island to where the blowholes are, and they stood for some time watching the sea force its way into the jagged caverns cut through rock until great pressure had been built. Then, with a mournful whoooosh, the water exploded upward through small holes in the rock and spouted many feet into the air, falling across the land like silvery rain.

"I have never loved anyone but you," Rachel said.

The lovers hid along this shore for five days, and the passion they must have known still lives in Leguois' *Lyrics from Makongai.*

In the meantime, Camilla was beside herself. She ranted about the island like a madwoman. "My only daughter has run off with a leper. We'll have to catch them and shoot them both for the good of the island." She carried on so that people began to become panic-stricken, and the young doctor who had let Leguois out of his hands after a prediction of leprosy was roundly accused.

Then Leguois and his perfect captive rode slowly into Nukualofa and he gave himself up. I can see them yet. The carriage was not a new one. A spring sagged so that the driver's side drooped toward the dusty road. The horse was an old one, too, but he moved fast enough that day. As the dreadful carriage moved slowly into town, people drew back. Here was the leper! Here was the leper and his lady!

At the hospital Leguois got out and tied his horse as carefully as if he were stopping by for tea. Then he stepped around to the other side and handed Rachel MacDonald down into the dusty road. We boys hung back and watched the lepers from a distance, quivering with horror. They walked slowly—as I recall the picture now, never to be faded, I think they walked with dignity—in to see the doctors.

Leguois was sent immediately to the leprosarium at Makongai, in Fiji. He was there for many hateful years and poured his heart out in the *Lyrics* which has become known across the world. The more terror he saw, the more pure his song became.

These were terrible years for Rachel. At first she was an outcast, for we all expected her to develop leprosy. Then, when it seemed safe that she would not, her son was born, and her religious mother used to stop any visitors to Tonga and in drunken accents tell them of the great shames that had fallen upon her family.

Rachel did not hear from Leguois for more than three years, although she wrote to him each week. Then it developed that the postmen in Tonga had been afraid of the leprous letters from Fiji and had burned them one by one as they arrived. I remember when this news reached our home. My mother cried and said that Rachel MacDonald was one of God's bright spirits and it was cruel that such things should happen to her. That was the beginning of the change in our attitude.

Her son Philip was a trial to the village of Kolovai. Perhaps because he knew his father was a leper, or because he knew he had no proper church-got father, he developed into a nasty child. He stole. He lied to everyone. And when he got old enough he took up with a native girl, a prostitute if we ever had one on Tonga, and ended up by trying to rape a white girl. He was sentenced to jail and, when he got out, settled in the bush with an absolute savage. Philip and this woman lived back of Kolovai, where he used to wait at night for the sacred flying foxes. He shot them and ate them, which is about as low as a white man can get, on Tonga.

Then one day a ship put into Nukualofa from Fiji and a thin, straight Frenchman came slowly down the gangplank. It was Leguois, and we all stood back.

But the news of his arrival sped about the island and soon there was a cloud of dust along the Kolovai road as Rachel MacDonald whipped her horse onto the quay. She burst through the hesitant crowds and threw her arms about the man she had never ceased to love. When he looked up at her—he seemed much shorter now—tears fell from his eyes and we had to look away.

He opened his old store in Kolovai and once a year he and Rachel would hire a horse and go over to the blowholes and watch the mighty ocean surge through the channels and explode majestically in the air. The violence of this sight pleased them, and when they returned he was not seen about the shop for some days. He was writing his poems.

We became accustomed to hearing Leguois referred to as a great poet. We did not truly understand his verse, because we like poetry that you can sing; but we did collect articles about him. He was compared with Gauguin, who, as you probably know, was a painter who visited Tahiti.

We often wondered why Leguois and Rachel did not get married, and my mother made so bold as to ask the minister. He said, "The man's wife is living. In Paris. She has refused him a divorce. She heard of his leprosy and said that it was her duty to stand by him. She did so. In Paris. Living on his income."

When word reached us of this woman's death—we were astonished that she was eighteen years older than Leguois—the cable man took it out to Kolovai himself, and that very night Rachel and the Frenchman were married by a civil official in Nukualofa. They were a strange couple, for he got shorter all the time and Rachel grew more stately. She was now one of those handsome Tongan women that journalists write about when they see our island, and she had the quiet beauty that seems to increase year after year.

She asked Leguois if later on they might get married by a minister, but he said no. He had nothing against the churches of Tonga, but churches elsewhere had done him grave wrong, and he preferred no contact with them. But two weeks later he went to Rachel's church and the minister married them properly.

By this time we all liked Leguois. We liked seeing a man who felt things more passionately than we did, and my mother said it was a shame a couple like that could have no more children.

Surely, the one they had was no consolation. Leguois sent messages into the bush, inviting the boy to come out and live with him. No answer. So Leguois hired a horse and went into the bush himself. He found Philip living in a grass lean-to. His teeth were falling out and he had made no effort to repair them. His wife was a slattern. They lived on taro and fish. Their little girl was being raised as a savage.

Leguois lowered his head in shame. "Philip," he begged, "can I not at least take the little girl?"

"Why not?" The beachcomber shrugged.

And that was how Taliesa came to live at the store in the village of Kolovai. I wouldn't say she was a beautiful girl. Not like her grandmother Rachel. But few women equal Rachel. Let's say that Taliesa was very attractive, could speak three languages, had a lively disposition, and was beloved by everyone who knew her.

Leguois never said much about her, but you could see that he believed his genius had been reborn in her capacity for music. That's the way things were when the Americans landed.

Well, to use a phrase I learned from them, they fell like a ton of bricks. They took her up in an airplane and down in a submarine. Under the bat trees in the malae they tried to kiss her, and in time a major from Cleveland, Ohio, succeeded.

His name was Roberts, Major Bob Roberts. He was a blond young man, very intense. He used to sit with Leguois in the store and talk about poetry. He said that he had read Leguois' *Lyrics* at the University of Chicago and that the professor there had thought them the best poetry yet to have been written on the South Seas. He produced some of his own attempts—with great embarrassment —but Leguois said they hadn't quite caught that mixture of fire and control that was poetry. Roberts said that was his own judgment, but he'd be hanged if he could figure out just how to get that mixture.

This American was no fool. He knew that if he wanted to pre-empt Taliesa he'd have to win Rachel's approval, too, so he used to show up at her house almost every day. He went into raptures over sandwiches she made: bread sliced very thin, a smear of Bovril, and some greens. He said they were the best he'd ever eaten and in payment smuggled canned food from the storehouse into Rachel's kitchen.

On Sunday night she and Taliesa would prepare dinner for all of us. The colonel would appear and Padre King, who ate like a horse. Rachel was the perfect hostess and in tribute to her wonderful qualities even the most austere Englishman forgot she had color and ate her food.

It was obvious to all of us that pretty soon Major Roberts would have to face up to that question that ultimately confronted every white man in the South Seas: *How much, in the conscience of God, do I care for this island girl?* And it was obvious that in Robert's case he cared a great deal.

I used to watch them in the evening. He would pull his jeep up to the store and hand Taliesa into it as if she were a queen. And when they got home at night she kissed him as if he were a king. Three nights she didn't get home at all, but on Tonga we don't gossip much about such things. Not when two people are in love, like Bob Roberts and Taliesa Leguois.

That name's what started the trouble. Bob wrote to his parents in Cleveland and said he was going to marry the daughter of a French poet and a white Tongan woman. His folks scurried to the public library and found that Leguois was known all over the world. In fact, the Americans thought more of him than we did right here in his home village.

So Bob applied formally to the colonel for permission to marry, and it was granted. The wedding was set for April, our loveliest autumn month, and Padre King went through the business of filling in the routine Army papers. But as a precaution—all ministers are conservatives, I guess—he came to me and asked me to witness the papers as a friend of the bride's family.

I have often reviewed what happened next and, although I acknowledge a personal responsibility, I cannot believe that had I acted otherwise the final results would have been different. At least I pray God that what I did shall not be held against me. But I said, "There's a mistake here, Padre."

"Where?" he asked, stuffing a sandwich in his plump mouth.

"This line. Rachel and Leguois are not the parents."

"They aren't?" he blustered.

"They're the grandparents."

"Oh, dear," he said, scratching out the names. "I'll have to type this whole form again." He poised his pen and asked, "Father?"

"Philip Leguois," I said. The pen scratched laboriously.

"Mother?" the chaplain asked.

That stumped me. I wasn't sure what Taliesa's mother was called. I hadn't seen her out of the bush for years.

"I think she's called . . . She's a bushwoman," I said.

As if in that moment he could foresee the future, Padre King grew very pale. With nervous fingers he put his pen away. He said hoarsely, "A bush girl?"

"Yes," I fumbled. "This boy Philip . . ."

Padre King rose in great agitation and looked out my door to the malae, where the foxes were preparing to leave the tall trees. He swallowed hard and said, "We must keep this quiet. A terrible thing has happened."

"What?" I asked.

"Marriage with half-castes . . . in the United States Army . . ."

"Half-castes!" I cried. "You've seen Leguois. You've seen his wife."

"My friend," the chaplain said in horrified tones. "The girl is more than half Polynesian. She could never become a citizen."

"Rubbish," I said weakly.

"And I am forbidden to marry an American man to such a girl."

"But this girl . . ."

"Is forbidden," the chaplain said solemnly.

I fell back into my chair and licked my lips. Of course, Taliesa wasn't half white, but there was never a finer girl on Tonga. I'd go as far as to say—all things considered—that she was as fine a girl as her grandmother. "By God!" I cried. "This is ridiculous!"

"My friend," the chaplain said quietly, "we dare not bluster. We're involved in what might become a tragedy. Carefully, now. Has Major Roberts met the girl's parents?"

"Nobody has. Not for years."

The chaplain buried his face in his hands. Then he astounded me by saying, "Will you forgive me if I pray?" He knelt beside his chair and when he rose he said, "We must do nothing until I can inform Roberts properly." Then he corrected himself. "You must go to the bush and find if this Leguois fils is still living."

I did not find Philip Leguois. The natives told me that he had moved on. I returned to Kotovai, frightened of what Roberts might do when he discovered the facts about Taliesa, and I was disposed to go at once and tell him of the impasse that had been reached. But Padre King would not hear of it, for we were to have a picnic that day, and he said, "We must not dynamite his trip to the Haamonga."

"You think we are dealing with dynamite?"

"Worse," he said. "We're dealing with love."

No one knows when this Haamonga was built. Ages ago, some powerful race inhabited Tonga and built a mighty altar in a corner of the island, two giant pillars of rock with another lying across the top. The Americans liked to take their girls there for picnics, and on this day the colonel outdid himself. It's in honor of Bob and Taliesa," he announced as he opened the festivities.

All afternoon, Chaplain King and I looked at one another with dismay. While the meats were being barbecued he showed me official dispatches from Nouméa forbidding United States citizens to marry Polynesians.

"But they aren't Orientals!" I whispered harshly.

"To Congress they are," he replied pathetically. "Did you find Leguois?"

"No trace of him," I whispered. "Gone bush completely."

Padre King shook his head sorrowfully and looked with much compassion to where young Roberts, happy and red-cheeked, stood with Taliesa, as bright a girl that day as I have known. Rachel sat with them, tall and gracious, and Leguois stood by the barbecue talking with the colonel.

Then suddenly Rachel's face turned ashen and she half fell toward the fire. The colonel leaped forward and caught her. She put her hand to her face and cried something in Tongan. At this Leguois looked up and trembled. "No!" he commanded. "No!"

But no one could stop what had to happen. Down the road came a worn-out horse hauling a broken carriage. In it sat a cruelly thin white man. He had no teeth, no luster in his eyes, no cleanliness about him. He wore a torn shirt, dirty white ducks and a rope belt. It was Philip Leguois.

Beside him sat his bushwoman, grotesquely fat and in a purple shift. Her hair was not combed, but she wore a flower, wilted and forlorn. I have never seen a carriage that looked more like a messenger of death.

Only four of us knew who this couple were, Rachel and Leguois, Padre King and I. The padre acted first. He leaped into the road and said sternly, "Go back!"

Have you ever seen a carriage and a horse so old that they had not the energy to stop? They were in motion and they must come on, bearing Philip Leguois and his grotesque bushwoman.

"Somebody sent for us," Leguois said dully.

"You are not wanted," King cried, his hand motioning them back, his strong voice urgent. "Go back."

"Boys came into the bush," the man persisted, and his horse stumbled on.

The poet Leguois, now a white old man, stood in the road and waited until the battered horse had delivered its frightful passengers into the midst of the picnic. Then he said, "*Bon jour, Philippe.*"

The younger man's eyes brightened for a moment and he said, "Hello, Father."

Rachel controlled herself and went to the wagon. She extended her graceful hand and Philip took it in both of his. Tenderly he leaned forward and kissed her on the cheek. Bitter tears ran into his beard.

At this Taliesa uttered a small cry and ran to her grandfather. "*Est que c'est . . .*" she began.

"*Oui. Il est ton père.*"

Without hesitation she went to the carriage. Reaching in and grasping her parents by the hand, she said, "You are welcome to the celebration." Then, as they climbed awkwardly down in all their matted filth, she turned to Roberts and the colonel and, when they came to her side, said, "These are my parents. I have not seen them for twenty years."

I have never cared for the Americans. In many ways they spoiled Tonga, but on this afternoon they were men. The colonel bowed gravely and ordered food for the new guests. As they wolfed it, young Roberts stood with his hands tightly clenched. For a moment I was afraid that he might faint, but he gained tight-lipped control of himself and found a place for the bushwoman to sit.

That night Roberts drove Taliesa to the malae and you would have thought that nothing had happened. The hordes of flying foxes flew out for their night rendezvous, and the young lovers watched them disappear in the dusk. Impassionedly the American caught the honey-amber girl in his arms and cried, "I love you, Taliesa, more than I do my own life."

In the days that followed Chaplain King was ruthlessly patient in explaining the brutal facts to everyone. He was especially careful with Roberts and Taliesa, whom he met together. He kept repeating, "The Army will not let you marry. There is no way for Taliesa to become a citizen."

"Padre," Roberts said brokenly. "You know damned well what that scene at the picnic meant to me. I . . ." He fumbled for words and seemed about to break up. Then he took a deep breath and said haltingly, "The humiliation could not have been greater. And yet, in spite of it, I want to marry Taliesa."

"I did not deceive him," Taliesa said softly. "I didn't know."

"My dear child," the chaplain began.

"Will you marry us?" Roberts interrupted sternly.

"No," Padre King said in a quiet voice.

"Does your religion . . ."

"Son," Padre King said slowly, patiently, "this is not religion. It's the law. It's not God's law. It's just the law. And I'm bound by it."

"What kind of law?" Roberts shouted. "In Hawaii soldiers are marrying Japanese girls. Look at this clipping."

"They're citizens," King insisted patiently.

"They're the enemy!" Roberts screamed.

"Son," the chaplain said slowly and very patiently, "there are times when you face the solid wall . . ."

"Will you marry us?" Roberts shouted again.

"I can do nothing."

"You can listen, damn you. Tell him, Taliesa."

The island girl looked at the floor and said, "We are going to have a baby."

Padre King sat very still for a long time. Then he dropped his head onto his arm for a moment. Then he blew his nose and said, "I have a daughter your age. Her boy . . . The one she wanted to marry . . . He was . . ." His voice broke and after a moment he said, "I think we should pray." He kneeled and sent impassioned words to God, as if he were praying in his tent in Georgia. The burden of his beseeching was this: "Guide us to what is right. We cannot know the way."

But curiously the way for these lovers led to the very oceanside where Rachel and the poet Leguois had gone years before. Our pair of star-enchanted wanderers went to the blowholes in a jeep, but jeep or horse, this journey is always the same. They watched the ocean surge in through the bowels of the earth and explode like sprayed fury into the moolight. They talked of what they might do, of how Roberts might earn a living if he renounced his citizenship and came to live in Tonga. They spoke of the unborn child—he was certain that it would be a girl—and of how she, as least, would be more than half-white.

All the tragedy of island life welled up between the lovers that night, and finally, in mad despair, Major Robert Roberts of the United States Army threw himself from the cliff. The violent seas caught him up, tumbled him in their arms, and sucked him forever into the jagged holes where spume is born. To this day his bones have not been found. He is part of us, forever a part of our island.

Now it is peacetime, and his daughter has been born. They call her Margaret, a name he chose that night. She is Margaret, great-granddaughter of Rachel, daughter of Camilla, daughter of Rose, daughter of Lucy, daughter of Talota and the murdering pirate Ross Lewin. She is attractive, and one day soon she will be twenty years old, in the Kingdom of Tonga.

$\longleftrightarrow$

Irresistible Force

The house was a gigantic stucco imitation of a French château, bright orange and monstrously ugly. It stood on a five-acre grassy knoll off Hollywood Boulevard, fenced around by a low stucco wall, also orange.

A taxi came roaring up the driveway, where ragged brown weeds sprouted abundantly in the gravel. Out of the cab jumped a hatless man in a sleek vicuna topcoat. He thrust a bill at the taxi driver and ran up the steps to the colossal orange portico, his long black hair flying.

"They're not here yet?" he said sharply to a little man with a high starched collar and a furtive face, who stood by the brass-studded oak door holding a bunch of keys.

The little man stared at the newcomer. "Good heavens, Mr. Fuave, you really came! I didn't believe—"

"Where are they?"

"They'll be here, sir—but—good heavens—"

"Well, it's a hell of a note. They only have to come from Culver City, and I came three thousand miles from New York, and I'm here first. Well, let's get the story straight, now. He's rich, and retired, you said?"

"Why—why, yes, sir—electrical contractor. Used to be small-time but made a pile on defense orders—very substantial party—how was your plane trip, sir? Dear me, all the way from—"

"Who likes the house—him or his wife or both?"

"Well, mainly Mrs. Erickson, I think—"

"Good, the wife usually makes the decision. What's she like?"

"Why, she seems very nice—"

"Look, Brewsters, I want information! What's her weakness? Why does she want this preposterous barn?"

"Oh—well, sir—" the real-estate broker's face creased in a sly grin—"to be frank, they—I don't think they know what to do with their money. I heard them talk about taking a trip around the world, or even settling in Paris. But I think Mrs. Erickson's decided to go in for a big splash here, to impress her friends, and—"

"What luck! *Nouveau riche* idiots. We're in at last."

"It does look hopeful, sir, that's why I phoned you—"

August, 1952

"The hell with hope." Jeremy Fauve lit a cigarette, looking at the broker with piercing, wild black eyes. "Do you know how long I've been trying to unload this mausoleum? I was drunk when I bought it, and I was rolling in money, and I was generally crazy. Now I've got to sell it, d'you hear, Brewsters? I need money. I will stop at nothing to nail these people down. Any maneuver that occurs to you, I'm for, d'you hear? Maybe we can pick up a silver-mink coat somewhere—tell the wife it goes with the house. A little thing like that can sway a woman, especially such a stupid one—"

"Pardon me, Mr. Fauve. My experience shows it's bad policy to try to influence a buyer. Any kind of pressure usually backfires. We'd better just hope—"

"Who's talking about pressure?" Fauve said irritably. "Just let me handle them, Brewsters, will you? This is the first nibble I've had in two years and I'm going to land them. It's a matter of salesmanship, of which you haven't an atom in your make-up. None of you brokers have, you're all sluggish leeches—"

"It's not an easy property to move, sir—"

"Okay, okay. Is that them?"

A new yellow Cadillac convertible came up the boulevard and turned in under the massive orange gateway.

"Yes, sir—"

"There's three people—" Fauve peered at the car like a hawk.

"The daughter is with them. Only child. That's the catch, Mr. Fauve. She doesn't want to move from Culver City. Says she'll be lonesome without her friends."

Fauve glared at him. "Ye gods, what do you mean, withholding such a piece of crucial information? Do you want to ruin me?"

"Really, sir, you gave me no chance," Brewsters whispered. The Cadillac had stopped and the doors were opening.

"All right. Be quiet now. I'll take over."

Erickson was a stout man with strands of yellow hair over a broad pink scalp, and rimless glasses that shone in the sun. His wife, trotting up the steps beside him, looked as though she had once been very pretty; her features were still doll-like under little puffs of fat, and her figure, lumping and bulging in a tailored beige suit, seemed like the ruin of a good thing. The daughter trailed behind, and Fauve noted unhappily that she was dragging her feet. He came down to greet them, holding out his hand to the wife. "I'm Jeremy Fauve, Mrs. Erickson. Happen to be in Hollywood on a pre-production deal, and so I thought—"

"Why, Mr. Fauve! What a surprise! What an honor!" The woman smiled and stared with hungry eagerness. "Dear, this is Mr. Fauve, himself—you know, the famous producer—" She fluttered her small, pretty hands.

"How do? Heard all about you, of course, from Brewsters and Eve here," Erickson said, with a trace of Swedish accent. "Don't get to New York much so I haven't seen your plays but—"

"You've missed nothing. The New York theatre is just a twitching corpse, Mr. Erickson—"

"Oh, don't say that," cried the wife. "I'm a New York girl myself, believe it or not, and the theatre is my first love. I still miss it. I even once had hopes—" she giggled—"before I got kidnaped to California, that is—"

"Of being an actress? My dear, you certainly look the part," Fauve said with a winning warmth which rendered the sudden intimacy quite inoffensive. "And let me congratulate you on escaping such a wretched fate. Mr. Erickson did you an immense favor by kidnaping you." As he talked Fauve sized up the daughter with swift side glances. She stood dejectedly one step lower than her father, her hands in the pockets of a blue cloth jacket.

The wife simpered, and Erickson said with heavy jocularity, "That's telling her, Mr. Fauve. She still throws it up to me that she was the star of her school show."

Fauve laughed merrily. "Well, let's not gossip here on the steps. Come in."

Mostly I want Ginny here to see it," Erickson said. "Missus and I have been through it twice. This is my daughter Ginny, Mr. Fauve."

"Delighted."

The girl looked dully at him and said, "Hi."

"I just love it," said the wife. "You've furnished it in such exquisite taste, Mr. Fauve."

"I suppose Brewsters told you," Erickson said, "that I have quite a large place in Culver City. I'll have to dispose of that before we talk business on this one—"

"Of course, of course."

Inside, the house was dim, cool, and musty. It had massive dark Spanish furniture and was liberally decorated with tapestries and armor and swords and heavy iron grill work. Fauve lagged behind with the bored daughter as the party drifted through the towering rooms on the ground floor. Suddenly, skilfully, he diverted her through a doorway, and they were alone in a pine-paneled study.

"Tell me, Ginny dear," Fauve said, in a good-humored mischievous whisper, "what's he like?"

Her eyes widened. "Who, Mr. Fauve?"

"The boy in Culver City."

Ginny was startled, and for a moment seemed ready to be rude. But Fauve's impish grin infected her; she gave him a low rich laugh. Her face brightened marvelously. She was about seventeen, short and quietly attractive, with brown hair and blue eyes.

"Well, Mr. Fauve! I've heard lots of legends about you. But I didn't know you were clairvoyant—"

"Mighty nice, is he?"

"He's wonderful, since you ask."

"College boy?"

"Oh, no, he's—he wasn't interested in college. He's—he's an actor. But a good one."

"Well! That's in my line. What's his name?"

"Oh, you wouldn't have heard of him. Burt Freeman—he's just nineteen—"

"Ginny dear, it's only half an hour by car to Culver City—"

"He doesn't have a car. He's poor as a rat. Oh, I'm sorry, Mr. Fauve, I know Mama loves your house, but—I hate to be the stumbling block—you see, Burt lives practically next door, and—this would be the end if—"

"My dear, my house is a meaningless trifle compared to young love." He laid his hand lightly on her arm. "The hell with my house. The hell with Mama. You stick to your guns. Queer the deal."

Ginny's eyes shone at him. "Thanks. You're terrific."

"Once, long ago," said Fauve, "I was as terrific as Burt Freeman. Would that I had known you then. Come on, drag through the formalities. But stand firm, dear."

"He's not a bad actor," Fauve said. He lounged in a corner of the control booth, out of the line of vision through the glass wall. It was late afternoon of the same day, and he needed a shave.

"Adequate juvenile. Dime a dozen," said the fat, pasty-faced man at the controls, glancing into the studio. Burt Freeman, a sandy-haired boy in worn tweeds, stood by the microphone, clutching a script. "All right, thank you, boy. Sit down for a minute."

The actor's voice boomed in the loud-speaker. "Thank you very much, Mr. Goldstone." He went scampering across to Ginny Erickson, who held her hands out to him, smiling, and her voice came through thin and tinkly. "Oh, Burt, you were marvelous—"

"No, I was fierce. I only hope he gives me another chance to—"

Goldstone flipped a switch and cut off the voices. He said to Fauve, "Want me to send them outside? You look silly hiding—"

"No, no, don't do that. Damn him for bringing her. Listen, Herbie, I want you to do exactly as I tell you. First—can you put him on one of your soap operas, any part, no matter how small?"

"Well, as a favor to you—though I don't know why you're so interested in him, he's a small-time nothing, believe me—"

"One thing, Herbie. It's got to be a program that originates in New York."

"Now, gee whiz, Jerry. What kind of crazy talk is that? You know the New York office does its own casting. A little squirt like him—it's preposterous to send him across the country—"

"I'll pay his expenses. Do you know someone in the New York office you can count on?"

"Well, Lloyd Fish'll do it for me—Jerry, what the hell kind of maneuver is this now? It's got a rich, ripe Fauve smell."

"Herbie," said Fauve softly, "how would you like to drop this trash and direct a comedy for me?"

Goldstone looked at Fauve with sudden doglike adoration. "Jerry—really this time? Are you going into production?"

"I have the new Cowling play."

"*Cowling?*" Goldstone whistled. "Last time I met him he spoke of disembowelling you on sight."

"I know," Fauve said. He drew himself up and his eyes became fanatically proud. "And I loath him and he knows it. He also knows that I alone can produce that play with the elegance and sensitivity it must have."

"Jerry, any time you say—I'll come running. I'd do anything to work with you again—"

"I will take you into my confidence, Herbie, because you are dear to me. Cowling has given me a sixty-day option on his play. I had to beg him even for that much time—the swine, the boor! He thinks I can't raise the money. I swore I had it already. But he's right. I'm broke, and I have no credit. But if I can get this pipsqueak to New York, I will have seventy thousand in cash within a week. See how important—?"

"Jerry, it's crazy. What has that kid got to do with—"

"Herbie, take my word for it and get him out of town on the morning plane! I'll tell you why in due time. Go on out there and tell him he's sensational. Then tell him he needs grooming. You're going to send him to New York to study with Erwin Piscator while he works in the soap opera. The agency will pay his expenses, you say. I'll give you five hundred dollars to give him. But tell him that unless he can leave tomorrow you're not interested in him. D'you hear?"

"Jerry, I—it's risky, tossing around the agency's name—"

"Am I asking you to put anything on paper, you ass? After he's been there a few weeks you can tell him he isn't developing properly, and kick him into the gutter. Go ahead. And phone Lloyd Fish right now, as soon as the squirt says okay. It's got to be absolutely legitimate for a couple of weeks."

The director shrugged and walked to the door.

"And turn out that damned light, will you?" said Fauve. "I want to watch this." Goldstone flipped a switch and the control booth went black. I needn't tell you that one breath of my name to that boy means sudden death to the whole enterprise."

"Don't worry, Jerry," said Goldstone wearily. "All he knows is he got a call from the casting office. His name was in the file. You're all clear."

Crouched in the gloom, Fauve observed with narrow eyes the pantomine beyond the glass wall. The young actor sprang up respectfully and approached the director as he came through the studio door. Goldstone began to talk. Freeman displayed astonishment, then delight. He asked several questions with wild excitement. He grasped the director's hand and pumped it. Goldstone patted him on the back, grinning tolerantly, and walked out. The boy rushed to Ginny Erickson, hugged her, and gabbled, his eyes glittering, his hands waving. He all but danced. The girl smiled uncertainly for a while, asking questions, then she began to look gloomy.

Fauve leaned forward, turned on the sound switch, and shrank back in his chair.

"—biggest chance of my life, sweetheart, can't you see that?"

"But when will you ever come back, Burt?"

"Well, I don't know. The main thing is, it's an *in*. Once I get set, why—"

"But why must they pick you for a radio show in New York? It seems so illogical—"

"Darling," he said in an injured tone, "it's just possible that I happen to suit the part. Actors aren't like cans of soup, you know. One isn't as good as another—"

"Oh, Burt, I know you're a wonderful actor. But there are a million actors in New York."

"You don't seem to grasp what this means. Studying with Piscator! Why, the agency's practically giving me a fellowship!"

"And what about me?"

"I should think you'd be as happy as I am—for me."

"You don't really care at all what happens to us, do you? You're not even thinking about it."

"Be sensible, Ginny. I have to make a living before we can be serious about getting married. Gosh, don't you believe in me at all? As soon as I'm on my feet I'll come back and marry you, or I'll send for you, I swear—"

"You never will. You'll meet somebody else. You, all alone in New York . . . you're very good-looking, Burt. This is the end . . ."

"Look, Ginny, if you want me to stay holed up in Culver City, getting old and bald while I wait for a break in pictures—"

"And I suppose it'll be fun for me holed up with Mama and Papa in that horrible orange monstrosity while you're dating a lot of New York debutantes and actresses and what all—"

"Sweetheart, it's not my fault you don't like the house."

"Oh you fool, don't you know why Mama wants that house? For me! So I can meet some rich society boy and—she's got it all figured out—"

"I trust you, Ginny. Can't you trust me?"

"You don't care. Not one bit."

"Darling, do you want me to swear on the Bible that I'll be true to you?"

"I don't want you to do anything. I don't care what you do. Go to New York. I'm sure you'll be a great star. Send me an autographed picture sometime."

"Ginny, you just aren't making good sense."

The girl strode rapidly to the door and went out. Burt Freeman took a step or two after her, then stopped and pulled the audition script from his pocket. As he turned the pages a self-satisfied smile spread over his face.

"There it is," Fauve said triumphantly, three days later, showing Herb Goldstone an advertisement in the real-estate section of the Los Angeles *Times*. They were having breakfast in the Wilshire Derby. "Waiter! Phone."

Goldstone peered at the ad. "Culver City . . . you're sure that's the house?"

"My child, I've driven past it ten times. Tudor-style fieldstone. That's it." The waiter plugged the telephone into the socket beside the table. Fauve called a number, saying aside, "Herb, you may as well look up reservations on the Chief, and—Hello, Brewsters? Fauve. I just saw the Erickson ad and—yes—yes—"

He nodded and nodded, smiling broadly. Suddenly his expression changed to a horrid glare. "What!" People at other tables turned at the agonized shout. "Say that again!" Then he smashed down the telephone.

"Damn young love!" he choked. "Damn it to the bottomless fiery pit!"

"Jerry, what—"

"I am ruined, Herb, ruined. Ruined by that girl! The whole bloody Erickson family is moving to New York!"

EDMUND WARE

◀──▶

The Diary of Death

ON A winter's evening, in his apartment in Boston, Mr. Usher sat down to read the record of events which had transpired during the previous year at his camp in the wilderness on Mopang Lake. The record was kept in diary form, with daily entries by the resident caretaker. Mr. Usher opened the volume at hand with marked anxiety. He had been able to spend but two weeks at his camp during the previous year, and this diary, which he had just received, represented the first twelve months residence of a new and untried caretaker, Zachariah Bourne.

Mr. Usher had hired Zack Bourne with strong misgivings. There had been no doubt as to Zack's woodsmanship, or his qualifications to live happily in the wilderness. He was a magnificent physical specimen, and he had lived in the wild lands all his life, but he had a reputation for lawlessness, and a primordial sense of justice which both attracted Mr. Usher and frightened him. Moreover, in his desire to protect Mr. Usher's interests, Zack had seemed overzealous from the start.

"Jest you rest easy, Mr. Usher," Zack had said. "I'll shoot the feet from under anyone I see fishin' in our waters, or huntin' in our territory."

"But you can't do that, Zack."

"I'm the best rifle shot in Mopang."

"So I'm told. I simply mean that the lakes and the forests are free to anyone. Part of your duty would be to keep the peace, as I have always tried to keep it here."

"Sure, Mr. Usher. I'll jest fix it so things'll seem peacefuler to trespassers if they stay away from here."

Mr. Usher probably would not have engaged Zack if it hadn't been for Zack's wife, Sarah. Sarah was city bred, and Mr. Usher saw at once that she would have a gentling effect on her tall, tough-minded husband.

"Zack Bourne!" Sarah had reproached. "Hush that wild talk."

Turning to Mr. Usher, Sarah had then explained that Zack had lately returned from visiting a crony who was in jail down in Mopang. The crony's name was Thomas Jefferson Coongate, and he was an evil influence on Zack, and a menace in the community.

October, 1941

"Coongate?" Mr. Usher had inquired. "I seem to recall the name. Isn't he the one-eyed poacher of Privilege?"

He was indeed, said Sarah Bourne, and briskly sketched the Coongate character. Old Jeff Coongate, according to Sarah, was composed solely of vices. He was a chewer of tobacco, a drinker of bottled goods in any alcoholic form, and a kind of marathon blasphemer. He was a sworn breaker of game laws, and an enemy of the State. He was a jacklighter of deer, a gill-netter of salmon, a dynamiter of trout, and above all else a plotter against the lives of game wardens. In fact, he was currently in the clink for shooting the stern off a game warden's canoe with an automatic shotgun. Happily the warden was a good swimmer.

When Sarah paused to draw breath, Zack said: "But he's a good feller, jest the same."

"That's what you think," snapped Sarah, "because you an' him river-drove, an' poached together, when you was boys. Every time you been in trouble, 'twas him got you into it."

This conversation more than half convinced Mr. Usher that Sarah had Zack under control, and he had hired Zack on the spot.

"I want you both to regard this place as your home," Mr. Usher had said to Zack and Sarah Bourne. "The canoes, and all the equipment are for your use, as well as mine. I hope you will love this camp, as I do. I request that you do not leave the place alone for more than two or three days at a time, except of course in emergency. And there is only one thing on which I insist. That is the regular, and accurate keeping of the camp diary, day by day."

"You mean," said Zack, troubled, "that I'm to write somethin' down every day? Every single day?"

"Exactly."

"I'll tend to that myself, Mr. Usher," said Sarah.

Now, in his apartment, as he read Sarah's careful entries in the diary, Mr. Usher's mind gradually relaxed. Sarah had done an excellent job. From the simple facts she had recorded, Mr. Usher got a clear picture of the seasons, the work, the weather, and events. Mr. Usher read with absorption, and fascination. The diary was vivid evidence of the reality of the place he loved beyond all others.

January and February told of blizzards, bitter cold, the crackle of northern lights, and the thunder of the ice at night. And always the loneliness:

"No one come by for seventeen days, too cold, 27 below today, mouse in back pantry, Zack has toothache, but hauled wood from choppin across dam."

March and April told of thaws and freeze which made travel on the lakes next to impossible. Then came May, and the last, deadly weeks of waiting for the ice to leave. And on the 23rd, the joyous entry:

"Ice went out overnight in northwest gale, flock geese landed in cove at sunset, Zack took me out in canoe, wonderful. Salmon fishermen be coming soon, and will have company here in this lonely place at last. Zack leaving daylight tomorrow for supplies."

So read Mr. Usher—on through June, and the fly season. He read of three deer feeding in the back clearing, a family of otter living briefly along the stream, and a moose sighted across the dam. Mr. Usher's satisfaction with his new caretaker was first clouded by an entry in late August.

"Game Warden Tom Corn stopped by today out of tobacco. Zack would not give him any, mean I call it. It was Tom Corn's canoe that Jeff Coongate shot stern of off. The warden reported Jeff Coongate gets out of jail October one. Oh dear. Hope he don't come to see Zack, we been so happy here, even through this long and terrible winter."

Mr. Usher began to read more rapidly. He had a feeling that the inevitable was about to happen, that the nefarious one-eyed poacher would soon arrive and lead Zack Bourne astray. On September 11th a swallow flew through the open kitchen window. Sarah wrote that this was a bad omen, that it meant that someone would be very sick, or get hurt. But the dramatic import of this was lost to Mr. Usher. It was completely over-shadowed by Sarah's description of the turning of the leaves in early October—and by the following entry under date of November second:

"A most awful day. Thos. J. Coongate come up lake in night, arrived here crack of day. He had whiskey, and offered to Zack. I would not let Zack touch it. He tried to get Zack to go to Little Mopang Stream to trap beaver, this against law. I would not let Zack go, as I know Mr. Usher would not like it. Finely I told that one-eyed poacher to go away from this place, and he went after darkness fell as he don't want no one to see him. Zack mad at me, says am not cordial to his friends. Cannot be cordial to that outlaw man, for fear Zack will get himself in trouble."

On November third, fourth, fifth, and sixth, Sarah reported that Zack had not spoken to her. But then on the seventh:

"Zack made up today, kissed me, so sweet, said he knowed I was right, and if it hadn't been for me he would of done something foolish. Was so sweet, hugged and kissed me, till I am bruised and squoze, he don't know his strength. My!"

The entry of November 10th told of Zack's last trip out to Privilege for supplies before freeze-up. Zack returned two days later with a canoe-load of provisions and the mail. November 13th:

"Unlucky day, Zack brought letter from my brother saying my sister very sick in Bangor. Must go to her, as if anything happened would feel awful, and shell ice on lake now in many places. Must go, hate to leave Zack alone, as don't know what will happen. Do hope and pray that one-eyed devil Jeff Coongate don't come back this way."

As he finished reading the above entry, Mr. Usher stiffened in his chair. He, too, hoped and prayed that the one-eyed poacher would not, or had not visited his camp when Zack was there without Sarah. November 14th, 15th and 16th were blank, indicating the time required for Zack to get Sarah out to Privilege en route to Bangor. On the 17th, Zack had returned to the job. The handwriting was no longer in Sarah's clear, even penmanship, but showed signs of tremendous effort. Mr. Usher remembered that Zack had seemed troubled when he learned that he was to write something every day. The first entry in the labored, masculine handwriting, was on the 17th.

"Hellish trip back uplake after leaving Sarah in Privilege, broke ice clear from Caribou Ledge and chewed canoe canvas plump to hell. Geese went South in night, big flock, wish was with them, lonesome for Sarah all ready, but brought plenty big supply medicine back with me, Hernando's Fiery Dagger rum an Old Blow-Torch gin, ha-ha!"

Mr. Usher's heart sank. This was the thing he had dreaded. But he had not realized that Zack would be so brazen as to write it down in his own handwriting. On second thought, he realized, Zack Bourne was exactly the kind of man who would do just that, and do it unblushingly.

From November 17th on to the end of the year, the diary of Mr. Usher's beloved camp was the plain, agonizing record of a bush-queer man going steadily and irretrievably to hell. It was both fascinating, and appalling. November 19th:

"Cold for two days, ice four inches caught pickerl through ice, will say anyone that can stand up on this black ice after drinkin pint of Fiery Dagger rum is sure good balancer. Fell flat a dozen times gettin ashore, found camp door open wide when got back, someone maybe comin. Wish Jeff Coongate would come, would have hell of time. Plenty rum and gin left."

This entry was enough to sicken Mr. Usher, but he didn't realize to what depths a lonely man would sink until, on December 4th, Zack Bourne became a squaw man.

"Down to Privilege over the ice with hand sled. Stopped at Injun Villige on way back, got a squaw here now to keep me warm nights, her name Elsie Brown Blanket. Found old cat, Daisy, had kittens in cloze basket, five. Elsie thinks kittens might be good to eat. Some squaw, all right. Big bull moose workin over in woods near cove."

December 5th to 10th, inclusive, were quite clearly given over solely to debauch. Mr. Usher, reading between the lines, saw the desecration of his camp, and his wilderness. The handwriting for this period had become an illegible, drunken scrawl. December 11th marked Zack's return to partial sobriety. Mr. Usher read this day's entry, his stomach revolting.

"Elsie been keepin diary for me past few days, but I can't read what she wrote, but I know what she wrote about, ha-ha, thats all we been doin anyway. Snowed last night an covered most all empty bottles an tincans in front dooryard of cabin."

Mr. Usher was but slightly relieved to note that, on December 14th, Zack Bourne had tired of Elsie Brown Blanket's aboriginal charms.

"Elsie wants to get marrid to me and raise famly, can you beat it? That's a squaw for you. I said did not plan to commit bigmy with her, but only a little adultry, ha-ha. She got mad an throwed hand axe at me, so am leavin today to take her back to Injun Villige. Good snow-shoein on lake, tempture zero, wind north, clear."

There were only a few more entries. Zack's year, reflected Mr. Usher, his heart heavy within him, was almost over. So was Zack's job as caretaker of the camp on Mopang Lake. If the record of decay had so far sickened Mr. Usher, the last few entries did even more. They froze his blood.

"December 20th:

"My two dogs, Buck and Slats, been chasin moose in woods across dam. Will go after moose one day soon."

"December 25th:

"Merry Christmas, like hell. Buck and Slats dogged the moose out on ice. He dropped with first shot, I got the bastid right back of ear, some shot, as I had drunk 2 qts. rum yestdy an was shakin so couldn't hold rifle ver stiddy. Was dressin out moose when game warden Tom Corn stepped out of hidin in thick brush on shore, an got me for doggin moose. He drawed his service revolver and right before my very eyes shot both my dogs, Buck and Slats, best friends I ever had. Then he said for me to get ready to go to Mopang with him to jail, an I said would come peaceful, an told him I would get some things from cabin if he would wait. He waited all right, and will say that game warden will never shoot another dog in this world. How I know is my bisness, but wish Jeff Coongate seen it happen, as it would sure pleased Jeff, as this warden will never trail him nor anyone no more."

Mr. Usher shuddered, and closed the diary of death. He did not know whether to try and get in touch with Sarah Bourne, in Bangor, or to turn the diary over to the police. He finally decided to hire a plane equipped with skis for landing on the lake in front of his cabin door. His decision as to what to do about Zack would depend to some extent on what he discovered.

Taking with him the diary of death, Mr. Usher flew to Bangor the next morning on the regular transport plane. From Bangor he proceeded north by charter plane for Mopang Lake. He had been fortunate in securing the services of a pilot who tended the wants of trappers throughout the north. The flier knew the country well. He set his ship down smoothly on the packed snow on the lake before the cabin. Mr. Usher noted that no smoke came from the chimney. Had Zack left the country? Had the game warden already been missed? Apparently not, for inside the cabin Mr. Usher found the stove warm.

The pilot, looking from the kitchen window over the lake, said: "I guess there comes your man now. Prob'ly been cutting wood over on the island."

Even at a great distance, Mr. Usher recognized Zack Bourne. He had harnessed himself to a hand sled, and he was leaning forward, his great shoulders straining. The hand sled was loaded with wood.

"I'll pick you up at three sharp this afternoon," said the pilot. "That is, if the weather holds."

"But won't you stay and eat something?" asked Mr. Usher. He felt strangely lonesome, now, and uneasy. He wished the pilot would stay, and told him so.

The pilot shook his head. "I've got to pick up beaver skins for six trappers over in the Golroy River district. There's a bulge in the market, and if I don't catch it, I lose their business. I won't be gone long, unless a storm comes up."

The plane took off, circled for altitude, cleared the big ridge, and was gone before Zack Bourne arrived with his load of wood. When he recognized Mr. Usher, Zack slipped out of the sled harness and strode forward, smiling as if his conscience were as clear as a child's.

"Say, if it ain't Mr. Usher! I'm sure glad you could come."

As they shook hands, Mr. Usher felt bewildered, and a little frightened. Now that he had arrived, he did not know exactly how to proceed. Moreover, every time he turned his head, Mr. Usher noted a new bit of evidence which added confirmation to his worst fears. Zack's deer dogs, Buck and Slats, were conspicuously absent.

"What happened to your hounds?" asked Mr. Usher, gently.

"Buck and Slats?" While he answered, Zack calmly went about building up the fire and preparing a meal. "Well, I was afeared they might get to chasin' deer on the snow, where the tracks would show too plain. So I left 'em down to Privilege when I took Sarah out."

The smell of frying pickerel brought forth corroboration of another item in the diary of death. The cat, Daisy, and her five kittens emerged single file from under the stove, and, with tails high and backs arched, rubbed against Zack's legs. Mr. Usher's stomach turned over, as he recalled the entry in which Elsie Brown Blanket had pondered the kittens' edibility.

"I—I—uh—suppose it must have been lonesome here without Sarah," essayed Mr. Usher, miserably.

"Turrible! I damn near perished nights," Zack answered.

Now, for the first time, Mr. Usher observed that Zack's left hand was bandaged. Doubtless this wound had resulted from Elsie Brown Blanket's throwing of the hand axe. Zack had apparently shielded himself with his left hand, and had been cut.

"How did you hurt your hand, Zack?" asked Mr. Usher, fearfully.

"Cut myself with the hand axe," came the brazen reply.

"How?"

"Splittin' kindlin' in the dark."

Zack set a plate of fried pickerel and potatoes in front of his employer. But Mr. Usher's appetite was completely missing. He somehow could not bring himself to break bread with a drunkard, adulterer and murderer. Zack himself ate with relish, and when he had finished, said: "I'd like to take you out 'round the place an' show you some things I done. Maybe you'd be pleased to see 'em."

Deciding to delay mentioning the diary until time for the return of the plane, Mr. Usher accompanied Zack on a tour of inspection. In between debauches, Zack had found opportunity for a prodigious amount of work. Mr. Usher smiled bitterly. Aside from the fact that his new caretaker broke all ten commandments, he was the perfect man for the job. He had built a cap-and-bunk fence around the garden, using dry cedar poles. He had cut the unsightly dead limbs from the great white pine which land-marked the place in Mr. Usher's mind and memory. He had shingled the shed roof with shingles he had split himself, with mallet and frow. He had re-canvassed three canoes as smoothly as a factory might have done it. But most pleasing to Mr. Usher was the magnificent axe work which had gone into the hewing of new sills for every building on the place.

"That's beautiful, Zack," Mr. Usher had remarked, momentarily forgetting that his man was virtually a self-confessed murderer.

" 'Tain't nothin' at all, hardly. You come in the workshop, an' see the paddles I made. Got six out of one big maple butt. An' I got the best one marked for you. It's got a spring, an' whip to it, an' the bird's eye in the wood makes it han'some."

Mr. Usher tested the spring of the blade, found it perfect, and set the paddle down with a sigh. "I am very sorry that your wife, Sarah, had to leave you alone so long, Zack."

"Me, too. But I think Sarah's sister'll die, an' that won't bother me a dang bit, neither, 'cause then Sarah can bury her an' come back."

As they left the workshop, walking toward the cabin on the path Zack had shoveled in the deep snow, Mr. Usher decided to have his showdown and get it over with.

"Zack," he said, "I have read the diary. I have read it all. That is why I am here, as you may have guessed."

At mention of the diary, Zack Bourne showed his first signs of uneasiness. His eyes no longer met Mr. Usher's squarely, and he replied irrelevantly, plainly avoiding the subject. Pausing at the cabin door, he pointed to the windows, and said: "I puttied every dang pane of glass this side of the cabin."

"Zack, I want to talk to you about the diary."

But Zack's reluctance to discuss the subject continued. His guilt was palpable. He looked off across the lake, and, after a heavy silence, said: "There's someone comin'. There's two men comin'."

Mr. Usher glanced at his watch. Plane-time was but half an hour hence, and the two men, who were approaching rapidly across the lake, gave him extra confidence.

"Zack, I'd like to go over the diary with you and ask some questions. I brought it with me."

They entered the cabin. Mr. Usher sat down at the kitchen table, spreading the diary open before him. Zack put some beech chunks in the stove, and sat down opposite his employer.

"Ain't the diary all right?" he asked, avoiding Mr. Usher's eyes by staring from the window at the approaching men.

"No. I am sorry to say it is not all right."

"Well, dang it, that's Sarah's fault then. She kep' it."

"She kept it perfectly. I refer to the entries made by yourself, in Sarah's absence."

Zack swallowed. His forehead glistened, as the sweat began to come. He stared steadily at the two men, who were by now less than two hundred yards away.

Mr. Usher turned the diary toward Zack, and pointed to the entry for November 17th, the first following Sarah's departure: ". . . brought plenty big supply medicine back with me, Hernando's Fiery Dagger rum an Old Blow-Torch gin, ha-ha!"

"What do you suppose I thought when I read that, Zack? What opinion could you have thought I would have, about the new caretaker to whom I had entrusted my place here?"

Zack's huge hands clenched. The red of shame suffused his face. He averted his eyes, but made no reply.

"And this entry," continued Mr. Usher, turning to December 4th. "With your wife gone, you turned squaw man. You brought an Indian woman here—the one who threw the axe and cut your hand."

Zack guiltily thrust his bandaged hand out of sight under the table. Then, with a groan, he stood up and walked to the cabin window, his giant shoulders slumped abjectedly.

"Zack," said Mr. Usher, "I am afraid I shall have to terminate my agreement with you. As for the entry about the shooting of—"

Zack had suddenly straightened and glued his face to the window pane. The two men were just entering the cabin dooryard. "Game warden!" said Zack. "A game warden with that—"

"The game warden," Mr. Usher asked gently, "couldn't be Tom Corn, could it, Zack?"

"Not unless it's his ghost," said Zack, turning fiercely. "He's been—transferred."

To Mr. Usher, the word "transferred," as it issued from Zack Bourne's livid lips, meant liquidated, purged, in short, murdered. But Zack's recent shame and guilt had suddenly dropped from him. He stood for a moment, tall, tense, savage. Then, with the quickness of a huge cat, he reached for his rifle, snatched it from the wall pegs, jacked in a shell, and flung open the cabin door.

"Zack! Zack!" cried Mr. Usher. "You can't kill another warden, Zack!"

"I don't aim to kill no warden," Zack snarled, as Mr. Usher followed him from the cabin door. "I aim to kill the bastid that wrote that diary for me. Step to one side, warden—jest a foot to one side, till I get a shot at that one-eyed Jeff Coongate!"

Standing behind, and a little to one side of Zack, Mr. Usher observed that the warden's body shielded the second man. As he watched, spellbound, a face of splendid and grinning malevolence appeared briefly over the warden's shoulder. One eye was missing from the face. The color of the other eye was a kind of baleful blue. There was also a stringy, white mustache, from which icicles hung, giving the one-eyed poacher of Privilege the appearance of a sardonic Santa Claus.

"Warden," said Thomas Jefferson Coongate, "it's your duty to pertec' me. I'm your prisoner."

The warden moved a little, not especially liking his view of the hole in the end of Zack Bourne's rifle. The one-eyed poacher moved with him, and for a second or two the warden and his prisoner resembled a dance team, shifting feet in perfect synchrony, no mean performance on snowshoes.

"Zack," said Mr. Usher, almost happily, "I think you better let me take that rifle now."

"Go ahead an' give it to him, Zack," said the game warden.

When the rifle was safely in Mr. Usher's hands, the one-eyed poacher cautiously showed his head and part of his body. "Git me down to that jail quick, warden," he said. "I ain't safe, loose, while ole Zack's mad at me."

"You'll have time to cool off, Zack," the warden grinned. "I think I can promise Jeff Coongate at least three months. He's been chloroformin' beaver over on Little Mopang Stream."

"An' to think," muttered Zack, leaning weakly back against the cabin wall, "that I dang near went with him, on'y for my wife, Sarah."

A few minutes after the game warden and his prisoner left for Privilege en route to the Mopang jail, Mr. Usher's plane landed. But Mr. Usher had decided to remain with his new caretaker for several days, so he paid the pilot off.

There were a few things that needed clearing up concerning the diary of death, but there was no longer any doubt about Zack Bourne. Zack's temper had cooled. Dark had fallen over the Mopang country, and in the light of the lamp in the kitchen, Zack read the one-eyed poacher's inimical work of art, and chuckled aloud.

"Why, that ole hellcat. There ain't a whisker of truth in him. What he wrote down, is jest what he wished was true, but knowed it never could be. It's a kind of a dream, like."

"Just how did it all get into the diary, Zack?"

Zack ruefully explained that Jeff Coongate had stopped at the camp for two nights, shortly after Christmas. To Zack, the writing of the diary had been an ordeal which he couldn't face. He had tried again and again, but in his fingers the pen had felt unnatural. As the days passed, and he had written nothing, the very sight of the pen had nauseated him, and he had continued his procrastination, brooding and ashamed. He had hoped that Sarah would return to fill in the empty days for him. But no. Instead came the one-eyed poacher of Privilege, who offered to take the whole thing out of Zack's hands and make a nice, interesting record. Zack hadn't even bothered to read what he wrote. Jeff Coongate had graciously wrapped the diary, sealed it and addressed it.

"Then you really did cut your hand splitting kindling," laughed Mr. Usher.

"Sure did. And Daisy sure had them five kittens, all right. 'Twas 'bout three weeks before Jeff showed up. He'd been clear out to Carterville to get chloroform for them beaver he'd located on Little Mopang Stream. An' I really took Buck an' Slats to Priv'lige, too, so's they wouldn't cause no trouble here. An' it's a fact about that warden, Tom Corn—he's transferred. An' that Jeff Coongate! Well, he's a good feller, just the same. But I figure he put that in about the squaw a-purpose to torment Sarah. He hoped Sarah might read about Elsie Brown Blanket."

"Zack," said Mr. Usher, "by way of apology, I'd like to renew my agreement with you for an indefinite number of years. Would you be willing?"

"Yes, sir, indeed I sure would. Me an' Sarah loves this place like it was our'n. But there's jest on'y one thing: don't you never tell her 'bout that diary, nor who wrote it. I wouldn't want Sarah to know that Jeff Coongate spent a couple nights here. He ain't a man that women understand."

STUART CLOETE

←————————————————————————————————————→

The Silence of Mr. Prendegast

"Avril Mason used to be the most beautiful woman I have ever seen," Prendegast said.

I was staying with the Masons. Someone had given me a letter of introduction to them, and they had asked me to visit them, so I was interested in what Prendegast said. He lived on the next farm and I'd dropped in to see him, the way one does in Africa. I needed exercise and had gone for a ride; and then, seeing his homestead, I'd thought I'd drop in. I was curious about him because Avril had said, "He's a queer character. We don't see much of him, and when we do see him he doesn't say a word."

Well, he seemed disposed to talk now. Perhaps because I was a stranger, perhaps because I was a writer and people seem to talk to writers. Writers are out of their world, unreal to them, like griffins and unicorns.

When I'd introduced myself, Prendegast had said, "The writer?" and I had said, "Yes."

"I read a lot," he said, "and I've enjoyed your books."

I was flattered and pleased, and took to him at once—this being human nature. But I was particularly interested in what he said about Avril. It confirmed what I had thought myself when I met her. She'd been beautiful. Twenty years ago or so, she must have been lovely. She still had the bone in her face, the structure was there; she still had great dark brown eyes; she still had a good figure and good legs. Her hair was grey now, of course, but she had masses of it, and it was strong and vital, with a natural wave. She blued it heavily and used a lot of make-up, but the beauty was all there underneath. She was like a picture postcard that someone has written over. Time had written over her picture, blurring it a bit, smudging it, fading it; but the picture was there, and Prendegast's remark brought it out again.

Avril Mason was beautiful (he went on). She had the kind of beauty that brings a man's heart into his mouth, and she was, as far as I was concerned, the very last kind of neighbor I could have wanted. In fact, if I had been asked what sort of people I should like least, I should have said a beautiful young woman

November, 1951

with an invalid husband. At least I should have said that if I had been smart enough to think of it.

I'll never forget meeting her. I was sitting on the stoep figuring out some stock returns when she walked in. I was a filthy mess, sweaty and covered in dust, having just come from the cattle kraals. Nothing more unlikely than a woman like Avril Mason walking up the steps of a South African farm stoep could be imagined. I looked up from my figures and there she was. Tall, dark, slim, beautifully turned out in a white suit with white gloves and a white felt hat.

"You're Mr. Prendegast?" she said.

I said yes, and then, "Where's your car? I didn't hear it."

"I left her at the back," she said.

I said nothing. I just stared, I think. She really left me speechless. It was a minute before I asked her to come in and sit down, and called the boy to make tea.

By this time I'd taken her in. The details of her dress, her lovely hands and slim legs and ankles. Her hair was long and she wore it in a knot at the back of her neck like she does now, only of course it was brown then—a lovely, rich, dark brown. Sepia color with almost a touch of red in it. Her eyes were brown, velvety soft. They were the color of dark sherry, very large and set wide apart, and they gave her a young, innocent look. Her eyes have changed a lot. I guessed her to be about twenty-five, and as it turned out I was one year out. She was twenty-six. It was years since I'd seen anyone like her.

She said, "We've been looking at farms and have more or less decided to buy Avalon."

It was quite undeveloped then. Just bare veld.

"I hope you do," I said.

"We'll buy it," she said. "I've just decided."

And I felt that her meeting me had clinched the deal in some way. As a matter of fact, that's an understatement. I knew it, but did not want to know it. I knew from the way she had looked at me, and from the quick way she was breathing.

Then the we dawned on me. " 'We,' " I said. "You said we. Is there someone with you?"

"Yes," she said, "my husband. He's an invalid—at least he's not at all well. And Phyllis. They're in the car."

"I'll go and get them," I said, getting up.

She went on, "My husband is Frederick Mason—Freddy Mason."

"The polo player," I said.

"Yes," she said. "He was badly wounded and has to live a quiet life in the country. That's the reason why we're buying a farm." Then she said, "This is good horse country, isn't it?"

I said, "Yes. We're high here. No horsesickness to speak of, and except for Mooi River and parts of the Karoo and Free State it's the best place I know."

"Then that settles it."

I said, "I'll fetch them," and went out.

The car was a big green Cadillac. In the front seat there was a native driver, and at the back were her husband and Phyllis.

"Come in," I said, "and have some tea."

Mason said, "Thanks," and got out of the car carefully. He was a man of about forty and looked very ill. Phyllis followed him. "This is Miss French—Phyllis French," Mason said.

We shook hands. "My name's Prendegast," I said.

Miss French was a small woman of about thirty—a rather fragile-looking washed-out blonde. She had tired blue eyes and she seemed very quiet. I remember thinking then that she looked rather like a governess.

They followed me in and we all sat down.

"My wife has told you, I suppose, we're thinking of buying the place next door," Mason said.

I said, "Avalon."

"Yes," he said, "but it really depends on my wife." He smiled at her. "She's got to make the decision."

"We'll buy it," she said.

"You've made up your mind, then," he said.

She looked at me under her lashes. "Mr. Prendegast has decided me."

I found later that this was typical of her. The double bluff in which the absolute truth was used to disguise the truth.

"What did he tell you?" her husband asked.

"He says it's good horse country; and then, having a civilized neighbor . . ."

I said, "Not so civilized."

She said, "Civilized enough."

Mason said, "I've got to lead a quiet, open-air life. She told you, I suppose."

I said yes, and then asked Miss French how she would like it.

"I don't really know," she said, "but I like a quiet life. Books," she said, "and music . . ."

"Phyllis is a highbrow," Mrs. Mason said, and laughed.

"And you?" I asked.

"Me?" She laughed again. "I can be happy anywhere."

Not much more was said, as far as I remember. The conversation became general and centered more or less on farming, cattle and horse breeding, shooting, the question of labor, and similar topics. They only stayed an hour and then left for Nylstroom, where they were spending the night at the hotel. They were going back to Johannesburg the next day to close the deal. When they said good-by, Mrs. Mason said, "We're staying at the Carlton, if you want to get hold of us, or are coming into town." I said I only went to Joburg once a year to see the dentist. "I hate the place," I said. And that was the last I saw of them for some time.

They were, however, in my mind quite a lot, because I couldn't get them out of it. Her looks, the sick husband, the sad-looking secretary or whatever she was. Why would people like that want to come into the wilds? What would they do with themselves? Avalon is a big place. Five thousand morgen—a morgen here, as you no doubt know, is a little over two acres. It was, as I said, quite undeveloped then but had good grazing and plenty of water. But it was hard to visualize them there. They belonged in England, America, or the South of France. It all puzzled me; and then I accepted it the way one does. One can't go on puzzling forever, and people should know their own business best.

What did puzzle me, though, was her interest in me. I'm not a ladies' man. Never was. But the look she'd given me meant something or I thought it did; and then I put that out of my head too. I was very busy losing a lot of stock with a pride of lions that had come in from the reserve, and one of my best bulls was sick. A bull meant a lot to me then. A bull's half the herd, especially when you're grading up on native cows. Funny, now that I can afford it I seldom lose anything. But then it was different—lions, wild dogs, leopards, jackals, every damn thing. Of course the place was wilder then. (He spoke almost regretfully. He was silent for a few minutes and then went back to Avril.) I was in such a mess when she saw me. That's what finally made me decide I'd been imagining things.

I smiled. Poor Prendegast didn't know women. He was a fine-looking man even now, and must have been magnificent then. Strong, bronzed, smelling of sweat and cattle. I saw him, in my mind, on his stoep with his returns in front of him. I saw his dusty face furrowed with sweat around the eyes and nose. I saw his strong hands holding the pencil. And I saw Avril as she was then. Sleek, svelte, finished to the last degree, excited by a man like this—the silent, lonely rancher of the novelists. A man. A new type. With her husband ill and no good to her, the picture was very clear. To come into the bush was the one thing she could never have done without a pastime; and for a woman like her there was only one kind of amusement—men. But he hadn't seen it then, and I rather doubted if he saw it now. Rough and strong, an outdoor man, virile but at the same time what we call a gentleman. He read a lot and he'd been about before he settled here. He knew how to behave, which knife and fork to use at dinner and things like that, so that the paradox of his existence had intrigued her. Why should he live like this alone, unmarried, miles from anywhere?

And then, like all women, even the best of them, she wanted power. Here was something she could get into her power by the use of her beauty. A strong man she could either use or shatter. But I didn't say anything to him. I wanted him to go on. I was sure he would, because no one talks as much as a silent man once the silence has been broken.

"Go on," I said, "tell me the rest."

"The rest?" he said. "All right, I'll tell you. Maybe you'll put it in a book sometime. . . ."

The rest, as you can imagine (Prendegast went on), is where I made a bloody fool of myself. And a cuckold of Mason. I'm not excusing myself, except that as a farmer I know very well that morality doesn't jibe with biology, and a girl of twenty-six, especially one like Avril, can't live without a man in her life. For two years I was that man. Mason got worse. It's only lately he's taken a turn for the better.

It began with the rides. I used to take her for rides. I knew this country like the palm of my hand. She was just friendly at first, giving me the rope I needed to hang myself. I was in love with her. I was mad about her. I could think of nothing but her. And then one day I showed her the Bushman cave in the Berg. It's only about three miles from the house and about eight from here. You can get the horses up to within a couple of hundred yards of it and leave them tied in a thick patch of bush. Then you've got to climb for about fifteen minutes before you come to it. There's a nice Bushman painting in the cave— a giraffe in ocher yellow with black markings. The cave's as big as a small room and has a little spring on one side that's a mass of maidenhair fern. It's what you'd call a romantic spot, with a view over the low country, and the drip of water, and the moss and the ferns. I'll show it to you one day if you like.

Anyway, that's where it happened. I'd hardly got her there before she was in my arms. . . . I must confess that she did not match my ardor. I did not know then, as I do now, that such was her instinctively subtle way of increasing my longing for her. It was not long before she was openly as mad about me as I was about her. I'd never known a woman like her before. She was all woman. Sometimes I thought of the Bushmen who had made love there for hundreds, perhaps for thousands of years, till they were shot off like animals when the Boers first settled in the country. As I held her, I often thought of it. And of men and women, and the strange things that happen between them. I felt nothing about Mason. In this sense he was dead. He wasn't a man. You couldn't take something from him that he hadn't got.

We made a bed of maidenhair fern. We took my two dogs with us, and they'd have given us notice if anyone came near. Looking back on it, it's unbelievable, but then it was the only reality. We'd meet on horseback and ride there day after day. She's a wonderful horsewoman, you know. Learnt to ride as a child on a sheep station in Australia. That only came out later when she had to manage the ranch. She'd been brought up to it, and then had got out of it owing to her looks. There'd been a good many men in her life before Mason, I gathered. But he'd found her irresistible and had married her. It would be impossible to call her immoral. Morals didn't mean anything to her. She was a woman. A beautiful animal who had made herself into a sophisticated woman of the world.

Well, that's the way it was till Max came onto the scene. Maximilian Ferdinand von Freidheim. He bought Elandsfontein—that's the farm on the other side of me—for its shooting. We used to laugh about him. He always wore riding breeches, boots, and a slouch hat. It was his idea of what a man should wear in Africa. He was a baron, all right—I got a friend to look him up in the *Almanach de Gotha*—and in some way related to the Hapsburgs. He built himself a big house near the Masons' boundary. Elandsfontein is L-shaped and runs right around my place. I bought it afterwards, but that's a long way ahead. As I said, we used to laugh about him, and all the time she was having an affair with him. I have no doubt that when she was with him she used to laugh about me—the simple farmer who was stupid enough to fall in love with a woman like her. I think she told him she was just amusing herself with me, to keep suspicion from falling on him. That was her story to me about Max.

"Darling," she used to say, "it wouldn't do if I rode only with you. And besides he plays the piano so well."

Phyllis used to take him messages from Avril, and Phyllis loved his music. He had a Bechstein grand and played magnificently.

I interrupted Prendegast at that point. "I was wondering about Phyllis," I said. "She must have known what was going on."

"Some of it," Prendegast said. "She knew about me, but thought Max was a blind, which was why she let him make love to her."

"You mean he made love to Phyllis, too?"

"Yes," Prendegast said. "She often went over to his place on her pony—she had a little cream Basuto mare with black points (what you call a buckskin in America, I think)—and looked very well on her. Though I must say I'd no idea she could really ride until . . ."

"Until what?" I said.

"I'm coming to that," he said. "I've left out some bits. Anyway, you've got the hang of the story now. A beautiful woman with a sick husband and two lovers that she played off one against the other, making fools of them both. It was a triangle," he said, "with Avril, me, and Maximilian. Mason was on the sidelines; and Max had a little secret triangle of his own with Avril and Phyllis."

"Yes," I said.

"Well, I must go back a bit. You can see that money was no object with the Masons."

I said yes, again, because it was obvious that money had been poured into Avalon. The house was lovely and beautifully furnished; there was a park where they kept their brood mares, a wonderful garden, and a swimming pool two hundred feet long.

They went into it in a big way from the beginning (Prendegast said). Within a year they had ten thoroughbred mares and a grey stallion by the Syrian Prince who was by the Tetrach. Avril used to ride him a lot, but not to meet me—you couldn't tie him, and he was hard to mount. But I should have realized that Phyllis knew about horses when, one day, while we were all together having tea at Avalon, Phyllis said, "I'm sure Pasha could jump a house. Just look at his quarters."

Avril said, "He won't jump."

And Phyllis said, "He'll jump wire."

"Only to get at a mare," Avril said.

"It's just that you can't make him," Phyllis said.

"No one can make him jump," Avril said. "He doesn't like it."

That little conversation slipped out of my mind till much later. But to get back to Maximilian. He was very rich, too. I was the poor man there. I was ranching for my living while they were checkbook farmers, amusing themselves breeding a few horses to run in local races and running a herd of mediocre whitefaces.

Well, there it was; and, when you come to think of it, a pretty nasty mess, too. And, like all such messes, it was filled with latent tragedy, though none of us suspected it at the time. I was even very happy in my love for Avril, and things had begun to pick up for me. A couple of good calf crops with a big percentage of heifers, and Max's hunting had cleaned out a lot of vermin. I was sitting here where we are now, just as I was when I first saw Avril, when it happened. I was reading *The American Tragedy*—which was a bit of a coincidence—when I heard a horse galloping like hell. It was coming from the direction of Avalon, straight as a crow flies. I jumped to my feet. There were no gates that way. To get to Avalon you have to come round the way you did today. And then, to my astonishment, I saw Phyllis coming hell for leather on Pasha. She was leaning over his neck and her hair was streaming out all mixed up with his mane.

My God, I thought, the fence—five barbed wires, with fourteen-pound iron standards eight yards apart, with four droppers between them. It didn't occur to me then that she must have jumped six fences before she came to this one. I ran out just in time to see her give the stallion his head and call to him. He changed legs, gathered his quarters under him, and soared like a bird into the air. He jumped big. When he landed with his forelegs, his hind were two foot above the top wire. She never checked him, but came right on, through the rosebushes in the garden, and only pulled up when his nose was practically on the stoep.

I went to his head. He was blowing hard; great gusts of air came from his flaring nostrils. He was nearly black with sweat, but he knew me well and rubbed the thick curds, where the reins had chafed him, against my chest.

"My God, Phyl," I said, "what's up?"

She threw her leg over the horse's neck and almost fell at my feet.

I caught her by the arm. "What is it?" I said. "And what will Avril say?" Avril let no one ride that horse.

"Damn Avril," she said. "She's killed him. She shot him. She pushed the pistol right into his chest and shot him."

"Shot who?"

"Max," she said. "Avril has killed Max."

I called a boy to take the horse and put him in one of my boxes, and then I led Phyllis into the house and got her a drink of brandy. I lit a cigarette and gave it to her.

"Now tell me everything," I said.

She gave a sort of choking sob, and then, pulling herself together, said, "She shot him when she found he was my lover."

"What?" I said.

"Yes," she said. "He was my lover. We were going to be married."

"My God," I said. "But why?"

"You fool," Phyllis said. "Can't you see it?"

"Why?" I said again.

"Jealousy," she screamed. "He was *her* lover, too."

I poured myself a drink. I needed one. So she had tricked me, the way I'd tricked Mason. The way she'd tricked lots of men. Phyllis was crying softly, now.

I said, the way one does at such times, just for something to say, "I never knew you could ride like that. Why, you ride better than Avril." It was odd, using her name like that, as if nothing had happened.

"Like Avril?" Phyllis said. "Why, I taught Avril to ride."

"What happened then?" I asked. "Was she accused of murder?"

"No," Prendegast said. "There was an inquest, of course, and she said she killed him in self-defense when he tried to assault her. She'd torn her clothes to prove it. She'd torn them herself after Phyllis left, and the fact that she'd shot him at such close range clinched the matter. Actually, Phyllis said, she walked right up to him and shot him. His silk shirt was all scorched with the powder blast. Anyway, he was a bad 'un, Max was, and no loss to society. I advised Phyllis to say nothing because nothing would have been gained by it, and a lot of dirty linen would have come to light.

"You see, Avril had something on Phyllis. They'd been brought up together, but Phyl had been in a lunatic asylum for a while, and Avril was always threatening to let it out if she ever left her, or didn't do what she told her. That was why Phyl had never married before. This time she thought she was safe, because she'd told Max. But now the boot was on the other foot and she had something on Avril; and once she got over the shock, she blossomed out. Very pretty she was, now that she'd lost that worried look. Max hadn't meant much to her, she realized afterwards, except as a way out, an escape, and it sort of eased her mind, my knowing and not being upset. But that's why we never had any children."

"No children?"

"Yes," he said. "We wouldn't take the chance."

"You married Phyllis, then?" I said.

"Yes," he said, "I married her, and for fifteen years we were very happy. Then she died. Come," he said, and got up. "I'll show you her grave."

We went through the garden till we came to the paddock fence; and there, cutting into it, was a little enclosure with an iron gate. It was planted with giant aloes. "I didn't put roses," he said, "because they'll die if they're not taken care of. But aloes go on. Nothing eats them, nothing can hurt them. And she loved them."

"Is this the place?" I pointed to the fence.

"Yes," he said, "this is where she jumped Pasha. He died only ten years ago. Avril gave him to us as a wedding present, provided she could use him at stud when she needed him."

"What nerve," I said.

"She's got guts," he said. "All guts and no heart. Phyl had both," he said. "Plenty of both, and the light has gone out since she died." He coughed, and then he said, "Afterwards, I made a clean breast of it to Mason. About me and Avril, I mean. And he asked me if I thought he was a complete fool.

" 'You knew?' I said.

" 'I knew that she couldn't live without love,' Mason said. 'And I knew she'd picked on you when she decided to buy the farm.'

" 'You knew then?' I said.

" 'Yes,' he said. 'If it had been a city, there would have been lots of men. I didn't like that. But I was out of the running and I didn't want to lose her. Just to see her gave me pleasure—just to watch her walk, watch her move. Like a race horse.' "

At dinner that evening, Avril asked me what I'd been doing. "Have a nice ride?" she said.

I said, "Yes, I rode over to Prendegast's."

"The silent rancher," she said.

"I'm going to see him again tomorrow," I said. "He's said he'd take me to look at a Bushman drawing of a giraffe in a cave."

"I'll come with you," she said. "I'd like to see it again. I haven't seen it for years."

What nerve the woman had, I thought. She looked lovely in a white evening dress with red and green sequins on the hips. She wore a diamond star in her blue hair, and a double rope of pearls. It was difficult to associate this well-preserved and distinguished woman with the story Prendegast had told me, but I believed every word of it. It was all there under the white-sequined dress, the girdle, the pearls and diamonds, the hair-bluing and eye shadow. Eve was there, and Artemis the huntress, and the harlot and the slut that exist latently in so many women. What matters is how much of it there is. It's a matter of proportion, and Avril had too much of it. Just as she had too much beauty and too much nerve. She was dangerous as an unsheathed sword.

I never saw the cave, because a wire came calling me back to town, but I often wish I'd stayed on to see Avril and William Prendegast, both in their fifties, looking at the scene of their romance. I've often thought of Prendegast's words: ". . . a woman like a race horse," and of Mason—a man who could look truth in the face, which is more than most men can do.

The truth. What is truth? How much was love? How much was cynicism on Mason's part? What had held Avril to him? I'd heard Prendegast's story. How different would Avril's have been, or Mason's? And it had happened twenty-five years ago. What I had seen was the residue of Life, the sediment of an old emotion, of old pain that now was just a story.

MANUEL KOMROFF

The Thousand and First Extra

IT WAS whispered about Hollywood that they would need at least one thousand extras for the mob scenes of Zeloff's great production of that picture, still unnamed, dealing with American democracy. The story of this million-dollar production was being serialized in many newspapers as part of the publicity for the picture and a lively contest was under way for the title that best fitted the story. The contest was open to all. The prize, $5,000. The judges were the two stars of the picture, Lillie Lang and Robert Headlong, and the producer, Joe Zeloff.

Word leaked out on Saturday afternoon that the cameras were all ready for the mob scenes. No other announcement was necessary. Monday morning at the break of dawn a handful of extras were already waiting at the gate for a chance to be part of a mob. By eight o'clock several hundred were gathered. At nine o'clock the gate keepers and studio police arrived and had these people form into two long lines, men on one side and women on the other. They were allowed to stand two abreast and ropes were strung up from posts to the gate paling. By ten o'clock when the fine limousines of the studio workers began arriving, the files extended for several blocks. The mob was orderly and meek. Each waited for the chance to appear in pictures and bring home the five dollars.

Gathered here were surely one thousand or perhaps even one thousand and one. And their faces? Each a hidden drama. The eyes? Sad far away remembrances. The bodies? Broken hopes still propped up on two legs. How many were too hungry to stand boldly, too weak for pride!

Take the first in the line; he came from Maine with a voice and the one beside him was a vaudeville hoofer who once played big time. On the women's side. The pretty blonde won a beauty contest in Texas four years ago. She is now a waitress in a cafeteria and beside her is a wardrobe mistress of the old days. Yes, she dressed the great ones, the footlight dazzlers, and now she does a little as a seamstress. From the first to the last, if you could weave them all together, you would have a tale as amazing as the Thousand and One Arabian Nights.

And the story of that red headed fellow in a khaki shirt? He was almost *The Kid* in the Charlie Chaplin production years ago, that's how close he got. Less than a flip of a coin stood between him and fame. Do you believe in chance?

And behind him there is one with a heavy three weeks' growth on his face. He is an old hand at this extra business and he knows that the casting director will sift the lines quickly and with an unshaven face his chances of being kept in the mob are four times as good.

Behind this unshaven one stands a green hand, though twice in the past month he brought home five dollars. And this was the only money Jerobi brought home in a long time indeed. He was no actor, and he came to California with no studio ambitions. But as an extra, part of a mob, one in a thousand— or perhaps the thousand and first—he thought he might possibly fit in. After all a mob is made up of all sorts and even an odd duck of a mathematician, forty-nine and with grey hair, could have a chance.

An hour later the gates opened wide. The uniformed guards called out, "Take it easy folks," and the lines moved forward into the lot. On a raised platform sat a group of men. The fellow in the white shirt with the megaphone in his lap is the director himself. The man with the dark sunglasses in a silk gabardine suit and purple shirt is the producer, Joe Zeloff himself. The skinny fellow with the big checked cap is the chief cameraman. The man with the big cigar is assistant to the director, he was formerly a gag writer and now has ambitions to become a producer. The man with the big nose in the blue shirt with the script in his hands is chief assistant to Zeloff. He is more than assistant. Sam is number one yes-man to the big boss. He is the main sounding board of Zeloff productions.

The director in the white shirt lifted the megaphone as three members of the studio police force stood among the extras and gave each a red card. Through the megaphone he called: "Keep the fellow with the unshaven face. Have him remove his necktie. And the blonde girl in the black dress, O. K., give her a white apron. The lady with the grey hair, O. K., but her face is too clean, send her to the make-up department. The fellow in the khaki shirt with the red hair, that's fine, only have him put on an old cap. His hair picks up glints of light. The girl in the tailored suit, better luck next time." She did not get a red card but all the others did.

While this was going on Erick Jerobi, formerly teacher of mathematics, perhaps number one-thousand-and-one of the mob, was getting more and more uncomfortable. He kept dropping back in the line as though he was trying to hide himself from someone on the platform. His turn was close, and they were about to thrust a red card in his hand, when he decided that he could not go through with it and looked about nervously for a chance to escape.

"Hold it a minute," called Zeloff.

"Hold it," cried the director through his megaphone.

"Go down there Sam and tell that fellow I want to see him."

Sam went into the crowd and pointed. "This one?"

"No. The fellow in the grey suit with the blue tie."

He picked him out of the line. "The chief wants to see you." And with these words he led Jerobi up the steps of the platform.

"O. K. Go ahead," Zeloff announced to the director in the white shirt. Then turning in his chair he said: "Hello, Erick, how are you?" and shook his hand warmly. "Give him a chair," he ordered.

And there were many in the line who had stood hours behind the grey headed gentleman, in a grey suit, and were quite surprised to see him brought up to the platform and seated in a place of honor beside the great Zeloff himself.

An hour later Zeloff led the way to his office and as soon as the door was closed he pretended to be very angry.

"Now you are a fine fellow," he began. "I have searched all over for you, ever since I heard you were in California, and never once did you ever try to look me up."

"I wanted to, Joe, many times, but somehow or other I kept putting it off and you know how time flies."

"That's not the reason."

"Well, there might be other reasons."

"You know that I would give you a nice welcome."

"Yes."

"And that if there were something I could do for you I certainly . . ."

"Yes. Yes, I know," he replied nervously.

"I heard you were in California through Monroe. You remember Monte in our class. Best high-jumper in the school. But he did not know your address. How long is it now since you are here?"

"Four years."

"Like it?"

He smiled. "No. Not much."

"What brought you people out here?"

"Our daughter Elsie had a tubercular hip. She was thirteen then and the doctors thought . . . Oh, she is fine now. Perfectly all right. We had X-rays recently and if we wanted to we could go back tomorrow . . ."

"Yes, I remember her when she was a kid. She used to play the piano. Does she still play?"

"Yes. She even has pupils; just kids."

"And you?"

"When we first came out I had a job with a prep school, tutoring boys' algebra, but it did not last long."

"That sure does take me a long way back. Remember the time you tutored me in algebra? That certainly was one thing that I never could get into my head. I was fairly good at some subjects, but algebra, phew! I would never have got through but for you. You seemed to know the exact questions that the professor was going to ask."

"Well, it's a standardized course and if they don't ask the question one year they ask it the next. Most professors haven't too much imagination."

"That is the time I came to you with all my troubles and you asked me to drop the Mr. Jerobi and just call you Erick. We boys thought that some day you would be head of the department."

"No, that was hardly possible. I could never be more than an instructor for I didn't have a Ph. D. These days it is quite necessary."

"But you knew a lot more than any of them. And I heard some years ago, from some of the old boys, that you had made an important discovery and that we would hear of you in a big way."

"It wasn't a discovery exactly. It was a theory I suggested that dealt with probabilities and chances. It was published in the Journal of Mathematics—purely a technical thing and not much good to anybody at the present time, not even insurance companies."

"Why do you say insurance companies?"

"Well, they use more mathematics than any large modern institution. They have the odd chance to consider."

"I see. Well, it certainly is good to look at you again, and I am still sore at you for not having shown up sooner."

"You, Joe, are a big success. We always knew you would make the grade."

"Well, you may call it success but I have lots of headaches. Come, let's order lunch, I want you to have lunch with me."

"Oh no, I think I'd better be going."

"Listen, Erick. You have plenty of time on your hands and you are not going anywhere. I have not seen you in years and between ourselves let's not humbug. We can have lunch served right here in the office where we will be alone." He rang the bell and added: "You know it's good to see your face." And impulsively he went up to him and shook his hand again.

"I'll be glad to have lunch with you, but really, Joe, I know you have other things to do and your time is very valuable. I really must apologize to you."

"What for?"

"Well, I'm a bit ashamed. I did not expect to see you; in fact they told me that only the casting director . . . And the two other times when I worked as an extra we never saw the producer at all."

"In my productions I see everything. I suppose you like the experience of facing the camera?"

There was a knock at the door and a girl from the studio lunch room entered with a menu in her hand. Erick was about to suggest the sixty-cent lunch for himself but Joe said: "Pick from the dollar dinner."

When the girl had left the room Erick said: "You certainly have a fine office. We always knew you would land with both feet."

"Well, a lot of it was really luck. In some ways I was very lucky. Been married now five years. We have a boy two years old. Mary is a fine girl and I want you and your wife to have dinner with us."

"We have not been going out much lately, but perhaps some time . . ."

"With us it is different. Old friends are old friends no matter what."

From time to time the phone rang and people came into the room to get a moment's attention or a quick decision from the busy executive. The lunch was served and when the waitress left the room Zeloff leaned across the table and said: "I guess I am keeping you from being an extra and missing a lot of fun."

"No Joe. I didn't come for the fun. Frankly, I came for the five dollars. You know I don't bluff. Between ourselves the reason we don't go out much or why I don't look up old friends . . . Well, we don't have the clothes or even the carfare and for the past year it's been kind of . . . Well, you know, hard sledding. My wife has been making underwear for a little Hollywood shop and doing other sewing jobs and even Elsie has brought in two or three dollars a week giving piano lessons to kids. It sort of makes me ashamed of myself to have to be supported and so . . . I'm no actor, but if the labor is worth the hire I am certainly willing to do what I can. You understand."

"Sure. I understand."

The phone rang.

"What?" cried Zeloff into the receiver. "We jacked him only a month ago. All right, it was six weeks then. He gets a grand and a half and not another nickel. Tell him there are poor people in the world. Tell him we've got a depression on. All right, if he wants to go let him go, and if fifteen hundred smackers a week aren't enough for him he can take his tunes back to Dishpan Alley. Hell, nothing against you. Sure, you're his agent and you want to see him get ahead. All right, a shoestring-and-a-half for the next production and sign on the dotted line. Tell him to be a good boy and go to work and earn his ninety per cent. No. No. I won't split anything with you. Fifteen-hundred cart-wheels a week. Sure, I know he arranged the music for a Broadway show. So what? He's only twenty-three years old and he's drawing down mazuma plenty and never heard of the depression . . . I'll tell you a secret. He'll never be Beethoven. All right. Yes. I don't give a damn where he writes the stuff. He can move the piano down to the cellar if he likes. With his talent he doesn't have to be temperamental. All right. He wants a Turkish rug under the piano like Monte has? Tell him Monte wrote four hits last year! O. K., we'll give him a rug. Let him sign the contract. Fifteen-hundred white chips, eight weeks. Good-bye. Hello, hello. Say, do me a favor. Tell him to learn to play with the left hand also." He banged down the receiver.

From time to time there were other interruptions. And Erick apologized again for taking up the executive's valuable time.

"Well," Zeloff admitted, "the time gets valuable when we have a mob scene going on that costs us five thousand dollars a day." He lifted the receiver and said: "Tell Sam I want to see him."

Sam, human sounding board of Zeloff productions, appeared immediately.

"How's it going?"

"Everything's fine, chief."

"All right, I'll be here in case they need me."

"O. K., chief."

"And just a minute, Sam. Meet my old teacher from school in the East, Mr. Jerobi. If he ever comes here, and I am out, you be sure and take good care of him."

Sam shook hands with Erick and was about to leave the room when Zeloff called him back.

"Wait a second, Sam. Tell me about those letters for the contest."

"We have a whole room full. Must be a million letters. Perhaps five million—nobody counted them. We've got them tied in bundles."

"Well, I was just thinking that we might need some clerical help and some people to sort and tabulate the results."

"Look, chief, there's a million letters. And every letter is different. What can you do with as many as a million letters?"

"Well, Sam, what can you do with a million letters?"

"Listen to me, chief. The easiest—the best—the cleanest—fair-all-around—no headaches—no expense—no . . ."

"All right, what is it?"

"Look, chief. Call up the carpenter shop and let the boys build a little chute outside from this floor right into the cellar window. And go in and close your eyes and say 'eenie-meenie-minie-moe' and pick out a letter. All right, it's Mrs. Schwartz from Brooklyn, and the rest go direct to the furnace in the cellar. Just one dump and it's all over."

"I'll think it over."

"There isn't much time."

"I know."

When Sam had left the room Erick said: "Don't worry about me, Joe. It looks like you're trying to scare up work for me."

"Well, we don't need a mathematician on the lot but there are certainly a lot of things that we do need done. . . . Over in the next building is a twenty-three-year-old dance-hall piano player who just had his agent call me up to try to get him two thousand dollars a week. He never went to high school and can hardly sign his name. But he's got tunes in his head that he can strum out with one hand."

"Some types of talent are in demand and others are of little intrinsic value," observed the schoolmaster.

"All right. Then you will let me help you if I can. My God, Erick, when I think of all the things you did for us boys. You were like a father to us and now . . . I'm not talking about charity or anything like that. We need clerical work from time to time and pay the people for office assistance somewhere between thirty and fifty dollars a week. That seems fair for that type of work."

"Really, Joe, I did not intend to have this come up, but you asked me so many questions and . . . I am too far gone to hold any false pride and a job is a job. When a man is long out of work he will accept anything."

"Now that's fine. At least it will be better than standing for hours in the street waiting for a chance to appear as an extra in a mob scene. And a little more certain."

"Joe, I never expected to call on you for help."

"You didn't call on me. I saw you in the line and I picked you out."

Again the telephone rang and again there was an argument on the wire.

From time to time telegrams were brought into the office and Zeloff dictated replies.

Then Sam came in and announced: "Better go down and have a look at the camera angles."

"What's wrong, Sam?"

"Well, you can shoot a cat from the top or from the bottom, but a mob scene is a mob scene and it's just straight business and no monkey business."

"All right, Sam. Have them hold it. I'll be right down." Erick rose to leave.

"This is rather important and I'd better get over there, but as we were saying . . . Yes, I will have something without fail and you'll be hearing from me, well, within twenty-four hours. It's been wonderful seeing you again, and my best at home. Oh, just a minute, you'd better leave me your address. Here, put it on this pad. Excuse me, I must run. Good-bye."

An hour later Zeloff found the address written on his pad in that neat refined handwriting that brought back memories of long ago. He glanced at it for some time and finally he lifted the receiver and said: "Send Sam in."

He handed him the pad. "Do you know where that street is?"

"That's way downtown in the old part of Los Angeles. Somewhere in that section."

"Listen, Sam. That man you saw in here, Mr. Jerobi, was my old teacher."

"Yes, you told me."

"He is more than a teacher. I worshiped that man with the same feeling that a boy worships his father. He is down and out. You saw. It just breaks my heart. We used to go to him for everything. If we have any decency left in us today it is mostly due to him. How would we rascals know about loyalty and honor and honesty if he had not explained it to us from time to time? No finer man ever walked in shoe leather."

"That's right, chief, you can see it in his face."

"Well, listen Sam. We've got this damn contest on and it's a big headache."

"Do what I explained, chief, and it's no headache."

"You mean I should pick a letter . . . Well, Sam, would you mind very much if Mrs. Schwartz of Brooklyn did not get the prize? I mean supposing we got a letter from a certain gentleman who lives downtown in Los Angeles, and in this letter was a title that we all liked . . . We got to send the check to someone. All right, so he gets the check instead of a plumber in Kansas or a soda-water squirt in New Jersey. And we—we have the title we like."

"Chief, you've got something. Do you know what kind of title you are going to like?"

"Yes, Sam. I have the title." He tore the sheet off the pad upon which was written Jerobi's address and on the clean page he wrote boldly the words: *March America,* and handing the pad across the desk said:

"Sam, that's it."

"Chief, it's a win! A natural. That's the story of democracy all tied up snug. Democracy unrolls in eight reels and with sound it just marches along. That's it—*March America!*"

"Well, I'm glad you like it. Now listen, Sam. Fold this paper up and put it in your pocket and take this address. Now be very gentle. You are sent by me to talk to him about some clerical work and then you suggest that he enter the contest. Sure, everybody in the U. S. A. has entered the contest, and if he has not read the serial then you can explain something about ı.. Tell him how the script was written and let him think up some titles with the word America in them and some that show progress or going ahead . . . And you hear the tramp of feet and then naturally he will say 'March of Democracy' and then you combine a couple until he says 'March America.' You know—suggest it. Then get him to write it down. But, Sam, take it easy and be gentle and don't try to be too smart. Remember Sam, Mr. Jerobi is a scholar and a prince and you will never, even if you live to be one hundred, be Socrates."

"O. K., chief. I understand everything. And that title is certainly a knockout. You want me to go now?"

"Yes, and come to the house when you are through. The thing is on my mind."

It was long after supper when Sam finally arrived at the Beverly Hills home of Joe Zeloff.

"Yes, I had supper," he said, seating himself, "but I could stand a good long drink." While the drink was being mixed he continued: "Look, chief. On a dice cube there are six sides and each side has a number. So what are the chances, one to six, no? Well, the professor says it's all wet. And there are fifty-two cards in a deck and the chances are . . . He says no. Toss up a coin and it should be even chances, heads or tails. The professor says it's crazy. But I can't figure out why. That's all in his theory of problems and chances."

"I guess you mean chances and probabilities. How did this come up?"

"Well chief, first I go and find the place. No number on the house. You go through an alley and it's in the back behind the Mexican bazaar and near the Jap village. Then you go up the stairs and hold your nose for the cooking smells. So I find the place and he ain't home yet. His wife and daughter talk to me and tell me how much they hate California. Well, so would I if I had to live in two rooms in that neighborhood. In about half an hour he arrives. He walked all the way from Hollywood and he was pretty tired. I was in the other room and he did not see me. He said he almost had a job in the studio but he just missed it by a hair. 'About a thousand were taken but I was the thousand-and-first,' he said. 'And that again proves my theory,' he remarked. But he added that he had had a good lunch and some bright prospects. Then they told him that a man from the studio was waiting for him. 'Yes, I knew Joe would keep his word with me. He was a boy of great integrity,' he said. 'Straight as a die.' "

"Here's your drink."

"Thanks . . . So we talk about this and about that and finally I ease over to the side of the contest. Then he asks me how many letters we got. And I said, a million. Then he said, if all chances were equal, one would reason that one letter was a million-to-one shot. But no chances are equal. That is how he started to explain to me about the dice cube and the toss-a-coin business, and I let him go on. And now and then I bring in the idea of progress of democracy. And he agrees with me in everything, and goes ahead with the chances business and how this branch of mathematics, which started by gambler's odds, is now of great value to humanity and science. And it was the march of progress that could not be held back. Boy! Right on the head. So I tell him it's a wonderful idea and he should go into the contest. He asks me who the judges are and he gets sus-picious. Then I tell him that Lillie Lang is a dumb blonde and when you say jump, she jumps. And Robert Headlong is playing in the tennis matches and doesn't have time for contest letters; and anyway what you say goes. So then he says 'no.' Even if he had a good idea he would not put you in an embarrassing position. So I say to him that right is right and the chief is square and friend-ship never could influence his integrity. Your worst enemy would have as good a chance as your best friend. But still he hesitated and showed me a pamphlet he wrote about the chances business. And he told me he tossed up a coin and thirteen times in a row it fell heads up. And a dice has six sides but even if it isn't loaded, it is just the same as if it were loaded. Can you understand that? How do you account for it?"

"Well, did you finally get the letter?"

"Yes, I got it. He wrote down three. One is *Win for Democracy* and another is *March, Progress, March* and the third is our one, *March America.*"

"Good. Mail it to the office so the stamp is cancelled and tomorrow morn-ing . . ."

"It's in the bag, chief, and I'm glad the damn contest is over. But how do you explain that dice business and thirteen heads in a row? That goes against my whole education."

"All right, Sam, so your education was no good. Don't lose the letter."

The next day the check was put in the mail and the winner of the contest announced in all the newspapers. When reporters called at the home of Erick Jerobi, formerly a teacher of algebra, he had only one phrase that he repeated over and over: "I am speechless."

The telephone rang in Zeloff's office. "Mr. Jerobi on the phone would like to talk to Mr. Zeloff."

"Tell him I am in conference. Let him call me tomorrow."

The next day he again refused to talk with him. "Let him cool off first," he told his secretary.

After several days Zeloff said: "Let him come to the office tomorrow morning at ten. I don't want to talk on the phone."

Jerobi was most punctual.

"Look," he began. "There has been some mistake and I bring back the check."

Zeloff did not reply. He kept folding up bits of paper with his nervous fingers.

"Here is the check. I did not quite understand at first. Your man Sam is a very slick fellow and most persuasive. I had walked home from here and it is a good many miles. I was pretty tired and we got to talking about chances and I explained some of the strange facts that led me into my theory and he kept talking about the contest and just as a sort of joke I wrote out several titles . . ."

"Well, the one you wrote is the one we like."

"No, Joe, there is something wrong about it."

"We are using it, aren't we?"

"Yes, but I realize now that it was a setup. It was only a plan to put something my way. It was phony. Your whole contest was a fraud! Joe, what have you done? You have swindled a million people who believed in you. And all these years I too have believed in you as one of the straight, honest boys and now . . ."

"I see nothing wrong in this. When you tutored me in algebra you gave me the right answers and that is how I passed the examination."

"Joe, don't say that. It's not the same thing at all. There are standard problems in algebra and there was no collusion between the professor who wrote the examination paper and myself."

"No, I don't say you two got together, all I say is, you knew the answers."

"But this thing is a crooked thing. I cannot be a party to it. I must—I am forced to . . ."

"Wait a minute, Erick. Think for a second. I am an old pupil of yours. You are not going to let me down that badly. Think again. The newspapers are not printing your tale of woe because we are heavy advertisers and they will not give us bad publicity willingly. Think again. You have another proof for your theory that all chances are not equal. Think again. You did lots of things for lots of boys and now one of them has done a little thing for you."

"A little thing! A big crooked thing!"

"Yes, Erick. Put the check back in your pocket. Go back to Connecticut where you will be happy and forget all about this California nightmare . . . And your opinion of me? . . . Well, I am sorry. All the high morality . . . Yes, you sent us out of school filled with integrity, decency and prune juice! It's all a lot of old ladies' morality. The business world . . . All right, so you lie—what of it? So the deal is a little shady. So what? A lot of bids come into the office and he gives the business to his friend. What of it?"

"Joe! How can you speak like that? I would never have believed . . ."

"And I'll tell you more. When I saw you among the extras, I said to myself here is my chance to show my old teacher what I have done in the world and how success is really made. And so I put all my cards on the table and say, look Erick, look what a stinker your boy Joe has become! All right, the truth hurts. Sure it hurts. It hurts goddam hard."

"Yes, it hurts. I do not blame a man for what he has become. It's the shock that is hard. But I cannot blame him. A hungry man has a different morality than a sheltered scholar would have."

"And a successful man is again a different thing."

"Yes, he is. Good-bye, Joe, and no matter what you have become, may God bless you."

With these words he walked out of the office. But his feet were unsteady and he stopped in the hall at the drinking fountain to take a sip of water. His eyes were flooded and the paper cup shook in his hand.

Several days later Sam helped him buy a second-hand car and dispose of the old piano and other household junk. At last the little family was packed up and started on its homeward journey.

"California has been a big disappointment to me," he confided to Sam. "Yes, the climate is fair, but the people are so lousy they don't deserve a good winter. It attracts all the fakers and numerologists. Now what do numerologists know of the laws of chances? Nothing."

Sam reported these last words to his chief.

"I am sorry," said Zeloff, "I lost his good opinion. There was no other way. Sam, it broke my heart to have to tell him that I have become a skunk and that I live now without either integrity or honesty. There was no other way. So the contest was a little phony and a man who needed it got the check."

"Who was going to read a million letters anyway?"

"That's not the point, Sam. The point is that you have known me now for eight years and you have been on the job every day and you know that this is the only shady thing I have ever done. The million letter writers may not forgive me if they ever know, but there may be a chance that there is a God in Heaven and if there is, then I am sure He will forgive me."

"It's more than even chances, chief. According to the professor, Fate rolls a pair of loaded dice."

THOMAS WOLFE

◄──►

The Hollow Men

HOW OFTEN have we read the paper in America! How often have we seen it *blocked* against our doors! Little route-boys fold and block it, so to throw it— and so we find it and unfold it, crackling and ink-laden, at our doors. Sometimes we find it tossed there lightly with flat *plop*; sometimes we find it thrown with solid, whizzing *whack* against the clapboards (clapboards here, most often, in America); sometimes servants find just freshly folded sheets laid neatly down in doorways, and take them to the table for their masters. No matter how it got there, we always find it.

How we do love the paper in America! How we do love the paper, all!

Why do we love the paper in America? Why do we love the paper, all?

Mad masters, I will tell ye why.

Because the paper is "the news" here in America, and we love the *smell* of news. We love the smell of news that's "fit to print." We also love the smell of news *not* fit to print. We love, besides, the smell of *facts* that news is made of. Therefore we love the paper because the news is so fit-printable—so unprintable —and so fact-printable.

Is the news, then, like America? No, it's not—

The news is *not* America, nor is America the *news*—the news is *in* America. It is a kind of light at morning, and at evening, and at midnight in America. It is a kind of growth and record and excrescence of our life. It is not good enough —it does not tell our story—yet it is the news!

Take the following, for instance:

> An unidentified man fell or jumped yesterday at noon from the twelfth story of the Admiral Francis Drake Hotel in Brooklyn. The man, who was about thirty-five years old, registered at the hotel about a week ago, according to the police, as C. Green. Police are of the opinion that this was an assumed name. Pending identification, the body is being held at the King's County Morgue.

This, then, is news. Is it also the whole story, Admiral Drake? No! Yet we do not supply the whole story—we who have known all the lights and weathers of America.

Well, then, it's news, and it happened in your own hotel, brave Admiral Drake, so, of course, you'll want to know what happened.

October, 1940

"An unidentified man"—well, then, this man was an American. "About thirty-five years old" with "an assumed name"—well, then, call him C. Green as he called himself ironically in the hotel register. C. Green, the unidentified American, "fell or jumped," then, "yesterday at noon . . . in Brooklyn"—worth six lines of print in today's *Times*—one of seven thousand who died yesterday upon this continent—one of three hundred and fifty who died yesterday in this very city (see dense, close columns of obituaries, page 15: begin with "Aaronson," so through the alphabet to "Zorn"). C. Green came here "a week ago"—

And came from where? From the deep South, or the Mississippi Valley, or the Middle West? From Minneapolis, Bridgeport, Boston, or a little town in Old Catawba? From Scranton, Toledo, St. Louis, or the desert whiteness of Los Angeles? From the pine barrens of the Atlantic coastal plain, or from the Pacific shore?

And so—was *what*, brave Admiral Drake? In what way an American? In what way different from the men you knew, old Drake?

When the ships bore home again and Cape St. Vincent blazed in Spaniard's eye—or when old Drake was returning with his men, beating coastwise from strange seas abreast, past the Scilly Isles toward the slant of evening fields, chalk cliffs, the harbor's arms, the town's sweet cluster and the spire—where was Green?

When, in red-oak thickets at the break of day, coon-skinned, the huntsmen of the wilderness lay for bear, heard arrows rattling in the laurel leaves, the bullets' whining *plunk*, and waited with cocked musket by the tree—where was Green?

Or when, with strong faces turning toward the setting sun, hawk-eyed and Indian-visaged men bore gunstocks on the western trails and sternly heard the fierce war-whoops around the Painted Buttes—where, then, was Green?

Was never there with Drake's men in the evening when the sails stood in from the Americas! Was never there beneath the Spaniard's swarthy eye at Vincent's Cape! Was never there in the red-oak thicket in the morning! Was never there to hear the war-cries round the Painted Buttes!

No, no. He was no voyager of unknown seas, no pioneer of western trails. He was life's little man, life's nameless cipher, life's manswarm atom, life's American—and now he lies disjected and exploded on a street in Brooklyn!

He was a dweller in mean streets, was Green, a man-mote in the jungle of the city, a resident of grimy steel and stone, a stunned spectator of enormous salmon-colored towers, hued palely with the morning. He was a waker in bleak streets at morning, an alarm-clock watcher, saying, "Jesus, I'll be late!"—a fellow who took short cuts through the corner lot, behind the advertising signs; a fellow used to concrete horrors of hot day and blazing noon; a man accustomed to the tormented hodgepodge of our architecture, used to broken pavements, ash cans, shabby store fronts, dull green paint, the elevated structure, grinding traffic, noise, and streets betortured with a thousand bleak and dismal signs. He was accustomed to the gas tanks going out of town, he was an atom of machinery in an endless flow, going, stopping, going to the winking of the lights; he tore down concrete roads on Sundays, past the hot-dog stands and filling

stations; he would return at darkness; hunger lured him to the winking splendor
of chop-suey signs; and midnight found him in The Coffee Pot, to prowl above
a mug of coffee, tear a coffee-cake in fragments, and wear away the slow grey ash
of time and boredom with other men in grey hats and with skins of tallow-
grey, at Joe the Greek's.

C. Green could read (which Drake could not), but not too accurately; could
write, too (which the Spaniard couldn't), but not too well. C. Green had trouble
over certain words, spelled them out above the coffee mug at midnight, with a
furrowed brow, slow-shaping lips, and "Jesus!" when news stunned him—for he
read the news. Preferred the news "hot," straight from the shoulder—socko!—
biff!—straight off the griddle, with lots of mustard, shapely legs, roadside wrecks
and mutilated bodies, gangster's molls and gunmen's hideouts, tallow faces of
the night that bluntly stare at flashlight lenses—this and talk of "heart-balm,"
"love-thief," "sex-hijacker"—all of this liked Green.

Yes, Green liked the news—and now, a bit of news himself (six lines of print
in *Times*), has been disjected and exploded on a Brooklyn pavement!

Behold him, Admiral Drake! Observe the scene now! Listen to the people!
Here's something strange as the Armadas, the gold-laden cargoes of the bearded
Spaniards, the vision of unfound Americas!

What do you see here, Admiral Drake?

Well, first, a building—your own hotel—a great block of masonry, grimy-
white, fourteen stories tall, stamped in an unvarying pattern with many windows.
Sheeted glass below, the store front piled with medicines and toilet articles,
perfumes, cosmetics, health contrivances. Within, a soda fountain, Admiral
Drake. The men in white with monkey caps, soda jerkers sullen with perpetual
overdriven irritation. Beneath the counter, pools of sloppy water, filth, and un-
washed dishes. Across the counter, women with fat, rouged lips consuming ice
cream sodas and pimento sandwiches.

Outside upon the concrete sidewalk lies the form of our exploded friend, C.
Green. A crowd has gathered 'round—taxi drivers, passers-by, hangers-on about
the subway station, people working in the neighborhood, and the police. No
one has dared to touch exploded Green as yet—they stand there in a rapt
and fascinated circle, looking at him.

Not much to look at either, Admiral Drake; not even those who trod your
gory decks would call the sight a pretty one. Our friend has landed on his
head—"taken a nose dive," as we say—and smashed his brains out at the iron
base of the second lamp post from the corner.

So here Green lies, on the concrete sidewalk all disjected. No head is left,
the head is gone now, head's exploded; only brains are left. The brains are pink,
and almost bloodless, Admiral Drake. (There's not much blood here—we shall
tell you why.) But brains exploded are somewhat like pale sausage meat, fresh-
ground. Brains are stuck hard to the lamp post, too; there is a certain driven
emphasis about them, as if they had been shot hydraulically out of a force-hose
against the post.

The head, as we have said, is gone completely; a few fragments of the skull are scattered round—but of the face, the features, forehead—nothing! They have all been blown *out*, as by some inner explosion. Nothing is left but the back of the skull, which curiously remains, completely hollowed out and vacant, and curved over, like the rounded handle of a walking stick.

The body, five feet eight or nine of it, of middling weight, is lying—we were going to say "face downward"; had we not better say "stomach downward"?—on the sidewalk. And save for a certain indefinable and curiously "disjected" quality, one could scarcely tell that every bone in it is broken. The hands are still spread out, half-folded and half-clenched, with a still-warm and startling eloquence of recent life. (It happened just four minutes ago!)

Well, where's the blood, then, Drake? You're used to blood; you'd like to know. Well, you've heard of casting bread upon the waters, Drake, and having it return—but never yet, I'll vow, of casting blood upon the streets—and having it run away—and then come back to you! But here it comes now, down the street now toward C. Green, the lamp post, and the crowd! a young Italian youth, his black eyes blank with horror, tongue mumbling thickly, arm held firmly by a policeman, suit and shirt all drenched with blood, and face be-spattered with it! A stir of sudden interest in the crowd, sharp nudges, low-toned voices whispering:

"Here he is! Th' guy that 'got it'! . . . he was standin' *deh* beside the post! Sure, *that's* the guy!— talkin' to anotheh guy—he got it all! *That's* the reason you didn't see more blood—*this* guy got it!—Sure! The guy just missed him by six inches!—Sure I'm tellin' you I *saw* it, ain't I! I looked up an' saw him in the air! He'd a hit this guy, but when he saw that he was goin' to hit the lamp post, he put out his hands an' tried to keep away! *That's* the reason that he didn't hit this guy! . . . But this guy heard him when he hit, an' turned around—and zowie!—he got all of it right in his face!"

And another, whispering and nudging, nodding toward the horror-blank, thick-mumbling Italian boy: "Jesus! Look at th' guy, will yuh! . . . He don't know what he's doing! . . . He don't know yet what happened to him! . . . Sure! He got it *all*. I tell yuh! An' when it happened—when he got it—he just stahted runnin' . . . He don't know yet what's happened! . . . That's what I'm tellin' yuh—th' guy just stahted runnin' when he got it."

And the Italian youth, thick-mumbling: " . . . Jeez! W'at happened? . . . Jeez! . . . I was standin' talkin' to a guy—I heard it hit . . . Jeez! . . . W'at happened, anyway? . . . I got it all oveh me! . . . Jeez! . . . I just stahted runnin' . . . Jeez! I'm sick!"

Voices: "Here, take 'im into the drug store! . . . Wash 'im off! . . . That guy needs a shot of liquor! . . . Sure! Take him into the drug stoeh *deh!* . . . They'll fix him up!"

The plump young man who runs the newsstand in the corridor, talking to everyone around him, excitedly and indignantly: ". . . Did I see it? Listen! I saw *everything*! I was coming across the street, looked up, and saw him in the air! . . . *See* it . . . *Listen!* If someone had taken a big ripe watermelon and dropped it on the street from the fourteenth floor you'd have some idea what it was like!

. . . See it! *I'll* tell the world I saw it! I don't want to see anything like *that* again!"
Then excitedly, with a kind of hysterical indignation: "Shows no consideration
for other people, that's all *I've* got to say! If a man is going to do a thing like
that, why does he pick a place like *this*—one of the busiest corners in Brooklyn?
. . . How did *he* know he wouldn't hit someone? Why, if that boy had been
standing six inches nearer to the post, he'd have killed him, as sure as you live!
. . . And here he does it right in front of all these people who have to look at
it! It shows he had no consideration for other people! A man who'd do a thing
like that . . ."

(Alas, poor youth! As if C. Green, now past considering, had considered nice
"considerations.")

A taxi driver, impatiently: "That's what I'm tellin' yuh! . . . I watched him
for five minutes before he jumped. He crawled out on the window sill an' stood
there for *five* minutes, makin' up his mind! . . . Sure, I saw him! Lots of people
saw him!" Impatiently, irritably: "Why didn't we do somethin' to stop him?
F'r Chri' sake, what was there to do? A guy who'd do a thing like that is nuts
to start with! You don't think he'd listen to anything we had to say, do you?
. . . Sure, we *did* yell at him! . . . Jesus! . . . We was almost *afraid* to yell at him—
we made motions to him to get back—tried to hold his attention while the cops
sneaked round the corner into the hotel . . . Sure, the cops got there just a
second after he jumped—I don't know if he jumped when he heard 'em comin',
or what happened, but Christ!—he stood there gettin' ready for five minutes
while we watched!"

Observe now, Admiral, with what hypnotic concentration the people are
examining the grimy-white façade of your hotel. Watch their faces and expressions. Their eyes go traveling upward slowly—up—up—up until they finally
arrive and come to rest with focal concentration on that single open window
twelve floors up. It is no jot different from all the other windows, but now the
vision of the crowd is fastened on it with a fatal and united interest. And after
staring at it fixedly, the eyes come traveling slowly down again—down—down—
down—the faces strained a little, mouths all slightly puckered as if something
set the teeth on edge—and slowly, with fascinated measurement—down—down
—down—until the eyes reach sidewalk, lamp post, and—the Thing again.

The pavement finally halts all, stops all, answers all. It is the American pavement, Admiral Drake, our universal city sidewalk, a wide, hard stripe of grey-
white cement, blocked accurately with dividing lines. It is the hardest, coldest,
cruellest, most impersonal pavement in the world: all of the indifference, the
atomic desolation, the exploded nothingness of one hundred million nameless
"Greens" is in it.

It came from the same place where all our sidewalks come from—from
Standard Concentrated Production Units of America, No. 1. This is where all
our streets and lamp posts (like the one on which Green's brains are spattered)
come from, where all our white-grimy bricks (like those of which your hotel is
constructed) come from, where the red façades of our standard-unit tobacco
stores (like the one across the street) come from, where our motor cars come

from, where our drug stores and our drug store windows and displays come
from, where our soda fountains (complete, with soda jerkers attached) come
from, where our cosmetics, toilet articles, and the fat, rouged lips of our women
come from, where our soda water, slops and syrups, steamed spaghetti, ice cream,
and pimento sandwiches come from, where our clothes, our hats (neat, standard
stamps of grey), our faces (also stamps of grey, not always neat), our language,
conversation, sentiments, feelings, and opinions come from. All these things
are made for us by Standard Concentrated Production Units of America, No. 1.

So here we are then, Admiral Drake. You see the street, the sidewalk,
the front of your hotel, the constant stream of motor cars, the cops in uniform,
the people streaming in and out of the subway, the rusty, pale-hued jungle of
the buildings, old and new, high and low. There is no better place to see it,
Drake. For this is Brooklyn—which means ten thousand streets and blocks like
this one. Brooklyn, Admiral Drake, is the Standard Concentrated Chaos No. 1
of the Whole Universe. That is to say, it has no size, no shape, no heart, no joy,
no hope, no aspiration, no center, no eyes, no soul, no purpose, no direction,
and no anything—just Standard Concentrated Units everywhere—exploding
in all directions for an unknown number of square miles like a completely
triumphant Standard Concentrated Blot upon the Face of the Earth. And here,
right in the middle, upon a minute portion of this magnificent Standard Concentrated Blot, where all the Standard Concentrated Blotters can stare at him,
and with the brains completely out of him—

—Lies Green!

And this is bad—most bad—oh, very bad—and should not be allowed! For,
as our young news-vendor friend has just indignantly proclaimed, it "shows no
consideration for other people"—which means, for other Standard Concentrated
Blotters. Green has no right to go falling in this fashion in a public place. He
has no business *being* where he is at all. A Standard Concentrated Blotter
is not supposed to *be* places, but to *go* places.

You see, dear Admiral, this sidewalk, this Standard Concentrated Mobway
is not a place to walk on, really. It is a place to swarm on, to weave on, to thrust
and dodge on, to scurry past on, to crowd by on. One of the earliest precepts in
a Concentrated Blotter's life is: "Move on there! Where th' hell d'you think
you are, anyway—in a cow pasture?" And, most certainly, it is not a place to lie
on, to sprawl out on.

But look at Green! Just look at him! No wonder the plump youth is angry
with him!

Green has willfully and deliberately violated every Standard Concentrated
Principle of Blotterdom. He has not only gone and dashed his brains out, but
he has done it in a public place—upon a piece of Standard Concentrated Mobway. He has messed up the sidewalk, messed up another Standard Concentrated
Blotter, stopped traffic, taken people from their business, upset the nerves of
his fellow Blotters—and now *lies* there, all *sprawled* out, in a place where he
has no right to *be*. And, to make his crime unpardonable, C. Green has—

—Come to Life!

What's that, Admiral? You do not understand it? Small wonder, though it's really very simple:

For just ten minutes since, C. Green was a Concentrated Blotter like the rest of us, a nameless atom, swarming with the rest of us, just another "guy" like a hundred million other "guys." But now, observe him! No longer is he just "another guy"—already he has become a "special guy"—he has become "*The Guy.*" C. Green at last has turned into a—*Man!*

ERIC KNIGHT

Strong in the Arms

POLKINGTHORPE BRIG isn't such a big place, even as villages go; but by gum, it can produce men.

In fact, for a place its size, as you might say, it has produced more famous men, in a manner of speaking, than any other place in the world.

For instance it has Sam Small, who once voyaged all the way to America and by his cunning managed to come back home safely to tell all about it. And then it's got Ian Cawper.

Ian Cawper is really famous. He's the biggest and strongest lad in all Yorkshire—which means, of course, all England. For everyone knows that inch for inch and pound for pound a Yorkshireman's worth two from any other county—especially Lancashire.

Of course, Ian's a little thick in the head; but they don't hold that against a man much in Yorkshire. And, true, he's a fearful man to see when he's angered; but that's very seldom. Most times Ian is pleasant enough and affable enough. Whenever there's anything heavy needs lugging in the village, the folk always get hold of a bairn and say: "Run up Ian Cawper's cottage and tell him there's summat here that nob'dy but him can do." Ian will come down, generally carrying the bairn on his shoulder, and after they've explained to him carefully what they want, he'll move or lug or lift whatever it is, such as a walnut bureau or a boulder or a cart stuck in the mud—and very pleasantly he'll do it, too.

But there's a thing or two about Ian that fair puzzles the older people in the village.

To come right out with it, the fact is that Ian doesn't look much like any other Cawper that ever lived, not even as far back as old Capper Wambley can remember. True, the Cawpers have always been a strong breed, so he takes after them in that. But Ian is a blond, blue-eyed lad, while all the Cawpers before him were very dark—so dark, in fact, that Ian's father was known as Black Cawper. Ian's blondness couldn't have come from his mother's side, either, for she's a Motherthwaite, and the Motherthwaites are a darkish clan.

It's fair puzzling, indeed it is, and that's the truth, as the village people say. Naturally, they don't say it when Ian's around, for Ian Cawper's a fearful man when he does get angry, and could break a man in two with his bare hands if so be he wished.

April, 1938

But people do talk once in a while, and one night Sam Small got talking down at the Spread Eagle. What his story means, you must judge for yourself. As to how true it is—well, Sam Small's as truthful a Yorkshireman as ever blew the foam off four or five pints of good ale in an evening.

Ian's father, Black Cawper—so goes Sam's story—was a big strong man who was ready to fight, feast or wrestle at the drop of a hat. He wasn't as big as Ian has turned out to be, but he was shrewder than Ian will ever be. And he was more given to sudden tempers and to daring other men and showing off his strength.

Black Cawper was a favorite chap up on the moor on Sunday afternoons. For then, as now, all the men of the village would meet up on the moor to show off feats of nimbleness or strength, or to ask each other puzzling questions and riddles, or to bet on their dogs. They'd run their whippets, or hold terrier contests by putting their tykes in a barrel with a score or so of rats to see how many the dog could kill in sixty seconds. And sometimes, by lucky chance, they might meet a bunch of men from another village who would be looking for a bit of a fight. That's the way it's always been on Sunday afternoons.

Now on this Sunday afternoon about twenty-five years ago, so Sam Small says, a stranger came cutting across the moor who seemed by his speech to be from over Malton way.

They asked him if he'd like to fight, and he said no; they asked him if he wanted to buy a dog and he said no; they asked him if he'd like to wrestle or run a race for a bit of a side-bet and he said no. They had just about concluded he was a pawky sort of chap until he said that if it were a matter of knerr and spell, by gum, he'd be willing to back himself roundly to the tune of a few shillings.

Now if there's anything the lads of Polkingthorpe Brig pride themselves on besides fighting and dogs, it's their skill at knerr and spell, a game requiring strength, speed and judgment. (Many years ago this game drifted from Yorkshire up into Scotland where, in a much deteriorated and simplified form, it became known as golf.)

So when the stranger said he'd play, he was rapidly taken up.

It turned out, however, that this lad was nobody's mug. He was a lanky, little chap with a click to his wrists when he swung that sent the ball sailing champion distances. One by one he took the money away from the Polkingthorpe men until there was only Black Cawper left, and the light was beginning to fade.

"All or nowt in a final match," Black Cawper offered.

The lad said it was so for his pile of sixteen shillings, and he put up such a mighty ding-dong battle that at the last stroke Black Cawper needed the well-nigh impossible score of 262 to tie, 263 to win. But Black Cawper only laughed and flexed the muscles in his big arms and spit on his hands. He tapped the tie-up smartly, and when the ball rose into the air he wrapped the springy club round his neck and swung. He hit the ball fair just as it was beginning to fall and belted that dobbie a giant clout such as the men there had never seen before.

Away the ball went, screaming away in a straight, rising line. Up it went, away and over a far hilltop, out of sight.

Black Cawper laughed his hard laugh.

"Two hunned and sixty-three," he offered.

This meant that if the stranger could reach the ball in less than 263 leaping strides, the score counted to him. If he couldn't, it counted to Black Cawper who thereby won the match.

The Malton lad looked up at the hill and shook his head. He was a fine judge of distances, and knew he couldn't reach the ball in the required number.

"Tha's t'better lad o' t'two on us," he said and conceded the game. They shook hands and paid off. The matches were over for that day.

"Well," Black Cawper said, "now let's off and find ma dobbie."

But the men all shuffled their feet and coughed and spat.

"Nay, Black," they said, "us'll away and meet thee later down at t'Eagle."

Then Black Cawper laughed, for he knew why they were backing away as they looked at the bleak hill, now rapidly sinking back into the evening darkness. For over that hill was Wada's Keep.

Most everyone in Polkingthorpe Brig had seen Wada's Keep—but not after dark.

You went up there in the daytime—a bunch of you together, of course—and even then it was bad enough. If you had courage, you went right up to it, plunging through the bracken and stumbling over rocks. For the land there was no longer flat moor, but rocky and broken into strange crags. You kept on, being wrapped deeper in the lonesomeness and barrenness of that place. And when you got there, you didn't dare to talk. All you did was stand by the Keep whose stones were damp and green with their ancient age. At least 1200 years old it was—that's what the schoolmaster said the day he went up there. He talked about Saxon defenders and cromlechs. That word cromlech, it made it worse, it did.

No one needed to talk of things like that when you could stand there in that silence and look at the round tower and its walls made of mighty boulders that no human hands could have lifted into place. But those boulders had been nothing for Wada, the giant. He'd lofted them up into place as nicely as a mason these days sets in a little brick.

You knew the awe of that place when you stood there thinking things like that, standing in the land where no living thing moved as far as you could see down on the wide stretches. You smelled the dust of the dried bracken and against it the damp smell of stones in unused places, and then you'd hear the fearful, lonesome cry of a peewit, and at that you'd shudder and start home, walking quickly and more quickly—all of you. Until you came over the moor and could see Polkingthorpe again, and then you slowed down and laughed and pretended you'd never walked fast with the terror of unknown things breathing on the back of your neck.

And that was the terror all the men felt that Sunday afternoon when Black

Cawper faced toward Wada's land and said he was going there in the dusk. He laughed in his hard, bold way, and said:

"Would ye leave a lad to find his dobbie alone?"

They rocked on their feet and coughed and spat. And then Black Cawper blazed into one of his sudden tempers—Cawper's mad higs, the men called them.

"Ba gow," he roared, "that's ma pet dobbie and Ah'm not off to lose it. Ah'm bahn up theer, and what's more, one on ye's cooming up wi' me to bear witness Ah showed no fear. Here, Sam Small, tha'll coom wi' me."

"Nay, not me," Sam said, stoutly.

"Tha'll coom when Ah say," Cawper shouted. And he jumped over and caught Sam by the scruff of his neck and slung him over his shoulder.

"Here, let me dahn, Black," Sam pleaded. "It's ma teatime, and Mully'll be mawgier nor owd hell if Ah'm late."

Black Cawper paid no attention to Sam. Instead he swung about and faced the hill. He shook his knerr-and-spell club and lifted his head and shouted:

"Now giant! If so be as tha' lives in them hills, clear out o' t'road! For here cooms Black Cawper, and w' a witness to boot!"

But when he said that from the skyline came a quick glow of light and then, far away, the distant rumble of thunder. And as the watching men drew in their breath sharply, one of the dogs lifted his head and howled in a manner like to curdle your blood. Then, like a flock of birds that obey an unsounded signal, all the men turned about, and a mad charge of men and dogs went stampeding off down to the village.

When they were gone Black Cawper stood a while, and then, slowly, one foot stamping down before the other, he started up that hill with Sam Small over his left shoulder and his knerr-and-spell club in his right hand. At the top of the hill he lifted Sam to the ground.

"Now lad," he said. "Us'll find ma dobbie. And tha'd better stick close to me; because t'owd Nick hissen knaws what maught grab thee if tha tried to run hoam alone this time o' neight."

He chuckled deep down in his chest, but Sam only shivered. He glanced around fearfully, Sam did, and resolved not to be left alone that night if he could help it. So he followed close behind Black Cawper and they kicked at the tufts of grass and pulled aside clumps of gorse as they looked for the ball. But nowhere was a ball to be seen.

"O' course it's not here," Black Cawper said. "It maun ha' gone far and away down into t'valley here. For surely it were the championest clout a lad ivver give a dobbie."

So they went deeper and deeper into the country, following the line the ball had taken as best they could. But no ball could they find.

"Now lewk here, Black," Sam said at last. "No man can say tha hesn't dared to hunt, but it's pitch black now and we'll noan find it in the dark. Sitha lad, let's coom up tomort morn and lewk for it."

"Us has gate to be at t'pit and digging coal by dawn," Black said, "and Ah'm bound Ah'm off to find ma dobbie toneight. There'll be a gradely moon out soon."

"Nay, coom away, Black lad," Sam coaxed. "Just think, Black, it's supper time and there'll be a nice fire i't'fireplace, and a fine, steaming pot o' tea, and some hot toasted scones or muffins, all swimming in butter; or a pikelet or two and some sliced ham, wi' a wedge of two o' nice cold pork pie—or happen a bloater, all fried to a turn. Tha likes bloaters, Ah knaw . . ."

"Nay," said Black.

"Eigh, but happen there'd be a gert big foaming quart o' fine beer. Wouldn't a like a mug o' beer that'd mak' a chap smack his lips and . . ."

"Nay," said Black.

"Not even if, happen, somebody were to stand thee that quart o' beer?"

"Nay!"

"Not for a quart o' beer? Not even if Ah were to say outright it'd be me what stood the price on it for thee?"

"Ah said nay," roared Black Cawper. "Ah've said Ah'm off to find ma dobbie, and find it Ah will—if it tak's all neight, and no matter whose bailiwick it chances to be in."

Right when he said that Sam shivered, for Black's great voice went rolling out into the darkness and rumbled up into the crags, and like an echo came back a voice that boomed like a peal of thunder, saying:

"Be this what th'art looking for?"

At that moment there was a lifting light and the rising moon shot from behind a ragged cloud. Black and Sam, standing stock-still, looked out across the rocky hollow and saw a man standing on a flat crag—a great, well-set-up lad he was, with a blond beard that shone in the moonlight.

For a long time they all stood without moving and the moments passed. The first sound was when Black Cawper laughed his bold laugh.

"Tak' this," he said, and he thrust his club into Sam's hand. Sam heard him drawing in his breath through his nose, drawing it in and filling his chest so that it expanded, wider and wider. Then, with his head thrust forward and his arms hanging wide from bent elbows, Black Cawper took the first step forward. He kept on steadily, evenly, his metal-shod clogs coming down regularly as he went forward, step by step to where the man waited.

Poor Sam's belly turned over with terror, but he felt that this was no time for a lad to leave his chum, even if he died for it. So he scrabbled along behind Black, gripping the club firmly.

Cawper went on until he reached the flat rock where the man waited with his legs far apart and his thumbs hooked lightly into his waist-belt. Within an arm's-length Black Cawper halted and took the same position—his feet planted apart and his thumbs resting inside the waist of his corduroy trousers. Thus they stood and looked each other up and down slowly and carefully, not saying a word.

Sam waited in fear as the minutes passed; for although Black Cawper was a well-set man, the bearded chap was bigger by almost a foot.

They said no word, and when the time was done Black Cawper turned and picked up the dobbie that was shining on the ground. The way he did it was a dare-devil way, for he turned his back completely on the other man as if he scorned him. It was a bold contemptuous thing to do, and Sam gripped the club firmly. But the bearded man made no move, only following Cawper with his eyes that seemed to smile.

Cawper turned the dobbie over carefully, pretending to examine every part of it, his back still toward the other man.

"Aye," he said finally. "This is ma dobbie."

He turned around and laughed loudly, in the face of the stranger.

"Now, Ah gate what Ah coom for, Ah'll be off on ma road hoam," he said.

He waited patiently, but there was no answer.

"Aye, that's champion," Sam said quickly. "Thanking this lad varry politely for his help, us'll be off."

Black did not look at Sam. He stared at the unmoving man on the rock.

"Nay, but on t'other hand," Cawper said, "Ah maught want to stay."

The other man did not move, so Black Cawper went near to him, and squinting his eyes and looking up through his knotted eyebrows he said:

"Ah nivver turned ma back on noa man yet be-out being politelike, as tha mought say. Soa Ah'm axing thee: wouldt'a like to feight, lad?"

The blond man laughed.

"Eigh, there's all neight for sport yet," he answered. "Sit thee down here for a while—if tha's gate time to spare."

"Ah've gate as much time to spare as ony other man," Cawper said, "and brass enow to sit ony place ma feet can carry me to."

So they sat, each on a boulder, facing each other. Sam, not knowing what to do, sat on the ground, hugging the club. For a long time nothing was said, but Sam, knowing Black Cawper, could see he was getting ready to do a bit of thinking. Nearly half an hour passed in silence, and then Black said, suddenly:

"If a hen and a hawf laid an egg and a hawf in a day and a hawf, how much would one hen lay in a week."

He looked cunningly at the big man, for Black Cawper prided himself on being a foxy sort of a chap at thinking. But right smack back came the big lad:

"Four eggs and two-thirds on the way to lay another."

Sam Small drew in his breath quickly, for he knew of no stranger who'd been able to answer that problem before. Many a pint of beer had Black Cawper won from strangers in the inn with that one. Moreover, the answer given was the right one, for that's what the schoolmaster had told them was the right solution when they'd first taken the puzzle to him to be worked out.

When this stranger gave the right answer, Black Cawper nodded his head, for he began to see he was up against a very unusual opponent this time. So he went back to doing a bit of thinking again. He thought and thought until the moon was rising up in the sky. Then he got up suddenly and walking to Sam took the club from his hand. Looking over to see if the stranger was watching, Black took the dobbie from his pocket. Not speaking a word, he threw it up in the air with a fine, careless twirl of his hand, and then swung back with his club. The dobbie flashed up in the moonlight and began to fall. Just when it was a little over waisthigh, Black's club came swinging round and caught that dobbie a crack that sounded sweet and true.

Away that ball went like a line of silver. Then it was gone, slanting up into the night. But even then they could hear it whooshing away with a dying moan in the black quietness. For a long time they waited, breathless, and the minutes passed. Faintly they heard at last the sound of the dobbie tacking and tumbling on the stones far across the valley.

Then Black nodded his head in satisfaction and sat down.

The big man said never a word, but he got up and looked carefully at Black's club. He took it in one hand and whooshed it round a few times. Black's club was a special one, so heavy that no man but himself could swing it with the flash of accuracy and speed that knerr and spell demands. However, the stranger seemed amused by it and put it aside. Instead he picked up a great ash cudgel and selected a rock. As big around as a man's two fists, that rock was. But the big chap flipped it up in the air and swung quickly. That was a crash as if the rock had exploded, and Sam Small blinked as if he'd been blinded.

How far that rock went, Sam never knew, for as he waited for the sound of it falling, there came a flash of light on the horizon and a mumbling and a bumbling of thunder far away.

"Eigh, they maun be hevin a storm up i' t'Malvern Hills," Sam said.

He felt he must say something, for the other two never spoke. They looked at each other, and the blond man smiled. Black Cawper knotted his brows in anger and suddenly cried:

"Ah'll run thee a race for ten bob!"

"Good! To the tower and back," the other man said.

At the mention of that tower, Sam did shiver for fair. But Black Cawper hesitated hardly a moment.

"Done," he said.

"Touch the tower wall and back to Tichie here," the stranger said.

At this Sam got fair blazing, for although he wasn't a big man, no one had ever called him Tichie before—for that word means a dwarf man in Yorkshire. But he consoled himself with the thought that now the stranger would be beaten, for few light men were as fast on their feet as Black Cawper, and surely no big men best him in a footrace. But before he could think much of this, Black shouted:

"Ready? Go!"

Away they went into the darkness and Sam could hear the mighty churning and awhortling of their bodies tearing through the thick bracken and the crashing of their feet upon the rocks. The sounds died away and then grew again.

Sam jumped to his feet to see who was first, and when they came into view they were neck and neck. But right at the last moment the stranger seemed to glide ahead without altering his stride and flying past he tapped Sam with the tip of his hand.

It was only a light touch, yet Sam felt as if he'd been struck with a jolt of electricity and he felt himself going rolling and abowling arse-over-ashtip down the rocks. When he picked himself up and got back Cawper was paying off the bet, his forehead knotted in anger.

Now that the blond man had won the footrace, Sam realized that Black Cawper was up against something the likes of which he'd never known before and that this night was to see a contest to be remembered. For Sam knew that Black Cawper would never give in. And neither he did. In that moonlight night up in Wada's country, Black Cawper matched the stranger at all the things he knew, one by one. They matched at games of cunning and games of strength; at jumping for height and jumping for distance; at heaving rocks for yardage and heaving rocks for aim; at lifting boulders of greater and greater size above their heads. And always the stranger won.

Finally Black Cawper had not a farthing left to bet with. So he jumped up in anger and tore off his coat.

"Now lad," he roared, "there's nobbut one thing left. There's gate to be a feight, between me and thee!"

"For what stake?"

"Nay, Ah gate nowt left. Tha maun feight me for t'fun on it."

"And varry happy Ah'll be to do so, too," the blond man said.

"That's spoken like a honest chap," Black said and tore off his shirt.

They both stripped to the waist, knotted their neckerchiefs carefully about their middles. Black Cawper flexed his knotty arms and lifted his chest, all covered and matted with black hair. The other man's skin shone in the moonlight, pink and hairless as a baby's backside.

"Now lad," Black said, "how'll us feight—standups or knockdowns? Us maun do this reight and proper."

"Nay, awther way tha says," the other replied, lightly.

Sam waited anxiously. For there are two kinds of fighting up in Yorkshire. The standup is a softy sort of fighting that is drifting in from the south counties, in which it is very useless to knock a man down, for all you must do then is stand back and let him get up again.

Now the knockdown is the real Yorkshire way of fighting, for if you once strike your man down then everything else follows in a sensible sort of way—for instance you may jump on him, or kneel on him and batter him, or if you think it best you may stand off and kick him sweetly. This is a most honest way of fighting, especially since the clogs of Yorkshire have fine, pointed toes that are capped with brass, whereas the men from the south counties have only blunt-toed boots.

So Sam waited breathlessly, for a man who feels he is to be beaten will always pick the cowardly Southern style which allows him to escape whenever he wishes to lie down and fight no more. But he was proud of Black Cawper when he roared:

"Knockdowns—onless th'art flaid!"

The blond man laughed and waved his hand to say it was all the same to him. Then, bending, their arms hanging low, they began to circle each other on the flat rock. For nearly five minutes they moved thus, and the only thing heard in the clear night was the shifting of their feet on the rock and the deep drawing of the breath into their chests.

Suddenly, without a warning, the blond man charged first. But Black Cawper was ready. Like the blink of an eye he swung his clogged foot and kicked the man in the groin. So fast that you could hardly see it, he kicked again—and a third time. Then they swung around and faced each other once more, and Black Cawper laughed deep in his chest.

The other man should have dropped, but instead he charged in again, and this time from the position of his feet Sam could see he was to kick at Black's crotch. But Black knew a trick worth two of that. Without giving ground, he half-turned in a flash, standing on one foot and holding the other foot with his hands. He held the foot knee-high, and with the metal-shod sole turned out. He did it just as the other man's leg swung forward, and it was like a shield in defence. Sam Small heard a sound as if the shin-bone were splintering when the stranger's leg crashed against the upheld foot.

But the big man gave no sign, and instead kept coming right in and the two locked their arms. For a time they circled, each bent over, head to head like stags in the mating season. They pushed and swayed, each feeling for a stronger hold and kicking at each other's legs. It seemed to be deadlock, until Black Cawper shifted quickly and reaching under grasped the other's beard. He pulled down with all his strength, yanking the man's head down; and at the same time he brought up his knee with a force that smashed it into his opponent's face and sent him staggering back, with blood gushing from his mouth.

Without halting a second, Black put down his head and charged. He caught his foe in the belly with his head, and the force of the butting charge sent the man flying back. His body went wildly through the air and crashed onto the rocks six feet below the flat crag. Even while it was falling, Black was following up, and charging over the rock he leaped out into space, meaning to come down feet first on the body of the man below.

But somehow the man managed to roll aside with a lightning twist, and scrambling to his feet he locked his arms tight about his enemy. Thus they stood, chest to chest, and Black grinned, for he had never yet met a man who could withstand his grip. So he squeezed tighter and tighter. Sam saw the cords and veins stand out on his neck as he put on the pressure, but the other man only waited.

At last Black was done, and then it was the other's turn. He pressed, tighter and tighter, seeking to crush in Black's ribs. But Black, waiting as the other had waited, could not be beaten that way, either.

At a deadlock again, they began trying to lift each other, to pluck their foe from his feet and throw him. But they seemed evenly matched there, too. They swayed and staggered, crashing about and panting.

Thus, while Sam Small watched, Black Cawper and the stranger fought all that moonlight night in the land beside Wada's Keep. They crashed over the rocks and locked together they rolled down the slopes. They tore themselves free and charged each other. They wrestled and struck and kicked themselves apart and came back to the locked embrace again.

So the moon sloped over the sky and the wind blew cold and the night went past as they fought on.

And then, slowly, Sam saw that Black Cawper was to be beaten. He charged as courageously as ever, but his arms were lifting more slowly. And in a final locked struggle, the bearded man at last bent Black Cawper back, further and further. Then he lifted him from the ground and hurled him across the rocks.

Black Cawper, his face covered with blood, lifted himself up and came back, but again he was thrown. For a second time he lifted himself, shaking his head savagely as if to get it clear. He charged in once more, and once more was thrown. And this third time, try as he might, he found himself unable to rise. He pushed with his arms upon the ground, but they would not lift his body.

But even then he was not beaten in spirit, for as the blond man advanced, instead of wrapping his arms about his head to protect his skull, the way beaten men do, Black Cawper lay there proudly and defiantly, looking up sidewise at his enemy, but without any pleading in his eyes.

The big man jumped down to where Black lay and drew back his foot. Then he said:

"All this neight us has contested, thee and me."

Black Cawper did not answer. All there was to hear was the breath coming and going as his chest heaved for air. He tried to lift himself and managed to push up his shoulders with his straightened arms. But he could get no further though he tried until the beads of sweat stood out on his forehead.

Then, with a quick movement, the blond man reached down and with a great lift hauled him to his feet. Without saying a word he helped Black into his shirt and coat. When that was done he lifted his head and looked about and said:

"But a little while longer and tha'd ha' beaten me."

His voice sounded sad and far away as he went on:

"Ah, and if tha nobbut had! For when there comes another like unto me, than Ah am released and may go ma way!"

Black sat with his head bowed. The big man looked about him, turning his head.

"Eigh, but Ah maun go. Fare thee well, lad."

Black Cawper rose suddenly and held the other's arm.

"Nay, that maun't go," he said. "Ah want thee to coom hoam wi' me and meet ma wife."

"Thy wife? What for?"

Black Cawper stood up firm and held the other's hand proudly.

"Well lad," he said, "Ah'm a Yorkshireman born and a Yorkshireman bred, soa Ah can nobbut speak like a true sportsman. Tha's bested me at cunning and tha's bested me at speed; tha's bested me at strength and tha's bested me at feighting. Soa there's nobbut one thing left for an honest lad to do.

"Ba gum, Ah'm bahn to tak' thee hoam and hev a pup off'n thee!"

The other shook his head quickly.

"Nay, Ah maun be off," he said.

He started away, and then suddenly he stopped as if struck by a surprising idea. He spoke almost as if to himself.

"For when there is another like unto me, then am Ah released and may go ma way," he said.

Quickly, gladly, he reknotted his kerchief. He started to smile and say: "Ah'll go wi' ye," but then faintly, yet loud as faint sounds are at dawn, there came a cockcrow from the village far away. Sadly, sadly, the blond man looked at the east and cried:

"Nay, nay! Ah maun go!"

He turned and raced away before they could stop him and was gone from sight like the winking of an eye. But from the hills came his booming voice, fading away, and Sam says he heard him call, saying:

"A month from today! Ah'll be back and tak' ye up on that—a mooonth from todaaay!"

Then his voice rumbled off into the hills and became one with the muttering thunder of a dawn storm.

Now that is the story that Sam Small tells. He says he can remember the exact date—as most men in the village can.

For coming down from the moor that gray morning, Sam Small and Black Cawper were so late they had no time to go home to their cottages. For they were on the 6 A.M. shift at the pit, and so they went right to work.

And that very day was the day of the big do at the Silkstone Pit Number Two. It was the day of the disaster when Sam, racing from his gallery, saw Black Cawper standing like a Colossus, his great back arched and holding up a sagging cross-timber.

Everyone knows that is true, for they still tell you about it in Polkingthorpe Brig—how Black Cawper held up that great timber and roared in his bull voice to the men to hurry, and how as the men in his gallery ducked under his arched body that great timber pressed him down, lower and lower.

Black Cawper never came out of that pit, for as Sam Small ran along toward the shaft there came a rumble and a roar and the roof behind them caved in. Sam Small and seven others reached the cage in safety, but in that level sixty-seven lives were lost. Sam and the other seven came out to tell the story.

So no one can mistake the date on which Black Cawper died. And no one can mistake the date on which Ian Cawper was born—ten months later.

Now we are not too handy on arithmetic and such tricky matters; but, as we say in the village, there seems to be summat varry, varry fooney somewheers.

But, naturally, nobody ever says anything much about it because—well, Ian's affable enough most of the time; but if he ever got real angry, why he could break any man in two with his bare hands. It's almost supernatural, how strong Ian Cawper is.

ALDOUS HUXLEY

Time's Revenges

It was warm, and there were the usual palms and hibiscus bushes and, along the edge of the terrace, a magenta glare of Mesembryanthemums. Lying back in her deck chair, Mrs. Peele alternately looked at the Pacific and, with a ghostly echo of the old delight, re-read the *Iliad*. She was near the end of the Third Book, and here, blond and beautiful, like that intoxicating Baron von Dittersdorf, who had told her by moonlight that his *liebe* was stronger than *tod*, and then, next morning, had borrowed five hundred dollars—here was Paris, ignominiously trounced by the man he had cuckolded. Here was bosomy Aphrodite to the rescue. Here was poor Helen, desperately trying to live down the past and telling her curly-headed baron exactly what she thought of him. Boaster, weakling, coward! And the baron's only answer—it had always been his only answer—was to carry her off to bed. The old *non sequitur* of love, the prehistoric sexual routine. But the one was convincing and the other worked. *Worked then,* thought Mrs. Peele as she lowered her book, *and still works today. Works in spite of Korea and atomic energy, in spite of all their Holy Years and Dialectical Materialisms. But not in spite of old age.* She sighed, took out her compact and, as she powdered her aquiline nose, peered at the image in the convex mirror. Fifty-one last June, and then nephritis; she looked a hundred and twenty.

There was a sound of footsteps behind her. She turned her head. Enormous, a football player on the verge of running to fat, young Peter Foss was ponderously bearing down on her.

"How are you feeling today?" he asked solicitously.

Even his voice was somewhat beefy, like a T-bone steak made richly audible.

Mrs. Peele shrugged her shoulders, couldn't decide whether she felt weaker by contrast or stronger by contagion.

Peter's laughter was the equivalent of an enormous filet mignon—thick, juicy, tender.

"How I love your wit!" he cried.

Mrs. Peele remembered the face in her convex mirror.

"There isn't much else to love," she said. "Just a skull and a skeleton."

"And a *soul!*" said the young man with emphasis. He laid a hand on the frail pipestick of her forearm and gave her a smile of almost filial admiration and tenderness.

October, 1951

Mrs. Peele smiled back at him. She was touched; but within her, at the same time, a small, dry demon of irony was making the usual derisive comments. How earnest he looked, how beamingly the Social Worker—almost the Moral Rearmer! And even if he did feel towards her like a son, even if he genuinely wanted to be kind and Christian, was it really possible for a young man in his position to behave disinterestedly? For, after all, who was he? The West Coast Representative of the Birnbaum Foundation. In other words, a professional fund-raiser. Or, in yet other words, a parasite on the aging rich. A parasite, of course. With the best of intentions, and for the highest of causes. But still a parasite. Like Franz von Dittersdorf—only a good deal less amusing. Peter's *liebe* wasn't any stronger than *tod*; it was hardly stronger than drugstore coffee. But at fifty-one that was all one was entitled to expect—the mildest kind of decaffeinized affection. In exchange for which these latter-day parasites considered themselves entitled to expect, not a mere five hundred for champagne and gambling debts, but forty or fifty thousand to finance a Report on Negro Housing in the Deep South—or was it Eskimo Housing in the Deep North? She burst out laughing.

"What's so funny?" Peter asked in a tone of slightly offended bewilderment.

"I was just thinking of igloos," she answered.

"What are you talking about?" he asked.

"Prefabricated igloos," Mrs. Peele went on. "Transported in deep freezers. The whole project financed by grants from the Birnbaum Foundation." Then, changing her tone, "Isn't it strange," she added, "the way rich people still go on giving away money in order to save their souls? Even when they know quite well that they haven't got the kind of souls that can be saved?"

Peter Foss opened his mouth to speak; then changed his mind and closed it again.

"What were you going to say?" she asked.

"Nothing."

Mrs. Peele was disappointed. She had hoped to provoke him into saying something *ernst* and eloquent about Life Eternal—and then, my God, how she'd have jumped on him! But, as she had had occasion to observe before, the boy wasn't nearly so dumb as he looked.

"We've got an interesting new guest at the hotel this morning," he said at last.

"Who?"

"No less a person than Oscar Hackett."

Mrs. Peele made no movement, uttered no word of comment. Her heart had started to beat very fast and she felt suddenly breathless. Did he know that she had once been married to Oscar? Why had he announced his arrival so abruptly?

"*The* Oscar Hackett," Peter went on, a little piqued, it was evident, by her show of disinterest.

"*The* Oscar Hackett?" she queried, feeling sure, now, that he knew nothing. After all, he'd hardly been born when it all happened.

"You know," he said, "the philanthropist."

"Of course I know," said Mrs. Peele in a sudden, startling outburst of gaiety. "Philanthropist. From *philein*, to love, and *anthropos*, man. He loves the human race. In fact, he just adores it."

At the thought of Oscar adoring the human race, and at the same time trampling with impartial insensitivity on every member of that race with whom he came in contact, she uttered a little snort of half-suppressed laughter. How ludicrous it all was, how utterly, bitterly absurd!

"There's nothing to sneer at," said Peter gravely. He leaned towards her, and suddenly his tone and expression were almost clerical. Speaking slowly and with a measured emphasis, he said, "I can't think of any man who has deserved better of his generation than Mr. Hackett. All those splendid gifts for World Peace . . ."

"And now," said Mrs. Peele derisively, "we're in the first year of the second Hundred Years War."

"And those Hackett Fellowships," Peter went on, ignoring the interruption. "And above all, his work for the Re-Union of the Churches. You see, he's a deeply religious man."

"Deeply religious," she repeated in a parody of his serious tone.

And yet, ridiculous as it now seemed, that was why she had fallen in love with him. There had been others as good-looking, others who were more attractive. But nobody else had radiated Oscar's crusading zeal, nobody else had ever marched into her mother's drawing room with the conquering air and prophetic manner of Richard Coeur de Lion.

"Mr. Hackett," Peter was saying, "is a dedicated soul."

The one dedicated soul in a world where everyone else was interested only in politely killing time and, in the intervals, making yet more money. He came charging into that world like an Early Christian bull in a china shop of frivolities. To a young girl who had just seen through all the elegant shams of her mother's existence and was still in a state of shocked revolt against the ugliness of its reality, the bull's performance seemed altogether wonderful.

"Truly dedicated," the young man insisted.

Yes, truly dedicated—but to what kind of a God? Deeply religious—but couldn't you say the same of Torquemada; couldn't you say the same of the High Priest of Moloch? It was not until after their marriage that Anne Peele had begun to ask herself those questions. In her own perverse and exasperating way, her mother had asked them long before. Shutting her eyes, Mrs. Peele could hear that soft voice drawling away across the gulfs of dead time. "He could hardly be handsomer," it said, "and he certainly couldn't be any richer. But did you have to choose somebody who was so revoltingly *good?*" At the time they were spoken the words had seemed almost blasphemous. But now . . .

She thought of Oscar, so hag-ridden by the ideals he had inherited from that ferocious old mother of his, so hoodwinked by his ready-made convictions of what ought to be, that he didn't notice, could hardly even see or hear, what was actually going on about him. "I'm a realist," he liked to boast, "I'm a man who always faces the facts." But the only facts he ever faced were the facts in Census

Reports and White Papers, in *Fortune* and *Foreign Affairs*. Of such humbler realities as a young girl's body, a young wife's feelings—anybody's feelings if it came to that—he had always been completely unaware. Being aware takes time, takes effort, and Oscar was too busy being good.

"Why can't they leave people alone?" she said aloud.

"Who?"

"All these damn philanthopists. Look at Korea. We want to do it good, the Russians want to do it good, the Chinese want to do it good. Why not leave the Koreans alone for a change? Let them stew in their own juice. It stinks. But at least it's *their* juice."

Peter smiled indulgently and shook his head.

"We can't stand by idle," he said.

"Why not?"

"We've got to do the good as we see it."

"But that's the point: you *don't* see it."

"That's why we need more men like Mr. Hackett," said Peter.

"*Mister* Hackett," she repeated, suddenly struck by the fact that, in the young man's conversation, the names of the very rich were never mentioned without their qualifying title of respect.

"Men with vision," he went on, "men with a social conscience, men with . . ."

"With eighty million dollars."

The young man looked at her for a moment in silence, then gave her another of those indulgent smiles of his.

"What is it," he asked, "that makes you want to seem more cynical than you really are?"

The answer, of course, was "You." You, Peter, the virtuous leech, the high-minded and altruistic tapeworm. But she left the words unspoken. After all, he was a very nice young man; and she a tired, lonely old woman. Mrs. Peele laughed and shrugged her shoulders.

"I suppose you think you know what I really am."

He looked at her for a moment in silence, then nodded his head.

"Better than you do yourself."

He had dropped his pulpit manner and once again, tenderly, admiringly, protectively, it was a son who spoke to her. A son . . . With excruciating vivid-ness she remembered the flushed thin face of the little boy under the oxygen tent. If he had lived, little Dick would be twenty-eight next December the third. A year older than Peter. Her eyes filled with tears.

"The self you know," she heard him saying, "is the self you've had to fabricate —in mere self-defense. What I know is the self you fundamentally are."

It was just uplift, of course, just Liberal Christian twaddle, just the patter of a good salesman, whose line happened to be organized charity rather than vacuum cleaners. Butter them up! Give the old girls something that'll make them feel good! Mrs. Peele would have liked to laugh, but was afraid that if she opened her mouth, she might start sobbing. For of course it was absolutely true. She *had* transformed herself into someone else, someone quite different from the girl who had set out with her Richard Coeur de Lion on a crusade to make the world a better place to live in. And it had been done in mere self-protection, just as he had said. She thought of those seven years of her marriage with Oscar; remembered the strange blue glare of his eyes and the cleaving chin, the eager profile—like the prow of an icebreaker. And the ice was alive and vulnerable. It was the body he had been too puritanical, too respectful of his mother, to do anything but furtively violate. It was the mind he had had no time to train or even understand. It was the personality he was forever snubbing and humiliating, not out of any perverse delight in cruelty, but merely because he had other, higher things to think about than a woman's sensibilities. She had gone to him defenseless, in a total self-surrender, and he had forced her into armor. Layer upon layer of it—snubproof, outrageproof, proof against the most penetratingly solemn words, the most idealistic eloquence. After little Dick had died, there was no occasion for her ever to take it off. Absolutely no occasion; for, each in his own way, Oscar's successors had been as bad as Oscar himself.

Toward Franz, it was true, she would always feel a certain gratitude. Gratitude for an apocalypse; for he had initiated her into the nocturnal mysteries, had revealed the impersonal otherness of her own deepest being, had made her taste the ineffable beatitudes of extinction. When he kissed her, there was no more armor and nobody any more to wear the armor. Only a blissful alienation, a dark yet living and conscious absence. But every darkness is the prelude to another day, and by day Franz was nothing but an impudent adventurer—a crook, and rather a stupid crook at that, who finally became insupportable.

But when Franz had been got rid of, there was poor Johnny McPhail, drunkenly oscillating between maudlin sentiment and brutality. And then, after Johnny, Lancelot. But Lancelot was an actor and could never be anything else, even at his mother's funeral, even in bed. And finally, when she turned in despairing revulsion towards the other pole of existence, she had found, not God, not peace, not charity, but an obscene mingling, in that unspeakable little Donald Peele, of Neo-Scholastic intellectualism with an almost infantile vanity, of erudite and unctuous talk about the Spiritual Life with a mean soul's petty spitefulness. In response to Donald, her armor had turned into a panoply of derisive counterattack. She was back where she had been with Oscar. Only now it was worse, much worse. For now she was old. There would be no more absences and extinctions, no new revelations of the otherness beyond personality. There was, and there could be, only her waking, daytime self—only this weary sense of being the victim of a failing body, only this constantly repeated realization that she had lost, irrevocably, all that had once reconciled her to existence, only this chronic consciousness of frustration. And the frustration was inescapable, because it had somehow been predestined. She was foredoomed to it, had no choice but to invite it. Frustration after frustration, through the whole gamut. And the latest of them was the frustration of her affection for this absurd boy. How touchingly ingenuous he had seemed at their first meetings, how kind and thoughtful, how genuinely concerned to do the will of God. And then he had talked about the Birnbaum Foundation, and everything was called in question. Was the goodness merely professional? Was the affection a stratagem? Was the religion just a part of his stock in trade? And now he was licking his chops over Oscar, was savoring in advance that juicy gobbet from the eighty-million dollar table of the deeply religious man of vision. How odious everything was, how senseless, aimless, hopeless!

Peter Foss glanced at the half-averted face beside him, saw the brightness of tears on the lashes, and, tactfully turning away, started to fill his pipe. *Thank you, dear God,* he said to himself; for he was grateful for having been inspired to say what was so obviously the right thing. To grow old with a heart of stone—no, not even stone, with a heart of tin, a heart of plastic—could one imagine a worse punishment? Somehow or other this unhappy woman must be rescued from her own suicidal flippancy and cynicism. He had realized that from the first moment of their acquaintance. And now God had shown him the way. He had spoken, almost at random, and his words had touched her, had actually made her cry. *Thank you, thank you.*

And all of a sudden another inspiration came to him. He was just taking the pipe out of his mouth in order to give it utterance, when Mrs. Peele abruptly broke a silence which she had begun to find oppressive.

"Do you know Oscar Hackett personally?" she asked in a flat voice.

Peter had to make an effort to repress his annoyance at the interruption.

"I only know his wife," he answered.

Mrs. Peele looked at him sharply.

"His wife?" she repeated; then remembered the existence of that awful Muriel.

"I met her last year," he explained, "at the Conference of Juvenile Delinquency."

"Does she go in for *that* kind of thing?" Mrs. Peele inquired.

The young man nodded.

"During the last year or two," he said, "Mr. Hackett has delegated almost all his philanthropic activities to her. You'll enjoy her. She's a lovely person."

A lovely person . . . As though by magic the words restored Mrs. Peele to her normal state of ironic equanimity. A really lovely person!

"And there she was in the lobby. I was never more pleasantly surprised in my life."

"Another old lady to use your charm on," said Mrs. Peele.

He made no comment and there was a long silence.

Suddenly the smell of tobacco and shaving lotion grew stronger in her nostrils. She turned and saw that Peter was leaning confidentially towards her with that look of beaming earnestness which always presaged the utterance of something edifying. This time, she decided, and smiled, this time she would really let him have it.

"Do you remember what I was saying just now?" he began.

"About what I *really* am?"

"About what you really are," he repeated in a tone whose seriousness was the implicit reproof of her levity.

"Go on," said Mrs. Peele. "I adore talking about myself."

"And that's why you haven't got any self to talk about."

Mrs. Peele laughed—but a little uncomfortably.

"If you pay attention to what you think you are, you'll never become what you really are."

"Then what should one pay attention to?"

"I won't tell you."

"Why not?"

"You'd only laugh."

"No, I wouldn't."

"And anyhow," Peter went on, "you know it already."

"I don't."

"You know it, you've always known it and you always will. But whether you'll want to do anything about it is another question."

Beef, evangelical beef. And yet, as the silence lengthened out, Mrs. Peele became aware of the young man as something more than this congenial and yet absurd presence—became aware of him as the source of a kind of radiance, as the center from which a life that was not merely Peter's communicated with a life that was not merely her own.

"The trouble is," she said at last, without looking at him, "the trouble is that, whenever I've tried to act on it, somebody's always come along and made complete nonsense of the whole idea." She thought of Oscar and the nonsense he had made of crusading idealism; of Donald and the slime he had spread over the saints; of Peter himself and his way with the old ladies. And then there was Franz—Franz the incomparable lover, the insupportable pimp. Even the dark gods had been desecrated for her. "Complete and utter nonsense," she repeated emphatically.

"But after all," he began, "truth doesn't vary with the people who speak it. It's independent . . ."

But once again he was checked in mid-career. Feet crunched behind him on the gravel and in a rather doubtful, questioning tone a shrill feminine voice pronounced his name. Frowning, Peter turned his head, then readjusted his expression and rose with alacrity to greet the newcomer.

"But how delightful!" he cried.

Under the concealing brim of her wide straw hat, Mrs. Peele wondered who on earth he was being delighted about this time.

"Thank goodness it's you!" said the shrill voice. "I'm so dreadfully short-sighted, I never know who I'm talking to. It's quite embarrassing when you discover you've been calling a perfectly strange man 'darling.' " There was a coy giggle.

Mrs. Peele raised the brim of her hat and saw a fat middle-aged woman, with dyed hair and wearing a pale blue print, in the act of sitting down rather cautiously on the chair which Peter had just vacated. The head came round, revealing a face which she recognized but could not put a name to. Then Peter did it for her.

"This is Mrs. Hackett," he said.

But of course! The lovely person—as large as life. Considerably larger even.

"I hope I'm not interrupting anything," said the squeaky voice.

"Nothing crucial," Mrs. Peele answered. "Or was it?" She looked up at the young man with a quizzical smile.

Mrs. Hackett gave him no time to answer. "Peter was telling me such *interesting* things about his survey of Negro Housing."

"Yes, isn't it *thrilling!*" said Mrs. Peele with ironic emphasis.

"I just *longed* to hear some more. That is, if you'll tell me."

Fascinated, Mrs. Peele watched her as she gave Peter the shy, coy smile of an adolescent making her first experiments in seduction.

Emollient, its native beefiness boiled down to the colloidal state of jellied consommé, the voice of Peter Foss came back to her.

"I shall be only too happy," it said. "But meanwhile I want you to know Mrs. Peele."

In Muriel's large myopic eyes Mrs. Peele could detect no recognition or questioning curiosity.

"Anne Peele," she specified.

Again there was no reaction from Muriel. And why should there be, after all? It was the best part of twenty years since they had met at somebody's enormous cocktail party in Washington. She had been Anne MacPhail in those days, and Muriel was already as blind as a bat and too vain to wear spectacles. If she herself remembered the incident so vividly, it was because she had been curious to see the woman whom Oscar had chosen as her successor. For a whole evening she had watched her from across the room—watched with an amazed amusement that gave place after a time to a painful sense of humiliation. For if *that* was what Oscar really liked, and if he had once liked her, then she must have something in common with Muriel. And Muriel was busily revealing herself as being everything she had always most cordially abhorred. Fluffy and twittering, infantile but a bitch; the sort of woman who liked to talk to men about Little Me; who behaved with deliberate silliness so that old gentlemen might smile indulgently and think she was too cute for words; who uttered baby laughter and lifted baby eyes, inviting all males to constitute themselves the protectors and would-be violators of an innocence well below the age of consent.

And now here she was again, twenty years after, but still Muriel—Muriel with a vengeance, Muriel raised, so to speak, to a higher power by the passage of time. For beneath an excess of the rouge and powder, the little, round, baby face was wrinkled now and had started to sag. And what had once been a charming body was now enormously out of proportion with the head—a mound of middle-aged flesh topped, incongruously, by a doll. But, meanwhile, her style of dressing, the tone of her voice, the things she said and the way she said them

—all were unchanged. Here were the same frills, the same ribbons, the same bright pale colors. And the same half-witted canary chirped the same imbecilities; the same parody of a child opened the same blue eyes and appealed for the same nauseating kind of avuncular lechery. Today the appeal was being directed, not to one of those elderly industrialists or professors of economics who were her predestined and legitimate victims, but to this boy in his twenties. Doubly incestuous, she was asking someone who might have been her son to become her daddy.

"And what about the organizational setup?" Muriel was saying. And, before Peter could answer, she turned to Mrs. Peele and said, in a stage whisper, "I haven't the faintest idea what organizational setups are. All I know is that Mr. Hackett is tremendously keen on them. But *tremendously!*" She gave vent to a teen-age giggle.

Peter laughed, too—laughed, to all appearances, with genuine amusement. What was it, Mrs. Peele wondered, what was it that made otherwise quite rational men succumb to this kind of female infantilism? Even Oscar. She remembered how, at that cocktail party, he had shown Muriel off to a little circle of bankers and politicians—like the proud father of an *enfant terrible*, like the impresario of a midget. Roaring with laughter, calling for silence when she was about to utter one of her priceless gems, repeating the inanities to those who had been lucky enough not to hear them. But she also remembered the brutal way he had cut her short when she interrupted a conversation that seemed to him important—remembered Muriel's hurt look and the mounting flush of humiliation, the gallant attempt to force a smile and pretend that nothing had happened. It had all seemed painfully familiar.

Mrs. Peele sighed profoundly. There was something, she reflected, unutterably dismal about the consistency with which people always lived up to character. As though they were acting in one of those old comedies, where every personage has a name corresponding to his nature—Sneerwell perpetually sneering, Belch forever in his cups, Horner indefatigably making cuckolds, and now Twitterbaby, at fifty, repeating word for word, gesture for gesture, the performance of Twitterbaby at thirty, Twitterbaby at twenty, Twitterbaby ever since the age of puberty. Nothing had changed except her weight. In the old days the actress was no heavier than the personage she represented. But now the part of Twitterbaby was being taken by one of those massive veterans who insists on playing Juliet, even though their status as grandmothers can no longer be concealed by tightest lacing, the most golden of wigs.

And meanwhile the two voices, the deep and the shrill, talked on and on. It was a sonata for canary and jellied beef—now a rich consommé punctuated by ecstatic bursts of twittering, now the sustained dickeybird, with occasional colloidal accompaniment. How eloquently one could write about it in the annotated program! "At this point there occurs the celebrated *legato* passage for unaccompanied beef. With indescribable tenderness the jelly quiveringly yearns for the canary's money; but the answer is only a coy *pizzicato* in the treble. Modulating in masterly style from G-minor to C-sharp major, our beef now proclaims its exclusive attachment to the birdie's soul and suggests the joys of heaven in a series of impressive chords, which are soon repeated, two octaves higher, in the *vox canarica* . . ."

How ludicrous it all was! And yet how painful, how humiliating! For this farce was the grotesque symbol of man's destiny, the epitome and caricature of human life. The life and destiny of incommensurable lovers; of mothers whose children are all changelings; of intimates incapable of communicating with one another; of island universes forever at cross purposes. And the farce went on and on, not through three acts, or five, but indefinitely. Each morning, one wakened afresh to the same degrading compulsion of having to utter the same stale nonsense, to act out the familiar futilities. Day after day, sameness after sameness, like one of those revolting processions of caterpillars, the horror of endless repetition. And then, abruptly, the other, the infinitely greater horror, not of endlessness, but of the end; the ultimate and total humiliation that was death . . .

"Mrs. Peele."

She started and looked up. Enormous, like a Hercules in tweeds, Peter Foss was standing beside her.

"Will you excuse us?" he said, laying a hand on the back of her chair and bending over her with his most touchingly filial smile.

Under his elbow, Mrs. Peele caught a glimpse of Muriel's broad blue posterior wobbling away in high heels towards the hotel.

"We're going to visit for a few minutes with dear old Mrs. Schlag."

Dear old Mrs. Schlag—owner of half an oil field. The high-minded parasite was on the march again.

"Thank you, Peter," she said and patted his hand.

"Thank me for what?"

"For cheering me up."

"But I haven't done anything."

"You don't have to do anything. You merely have to exist."

In silence, because he did not know what to say, Peter looked down at her. It was a thin, worn, suffering face; but in their bony sockets the grey eyes shone with mischief and the rather full lips were curved into a smile of delicate irony. A most disquieting smile. But a moment later Peter remembered to feel sorry for the poor woman. To this unhappy victim of her own tin and plastic heart, of course it must seem comic that anyone should be a Christian.

"May we go on with our talk some other time?" he asked in the intimate and meaningful tone of one who shares sacred secrets.

This time, thought Mrs. Peele, the voice was a *pot au feu*. Beef at its most domestic; chunks of poor old Bossy simmered for hours in the smelliest corner of a fourteenth-century kitchen; the food of simplehearted peasants, masticated by candlelight and to the sound of the *Angelus* . . .

"With the greatest of pleasure," she answered airily. "And now you must run away from dear old me to dear old Mrs. Schlag."

He started to protest; but she gave him a little push to speed him on his way.

"Good-by, my pet, and good hunting."

The large heavy feet went crunching away over the gravel. Mrs. Peele laughed noiselessly, then all of a sudden felt herself overcome by a kind of dry misery, a sense of inner hollowness, of being dusty and desiccated to the very core. After a few minutes she got up, walked back to the hotel and went up to her room. For lack of knowing what else to do, she changed her dress and, yet again, carefully made up her face; then switched on the radio. A preacher was shouting something about the blood of the Lamb. She turned the knob. ". . . . a touch of acid indigestion," said a voice almost as beefy as Peter's. Turned again, and it was a hooting contralto, hungry for somebody's lips. Again, and the news from the front was worse than ever. The wheel had come full circle, from blood through the stomach and the genitals, back to blood again. She silenced the machine and walked out onto the balcony. Below her were the same old palm trees and the gaudy magenta carpet of flowers, and beyond the flowers, rising to the level of her eyes, the vast, mild blueness of the sea. And this was the view for which one paid three dollars a day extra on the price of a room. It wasn't worth it.

She turned her head and was startled to find that, separated from her only by a stucco parapet, a man was sitting on the balcony next to hers. His chair was turned so that she could see only the back of his head and the silhouette of his left cheek and temple. But that was enough; for that was all she had ever seen of Oscar, when she ventured into his study—a back and one surprisingly small ear and the vanishing third quarter of a face deliberately averted from all intrusion on his enormously important labors.

"Darling," she would venture to murmur at last, and again, more apprehensively, after another twenty seconds, "Darling?"

At the third or fourth repetition he would say, "One moment, please." And finally, perhaps a minute later, the head would come sharply up, the swivel chair would whirl round and she would find herself confronted by the sternly noble face of a crusader who has just been interrupted, in the midst of his final, heroic assault on Jerusalem, by the most imbecilic of blondes on the most frivolous of pretexts.

"What is it?" he would ask in a tone which made it very clear indeed that he was not to suffer fools gladly. "What is it?"

In the beginning, Mrs. Peele remembered as she looked at Oscar's immobile back, in the beginning, before she had forged her cuirass of indifference, her reaction had been to feel and behave like the fool he proclaimed himself unwilling to tolerate. Fear turned her into an idiot, incapable of saying anything, or, if she did speak, talking only nonsense.

"And what *precisely*," he would ask with an icy sarcasm, "what *precisely* does *that* mean?"

And she would stammer more incoherently than ever and, sitting there in judgment upon her, the indignant crusader would listen, his lips ever more tightly compressed, his brows ever more darkly frowning, until the tension of righteous exasperation became too great to be borne. And then, like a thunderclap it was out—the harsh and hurting word of contemptuous anger, irrevocable, irreparable.

Yes, irreparable, Mrs. Peele repeated to herself, irreparable. For Oscar had never known how to make reparation. If he had, if he could ever have used a wholehearted regret for having hurt her as the means to a better understanding of himself and his victim, she would have welcomed these humiliations. But no, he must always be the crusader, ceaselessly possessed by a devil of abstract idealism and therefore convinced of his own virtue and incapable of humility. When he tried to make reparation, it was not from below, but from above; not from an abased sense of having done something less than human, but from the lofty standpoint of a superior being who has unintentionally, and by the mere fact of being superior, wounded a member of the lower orders. Instead of repentance, he offered her, out of the treasury of his own strength, condescending encouragement and a little sermon on how to behave better next time. And sometimes, incongruously and suddenly, the crusader would be overcome by the temptations of the flesh. Without transition, without a preliminary word, the homily would give place to the most brutal and unskillful of caresses. And afterwards, whatever might have happened—whether she resisted this irrelevant outrage of her feelings, or surrendered to it in the hope of transforming it into a more human relationship—afterwards, he always felt ashamed of himself, and the shame made him so resentful of her part in contributing to his fall from crusading dignity that he would go out of his way to find new pretexts for blaming and humiliating her. And yet, incomprehensibly, she had always loved him, or at least she had always hoped that, someday, he would make it possible for her to love him. But he never had, he never had.

Mrs. Peele sighed and then, shrugging her shoulders, crossed over to the parapet that separated the two balconies.

"Well, Oscar," she said almost playfully, "a penny for your thoughts."

Not, of course, that they were worth a penny. For who wanted to hear about organizational setups? Who cared two pins about the dilemmas of the very rich, torn between Negro Housing, World Peace, and Fellowships in Applied Sociology?

"A penny for your thoughts," she repeated more loudly.

There was still no answer. In his old age Oscar must have taken to overacting his own role.

"A penny for your thoughts," she almost shouted.

The man started and turned his head.

"Either you're deaf," Mrs. Peele began, "or else you . . ."

She broke off and stared in horrified silence at a face that was still recognizably Oscar's, and yet belonged to someone else, someone utterly different from the all-too-noble crusader of her painful or ironic memories. And it was not merely that the face was now that of an old man. Those lines across the forehead and around the tense closure of the lips were the tracings, not of time, but of despair. And the same despair looked out at her from the wide, fixed eyes—an agonizing extremity of hopelessness, a knowledge of irremediable perdition.

Mrs. Peele was filled with a kind of panic terror.

"Oscar!" she whispered in a tone almost of protest.

He opened his mouth, but no words; tried again and finally spoke.

"Were you talking to me?" he asked.

"Oscar, don't you know who I am?"

"Who you are?" He stared at her for several seconds in silence, then went on doubtfully, "It's not Anne, is it?"

Mrs. Peele nodded affirmatively. Her first startled terror, as though at some apparition from another realm of being, had given place to compassion. She gave him her warmest, her most friendly smile.

There was another vacant interval. Then, with an enormous effort, he tried to smile back at her. The corners of the mouth twitched spasmodically and there was a movement in the folded skin of the cheeks. But all the time the eyes continued to deny the very possibility, not merely of joy and laughter, but of all human sympathy, even all awareness. The lost spirit within knew nothing but its own perdition.

As though conscious of the incongruity of his grimace, he turned away from her.

"It's been an awfully long time," he muttered.

"An awfully long time," she agreed. "And yet one remembers."

"Yes, one remembers."

His voice trailed off into silence.

Sameness after sameness, the endless procession of caterpillars . . . But this was worse. For here there had been an ending, a mortal transfiguration, an actual death in life.

Mrs. Peele leaned over the parapet and laid a hand on his shoulder.

"Oscar, what's wrong?"

At first he wouldn't look at her, but only shook his head and went on staring sightlessly at the sea.

"Maybe I could help you."

Again he shook his head.

"Tell me," she insisted. "It'll make you feel better."

Her words and the passionate concern with which they were spoken made her think of that time she had found little Dick crying his heart out in the summer house at Mount Kisco. "Tell me, my darling, tell me." And at last it had come out—the small, trivial tragedy of the broken vase, of mademoiselle's refusal to listen to his side of the case, of the unfairness of a punishment he hadn't fully deserved. The memory of the suffering child deepened her pity for the man before her.

"Won't you tell me?" she begged.

"It wouldn't be any good," he said at last, almost inaudibly.

"Why wouldn't it be any good?"

"Because I'm no good."

"You?" she questioned incredulously. To the trampling and infallible Oscar she had known, the no-goods were everyone except himself.

"Sometimes I can forget for a little," he went on. "But then it all comes back."

"What comes back?"

For a reply he covered his face with his hands and shuddered.

"What comes back?" she repeated with an eager insistence.

There was still no answer.

But to Mrs. Peele his silence was itself a confession. Why wouldn't he speak? What was the shame that forced him to hide his face from her? With a triumphant leaping of the heart she suddenly knew the answer. Knew it, not with her head, but in her bones; knew in the teeth of all the probabilities, because she so passionately wanted it to be true; knew for an absolute certainty that Oscar had come at last to realize what he had done to her during those years of outrage and humiliation—to realize and regret. The knowledge filled her with an almost exultant happiness. For in some obscure way everything was now changed. She had loved this man; and he, with his every word and act, had robbed her love of its meaning and taken away the reason for its existence. It had been a total denial, a *reductio ad absurdum* of her innermost being. But now he was sorry and his contrition proved that even in the most ruthless idealist there lurks a human being, sensitive, humble, capable of love and understanding. And if that were so, then she had been justified in feeling for him as she did. Retrospectively, the farcical chaos of her existence took on a kind of sense. And this sense would become plainer as time went on. For, if Oscar were sorry, she could forgive him—oh, how gladly, how unreservedly! And along with forgiving would go plain giving—a giving of heart, time, strength, her whole self. Giving, she would receive; giving, she would be made whole again and happy.

It was what Peter was always saying. Twaddle to catch the old ladies with! And yet, "You know it and you've always known and you always will." This time, at last, she was going to be able to act on the knowledge.

She leaned forward and, for the third time, repeated her question.

"I can't tell you," he muttered.

"But you must."

He shook his head.

"Please, Oscar, please!"

"I can't."

There was a silence. Then she made her decision. If he couldn't bring himself to take the first step, she would take it for him.

"You can't," she said slowly, "because it's something about us."

He took down his hands and looked at her.

"About us?" he repeated uncomprehendingly.

"At Rome, do you remember? And then Sorrento. And Capri. And Taormina . . ." She was listing the successive horrors of their Italian honeymoon—one violation after another, and in the intervals, so exhaustingly educative it almost atoned for what the Puritan in Oscar could only regard as a criminal indulgence, long hours of penitential sightseeing. "Do you remember?" Mrs. Peele repeated. Her eyes were bright, her face transfigured by a smile of anticipatory forgiveness.

He continued to look at her in bewilderment, then shook his head.

"I don't know what you mean," he said at last. "It wasn't as if there was anything wrong."

"Nothing wrong?" she repeated, not wishing to believe that she could have heard his words correctly.

"After all, we were married."

Mrs. Peele felt as though a noose had been thrown around her heart and suddenly tightened. Then, in spite of the pain of that horrible constriction, she began to laugh.

"How can you!" he cried reproachfully, and once more covered his face.

"I'm sorry," she gasped between two paroxysms.

She tried to stop laughing, tried to tell him how deeply she felt for his unhappiness, how passionately she longed to help him. But her body was as though possessed by something alien and malignant, something that shook her from within, something that clutched at her throat when she tried to speak, and brought the tears into her eyes.

"Terribly sorry, Oscar."

The rest was drowned in a kind of whooping asthma of hilarity.

And suddenly, as though to justify himself against the implied criticism of her laughter, Oscar began to talk in a tone of agonized self-accusation about his sins. And his sins were not the driving insensitiveness, the blind idealism of which she and so many others had been the victims; they were his weekly visits, between 1937 and 1939, to a redheaded girl called Patsy, who lived in an apartment on East Sixty-seventh Street.

The laughter died down, and Mrs. Peele was able to listen to him with all the appropriate marks of understanding and compassion. But in fact they were back again where (except in her own sentimental imagination) they had always been —in the middle of the fifty thousandth act of the old, old farce. And the farce had taken a disquieting turn for the worse. Their worlds, as she had discovered in the first months of marriage, had always been different. But today the separating distances were immeasurably greater. He had moved, as it were, from Mars to Sirius, from Sirius clean out of the galaxy and into chaos.

"There's nothing to be so upset about," she said consolingly.

But no, he insisted, there had been no excuse. Even the fact that Muriel was much too pure to wish to have anything to do with him was no excuse. He ought to have had the strength to control his lusts. But when Patsy came along he had fallen immediately, without resistance.

"I hope at least she was pretty," said Mrs. Peele. "I hope she knew her business."

He refused to be laughed out of his misery. Patsy wasn't a joke. She was the symbol and occasion of all evil. For two years he had bought his right to her by endowing World Peace. Then came the invasion of Poland. It was a judgment, a manifest condemnation. On September the fourth, he wrote Patsy a check for five thousand dollars, returned the key to her apartment, then went home and confessed to Muriel, who, being a wonderful woman, forgave him.

"*I'd* have forgiven you," Mrs. Peele could not refrain from saying, "if you'd ever asked me to."

He looked at her in surprise.

"But you never had anything to forgive me for," he said. "I mean, I was perfectly faithful."

"Perfectly faithful!"

That, surely, was the opening line of the fifty thousandth and first act.

"Whereas with poor Muriel," he groaned, "with poor Muriel . . . Oh, God! And yet she forgave me."

"And so all's well that ends well," said Mrs. Peele.

"But it hasn't ended," he protested.

"You mean she still throws it in your teeth?"

He shook his head emphatically. Muriel had been absolutely wonderful. Never a reproach, never so much as the dropping of a hint. Complete forgiveness.

"Then why go on worrying?"

Because however complete the forgiveness, the offense remained; so did the offender. The one was a shameful fact of history, the other, a living defilement.

"After all," said Mrs. Peele, "you're not the first middle-aged husband to sleep with a pretty girl."

But Oscar was not listening, did not even hear her.

"Unclean," he kept repeating, "unclean."

"Nor the last," she added, interrupting in her turn; for she was determined to finish her sentence.

"I ought to be dead."

His voice trembled and broke, and she saw that he was crying.

"Oscar!" Her pity was mingled with an exasperated protest against such an inordinate ado about next to nothing.

But Oscar paid no attention. Sunk in the hell of his own despair, he was beyond her reach. She stood there helplessly, murmuring the kind of consolations one addresses to a stricken child, but conscious all the time that it was all completely useless.

"Oscar," she wheedled, "dear Oscar . . ."

"Oscar," shrill echo startlingly repeated.

Mrs. Peele looked up. Sky-blue and enormous, Muriel was standing in the open doorway between the balcony and Oscar's room. The doll's face was frowning, the baby voice was harsh with annoyance.

"What's all this nonsense?" she crossed the balcony, laid a hand on Oscar's shoulder, and shook him roughly.

"I ought to be dead," Oscar moaned.

"Stop it!" cried Muriel angrily. Then she turned to Mrs. Peele. Her breath smelt of alcohol. Dear old Mrs. Schlag must have provided cocktails. "I hope he hasn't been bothering you," she said solicitously.

"Not bothering me," said Mrs. Peele. "But of course I couldn't help feeling extremely concerned.

Muriel smiled contemptuously.

"There's nothing to be concerned about," she said without compassion. "Once they get into this state, they go on and on."

"They?" Mrs. Peele repeated. She looked at this bowed and sobbing creature who had once been a man and was now merely one of "them," merely a typical specimen of some inferior species. "They?"

The doll nodded so emphatically that the blue bosom began to quiver.

"They all do it," she said with an expression of self-satisfaction. "Dr. Knoblock says it's like the rash in measles. Just one of the symptoms, that's all." And suddenly she gave a squeaky imitation of Oscar's despairing phrases. " 'I ought to be dead, I ought to be dead.' " She hiccoughed. "Pardon me." Then back to the impersonation. " 'I'm unclean, I'm no good.' Did he treat you to all that?"

Mrs. Peele nodded, and the doll laughed delightedly at her own cleverness.

"And I bet he told you about his girl friend," she went on, talking over him, talking past him, as though he were only a piece of furniture, or at best some kind of mindless animal. Then, warmed by the dry Martinis into confidential affectionateness, she leaned forward and laid a hand on Mrs. Peele's arm. "I like your dress," she said. "It's stunning."

"Thank you," said Mrs. Peele with cold distaste.

"But that isn't what I wanted to say. Only that dress is so fetching. Pardon me." And again, "Pardon me. My dear," she went on, lowering the squeak to a tragic whisper, "you have no idea what I've had to go through. Simply no idea. I mean, before *this* happened." She indicated Oscar. "And it's only two years since the first attack. And after his shock treatments he goes back to normal."

"Back to normal?"

"Almost worse than normal," said the doll. "But then, after a month or two, this thing hits again." She sighed, she did her best to look mournful; but the blue eyes beamed with irrepressible triumph.

There was a starchy rustling and an instant later a plump little woman, all in white, came hurrying out onto the balcony and briskly patted Oscar on the head.

"Well, have you been a good boy while Nursie had her lunch?"

Oscar made no answer, did not even lift his head.

"Take him in," said the doll.

Mrs. Peele watched him go, then turned and, ignoring Muriel's protests, went back into her room and closed the door behind her.

MARK SCHORER

$\longleftarrow$ ———————————————————————— $\longrightarrow$

The Long Embrace

THE ACCIDENT took place on a foggy evening, at about six o'clock, just outside the city, and very near one of the big municipal hospitals. It was no time at all before the ambulance had picked up the patient, who was unconscious, and had her in the hospital. In the operating room her eyelids began to flutter, and the attending surgeon, an elderly man, ordered ether. "Keep her under," he said. "This looks like a long job. And get Carver at once to handle that pelvis. I don't want to touch it, and there's plenty to keep me busy. Checked the heart action?"

"Abnormally slow."

"Prepare adrenalin."

The fluttering eyelids of the patient opened wide just before the ether mask covered her face. In her condition, she submitted to the anaesthetic without struggle, in fact, as it seemed, eagerly . . .

. . . you might have been under the sea. The trees had lost the spininess of earth, had been turned to veils which undulated gently and with infinite luxuriance in the slow currents that ceaselessly brush across the incalculable bottom of the sea. It was late afternoon, and there was a green light in the air still which intensified this sense of a submarine world, and only the greenness saved vegetation from monstrous appearances. And somewhere the sun was shining, curiously, and sending strange, horizontal beams of light, pink and yellow, through the thickness, rays which died in the very act of penetrating the fragile, inexorable barrier of fog, but which, still, before they died, hurt badly, cut like spears, sheared like knives, grated cruelly like bone splintered in the thighs, the stomach and the chest, the very head and brain. And yet the fog saved her from the ultimate, grinding pain, blurred things softly, and let pain swim in almost dreamlike waves against her, as she herself swam dreamlike, boneless, in the fog, in the remote depths of water.

Then, out of the billowing gray, a voice began to come. "Back her up," it said flatly, distantly at first. "Back her up, back her up, back her up. There you are, there you are, there you are."

Through what immeasurable depths of ocean did this familiar repetition of sounds float? "Back her up, back her up, back her up." The cold and metal voice, the dying, dropping sound? "Back her up, back her up, back her up,"

and, "There you are, there you are, there you are." This was a dead, metallic
voice which she knew, a voice which made no effort to lift itself above the
steady, monotonous hum of motors which was like the deadened roar of waves
on a distant beach, yet effortlessly detached itself from the whole background
of throbbing sound and flatly said, "Back her up, back her up, back her up."
The voice was empty of everything but metal words, no fear, no pity, no dread
of castastrophe, no love of it either, was merely catastrophe itself, articulate and
cold: "Back her up, back her up, back her up."

In the glistening, slightly tilted mirror she saw behind her how, in that sub-
aqueous world, a corridor appeared, empty and cold and infinite, its narrowing
length beyond the power of the mirror to tell, but infinite, infinite, white and
gleaming and cruelly empty, endless as it narrowed down to a point no eye
could truly find, stretching endlessly through the gray, green, billowing world.
And, "Back her up, back her up, back her up," the voice said relentlessly, over
the rising roar.

Then, as dread accumulated and mingled with the already experienced pain,
these two illogically mixed, the fear and the fact which was feared; then, as all the
motion of the world took on both violence and order, the green fog swirling now
into patterned arrangements of wheels and wheels and wheels, and the rays of
curious sunlight suddenly swinging up, much brighter, as from points of earth
and wheeling out in patterned revolutions piercing the fog but never finding
sky; then, as all sound came together in the powerful and helpless drone of one
motor, and that somewhere above, lost in the depths, and for which the lights
made their vain and ordered search—then, fixing her glance with sober frenzy
on the mirror in which the endless corridor stood askew, she began to back,
back, back, first fearfully, and slowly as the voice was slow, then, as gradually it
spoke more rapidly, terrorized, and faster, faster, faster; and at last the machine
was moving backward with such terrific speed that she knew that she was no
longer driving it, but that it was compelled, pulled back by space itself, the magnet of space fixed on the helpless object of time, which now charged back and
back and back, as still the voice said, "Back her up, back her up, back her up,"
and dread became an unendurable ecstasy of suspense. And then abruptly the
voice changed, and it was the old man's voice, quavering and uncertain, yet speaking the same words; and as the machine fled ever backwards, the old man himself
appeared, a crazy, yellow figure dancing like fury before her, down the limitless
corridor, forever down, and always faster, faster, faster. But with the change in
the voice, dread dissipated itself, and now she was laughing at the joke, and
the old man, dancing in his painful fury before her, laughed too, with his toothless gums, in his yellow, ancient face. And then at last, with an effortless transition from concrete to air, the machine lifted itself from the ground, from the
corridor, from the old man, was in the fog itself, and, in the revolving lights,
found its own orbit at last. Then there was once more the infinite luxury of submarine motion in her body, and all pain was gone; only the undulation of the
orbit itself, in the bright light, as the light went ever out and out into space, and

the orbit with it, the marvelous magnetized arc in space which held her, orbit in space dipping, dropping, rising, falling, out, out, out into the darker air, the sound of the motor above fainter and fainter, the voice retreating, retreating, a vast silence preparing itself for the secret she was to learn at last out here, in space unendurably cold yet not felt as cold, as the orbit was graying, then was lost, and fog lost, sea lost, sound lost, voice lost, only cold and black left as out, out, out toward knowledge she comfortably moved.

The mask was lifted from the face. "Under," said the attendant. "Observe the heart action closely," said the surgeon to the nurse. A young man, black eyes alert above his mask, came into the brilliant, shining room.

"Hello, Carver," said the older man, and with his glittering instrument he indicated the patient's pelvic region.

The young man grunted and glanced briefly at the face.

Quite suddenly, and, as it seemed, not curiously, she was on solid earth again, in a familiar world. Her hard heels struck sharply on the sidewalk as she went rapidly down the street from her mother's house to the garage where she kept her car. It was a late September afternoon, heavy with fog, and she was anxious to get to the airport where, she knew, Dave was soon going to make a landing that would not be easy. He would not be pleased to see her there again, but it was a funny thing the way you got over shame, over the most terrific insults to your pride, got over your pride itself, when you were really put to it.

She pushed the heavy garage doors apart and slid in through the aperture. Ether Voice was scraping spark plugs at the repair bench. "Heigh," she said:

"Hello, Miss Walton. Going out?"

"Yes."

"It's a bad afternoon."

"Not too bad."

"Pop'll help you out."

The old man was beside her, bobbing up and down a little, his zany's grin on his parchment face.

"Hello," she said to him, and, smiling to herself, walked back along the rows of cars to her own, with the old man limping along behind her. Sometimes she wondered why the old man amused her so, what it was about an old man with yellow skin, no teeth to speak of and one foot in the grave that was funny. Most people would pity him, she supposed, so old, and having to work still, and in a garage that was not any too warm and cozy in winter, sleeping in a chair through long winter nights in the drab, concrete office, which is what he had to do when he was on night duty, and that was most nights, because his son had to get real sleep to run the place in the daytime when the real work was done. It was that he was both so old and always so foolishly chipper that was funny. She was fond of him, as one might be of someone mildly defective, and she had a pet name for him, and one for his son, too. To herself she called the father Old Death, and what an archaic clown he was! The other, because of his flat, monotonous voice, like the emotionless voices one hears under anaesthetic, she called Ether Voice. Their real names she did not know.

She edged her way through the narrow space between her car and the next and climbed in behind the wheel. The old man stood in the clear space in front, his hand up, prepared to signal her to come ahead. She started the motor, glanced at him, smiled, and heard him say in his high, croaking voice, "All right, bring her out, bring her out, bring her out." His bony old hand beckoned her in a circular motion.

She put the machine in gear and let it move slowly ahead. Almost at once it scraped up against the fender of the car on the right. She pulled on her brake and stopped short. The old man was grinning helplessly and shaking his head, and Ether Voice, who had looked up sharply, came toward them at a run.

"By God, Pop, you gotta watch what you're doin'!" he said in his metallic voice, from which one could not have known that he was angry.

"I thought them wheels was straight," the old man wheezed.

"Okay," said Ether Voice, and, looking up at her, "Half our profits the old man uses up in the fenders and bumpers we gotta repair. He can't get a car in and he can't get it out without somethin'."

She put her head down on the steering wheel and laughed. "Every time," she cried, "every time! He doesn't miss a chance!" Something in these little accidents, these parodies of catastrophe, for which the old man was always responsible, seemed almost unbearably amusing to her; now she was laughing so hard that tears came to her eyes.

"It ain't funny any more," Ether Voice said, and looked briefly at the old man who stood there grinning, ashamed of his ancient incompetence, and, with his good foot, kicking at a post like a schoolboy.

"All right, Miss Walton," Ether Voice said. "Turn your wheels sharp and back her up."

She put the car into reverse and straightened the wheels.

"All right, back her up," he said in his flat tone, his hand waving her back. "Go on, back her up, back her up. There you are."

She was about to move the car forward again when they heard the telephone in the office ringing loudly.

"Wait," said Ether Voice, "till I answer that."

He trotted up to the front of the garage, disappeared, and in a moment came back again. "It's your mother. Wants to know if her daughter is here. Wants you to come home a minute."

"Oh Christ!" she said.

Ether Voice said, "All right, now. Bring her out, bring her out." Slowly she edged the car out of its space, and then swung it round to face the doors, which the old man was straining to open. Ether Voice walked along beside the car and said, "Now take it easy, Miss Walton. It's bad driving."

"Okay," she said, and, waving to the two of them, slid out into the gray-pink fog. Once she had heard him say to the old man, "Any dame that drives like that one's got somethin' eatin' at her," and she could remember the old man's meaningless grin which almost suggested relish. And now, in her impatience, she pressed her foot hard on the gas and drove the few blocks to her home swiftly, recklessly through the mist, pulled up in front of the house with a jerk, jumped out, slammed the door, and ran up the steps. She went directly to their sitting room where she knew her mother would be, and there she was, sitting heavily in the firelight on a little settee which she seemed to crowd, a decanter of sherry and two glasses on the table before her, her fat legs stuck rather ridiculously out, the great knees apart, and her little hands folded tidily in her lap. Something in the neat arrangement of waves in her mother's hair, something about the genteel gray hair itself, so well-kept and glistening in the firelight, outraged her.

"What is it?"

Her mother smiled with studied patience. "Sit down, dear."

Marge gave a tug at her hat. "Well, what?"

"Sit down."

Impatiently she sat down on the edge of a chair. "What?"

"Darling, you're looking lovely. That blue, fuzzy wool becomes you—your eyes, and your hair. It makes your hair positively yellow! I like it combed down that way, around your shoulders. Makes you look like fifteen."

"Come on, mother, what is it?"

"Don't always be so sharp, dear. It's only that when I saw that you'd gone out, without saying anything, I was worried. That's all. Where were you going?"

"For heaven's sake!"

"I'm serious, Marge. Do take off your hat. Have a glass of sherry with me. Be my daughter for a change."

"Daughter! What rot. Come on, Mother, what do you want?"

Her mother hesitated, and then, in a helpless little voice which was comic in a woman so heavy, she cried, "Oh Marge, what's wrong with you? Tell me. What is it?"

"If you didn't have a pretty good idea, you wouldn't be worried."

"No, Marge. Just your driving. That's enough to worry me enormously."

"What about my driving? I like to drive, that's all. I like machinery. I like to make it go."

"But you're so reckless."

"Anybody who knows how to handle a car can't be reckless. Now what is it, really?"

Her mother bent over and poured sherry into the glasses. "Here, dear," she said.

"I don't like the stuff, thanks."

Mrs. Walton sipped at her glass. "Well, there is more than your driving, then. You haven't always been this way. So—nervous, distraught. So abrupt with me."

"Oh, I'm sorry. But look, I am in a hurry. May I go now?"

"Where are you going?"

"You know perfectly well."

"To the airport?"

"Yes. To see Dave Roberts make a landing."

"That man."

"A good man, Ma. Too good for me, I guess."

"What do you mean? You, who have every opportunity. Think of the expense to which I went to educate you, then to bring you out properly, and now you won't have anything to do with your own kind of men. Or the girls, for that matter."

"Bores, mother. The most terrific bores, all of them. I can't stand them. I'm sorry about the expense, but it was never I who wanted to come out. Or any of the rest of it."

"But that man—that *Roberts!*"

Marge stood up. "Get something straight, Mother," she said. "I'm in love with him. In love? No. Crazy. Absolutely crazy about him. I'd give anything to get him. *Anything* at all. You're right. Something is wrong. I'm slightly nuts."

Mrs. Walton struggled to her feet, and her lacy teagown fell about her short legs in heavy folds, shrouded her dainty feet. "Marge, stop! I won't listen to this from you. I won't, I tell you."

"You asked for it," Marge said quietly.

"Do you mean to *marry* this man?"

She laughed. "Marry? Listen, a girl in my position doesn't hold out for marriage."

"What are you talking about?"

"I mean he thinks I'm so much dirt."

"Oh!" Her heavy shoulders hunched up in outrage, and her bosom rose and fell above her folded arms.

"It's true. How about it? Can I go now?"

"No. Sit down another moment. I want to tell you something." Mrs. Walton spoke quietly, with an effort.

"Well, what?"

"You know that I've not had an easy life. Bringing up a child, always headstrong and increasingly so, and in all these last, difficult years, I've had no help, I no husband, you no father. And now, Marge, don't you see, this hurts doubly, because somehow it must be *my* fault. If your father had lived, if you had a father now who could talk to you, I'm sure—"

"Rot, mother. It isn't a *father* I need."

Mrs. Walton blinked rapidly. "Marge, you wretched girl!"

"Sure. Don't I know it?"

She stood up to go, and as she stood up she felt a sharp twinge of pain in her chest, or her bowels, and slowly, as she stood there, and the room began to fade from sight, it grew into a terrible pain in her whole body, a ripping, tearing pain, and as she cried out, she knew that what she said had never been said. "Oh my God, Mother, help me!"

"*Mask! Mask!*"

But her mother was already gone, had vanished in the mist which was swirling in the room, and the glow of the firelight had transformed itself into beams of searchlights, and the roar of a motor grew loud in her ears again, and it was suddenly very cold as she was driving faster and faster and faster until she was shrieking with terror, and shrieking a strange thing, something else she had never said, "Father, help me, father, father!" But when at last, in the cold blackness, she was free of the car and found herself moving slowly out and out into the space beyond, where there were no longer any searchlights but only a few distant stars, or any sounds, or any pain, she moved with strange, compliant comfort, until she knew that in a moment she would have moved out of mind and into that knowledge toward which she yearned now in agony and joy.

"Okay. Way under."

"Pulse?"

"Dropping."

"Watch it."

And then she was on the ground again, driving now, fast but safely, the fog heavier and the day a little darker, taking the last curve on the highway before she turned in at the airport, then swinging her wheel sharply, and coasting into the nearly empty parking space. She pulled on the brake, jumped out, rushed into the brightly lighted, metallic place, and asked the first person she saw, "Is Roberts down yet?"

"Coming down now, ma'am."

She ran on down the shining corridor and out again, into the fog. She heard a droning motor above her in the mist, and she saw how all the sentinel lights were obscured on the ground in the deepening fog. The big searchlights were on, playing on the air, and in their powerful, barrel-like beams, the fog swirled in clouds. But the beams, even before they narrowed, were drowned, dissipated, blurred, unable to penetrate far the incredible murk. She glanced up at the controls tower where she could see the operator through the big windows, and she wished that she could get up there and listen to them bring him down, but she knew that they would prevent her. She clutched a moist, chromium railing and waited, listening to the steady roar of his motor as he circled the field.

As she stood there, she had only one desire, to be up there with him, to feel what he was feeling, to know what it was like to identify so perfectly the will and the mechanism and make this mechanical triumph over these non-mechanical obstacles, and come down smoothly, sweeping onto the ground exactly as you had calculated, but never knowing that you were going to; or not making the triumph, and come booming down from the soft, treacherous fog into the solid, smashing concrete as you had not calculated. The tension in either case was something which, even as she stood there on the earth, she could feel, she was certain, as powerfully as he, whose tension it was.

She clutched the railing with both hands and strained her face upward.

His motor now sounded farther away, then seemed to have stopped entirely, then picked up again with a sudden, nearby roar, and in the next moment she saw him come taxi-ing down the concrete, the glittering, silver machine through the fog like an obscure monster in a dream. She waited for him. When he came through the gate she stepped up to him. "That was very neat," she exclaimed.

He paused and stared at her. "My God," he said. "Again!"

"Sorry."

She walked along the runway with him, trotting at his side to keep up with him, and into the bright interior. He stopped abruptly and turned to her, his face red with exasperation. "Listen—" he said.

"Oh, don't say it!"

"Well, good Lord—"

"I know, I know. Just don't say it again."

"Now, listen—"

"No, no, don't."

"I've got to report," he said.

"Okay. I'll wait," she said, and watched him disappear up a little flight of metal stairs. Presently he came down again and, without speaking, walked by her into the restaurant. She followed him in and sat down beside him on one of the leather topped stools at the bar.

"Coffee, Marie," he said, pushing his pilot's cap back on his head.

"Two."

He turned and looked at her. "What do you want, anyway?"

"Don't be silly."

"Well, why don't you give up? No kidding, I'm not interested."

"Listen, Dave," she said, watching her fingers as she unwrapped one of the squares of sugar and dropped it into her coffee, "I'm not asking for much. I'm not trying to involve you in anything. I know you don't want to get mixed up with a woman. But you won't, don't you see? What I can give you, you probably pay for other places. And you'd be just as free."

"Jesus, what a woman!"

"Well, why not? Am I ugly? What's the matter with me? Am I ugly? Do I smell?"

He almost smiled at her. "You know you're damned attractive, that you've got everything a girl needs, including bucks. You got so much that you ought to have better things to do than chase me."

She put down her cup. "Sorry. I haven't."

"Well, why me?" he suddenly cried, so that the girl behind the counter heard and turned her bleached head sharply to stare at them. "Why me?" he asked more softly.

"Why? I don't know. It just is you, that's all. You just happen to be everything, see? I don't know why. Maybe it's the way you can bring a plane down. Besides being so beautiful."

He stared at her curiously. "You know, you make me uncomfortable," he said, "because I don't think it's me at all. It's something else you're after, something you got me mixed up with. Maybe just flying. Well, there are a lot of better fliers than me around."

"Something else?"

"Yeah. Girlish fancy about speed, or danger, or something."

"Maybe," she said. "But there it is."

"I can't accommodate."

She paused. "Look, there is something else. I'm no tart, you know, if you happen to think so. Fact, I'm what they call a virgin."

He laughed briefly. "Don't I know it? You'd have to be to be so dumb, and to hang on so. Sure, I know it."

She looked squarely into his dark eyes. "Dave," she said, "didn't you ever do anything you didn't want to do particularly? Just to be generous? Just to help someone out who was in a bad way? Didn't you?"

"Sorry," he said, "I got a girl, and I don't want another. It just happens. Besides, she wouldn't like it. Which reminds me, I got a phone call to make. Excuse me."

He got up and started toward the door, and she stood up too, and ran after him. She caught his arms, and he swung round to face her. She half-moaned, "Listen, take me outside for just one second. Embrace me for just one second. Kiss me, just once!" There were tears crowding out of her closed eyes.

"For Christ's sake!" he said, pulled his arms loose, and went out.

"Dave? That girl?" she cried, and her terrible yearning turned into pain.

He disappeared, and as she stood there, with her hand out, the pain spread in her chest and bowels again, slow at first and not hard, but then growing, and growing, and then she was calling loudly to Dave, something she had never said, she knew, "Dave, for God's sake, help me, you hurt me," and then the pain was so terrific that it seemed to lift her from the ground, and she saw how the fog was pouring in through the windows, filling the room, and the room vanishing, and Dave vanishing, and herself alone again, somewhere in space, in one of those beams again, moving out and out, and in her car again, driving furiously, furiously, out and out and out toward the blackness and the tiny stars, and with the knowledge suddenly that she was going to learn something, hear a voice from the motor drone, hear something which would explain everything, so that she would know at last, in the empty blackness, from the furious speed, what her whole life was a struggle to learn, if she did not smash up first, if terror did not drown her, learn what this fog, these lights, this roar of machinery, this grinding pain, these cries to him for help, were for . . .

"Mask, quick!"

"Here."

"*How is the heart?*"

"*Slower, doctor.*"

"*Adrenalin.*"

"*This is ticklish,*" *the young doctor muttered through his mask.*

"*There, she's going under again.*"

. . . and now out and out into the blackness, where pain ceased, and danger ceased, and sound and light and real motion, and you were hurled smoothly in this curious way to the secret of everything which was all you yearned for in the blackness and the unfelt cold . . .

But then, once more, everything was real enough again, and she had learned nothing except that now it was necessary to drive as fast as she could, tear up the highway, away from him, racing back to what? Home? The garage? She did not know. But she knew that she had to press the gas down as hard as it would go and take these corners sharp, let up a little as she came to them, and then, as she went into the curve, press down hard so that the tires stuck on the right side and she swept out free and fast into the straightaway.

Somewhere the sun was shining, sinking, sending a curious pinkness through the fog, and the air was faintly green, because it was day still, but the trees which shed the greenness on either side of the highway were limp and strange, like trees under water, dripping and waving like vegetation under the sea, listless and graceful, like dancers waving their arms.

Careful! She jammed her foot on the brake so that her tires screamed, swept up on the wrong side of the curve, but met nothing, and coasted over again on the right side, and then once more let the motor out. Her hat was on the seat beside her, and her hair streamed in the wind like a flag and the wet air struck her face sharply like hands. Ahead, the fog was red with the lights of the city going on, and now, through the thinning trees along the highway, the lights of houses shone. She pressed down hard on the gas and heard the soft roar of her engine in the deepening dusk, and the machine fled, or charged, along the dim highway, swept round curves, leapt up rises and roared into declines like an armored beast, enraged and incredibly powerful. She drove with a controlled fury, her hands exerting only a normal pressure on the wheel, but her foot pressed down hard, and her face lifted, almost expectantly, as if this speed were about to reveal something momentous to her, as if this speed were itself an answer to something, this speed which then seemed more important than anything in her life, even life, even Dave.

She was coming to the intersection with the highway which led directly into the city, and she took her foot off the accelerator. At the intersection she stopped for lights. She was breathing hard with excitement. Then she got her signal and turned sharply right, on to the city highway. Here the traffic was heavier, and she had to drive more slowly, but still she drove faster than she should have, unable to keep her speed down, darting in and out between cars, expertly, and not troubled by the fog now because the highway was illuminated, not troubled, as long as she kept up her speed, by thought.

She came to a stretch without traffic, and she let out the motor again. The powerful purr of the engine pleased her, and, leaning forward a little, her hands light on the wheel, she smiled. Only then she saw that she was taking a curve, sweeping out on the wrong side, and, too late, sweeping ahead at lights, a great shape, a truck, then a tremendous jolt, and then nothing at all . . .

. . . nothing but blackness, out into which she kept moving, free of her car now, and moving wonderfully in a regular circle, a circle which widened and widened, and as it did so letting all sensations, one by one, fall away. A familiar voice was saying, "Back her up, back her up," a flat, metallic voice, a voice without feeling or meaning, a voice at once strange and familiar in its curious, mechanical repetitiousness. This voice, in the blackness, was her only sensation. Lights and roaring and pain had gone, and in the blackness, as she swung ever out and out, nearer toward what seemed to be a few cold, distant, unblinking stars, only the voice stayed with her. Now even that was changing, changing to the older voice—and as the voice changed, she felt her whole being wracked with longing—the slightly wheezing voice, the clownish voice, and the words changed, and now, as she seemed to straighten her course and soar swiftly and cleanly out toward the distant stars, the new voice said, "Bring her in, bring her in, bring her in." Everything she had ever felt seemed concentrated now into a single yearning desire to be with the voice, and then presently, in the blackness, the form itself appeared, the old man, motioning with mechanical regularity, until, weeping, she came to where he was.

And then she began to laugh, as, in that outermost place, she felt his arms grip her and, in that embrace, they moved further out together. She was laughing, and wanting to say something, for now everything was clear. She looked close into his face as they sped through blackness, at the old skin, and the toothless jaws, and the zany's relishing grin, and she laughed again, as she had often laughed at him without knowing quite why, this ancient clown. But his arms were sinewy around her, and there was no longer any wondering in her mind, any yearning in her anywhere. She closed her eyes, and this embrace was everything—Dave, mother, father, life—and her laughter died to a smile. She opened her eyes and, in his thin arms at last, swam out with infinite pleasure, in the cold blackness, toward those cold and distant stars which now, slowly, were blinking out.

Later, in the doctors' dressing room, the two men were talking.

"Who was she?" the young man asked.

"She's just been identified," said the other. "Her name was Marge Walton. Rich girl."

"Marge Walton! No fooling? I've seen that car. What a baby!"

"So?"

"Big, open, high-powered foreign job. Black, with a lot of chromium on it. Long as a boat. Like a big, roaring beetle. What a waste!"

"You could probably pick it up cheap now."

"Yeah!" laughed the young man. "After she tied it up in knots."

The old man was buttoning his shirt and suddenly paused. He looked at the young man and shook his head.

"I don't understand it. She was banged up pretty badly, it's true, and she had lost some blood, but not enough to cut her off like that. From the moment she came in, everything began to slow up. The adrenalin didn't begin to take hold. She wasn't trying very hard, I'm afraid."

And the young man, who was about to leave, said, "Some want to live, some don't, they say. Something we don't know about, and something they don't—until they go under. Well, I'll see you."

FRANK O'CONNOR

Orpheus and His Lute

Du holde Kunst . . .

"THE changes in this city—!" said the old man, and then paused as though overcome.

"What changes?" I enquired.

"Ah, well," he concluded in a shocking anti-climax, "'tis God's holy will."

"But what are the changes?" I persisted.

"What are the changes? Isn't it change enough for anyone that the two things the people of this city were fondest of under the sun, the two things they'd give body and soul for, are after falling into disrespect?"

"And what are they?"

"Why, porter of course, and music—what else? Sometimes it was the music got the upper hand and sometimes the porter, but the one and the other were in every bit of sport and mischief there was. When I was a growing boy a man would cut his neighbour's throat for a pint of porter and travel Ireland to learn an old song. I knew wan two men that followed a fiddler all over Munster to pick up a solitary tune. I did so. But did I ever tell you the story of the Irishtown band?"

"You did not."

"Well, now 'tis a little story worth telling, just to show you the sort of *criothans* that pass for musicians nowadays. In those days—I'm speaking of fifty years ago—every parish had a band, and some had two bands and even three bands, but the Irishtown band was the best of the lot. There wasn't a man in it that wasn't born and reared as you might say between bar lines, and every one of them would drink Lough Erne dry. That was a well-known fact: a man wouldn't have a chance of being taken in the band unless he could do something remarkable in the way of drinking, and it used to be said of a certain notorious cadger: one, Daaza: that after a band promenade or a procession, with respects to you, he could get blind drunk on the emptying of the instruments.

"They were lovely musicians—'twas given up to them—but everyone was beginning to get sick and tired of their begging and blackguarding. They were forever collecting at the chapel gates for new this and new that, and of a cold winter's night you'd hear a knock at the door, and when you went out you'd see a couple of them outside with a collecting box, and they not able to stop it rattling with the shivering and the lust for drink that would be on them, and one of them would up and say 'Sorry for troubling you, old flower, but 'tis the way we're collecting for new uniforms for the band.' Uniforms! No one ever seen tale or tidings of anything new on them, and the old rags they had, there wasn't a vestige of a seat in one of them.

"You wouldn't remember it, but in those days it used to be a common thing for bands to serenade supporters of their own; Aldermen or M.P.'s or big butter merchants, more particularly when they were giving dinner parties, and when dinner was over the man of the house would come out and slip the bandmaster ten shillings or a pound to get drinks for the men. But in the latter end no one would open his doors to the Irishtown band for as sure as they got any sort of an innings, they'd be up week after week and night after night, puffing and blowing outside for hours, and midnight wouldn't see a sign of staggering or giving out in them till they got the price of a wet. And that was the rock they perished on, for one by one they lost all their backers, and towards the end even the dirtiest old ward politician wouldn't have the nerve to give them a show.

"Well, one cold, wet night in February they all gathered in for a practice. Practice, my eye! Damn the bit of practice they were fit for, any of them! They sat down round the fire, the whole lot of them, in the jim-jams, and 'twas two fellows called Butty Bowman and Ned Hegarty that weren't as bad as the rest that were lighting the pipes for them. That much they couldn't do for the jigs in their hands, and whenever the door opened or a cinder fell out of the fire, the whole bloody lot would give one loud shriek and jump three feet into the air, chairs and all.

" 'Boys, boys,' says the bandmaster, trembling and rubbing his hands, 'what in the name of the sweet and suffering God are we going to do this night?'

" 'Send out the conjuring box quick!' says Shinkwin, the big drummer.

" 'But who will we send it to?'

" 'Send it to the pubs. Crowley's at the bridge ought to be good for a bob anyway.'

" 'Here, Hegarty,' says the bandmaster, 'take a turn at it you now, yourself and Butty Bowman. And to make the one errand of it ye might as well take the jug as well.'

" 'So off with Hegarty with the collecting box, and little Butty Bowman behind him with the jug; and there were the rest of them, some not able to sit down, but walking up and down, clenching their fists and grinding their teeth; some too bad to move stretched out on the benches, and the whole lot of them shivering and moaning like men in their last agony, 'Oh, Mother of God, have pity on me! I'm dying, I'm dying! Oh, will this night ever be over me!' And every few minutes the bandmaster would be hopping to the window looking up across the bridge, and all the poor penitents crying together, 'Joe, Joe, are they coming yet?'

"After three quarters of an hour back comes me two buckos. The bandmaster made one wild dive for the jug and when he looked into it he gave a holy oath and covered his face with his hands. Butty Bowman held out his palm and there were three coppers in it. All at once the whole band began to shriek and shiver again.

" 'Boys!' says the bandmaster.

" 'What is it, Joe?' says a few of them.

" 'Ye know me a long time, boys,' says he, 'don't ye?'

" 'We do so, Joe,' says they.

" 'And ye'll bear witness,' says he in the voice of a man that was inviting them all to his funeral, 'ye'll bear witness before the world that I'm a musician to the eyelets of me boots.'

" 'You are, Joe,' says they, 'you are, of course, but how's that going to help us in our troubles?'

" 'Well,' says he, standing to attention and thumping his chest, 'I don't care who hears me say it but I was a man before I was a musician. . . . Butty, run down to Coveney's and tell them to send up the donkey and butt.'

" 'Erra, what's up with you, Joe?' says Butty, thinking, you know, the band-master was after going dotty with the need for drink.'

" 'Do what you're told,' says the bandmaster, and the teeth chattering in his head, 'do what you're told and do it quick, for be the Lord above me, I'm not responsible for me actions at this present instant.'

"Well, the bandmaster being twice Butty's height and a man that would crack your skull in a procession if you played a wrong note, away with Butty, and no sooner was he out of the room than the bandmaster breaks down, and sits in by the fire, shivering and crying. They didn't like the look of him at all, and no one went next, nigh or near him till Butty Bowman came back and tapped him on the shoulder. He got up without looking at anyone, took the keys from his side pocket and opened the instrument cupboard.

"At the sight of this they all brightened up like one man, because though only a few of them guessed what he was about, they all knew there was hope in sight.

" 'One minute,' says Ned Hegarty, 'can we do this without a comity meeting?'

" 'I'm the meeting,' says the bandmaster.

" 'But shouldn't we have a resolution or something?' says Ned.

" 'I'm proposing it,' says Shinkwin.

" 'I'm seconding it,' says another.

" 'Any objections?' asks the bandmaster.

" 'Anyone that have,' says Shinkwin, 'just leave him take off his coat and I won't be long dealing with them.'

" 'Passed unanimously,' says the bandmaster. 'Hurry up, boys, or ould Moon's will be shut.'

"With that, out with them all in a scramble, every fellow carrying his own instrument, and Shinkwin cursing, trying to get the big drum downstairs. They put the instruments into the old donkey butt and covered them with bags and tarpaulins, and off with them, beside the butt, in the pouring rain.

"Old Moon, the pawnbroker, thought they were mad when they came in, one by one, each of them with his own contraption. He didn't want to take the things at all, but they would not listen to his objections.

" 'How much so?' says he.

" 'Ten quid,' says the bandmaster, like a shot.

" 'Erra, what ten quid?' says old Moon.

" 'Ten bob a man?' bawls the bandmaster with his fingers doing the Morse code on the counter. ' 'Twill only quieten the drouth in us.'

" 'Five,' says the pawnbroker.

" 'What five?' says the bandmaster. 'The drum alone is worth more than that.'

" 'And a lot of use a drum will be to me if ye don't release it!' says Moon.

" 'On the sacred word of a musician,' says the bandmaster, 'we'll release the lot on Saturday night. . . . Take pity on us, Mr. Moon! For the sake of your dead mother, Mr. Moon, or your dead father, or whoever is dearest to you of all that's dead and gone, take pity on us this night.'

" 'Seven ten,' says the pawnbroker, and not a ha'penny more would he give them if they lay down on the floor and breathed their last on him. Well, when they got the money out with them in one mad rush like a lot of demented creatures after escaping from the asylum, seeing who'd be first to reach the pub, when all at once Butty Bowman gives a yell at them. They stopped, and the eyes hopping out of their heads.

" 'Jacus,' says he in a disgusted voice, 'are ye going to spoil it all, are ye? Are ye going into that pub with our sorrowful seven pound ten to blow it to the shawlies and cadgers of Irishtown? How long will it last ye? Be said by me, and in God's holy name, have grace about ye and leave the bandmaster order it, and we'll bring it back in the donkey-butt.'

"They all saw the sense in that, and, holding up their stomachs the way they wouldn't drop out of them with the drouth, they went round to a quiet little pub along with the butt, and by the back way they brought out four half-tierces. Then back with them the way they came, and when they got inside the band-room, Butty Bowman turned the key in the door and went upstairs to the window.

" 'What are you up to?' says Shinkwin.

"With that Butty threw the key clean over the bridge into the river. They all applauded him for this, and well they might, because it wasn't long before one woman and two women and three women began to hammer on the door below.

" 'Leave them hammer away to hell now!' says Butty.

"Then they set to it and they didn't leave much of the liquor behind. What made it worse was the wild mob that was after gathering outside. The women were dancing and shouting and screaming for drink, and when they wouldn't get it they drove in the window with stones, and when that didn't serve them they took a ladder to it. Butty Bowman and the bandmaster had rare fun knocking them off it again. The last I saw of the spree before I went to bed that night was Big Shinkwin and he with the jug in his hand pouring down the drink on top of them. They were trying to catch it in buckets and basins.

"The following night there wasn't a shilling left of the seven ten, and the bandmaster says, 'Boys, we'll have to steady up now and try to release the old instruments. And as we're about it, I'll start taking the subscriptions from ye.'

And what he collected was the sum of fourpence ha'penny. 'This won't do, boys,' says he, 'this won't do at all at all. Seven and six a man is what I want from ye, and I want it in a hurry.'

"He might as well have been asking a slice of the sky as asking seven and six from that crowd. Weeks passed and a month passed, and three days before St. Patrick's Day they had five and ninepence collected between them. 'Oh, boys, boys,' says the bandmaster, 'this is shocking. On Sunday morning I want every man jack of ye at the chapel gates and if that money isn't collected there'll be bad work.' And to make it more solemn he got special labels for the old collecting boxes printed 'Great National Appeal.'

"Mo leir, 'twas the sorrowful national appeal for them. The people went in and went out without as much as good morrow to the boxes or the men that were rattling them. One gentleman they stopped put the whole thing in a couple of words. 'After yeer last escapade,' says he, 'no decent man will ever put his hand in his pocket for ye again.' At the end of that day they had twenty seven and six. The bandmaster was crazy.

" ' 'Tis the end of the band, boys,' says he.

" 'Erra,' says Shinkwin, 'we won't go down as easy as that. We'll make a house-to-house.'

" 'Take an oath first then,' says the bandmaster . . . 'Not a drop of drink till the instruments are back. . . . Right hand up, everyone . . . So help me, God!

" 'So help me, God!' says they all.

" 'That I might be killed stone dead!'

" 'That I might be killed stone dead!' says they.

" 'Well, for God's sake will ye remember it?' says he.

"And they did. They stuck to that as they never stuck to a pledge before. And much use it was to them. They made another pound out of the house-to-house. 'My God,' says the bandmaster, beating his head, 'we'll be the laughing stock of Ireland if we don't turn out o' Patrick's Day.' They all had the scour on them now. Every hour or two one of them would be racing round to the bandmaster with a shilling or sixpence or even a couple of coppers he was after collecting somewhere.

"The bandmaster's hair was turning grey with anxiety.

"On Patrick's Eve up with him to the pawn.

" 'This and that, Mr. Moon,' says he, 'we'd be eternally obliged to you if you'd give us the instruments on loan for the one day.'

" 'What a fool I'd be!' says old Moon laughing in his face.

" 'For the love of God and the souls of the faithful departed!'

" 'No,' says old Moon, being a Lutheran by persuasion.

" 'Then,' says the bandmaster, 'hire 'em out to us.'

" 'No,' says old Moon again.

" 'For a quid.'

" 'No.'

" 'For two quid.'

" 'No.'

" 'For three quid then, and that's every ha'penny we have and more, and may the shining angels make a bed in glory for your soul this night.'

" 'No, I tell you,' bawled old Moon.

" 'You dirty little Protestant scut!' says the bandmaster. 'Hell is too good for the likes of you.'

"After that Shinkwin went in and by main persuasion got the pawnbroker to agree to put the instruments on separate tickets. The first thing he released, naturally enough, was his own big drum, and that walked away with one pound ten of what they had; then he took out a trombone, a B flat cornet, a euphonium and two clarinets. That left them without a penny in the world and there was Shinkwin with tears in his eyes begging old Moon for the sake of the souls in Purgatory to throw in one of the side-drums, and he wouldn't, he was that black.

"They put what they had on the donkey and butt, and 'twould break your heart to see them, one by one, running in distracted, crying out, 'Mr. Moon, Mr. Moon, throw in the old piccolo and I'll pay you o' Saturday!' or 'Mr. Moon, Mr. Moon, take pity on us and give us the little drum!' They were bad for drink but they were worse for music, and after the pawn shut they were still there, decorating the wall outside, and every now and then one of them would give a tap on the window and if old Moon looked out they'd be all winking and crying and pointing with their thumbs.

"In the latter end they got desperate entirely and up with a couple of them to Father Dennehy at the presbytery, begging him to intercede for them, but all the satisfaction he gave them was to say he'd be glad if the instruments were at the bottom of the sea instead, for all the mischief and scandal they were after causing in the parish.

"That finished them. Next morning, down with them to the bandroom and in the cold light of day there wasn't one that could face the thought of a turn-out with their couple of mangy instruments, and Melancholy Lane band appearing for the first time in their new uniforms. So off with them all behind the bandmaster to get what little satisfaction they could out of jeering the other bands. They took up their stance at the end of a lane where there was a flight of steps, and no one that saw them but was sorry, they looked so lost and miserable.

"Well, you know the sort of turn-outs there used to be in the old times: bands and banners and floats and drays with living pictures of Brian Boru and St. Patrick and Mother Erin playing her harp and National Foresters with their horses and big feathers out of their hats, and the devil knows what else. A procession like that would take two hours to pass, and there were the bandmaster, Shinkwin, Butty Bowman, Ned Hegarty and the others, with their tongues hanging out, and anyone that wouldn't jeer them, be God, they'd jeer him, but you could see 'twas the way the music was after going to their heads.

"However, that was nothing till the Melancholy Lane Brass and Reed came by in their new uniforms playing—of all the tunes they could find—'Defiance,' a march the Irishtown fellows were very fond of. Now, some to this day maintains that Melancholy Lane were to blame, and some says Irishtown; some says the bandmaster of the Melancholy Lane gave the order 'Eyes Right' and some says 'twas pure curiosity made his buckos turn their instruments all together on the poor Irishtown contingent. But, whatever it was, there was a roar raised, and the next minute the two bands were at one another's throats, and the new uniforms that Melancholy Lane took such pride in were wiping the mud off the streets so fast that you could nearly eat your dinner off it.

"Well, as God done it, Butty Bowman happened to have a bit of a heavy stick with him and with one lucky swipe he opened the head of a flute player and grabbed his flute. Then he made a run after the procession, and, falling into step as if nothing had happened, he struck up 'Brian Boru's March' on his own. And whether 'twas the warlike sound of that or the way they were after being starved for music for a month past till they were more like hungry lions and tigers than men, the Irishtown fellows laid out all round them, and one by one they were belting after Bowman with cornets, clarinets, piccolos and trombones; and, if they were, their supporters were springing up from every quarter and falling in two deep at each side of Bowman and the others, swinging big sticks and daring anyone to interfere. And still the band kept running up with bleeding noses and broken heads and faces that were after being painted and decorated with mud. The last out were the bandmaster and Shinkwin, fighting a rearguard action with the big drum.

"Within five minutes of the first blow being struck Shinkwin gave the three taps on the drum and if that band didn't play 'Brian Boru's March' it'll never be played in this world.

"But every good thing comes to an end and so did the procession. The band came back by the Stream Road, and by that time they had a force, three hundred strong, behind them ready to shed blood or tear iron. Just at the bottle neck bend they saw a cordon of police stretched across the road. The inspector stepped out and signalled them to stop. The crowd began to wave their sticks, and the bandmaster paid no heed to the signal. The police drew their batons but still the bandmaster marched on. Then, about six yards from the cordon, he suddenly swung round, marking time. And as if they had it all planned the band marked time too and began to fall into concert formation in front of him.

"A dead silence fell in the road as the raggedy-bottomed brigade struck up 'Auld Lang Syne.' They played it like angels, they played it so that no one who heard them ever forgot it, they played it as if they were too full of music and couldn't get it out of their systems. On the last bar the bandmaster snapped out 'Piano!' The people knew then they were in for a treat. The Irishtown fellows were famous for their *piano*: they could make those instruments sing like angels and never blur a note. The tears began to come to the people's eyes as it went on, and just when they thought they couldn't stand any more the bandmaster yelled so that he could be heard at the farthest corner of the crowd '*Pianissimo!*'

"At that word everyone held his breath. They knew now the band was out to beat itself. For about six bars Shinkwin tapped out the time very softly on the big drum before the band joined in. All the other instruments except the clarinets and the flutes came in on a whisper, playing staccato so that they sounded somehow or other like the voices of women sobbing in the next room, but the six clarinets took up the tune, and I never heard fiddles to compare with the Irishtown clarinets for sweetness. Then Hegarty the champion piccolo-player of Ireland, began to improvise a very melancholy ornamental passage above the clarinets—a thing he never did in his life before and that might have spoiled it all, but that day not a man in the Irishtown band could have made a mistake if you paid him for it. They were inspired, and Hegarty was inspired, and that one lonely voice, playing trills and shakes over the clarinets, gave the last touch to it. 'Twill show you, after the first bar the Inspector of the police took off his little round cap and every man there followed him.

"When the tune was over there was silence as if everyone was coming back to earth by a slow train, and then the inspector laid his hand on the band-master's shoulder.

" 'I have to arrest you and your men, Mr. Dorgan,' says he, 'and I assure you no arrest I ever made caused me more regret, because in my opinion you're a genius.'

" 'You needn't arrest us, inspector,' says the bandmaster, and some say there were tears in his eyes. 'We'll go to the Bridewell ourselves. The holy spirits are round us, and we must treat them gently.'

"And there and then they walked back to the Bridewell and surrendered without striking a blow."

"And did they get back their instruments?" I asked.

"They did not," said the old man. "They never played again. The Saint Patrick's Temperance Sodality bought the instruments they had and the tickets for the rest for a couple of pounds, and the band had one terrible night before they broke up for good—some time or other I'll tell you about that night.

"But sure The Temperance Sodality couldn't play for toffee. Temperance and music don't seem to go together somehow."

GERALD KERSH

Ten Old Tigers

"**Y**OU WANT to think of this," said Cattle, "whenever people get round to talking about the way people die, and what people die for—in general, when people begin to talk about things like Bill Nelson's death. Because there are times when there really does seem to be a Destiny that saves us, like cards to be played at the end part of a game." We talked about France, about the fall of France, and the nice rough wines of this part of France, and the smooth wines of another part; and the way wine is made.

Then Captain Ix said this:

"You may crush men likes grapes in a wine press. You can trample all the sweetness out of them—stamp them down until they look like a flat, down-trodden mass of rubbish. Do that. But don't forget one thing: out of the smashed remains of the grape harvest, my friend, brandy is distilled. Not much of it, but potent. And one whiff of good brandy carries with it the character and quality of the whole ravaged vineyard. Do you understand that? So with men. Squeeze a nation! Smash it and flatten it and twist out of it the last drop of its blood. But listen: out of the trodden-out debris of the people there comes a strong and vital spirit. It is there, fermenting, growing strong. And out of the agony of the crushed grapes, remember, comes the glory of the wine. Out of the agony of the people comes the glory of the nation.

"You can squash out the external appearance of a grape: but in doing this you give it an ultimate magnificence. It is like that with a man. A man on his own is a soft thing that spoils easily—like a grape! The press and the dark cellar bring out the undying spirit of the grape—as of a man!

"I am a Frenchman. I am one of the trampled grapes. But it is I who am telling you that even at this moment, in the dark, there is going on a stir, a ferment. And drip . . . drip . . . drip . . . drop by drop, there is gathering the rare, biting, imprisoned spirit of my people.

"Look here. I have been beaten like washing in a stream. I have been chewed up like grass. But it was I who went out to die with the Ten Old Tigers."

And Captain Victor Ix raised a glass of English bitter, and said, in a deep and resonant voice: "The Ten Old Tigers and the greater glory of France!" He gulped the beer; pulled a face. "Listen," he said.

I do not need to tell you much about our retreat. It was a debacle and a crash.

November, 1945

To my dying moment I shall carry in my nostrils the smell of that defeat—a smell, my friend, of doom: of high-explosive smoke mixed with petrol and burnt oil and dust and ashes. That was the smell of the Boche advance. They came on like driver ants in a jungle, over heaps of their own dead. The tanks roared like devils. It was like seeing a city on the move—tanks which looked greater than cathedrals, spitting shot and shell. And above them, airplanes as numerous and awful as the horde of Satan falling into hell—coming down howling, my friend; that is the only word. Their noise alone stunned us. But we held. My company did what was possible. I went mad. I raved. I swore like a maniac. But my little men went down; and my good old friend Xavier, the Lieutenant, he went down in a fine spray. The French Army was cut to slices like a ham—torn to bits like a pineapple. A bridge which should have been blown up was not blown up. The tanks came over in a black cloud. France was rolling over in her last convulsion. Germany was at her throat. The great thumbs of the tank and airplane offensive had a strangle hold, right behind the great artery. We could only gurgle and kick. And our kicks grew weaker. Our heads swam. Delirium! Blackness! Of my company, seventeen men were left.

I took them away. Then I was ashamed and wanted to go back: but then they took me away, for I was slightly wounded and not quite myself.

Yes, the man you see before you now, Victor Ix, retreated with the washed-out remains of his company.

I thought that although we had been pressed back, the rest of our forces were holding out; that I could come back soon with a new company and beat the Boche back to Berlin, as before. I did not know that the way had been cleared for the Boches, and that France was sold. It did not enter my mind, because I thought such things were impossible.

To the downfall of all traitors I will drink even another glass of this execrable beer: and one more still to the Ten Old Tigers. . . . To the ten grey and magnificent Old Tigers of Tolly.

We reached a tiny town called Tolly. Now I knew Tolly, for I had lived there for a little while when I was young. It is a little town like other little towns. Nothing happens there. Nobody does anything beyond a certain dead-alive routine of living. Tolly had only one thing to distinguish it from a thousand other such towns: a kind of Soldiers' Home.

Many years ago, after the fall of Napoleon Bonaparte, a certain military-minded wine merchant endowed a small row of cottages. He gave them to ten old soldiers, veterans of the wars, who had permission to live there in their old age rent-free. The will of the merchant provided, also, some small weekly sum for the purchase of tobacco and wine. The town provided a few francs' worth of lighting and heating. Thus, with their pensions, the old soldiers who lived in those cottages and waited for death were able to rest in some little comfort.

These poor old men were pathetic.

They had spent their lives in camps and barracks. They knew nothing but soldiering. A clause in the will that provided for them insisted that only men without families could enjoy those poor little amenities. So the ten veterans of

Tolly, who are now in Heaven, were men alone in the world: men who had devoted their entire lives to the Army of France.

When I was young and was at Tolly, I often saw them. They drew their pensions and spent the money on necessities. They were regimental, however, those poor old men. They received, every Saturday, a sum of three francs apiece for wine and tobacco; and so they went out to spend those few pence on wine and tobacco alone. And every Saturday morning, punctually at eleven forty-five, the ten old soldiers would march out to the Café Roche on the corner, and sit, each with his glass of red or white wine, smoking and talking. They amused people. It was funny to hear them discussing battles and skirmishes that everybody had forgotten, in places nobody had ever heard of.

Now and again, some person, slightly drunk and jolly, would say, "What about Indo-China?" And one of them, who had fought some shocking encounters out there, would square his thin old shoulders and begin to explain. . . . "We were here . . . they were there. . . . And then the Commandant said to me . . . and then I said to the Commandant . . . " Real old soldiers' talk. And then somebody would buy them drinks. Once in awhile one of them would get rather drunk. The townspeople enjoyed this very much—the spectacle of a seventy-year-old soldier singing forgotten songs in the ghost of a voice and reeling, supported by a comrade of seventy-two, back to the almshouse.

They were old and shabby. They had just enough to eat, but never quite enough to drink and smoke. They cadged a little. They sometimes attached themselves to total strangers and, talking of the weather, complained of thirst. Sometimes they were a bit of a nuisance. They tried to get small jobs of cleaning, or gardening, for the price of a litre of white wine and a packet of the worst tobacco. They used bad language when they forgot themselves . . . and as they grew older they forgot themselves quite often.

They talked mostly of battles; and when they talked, their skinny old hands lashed the air in savage gestures. One veteran of North Africa, a Sergeant-Major of more than eighty, whose elder brother had fallen at Sedan, used to demonstrate, with a decanter, how he had killed an Arab with a rock, and so saved the life of his commanding officer. The breasts of all of them tinkled with medals They all cultivated fierce mustaches. Most of them shaved every day, and walked upright.

The people of Tolly called them the Ten Old Tigers.

We got into Tolly, as I was telling you—used-up, finished, dead on our feet. The town was almost empty. The people had fled. There was an echoing silence. "What is this?" I wondered. We passed the Café Roche. There was a sound of merrymaking inside . . . a sort of crackle of senile laughter.

I staggered to the door. The café was empty. Only ten familiar figures occupied the center of the place. They had bottles of the best wine before them. Eight of them were smoking cigars. Yes, they were the Ten Old Tigers. I was nearly dead of exhaustion. I heard myself saying: "What, Sergeant Bonenfant—is it you?"

And a very old man said: "Vi l'capitaine," and sprang to his feet. He said:

"It is fifteen years since I saw your face last. Let us see—only four of us have died since then. There are four new ones. For the rest, we are still here . . . " He was happy with wine. "Listen, mon Capitaine, they have all run away. The café is ours. Drinks are on the house." This Sergeant Bonenfant was a wicked old man, who was disrespectful to officers and feared neither God nor man. He laughed and said: "They think the Boches have beaten France!"

All the rest roared with laughter.

I said: "They are coming in tanks." Then I felt my legs giving way. I said to my men: "Find yourself to eat and drink." And I sat down. And then the place whirled round me like a wheel, and there was a redness, and a purple, and a darkness. . . . And I came to myself on the floor.

One of the old men had propped my battered head on his bony knee. Another was pouring most of a bottle of brandy down my throat. A third was saying: "Bite his ears: that brings them to" . . . and another was replying: "I have no teeth." A fifth was slapping me in the face: an old soldiers' remedy for unconsciousness, it appears.

"My men?" I asked when they had finished pouring the brandy.

There was a mutter of horrible oaths and curses. The old sergeant, Bonenfant, said:

"The ——s have run away. There is some fairy tale. There is some legend. The Boches are almost here, one says. Then why not go and stop them, I say. But no. The seventeen of them, your men, throw down their equipment and run off. They say, 'Against tanks, what use are rifles? Besides,' they say, 'we are betrayed and sold.' It is a question of morale. They run. As for me, I say: Bah!"

I sat up. "There is something here that I do not like," I said. "We were retreating, yes . . . but . . ."

There was a crash. There was a smash of glass. A very old man, the oldest of all the Tigers, none other than the old Sergeant-Major whose brother had perished at Sedan, had thrown a water carafe through the window into the street. It was not drunkenness. It was rage. Yes, rage. That old, old man was bristling like a grey wolf. He stood up. His timeworn throat jangled like a broken piano. He shouted:

"Silence!"

There was authority in that voice, my friend. We all listened, out of force of habit.

He let out a string of old Army endearments:

"Silence, you dirty maggots! Silence every one of you, you this-and-that offspring of so-and-so! You drunken, noisy dummy-headed blank spawn of little frogs! Shut up! You in the rear—put down that pipe while I'm talking to you! Are you attending to me? Right. You'd better. You imbecile idiot scum of puddles! . . . Stop shuffling those feet!

"The Boches are coming. This is serious. Do you understand? They say that France is sold. I don't know. I know that there is something strange here. I know that in time the Boches would have come here only through a thin paste and that thin paste would have been me—and it would have been you, too, if

I'd been your Sergeant-Major! I'd have blown myself to dust to get in their eyes! And so? What has happened? Everybody runs. Civilians, yes: they are only jokes. They ran. But when soldiers run, my comrades, there is something funny. Soldiers are paid to fight, not run. It is a career: to fight, not run.

"Then what? We are old men. But we are men. We are ancient soldiers. But we are soldiers. In Africa we stood alone against thousands, and we did not run. What have we fought for all our lives, if people run away now when we are nearly dead? What have we lived for, to see everything we made go away like tobacco ash in the wind?"

A growl of rage from the other nine Tigers. They were sober now, and they growled. I felt myself growling with them. He went on:

"For myself, I have only about twenty years more to live. But—name of a name of a dog of a dog of a pig!—I have spat in the eye of death twenty thousand times ever since I was born, and got away with it! So have you all, you young pups! So have you all, you whipper-snappers; for you're soldiers like me! Good. At Sidi-Faouzi the raw recruits broke like string. The veterans, the old ones, it was they who saved the day with pig stickers, with naked steel. Good. It is the veterans who will save France now. Look! They have thrown down their rifles and their pouches. Good! Here are rifles, ammunition and bayonets. What more do you want? A regimental band? Bah! Get on that equipment! It is an order! To arms! Long live France, and down with the Boches!"

And my friend, my friend, as if in a dream I saw those ten old soldiers, those aged, superannuated, worn-out, battered, broken-down veterans of all the wars of the Empire—I saw them stuff their pipes into their pockets (incidentally, like good old soldiers, helping themselves to packets of tobacco) and struggle into the belts and pouches my men had left. They put the stuff on wrong. It didn't matter. They had their bayonets on their shrunken left hips. They loaded their rifles. The youngest of them—a man of sixty-four whom they called Bobo, who had been in the cavalry in the last war—showed the old Sergeant-Major how to load his rifle. The present pattern was quite new to him: in his day he had handled the ancient chassepot, and the forgotten Lebel.

The Sergeant-Major addressed them again: "Now, come on, you sons of dogs! Do you want to live forever?" It was the greatest war cry I had ever heard. I tore a strip off the tablecloth nearest my hand. I tied it 'round my head where I was wounded. I rose. I stood as on parade. I bellowed at them:

"What the devil is this? Sergeant-Major, are you forgetting yourself? Why, confound and blast you, man, I'll break you for this if you don't watch out! Who's commanding this company? Did you ask permission to speak? Now then! Get into line, there! Why, you ratty mongrels—are you sons of men? Or are you rookies? As you were! 'Shun! As you were! Company . . . slooooope arms! By your leeft . . . quick . . . march!"

It was a dream. It was a fantasy. At the head of ten men, the youngest of whom was over sixty—whose combined ages added up to something like seven hundred years—I marched out to hold back the shattering advance of the German tanks.

There went, up that ruined road littered with the debris of an army that had fled, seven hundred and forty-odd years of French glory.

I was the odd forty years.

The tanks had passed. The mass of infantry was following. I found a position in the face of the advance. There was natural cover. I hardly cared. To me, this was not a battle, so much as a gesture. It was my duty to die with France, I thought. And I was going out to die. Those wonderful old men had shamed me into it.

We saw the Boches coming. We had only our rifles, and about forty rounds of ammunition for each man. I was lying next to Sergeant Bonenfant. He was crooning over the butt of his rifle, caressing it with his cheek, and crying heavy old tears of joy. His poor aged hands were clutching his weapon. I could see the blue veins like cords, and the dried old fingernails dead-white under the pressure of his grip. The Germans came in sight. "Hold it," I said. The word went along. At a hundred yards I said: "Ready." At seventy-five yards I said: "Fire!" I roared it, and picked off an officer. The ten other rifles went off in a ragged little volley, but nine more Germans went down.

They must have thought that there was some huge counter-attack brought up to surprise them. They stopped. They took cover. We fired at will, picking our men. Ah, my poor old Tigers of Tolly . . . their muscles could no longer work with their eyes! Only one bullet in five hit anything, although the Boche was horribly exposed. Oh, for a section armed with light machine guns! I could have inflicted astronomical casualties. But it was better as it happened. Yes, it was greater. They were great, those men who had exhausted themselves in the quarrels of France.

We went on firing until our ammunition was exhausted.

Meanwhile, the Boches had let loose machine guns.

Bonenfant went down first. I saw one drop of blood, like a jewel, on his white mustache. No more. He died smiling. He thought he had hit the man he aimed at. But the man got up afterwards: he had simply ducked. I fired my last cartridge. "That for you, Bonenfant," I said. Then I got up. I yelled: "Charge!" In one hand I held a bayonet: in the other my revolver. "Charge!" I shouted . . . and even as I shouted, I felt a kind of hammer hit my knee. A ricocheting bullet had smashed it to pieces, and I went down like a skittle, sobbing with rage and disappointment. I wanted to die with my grandfathers-in-arms.

I lay, helpless. And I saw the last of my Old Tigers advancing with fixed bayonets upon the enemy. Four old men, carrying their bayonets at high port, ran as fast as their rheumatical legs would carry them—against twenty thousand German soldiers.

A machine gun went at-at-at-at-at. The old Sergeant-Major and one other tripped and rolled over. The last two kept advancing. I believe that even the Germans were touched. They held their fire. An officer stood up and waved his hands, and shouted something. The last two Old Tigers ran faster, with the little jogging steps of exhaustion. The officer fired his pistol. One fell. With his last ounce of strength he tried to throw his rifle at the Germans. But his arm was too weak.

And so the last of them all came down on the great German army.

Ten yards away from the officer, he stopped. I could see his chest and shoulders heaving. He was exhausted. Not even his will could take him a step farther. I was mad with pain and misery, and the shame of having fallen. I screamed: "Vive la France!" The last Old Tiger found breath enough to cry back—such a poor, pitiful, quavering cry; and yet so stupendous and so noble that the earth seemed to stop in its orbit and the sky seemed to stand still . . . "Vive la France!" Then he simply fell dead, because his heart had stopped.

That was the end of the Ten Old Tigers of Tolly.

I lay there, nearly dead. I lay for three days. I was found, then. I lost my leg. I am glad I lost my leg. All of me could not be buried with those great old men: but at least a part of me is honored by their presence in a grave.

A nation is great only as its finest sons are great. France is as great as the Ten Old Tigers. They are planted in the earth like seeds. Out of them there will grow something stronger and more beautiful than trees. Such men do not die. God send me such an end.

JESSE STUART

Not Without Guns

I<small>T WAS</small> in April. I was working on the hill. I was plowing corn ground. Erf Ealey come up the hill to me. I saw him climbing over the furrows. I stopped my mules and waited to see what Erf wanted. He come up the hill with his face all flushed red. He was getting his breath hard. I could tell Erf was skeered a little.

"What's wrong Erf?" I says.

"Plenty wrong," says Erf, "ain't you heard about it?"

"No," I says.

"Well the Short Branch boys and the Coal Branch boys have bunched together," he says, "and declared war on us Whetstone boys! Said they dared us to come to the Protracted Meeting tonight. Said we'd get our heads peeled with clubs. Said for us to quit taking the Short Branch and Coal Branch girls home. Said they's ending the whole thing."

"How did you find it out?" I says.

"Feel of the knots on my head," says Erf. "That's how I found it out! Ain't you heard about 'em waylaying me and beating me nearly to death?"

"No," I says.

"It's the news all over Whetstone today," says Erf. "They piantly laid it on me last night. I took Susie Abrahams home. Her brother Dick Abrahams was one of the gang that laid the clubs to my head. If I hadn't tore loose and run to the brush I believe to my soul and God they'd a-killed me."

"You go around and round up all the boys," I says. "I've got to get this patch of corn ground plowed. If I don't Pap will raise hell. He says I've been doing too much sparking and too much churching here lately. Says I ain't been wide awake during the daytime since Brother Stokes started the Protracted Meeting at Short Branch. Pap told the truth too. I'm getting like an owl. I see better at night."

Erf went up Whetstone to round up the rest of the boys. I'll tell you the pump knots on his head were big as guinea eggs. I felt sorry for old Erf. "Let that gang try it tonight and they'll get the hot lead," I thought. "They won't be jumping on the least man on Whetstone. They'll be bucking up against some real men. I'm as good a man myself if I do say it as ever packed a pistol or wore a pair of pants."

I finished plowing Pap's patch of corn ground. I took the mules to water.

July, 1939

Then I took them to the barn—unharnessed them. I put them in their stalls and fed them. I could hardly remember the right number of corn ears to feed each mule. I was thinking about the fight we would have with the Short Branch boys and the Coal Branch boys. When they come at us with their clubs we'd answer them with a load of hot lead.

I et my supper. Then I changed my clothes. I put old Hulda in her holster. I put on a coat to hide my holster. I was ready for church. "Boys go to church nowadays," says Pap, "to spark gals. They go to drink and fight. They don't go to hear what the preacher says. The world is on the road to hell and damnation."

"It may be Pap," I says. "I don't know. I just know I like to go to church. I go because they ain't no place else to go."

Pap looked hard at me. But I walked out'n the house and down the road. I'd meet the rest of the boys at the forks of the road. Then we'd turn to our left—climb the pint, go through a pine thicket on top of the ridge and then we'd turn over yan side the hill to Short Branch Church. The church was right on the divide between Short Branch and Duck Puddle and Duck Puddle flowed into Coal Branch. All the Coal Branch crowd had to come up Duck Puddle to get to the Short Branch Church. I guess that's what made them friendly with one another. We's on the other side of the big hill over on Whetstone and they hated us.

"Well," says Erf, "we are here. If this ain't enough to subdue 'em we can get reinforcements. Price Taylor said he wasn't brewin' for trouble but said if it broke out tonight and they got too hot for us to send a boy back over the hill and let him know. Said he'd come with his autermatic shotgun with high-powered shells filled with chilled-buckshots. Said he used 'em for dogs among his sheep."

There was Lum Sperry, Butch Noell, Jack Todd, Ephriam Bates, Andrew Duncan, Rufus Powell, Bad-Eye Flannery, Steave Walker, Tom Brown, Estill Brooks, Erf Ealey and myself. "There's a dozen of us here," I says, "and they'll have at least three men to our one."

"That won't make any difference," says Butch, "we've got the difference between men on us. Every one of us is ready. We ain't taking no foolishness. We ain't thinking about fighting with clubs nor our fists either. We're going to take our girls home."

"Don't ever think they won't have more than clubs tonight," says Erf, "after the way they beat me up. They'll be prepared for us. They'll be ready and waiting. The club practice on my head was just bait to draw us all out tonight!"

"Well they've got us," says Lum.

"What can they do with us?" says Estill.

"Let's get going," says Bad-Eye Flannery. "Church will soon be started. We'll haf to go in late—all bunched together and have everybody watching this Whetstone crowd come in! I don't like to walk in a church house and have everybody to start staring at me and quit a-listening to what the preacher says."

Bad-Eye carried our whiskey. He had two one-gallon jugs with a strap buckled between the handles. He put the jugs over his shoulder to make them balance.

Erf Ealey led the way up the path. We started over the hill to Short Branch Church. The moon was out. It was light enough to shoot a rabbit. The path wound up the hill like a snake. It was too steep for the path to go straight up the hill.

A rabbit jumped from a stool of briars. Bad-Eye jerked his pistol and aimed.

"Don't shoot," says Butch, "save your cartridges. We might need them tonight. That old rabbit's liable to have youngins any way this time of year. You can't tell. Save the rabbits to shoot at next year."

Bad-Eye lowered his pistol. He put it back in the holster on his hip.

"I've always said," says Lum, "when a rabbit lives the season through here and dodges all the bullets shot at it, then the rabbit ought to be left alone until another hunting season comes around. It's only fair, boys, to the rabbit! If we hunt next year we've got to leave a few rabbits for seed."

"All right boys," says Bad-Eye, "hush your mouthing. I've put my pistol up. I don't intend to shoot at a rabbit. I's just limbering up—practicing on gettin' my pistol out'n my holster."

We's gettin' hot under the collars by the time we got to the pine woods on top the hill. Bad-Eye was sweating and panting with two gallons of licker swinging across his shoulder. "How about swigging a little from these jugs?" says Bad-Eye. "It'll kindly lighten my load a little."

"Suits me," I says. "I never was so thirsty."

Well we stood in the moonlight and passed the jug around. Every one of us took a big swig. Then we passed the jug around again. We took another big swig apiece. After each man took his swig he would go "aham" and spit on the ground. It was good whiskey. It was the real corn. It would put life in you. It would make you want to fight. It would make you take your part. It would make you wade right into a bunch of clubs. When you got this moonshine under your belt you didn't even fear the Devil himself.

"This jug's emptied," says Bad-Eye. "Now we must keep the other jug to nibble on while we are in church."

"Who's going to guard the jug," says Erf, "while the rest of us go in the church house?"

"I'll guard tonight," says Rufus Powell. "You guarded last night didn't you Bad-Eye?"

"Yes I did," says Bad-Eye.

We's feeling higher than the Whetstone pines above us. We felt the new life coming into our bodies. All of us had been plowing, or sprouting ground, or digging coal all day. But we wasn't tired now. We's rested and ready. We could see the white church house in the moonlight down in the shoulder of the hill below us. We could see the white strip of path winding around down the hill like a snake below us. We were on our way to the church. We could even hear them singing and hear the organ playing. We could see the bright lighted winders. They were brighter than the moonlight.

"Now boys," says Rufus, "when one of you feel the urge for a swig I'll have the gallon right out here by this black oak—right here next the graveyard. Don't all of you come at a time. We might be indicted next Grand Jury for disturbing Public Worship."

"It's a damn shame," says Butch, "that we have to have a man to guard our licker at church. Of all the places on this earth you'd think your licker would be safe at church. But I've lost more licker at this church than any place in the world. Boys just come here and never go inside. They just run around the house like heathen and pilfer—hunting for licker. You haf to watch it here."

"Reminds me of crows," I says. "One will stand up in a tree above a shock of corn while the others get down and fill their bellies. The crow in the tree will caw-caw to the crows on the ground when he sees a man coming. Then they fly up and fly away. They work with one another—just exactly like we do. We have one of our crowd to watch our licker every night to keep a Short Branch man, or a Coal Branch man or a Duck Puddle man from stealing it."

"I've always said," says Steave Walker, "that they ain't any difference much between men and crows! They are all thieves and rascals. But they hang to their own gangs. They've got to do it in this world boys! Now look how Erf got beat up when he's by hisself the other night! If we'd a-been with Erf it wouldn't a-happened. W'y I can shed tears every time I think of the pump knots on top his head! I run my hand over his head and it felt just like sweet-tater ridges!"

"Quiet boys," I says, "we're at church. Let's go in and act like men. Let's show Brother Stokes how nice the Whetstone men can act!"

"It's a go," says Butch. "We don't want a jail sentence for disturbing public worship nohow."

Brother Stokes was preaching when we went in. There was a big long seat in the back of the church. It was empty. We got this seat and we all sat together. Just across the aisle from us I saw the Coal Branch boys. They's on two big seats. They's off to themselves. In front of us was another long seat and it was filled with Short Branch boys. There was half of another long seat in front of us filled with Duck Puddle boys. I wondered why they weren't all together. But when it come to fighting us, I knew they'd soon be together. They didn't like the Whetstone boys. We had about the same love for them.

"This Protracted Meeting," says Brother Stokes, "is bound to be a success. Look at the young men from every creek and holler around here! Look at them won't you! They have come out here because they are interested in their souls! The older people all ought to be ashamed to let these young men come out and beat them! When so many young men come out, my Protracted Meetings are always a success. It shows that the people of the community are hungry for the Spirit. It shows that they crave the Spirit and they come."

We looked straight at Brother Stokes. We didn't make a lot of noise. Just one of us at the time slipped out to the jug Rufus was watching. After we got our swig we slipped back and let one of the other fellars go. We didn't make a lot of noise. We were quiet about it. I've seen men turn the seats over getting out. But that ain't in the blood of a Whetstone boy. We never acted like that around God's house of worship.

We listened to Brother Stokes preach his sermon. We looked over the house too sorty until we found our girls. We didn't do a lot of neck-craning like the other boys. We behaved ourselves. Brother Stokes says: "I want to thank you boys for your good behavior tonight. I want you to come back until this Protracted Meeting is over. Maybe you will want to consecrate your lives to God." Brother Stokes dismissed us with a word of prayer. Just soon as he said the last word we made for the door to get our girls.

Nine of us got Coal Branch and Duck Puddle girls. Three of our crowd got Short Branch girls. They would be separated from us. They would be going back the other way. They would be going toward Little Sandy River. Our crowd was divided. Butch, Rufus and Bad-Eye went back the Short Branch way. They were hanging onto the arms of awful purty girls. I didn't much blame them. Maybe they forgot all about the trouble we were going to haf to face.

I looked back as we started over the bank toward Duck Puddle. I saw a whole army of boys standing under the oaks in the Short Branch Church yard. I thought they were brewing trouble.

Then I thought about the three Whetstone boys that went down Short Branch. They could beat them to death and the rest of us would be over on Coal Branch and Duck Puddle.

"Boys," I hollered to our gang going over on Duck Puddle and Coal Branch, "soon as you take your girls home, come back to the foot of this hill that leads up to the church house. Come here and wait until all nine of us can get together. Boys pass the word on to one another."

I took Susie Munn home. She said her Brother Jack Munn was hanging around the church house for something with a lot of other boys. Said they'd been getting together all day and plotting. Said she thought they were sore because our Whetstone boys had been going with the Coal Branch, Duck Puddle and Short Branch girls.

I just let her go on and tell all she would. I wanted to get the lay of the land so if we had to fight we would know a little about their numbers and strength. If they were armed with clubs we had the advantage. If they carried the difference then we would be outnumbered three to one and we would haf to take cover and shoot from ambush. We'd haf to bushwhack.

The moonlight was so purty on the April fields. Susie was a purty little doll. But I couldn't love Susie an awful lot for thinking about what was to come in just a matter of hours. The plowed furrows looked good in the April moonlight on the Coal Branch hills.

The night was so purty. It was the purtiest time of the year. The apple orchards were white with bloom. There was the smell of wood smoke in the bright-blue night air. The Coal Branch farmers had burned their clearings and the smoke had settled down in the valley. The wind from the apple orchards was sweet to smell.

I took Susie to her door. I squeezed her right tight and kissed her a lot before I let her loose to go in the house. She didn't seem to be in a great hurry to get in the house.

"Oh if it wasn't for that infernal gang," I thought, "we could spark these purty girls in peace. Wait until that bunch comes to Whetstone and we'll be just as kind to them as they have been to us."

I hurried back down Coal Branch. It was nearly twelve o'clock. I didn't know how far the other boys had to take their girls. Some had to go a fur piece. Some had to go to the head of Duck Puddle. I spect it was every bit of three miles that I had to take Susie. I'd trot a little bit. I'd get to sweating. Then I'd walk until I got cool. I wasn't long getting back to the foot of the hill. Jack, Tom, Ephraim, Estill, Andrew, Steave and Erf were under the big oak tree at the fork of the roads waiting. They's smoking their pipes, cigars and cigarettes and talking to each other.

"Waitin' on you Oscar," says Jack—"all here but you and Lum! Where did you haf to take your girl nohow?"

"Must a-been to the head of Coal Branch," I says, "I've run nearly all the way back. I nearly walked Susie to death gettin' her there. I just thought you fellars would all be here waiting on me. I'm hot as a roasted tater."

"There comes old Lum," says Andrew—"bet he had some fur piece to take his girl!"

"You happy tooten," says Lum. "You said it boy! After we got to the head of Duck Puddle, Bertha says: 'nother hill to cross.' After we crossed that hill Bertha says: 'One more hill to cross.' But I found us another gallon of spirits. Boys our night ain't started yet—it's jest beginning—I've been thinking about poor old Butch, Rufus and Bad-Eye."

"You couldn't a-picked three from our crowd that would come nearer takin' care of themselves," says Erf. "All good shots. All tough as the devil wants them to be. Ain't afraid of hungry lions!"

"Just the same," says Ephriam, "we'd better kill what's in that jug and be on our way. We can't tell what has happened!"

We stood under the oak where the roads forked. One road went up the hill to the Church and down Short Branch. The other road went up Duck Puddle and down Duck Puddle to Coal Branch.

We passed the jug around and each man took his swig in turn. That is one thing you can say for the Whetstone boys. They know how to drink out'n a jug. They ain't hoggish. Each man gets what's coming to him. Seems like he knows just how many swigs to take without counting them. He ain't stingy with his whiskey either. He divides with his friends.

After we killed the gallon we started up the hill. The sky was not as purty and bright as it had been. Little dark clouds had began to gather on the sky. The April air was so warm it felt a little like rain. We walked up the hill. We didn't talk. We were going toward the church house. We thought the gang would be there. They were there. They knowed we had to come this way. There wasn't another way for us to get back to Whetstone. It looked like an army of men. They were waiting for us in front of the church house.

"All right boys," we heard one say, "here they come. Get your clubs ready!"

"Hands on your guns, boys," I says.

They walked to meet us. Their clubs were the purtiest clubs you ever saw. They were peeled clubs. They were purty and white. They held them high in the air and marched toward us!

I held Hulda in the air. I shot twice!

"Who gives a damn for your guns," says one of their men. "We got our guns too. If you start gun shootin' we'll wipe your little crowd out in two minutes."

One of their men pulled a gun and shot twice.

"To the woods, men," I says.

We broke for the woods. We tore out hard as we could go. It was a patch of oaks over across the road from the church house. They follered us to the fence and batted us across the behinds as we rolled over the fence. When we hit the ground on the other side of the fence, we hit the ground running for the patch of oaks. We fell on our bellies behind the trees. The big gang didn't follow us. They took cover in the church yard. They couldn't find enough trees. They run to the graveyard and got behind the tombstones.

"Yaho," says Butch—"where are you boys?"

"Take cover," says Ephriam. "They are behind the church yard trees. They are behind the tombstones. Get cover quick."

I don't know who shot first. I don't know how it all started. It was a gun battle. We turned our bodies straight out from the trees with our heads up close to them. We laid on our bellies and shot rapid fire at the white tombstones. We shot at the sight of their gun flashes in the church yard. For every shot we fired they must have fired seven.

"Shoot low," I would hear them say. "Shoot low!"

Then we heard three guns barking on our right. It was Butch, Rufus and Bad-Eye. They had found a hiding place. They were firing from our right. We almost had to shoot over them. We could see the flashes of their guns. The bullets wheezed in the brush above us. They cut limbs from the trees. The limbs fell on us. If one of us had raised up we'd a-been a goner.

"I hate to shoot into a graveyard," says Erf, "but I haf to. Ma always told me it was a sin to step on a grave. I never do. I guess we won't wake the dead up. They won't know about their kin folks shooting over top of them and plowing the dirt with bullets above them."

"Shoot to bust them," says Ephriam. "Remember the pump knots on Erf's head. Remember a Whetstone boy can't come over here in peace. Pour the hot lead to 'em between the eyes!"

We could hear them holler. Then they would shoot. We'd hug the ground. The bullets would pass over us. I could remember the times when we'd go rabbit hunting and if we couldn't find a rabbit or quail to shoot at we'd stand off and shoot at each other. We'd get fur enough apart not to kill one another because it was in fun. We'd just sprinkle each other—make it smart—burn the hide a little bit. But I never was in a gun battle like this one.

The moon went under the clouds. We's still pounding away at one another. We'd wait until we saw the fire flash from their guns. We'd shoot at their fire. Our shooting wasn't fast as it had been. Our ammunition was getting slim.

"Go after reinforcements Erf," I says. "You know who to get. Crawl over the bank on your belly. Walk low until you reach the top of the hill. Wait until we sorty stop firing."

We eased up on firing. They took it as a token of truce. They eased their firing. Erf slipped over the bank—twisted out around the hill. Then he started to climb toward the top. They just fired a few times when the lightning flashed. We could see a ditch we'd been shooting over in the cow pasture. There was a big deep gulley. We could see Butch, Rufus and Bad-Eye in the ditch. They had stopped firing. Must be they were out of ammunition too. They's just laying down and hugging the bottom of the ditch.

"When we get chilled buckshot we'll run 'em from behind the tombstones," says Ephriam. "That ain't over 125 yards over there. Super shells with chilled buckshots'll send them screaming to the woods."

It must have been two in the morning when our reinforcements come. They crawled on their bellies up to the patch of woods. Erf was in front. He led them to us. We's just shooting every now and then to let each other know we's still there. We didn't know whether they'd sent for reinforcements or not. We didn't care. We had the best position to shoot from. We's a little higher up on the hill. When the lightning flashed, we could see the tombstones.

"Seven new men," says Erf. "Five autermatics with shells used for killing dogs that kill sheep. Two rifles—one a 30-30 Springfield. One a muzzle-loader. Price Taylor, Chilly Bain, Pluck Reed, Wid Callihan, Jake Henson, Mart Fields and Harlan Wurts."

"All right boys," says Price—"just where are they hiding?"

"Wait until I shoot," I says. "Then you watch their gun fire and get their range."

I fired my pistol. There was a flash of fire from the graveyard. Fire flashed from the trees in the church yard. Our autermatics begin to roar. Great streaks of fire jumped from the barrels like lightning. The lightning flashed over head. The rain started falling. I guess the rain helped a lot of them. We heard them hollering when the chilled shot begin to sprinkle the graveyards. We heard them take to the woods above the church. When they got above the house we barely could sprinkle them. We poured the hot lead at that bunch of rascals. They'd been pouring it to us.

"Where are you Oscar?" hollered Butch. "Watch we're coming! Don't fire this way."

We stopped firing until Butch, Rufus and Bad-Eye come running low and then fell on their bellies and scooted on the muddy ground in amongst us.

"Welcome home boys," says Jack.

"I lost a finger," says Bad-Eye. "Rufus tied it up with his handkerchief. A bullet nipped it off clean as a whistle when we's taking cover. They had open field at us. We come up the road—we didn't know you's lined up already to fight."

"We've sent back and got reinforcements," I says. "Erf went back and got a few of the old hunters. We've run 'em through the woods!"

"Reckon anybody's been killed?" says Jack.

"Don't know," says Chilly—"if they have been they're close the church house to have their funeral preached and close a graveyard to bury them in. We ain't worrying about that. You boys will be safe in going back to church. I'll bet you two gallons against one. This would put the fear of Whetstone into that bunch!"

"The fun is all over," says Pluck Reed. "We'd better be on our way across the hill. Don't light your pipes or cigarettes yet. Someone may shoot at the light."

We walked up the path in single file. My leg felt a little stiff. I thought it was from laying down behind that tree so long. We walked through the rain— we were wet as possums. We had to hold to the sprouts to get up the slick path. The rain was still falling. We had to nearly feel our way. We took hands and held to one another. We finally reached the top of the hill. It wasn't raining so hard in the pine grove. We got under the pines—Chilly held his flashlight while we filled our pipes, lit our cigarettes and cigars.

"I've been scint on the leg with a bullet," I says. I looked down and blood was oozing from my leg.

"Let me see," says Chilly. He took the flashlight and looked at my leg.

"No more than a briar scratch," says Chilly. "Let it bleed, that will be good for it. This has been a lot of fun. Wait until you see a real battle. I was in a few not so long ago. You are just boys. Old Pluck and me's been there before! We put 'em on the run didn't we? It's hard to beat chilled buckshot for close range fightin'. Sawed-off shotguns are awfully good for real close fightin'."

We stopped at Chilly's house when we got down on Whetstone. He give us a swig around. "Not much, boys," says Chilly, "but it's enough to keep you from takin' cold."

"Now boys," says Pluck, "before you all scatter out—you go back to church tonight. You don't know anything about all this shooting. You take your girls home just like nothing had ever happened. If they have you before the Grand Jury you don't haf to indict yourself. Remember it has been a dark night. You ain't seen no guns. You ain't disturbed no public worship. Be kind to Brother Stokes and help him all you can with the Protracted Meeting. Remember you won't have as many there tonight as you had last night. It's too wet to plow to-day and you fellars can get some rest. Remember you'll hear of a lot of fellars being in bed sick with the rheumatics, with colds and the flu after this gun battle tonight. Just remember Oscar you all can go in peace now. They won't want to bunch on the Whetstone boys. It's all over. They've been weaned like suckling calves."

SECTION THREE

Graphics

INTRODUCTION

TWO POINTS OF POLICY were pronounced in the very first issue of the magazine and could be restated today with greater applicability to current issues than they might have enjoyed at some of the interim stages.

We said at the outset (October 1933) that in page layouts, typographic dress and general layout we had tried to allow this magazine to take on an easy natural masculine character—to endow it, as it were, with a baritone voice. We said that it would have been easier to follow the much fancier handling that characterizes so many of the general magazines that are calculated to captivate the woman reader, but that we thought you'd welcome a change from that, so we had consciously tried to avoid all fuss and feathers, in dishing up the magazine's content.

The other point we made at the beginning was that the use of color gave us a chance to give the cartoons a variety of treatments that would not otherwise be possible, and that we felt that some of them came very close to being classifiable, with equal applicability, under the heading of art as well as humor.

As for story illustrations, we early defined our policy regarding them, by saying that we wanted them to be "almost never illustrative." We meant that we aimed not at a definite illustration of the text alongside which they appeared, but at a translation into pictorial terms of its general mood or tone.

We inveighed against the then prevalent practice of slick-paper magazines of beginning stories on double-page spreads with fully eighty per cent of the area preempted by a big illustration, captioned by a catch-line taken from a high spot of the text. It seemed to us then (and still does) that such illustrative treatment is an affront to the readers' intelligence—as if the premise is that he's such a lackluster lug that he must be teased into making the enormous mental effort involved in concentrating upon the plain type long enough to spell out the words. Our point then (and now) is that in magazines addressed to the attention of adults, the *telling* of the story is the job of the author, not the artist.

Perhaps fortunately for this section of this book, that illustrative policy was ill-kept, over the years, with the result that there are some prettier pictures coming up in the subsequent pages than might otherwise have been the case.

As for the content of the cartoons, we long ago conceded to *The New Yorker* a near-monopoly on sophisticated whimsy, so we set out to try to get a corner on something known (if only to ourselves) as Whamsy. Based on the principle of aesthetics designated in the textbooks as *Einfühlung*, it represented

351

as close an approach to audience-partici-
pation as the cartoon could ever conceivably come, short of some printing-press
equivalent of 3D. The most memorable
example of this "Wanna Make Something Out of It?" school of comic art
was undoubtedly the drawing of the
Petty girl looking you straight in the eye
(after the manner of Uncle Sam on recruiting posters, so that from whatever
angle you regard it there's no escaping
that direct gaze) and captioned, simply
but eloquently, "Oh, you would, would
you?"

Cartoons like that brought scads of
letters asking us to explain the point.
We had to answer that there wasn't any,
except as made by the mind of the be-
holder.

We used to attempt to explain, to
those who found the incongruity between
the text features and the cartoons a disturbing evidence that "Esky" was suffering from schizoid tendencies, that the
cartoons are to the content as a whole
about what cosmetics are to a woman's
personality—a conscious and purposive
brightening up of the magazine's face,
to appear interesting enough to insure a
second look.

To apply the standards of another age
would be to assume that a woman who
uses lipstick or rouge is therefore morally
abandoned. You can at least get your
face slapped, and perhaps get tossed into
jail, if you are consistent in jumping at
conclusions like that.

But the point was better made, than
we ever made it, by a man who wrote in
to *The Sound and the Fury,* "I find no
fault with *Esquire* that I do not find
with the age that has produced it."

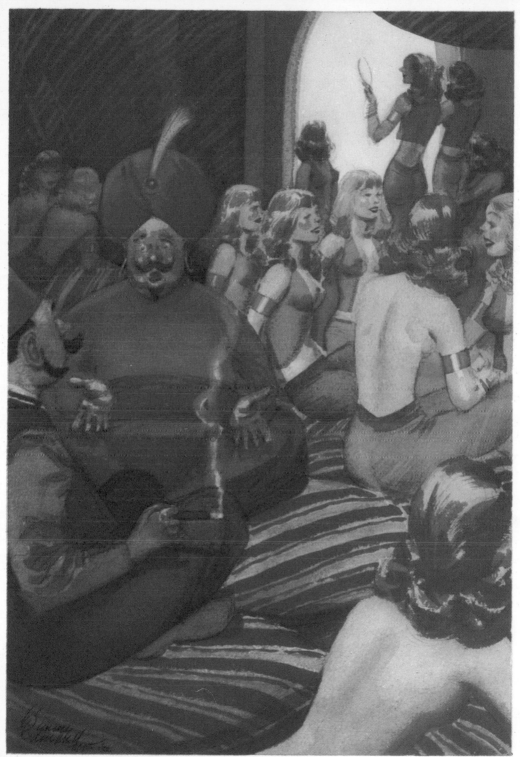

"Sometimes I feel just like selling out."

by E. Simms Campbell

Shall We Join the Ladies?

Raising our spirits high
by ELDON DEDINI

You finish it!

Ooo! What's in this!

I don't care, mix me anything!

The "manly" drinker

May I have your olive?

The usual, Sam

Just a "teeny" bit

by Dorothy McKay

"Stop looking at my cards!"

by SYD HOFF

"I hope you don't mind, but we just couldn't get a chaperon." by IRVING ROIR

"Now in this round, lead with your left, feint with the right, jab with the left, cross with the right—get up at the nine count." by ALEX YOUNG

"O.K. buddy, break it up." by E. SIMMS CAMPBELL

"I've discovered more movie stars this way." by ELDON DEDINI

"... and this one has everything."

by IRWIN CAPLAN

"I'm not sure, but I think in a dictatorship you _have_ to have children, but in a democracy they leave it up to you."

by Barbara Shermund

by SAM COBEAN

Well, it used to be out in the country

Country Club, U.S.A.

Keep your golf score down, your credit up, and—keep an eye on your wife

by Dorothy McKay

I'm afraid it was a mistake having the runner-up present the cup

Do you have an appointment?

Fore!

May we play through?

Keep your eye on the ball,
or as near to it as you can

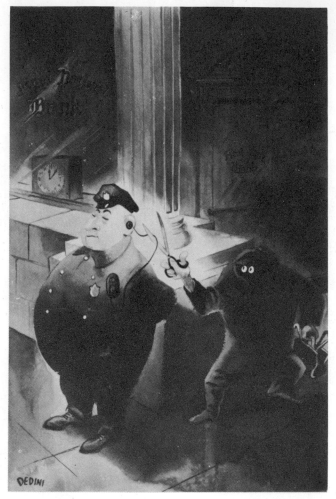

by ELDON DEDINI

Illustration for "Cybernetics"   by Boris Artzybasheff

Illustration for "Jazz on a High Note"   by ROBERT RIGGS

detail from illustration above

Il Duce   by ARTHUR SZYK

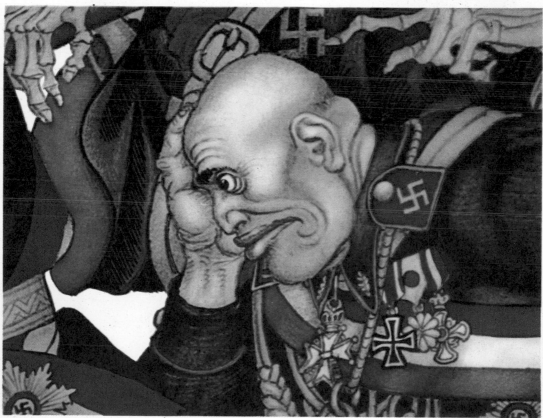

detail from painting above

Afghan Hound

Irish Setter

Dalmatian

Great Dane

Saint Bernard

Sheep Dog

Boxer

Greyhound

Bloodhound

Illustration for "The Office Party"   by ROBERT OSBORN

Illustration for "The Crusher"   by BEN STAHL

all photographs taken at Stillman's Gym

Photo illustrations for "The Amiable Tigers" by WALLACE LITWIN

Illustration for "Wall Street, Men and Money" by JOHN McDERMOTT

detail from illustration above drawn at the American Exchange

Illustration for "The Shame of Our Colleges"   by Naiad Giblan

Illustration for "The Ishikawa Follies"   by JOHN GROTH

Illustration for "The Crake"

by JOHN GROTH

*detail
of this
painting
at
lower right*

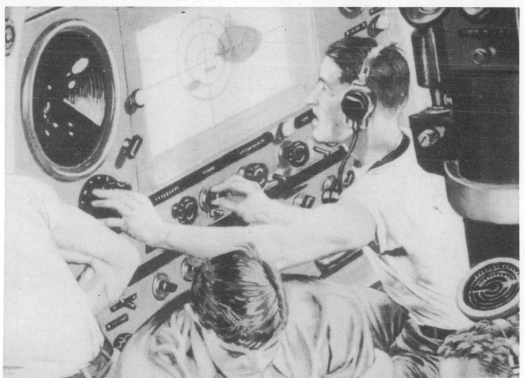

Illustrations for "Mission in 1956"   by FRED FREEMAN

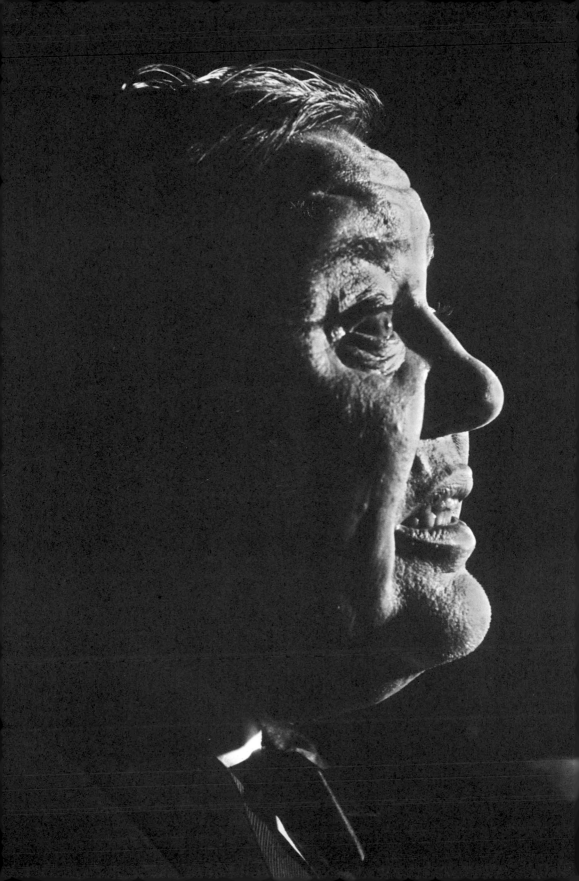

Raymond Loewy   personality photo by RICHARD LITWIN

Charles Laughton   personality photo by BURT GLINN

Types of American Beauty
Sculpture by Frank Nagy
Photographed by André de Dienes

Pomona

Dryas

Denise Darcel

personality photo by PHILIPPE HALSMAN

Janet Leigh

personality photo by PHILIPPE HALSMAN

The Esquire Girl

by GEORGE PETTY

The Esquire Girl

by VARGA

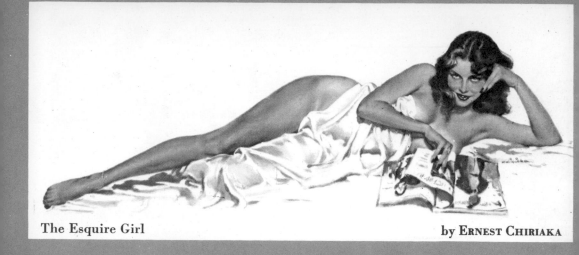

The Esquire Girl   by ERNEST CHIRIAKA

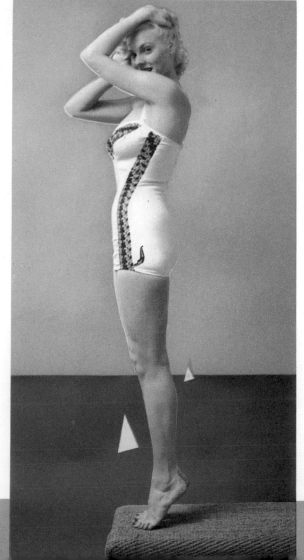

The Esquire Girl   photographed by
                                               RONNIE JACQUES

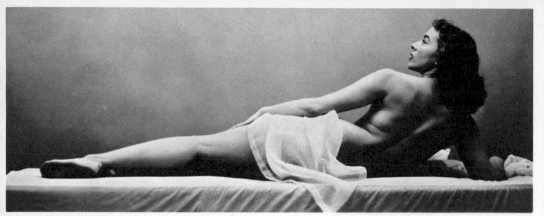

The Esquire Girl   photographed by Ronnie Jacques

The Esquire Girl   by Al Moore

"*I don't know what calibre I should get, but my husband is about that size.*"

by E. SIMMS CAMPBELL

"There are two ways of becoming a star, Miss Tulare—one is by industry, concentration and perserverance—the other I think might interest you." by HOWARD BAER

"I got fed up with the same old grind."
by ROBERT HOLLEY

"I've got a surprise for you—I'm going to be your mother." by RAEBURN VAN BUREN

"All right, so I'm dumb—so what would you do with a cultured woman." by HOWARD BAER

"He was just about the most unforgettable character I've ever met." by ELDON DEDINI

"She said her husband was out of town and I was fool enough to believe her."

by ABNER DEAN

A Hunting We Will Go—

A manual for modern deerslayers and their companions of the trail.

drawings by ELDON DEDINI

Bullet Man: **Thinks everything in the wilds is out to get *him*. Preparedness is his motto and he can throw more hot lead than a Balkan guerrilla.**

The Sunday Hunter: He's in rabbit territory, but imagines more animals than are found in the Bronx Zoo.

Camp Cook: Favors a simple sort of menu.

Tall Story Teller: Mountain nights and the stars inspire talk never heard elsewhere. As the campfire dims, fact and fancy melt together into a convincing, pleasant mixture.

The Guide: Reads trails like you read your newspaper. But for the smoothest trip through the hills, let him read the numerals on a twenty-dollar bill.

"High" Sierra

Night Song

by ABNER DEAN

"Shall we take the telephone, dear, we may get some calls while we're gone."

by BARBARA SHERMUND

"I don't see any sense in painting the same old vase over and over again."   by GARDNER REA

"Then I asked him where he got that illiterate stuff—my mother and father were married."

by HOWARD BAER

by E. Simms Campbell

"*He was a perfect gentleman—but we ran into that wildcat wife of his.*"

by BARBARA SHERMUND

"Stand back! All I want is a little gasoline."
by ABNER DEAN

"I thought you said there were three girls to every man in this town." by GARRETT PRICE

"We thought we'd never get here."
by JARO FABRY

"It's Mr. Aldrich, Mother. I dampened his ardor." by BARBARA SHERMUND

"Come, come, let's not quibble about price—she's not only a dancer!"

by E. Simms Campbell

SECTION FOUR

Fact and Fancy

INTRODUCTION

WE HAVE NEVER claimed that *Esquire* is the most thoroughly read of magazines. If there were some foolproof way of putting complete non-skipping and cover-to-cover readership to the test, our own guess is that *Time* would probably win off by itself. But *Esquire's* contents are dished up in a different way and for a different purpose.

Our idea, from the beginning, was to provide a monthly magazine in that literal sense of meaning a magazine that will last a month. With very rare exceptions, *Esquire's* contents do not become dated after a week, a month, or even a year. It is laid out to be read with equal ease by the busy man who seldom has more than a few minutes to spend with it at any one time and the leisured man whose reading is not subject to interruption.

Also there was a studied motive in making it so big. We wanted to be sure that a man could pick it up again and again and still find it packed full of things he had not yet read. We were simply aiming to make a magazine too big to be thrown away.

A man won't throw away a half-filled package of unused merchandise of any kind. And that's what a copy of *Esquire* is apt to be at the end of thirty days. Bookish people can and do devour it from cover to cover. But the average reader figures to be about half through one issue by the time the next one comes

out. If he buys that one it's either because he sees in it something he wants to read or just because the magazine is habit forming. But he doesn't, or at least he's not very likely to, throw the old one away. It's still a half-filled package.

That this is not just a sophistry that we ourselves have thought up in a promotion-minded moment is proved by the postman, over and over again, as each week brings new evidence that a copy of *Esquire*, like England's second Charles, is "an unconscionably long time a-dying."

For example, it was well over six years ago (June 1947) that our Swiss address was last listed on *Esquire's* table of contents. Yet hardly a week goes by, even now, that we don't get at least one, and sometimes several, letters forwarded from that address, asking for or about something featured in issues dating back of that time.

For that matter, hardly a month goes by that the mail doesn't bring in some inquiry about items featured as far back as the war years, and at least twice during the past year we have had inquiries pertaining to 1939 issues.

Speaking of the post office, our troubles with them neither began nor ended with the famous four-round bout with the Postmaster General. We won that one, by a Supreme Court decision. But there's another one that we're long since reconciled to losing; *Esquire* has been a pain in the post office neck for twenty years as the most persistantly swiped magazine that uses the mails. Nor does the swiping stop there.

We keep getting pictures sent in to us from libraries and clubs, and even from waiting rooms, showing copies of *Esquire* chained and tethered to desks and tables like so many horses to hitching posts.

Each time the letter accompanying such a picture is written with a little Jack Horner air of ingenuity triumphant, as if nobody else had ever encountered trouble safeguarding a copy of *Esquire*.

Well, we long ago said that the last thing we want this magazine to be is respected. We'll take love or hate but save the respect for *The Atlantic*. We're content not to be the most-read, if we can feel fairly sure of being one of the *longest*-read, and certainly the most widely swiped.

We've always thought of the magazine's table of contents as being comparable to a smörgasbord, or to a hotel's wine and liquor list—something offering the widest possible variety, but not offered with the idea that the whole thing must be devoured at a sitting.

Hence the heterogeneous nature of the offerings in this next section, compounded in almost equal parts of fact and fancy and—to our admittedly prejudiced view—remarkably little dated for all their assorted ages up to twenty years.

ROBERT HENDERSON'S
"The Pre-Occupation of New York"

It is *The Bedside Esquire's* hard luck and this book's good fortune that "The Pre-Occupation of New York" came into our hands just too late to make that earlier collection.

Here's how we greeted it on its original appearance in our issue for April 1940:

We don't exactly know what or whom to thank for the fact that we were able to include "The Pre-Occupation of New York" in this issue. Since Robert Henderson is a young man on the staff of The New Yorker, *our hunch is that this little gem of satire fell into our waiting and willing laps thanks to the preoccupation of Mr. Harold Ross. We could easily be wrong, as we so often are. Maybe they do things differently, not to say better, there. In any case, if* The New Yorker *saw, but couldn't see, "The Pre-Occupation of New York," then we're thankful that editorial eyesight is not universally uniform.*

WILLIAM ATTWOOD

◄──►

Ishikawa Follies

A FEW weeks ago, I tasted *sake* for the first time in more than four years, when a friend, who has been stationed in Tokyo since the end of the war, sent me a bottle of the cloudy, bitter-flavored liquor. On an enclosed card he wrote: "This will remind you of the good old days on Okinawa." Although I have never thought of those old days as being particularly good, I discovered, with the first sharp swallow, that the Spring of 1945, good or bad, was not so very far away, after all. Like Marcel Proust, munching his tea-soaked *madeleine* to recall his childhood, I found myself sipping my *sake* and sliding backwards in time, away from an apartment on East Fifty-first Street, across a continent and an ocean, and back to an island still redolent of the once-familiar, sweetish stench of crushed sugar cane and death. Another swallow and I could hear the rumble of artillery above the noise of traffic on Lexington Avenue. And then, all at once, there I was, draped in mosquito netting, dancing foolishly on the beach of Ishikawa, while someone (Rowe? Roth? Ross!)—while Herb Ross sang *Alice Blue Gown* at the top of his lungs in a semicircle of a thousand laughing, cheering, crazy Okinawans.

Sake is strong stuff. It is made from the fermentation of rice and, according to one encyclopedia, "produces a speedy but transient intoxication." It has long been Japan's national beverage, and I remember that among the men of my division, few of whom had tasted anything stronger than G.I. beer for several months, the prospect of finding vast stocks of *sake* on Okinawa was the most, if not the only, enticing aspect of the invasion which started on Easter Sunday, April 1, 1945. By the end of the month, however, it was clear that the Japanese had either drunk up most of the liquor on the island before we arrived, or were drinking it as fast as they retreated. The bottles we found in abandoned Jap caves and command posts were invariably empty.

In the early days, of course, you could generally get a quart of whiskey from one of the Navy transports anchored off Kadena Beach in exchange for a few Jap battle flags, and for a while my outfit even had a pfc detailed to barter duty. But very soon the souvenir market depreciated to the point where you had to have a whole arsenal of pistols and swords to get so much as a drink, and by the first week in May, when my division was pulled out of the line for a rest, my idea of a party was to heat some C-ration cocoa and invite the chaplain, who played chess, to come over to my tent for a couple of games.

May, 1950

It was during this rest period, I remember, that Ross, a former San Francisco insurance broker who had been a corporal for two years, suggested that we take a jeep and drive up to Ishikawa for a few days' swimming. It seemed like a good idea. Ishikawa, a village on the island's eastern coast, had escaped the brunt of the invasion, and the beach was still sandy and clean. Also, it would be quiet, as the town had been taken over by Military Government as a civilian concentration area and was out of bounds to troops. We would be able to by-pass this regulation, I knew, on the pretext of interrogating natives for tactical information, so I invited our young Nisei interpreter, Miles Matsumoto, to come along and add plausibility to our pretended mission. The fourth member of the party was Pfc Emerson Way, our jeep-driver. Way, a crusty ex-bartender from Apple Creek, Ohio, had been attached to my outfit just before the invasion, since the division band, to which he was regularly assigned as a cornet player, did not function during combat. "I think I'll take my horn along," he said when I told him about the excursion. "Driving this jeep's got my lip out of shape." I said that was a good idea.

It was a two-hour drive to Ishikawa and we decided to get started early in the morning. After getting the colonel's permission at breakfast, I told Way to fetch the jeep and sent Ross to pick up a couple of cases of ten-in-one rations from the mess officer. I strapped up my bedroll and was sitting outside the tent smoking a cigarette and enjoying the fresh breeze, when I caught sight of Matsumoto coming through the cane field that sloped away from our command post. With him was a bedraggled, middle-aged Okinawan wearing odds and ends of a Japanese uniform and a floppy fedora. As they approached, the native took off his hat, smiled, and bobbed his head up and down several times. I looked inquiringly at Miles.

"This guy works for the medics in the civilian dispensary," he explained. "I mentioned we were going to Ishikawa and he wants to come along. He's got a brother up there."

I shook my head. "Nothing doing," I said. "The jeep's crowded enough as it is."

"Wait a minute, Lieutenant," said Miles. "The guy also says he knows where there's ten gallons of *sake* buried and he'll split it with us if we give him a ride and help him dig it up."

I looked at the Okinawan, who resumed bowing and grinning. "*Hai! Hai!*" he said. "*Sake!*"

Just then, Way drove up with the jeep. "Who's your gook friend?" he asked as I handed him my bedroll. I explained about the *sake*. He stared at the native and then at me. "Well, what the hell are we waiting for?" he said. "We can get some picks and shovels at the motor pool. Where'd he say the stuff was buried?"

"He claims it's in the back yard of a house in Shuri," said Miles. "That's just up the road."

We had nothing to lose. "Okay," I said to the native. "*Hai!*" He put on his hat and scrambled into the jeep. Ross arrived with the provisions a few minutes later, and we all climbed aboard and started off. At Way's suggestion, we picked up a couple of five-gallon jerrycans along with the tools. It was a fine May morning, and for the first time on Okinawa I felt in a holiday mood.

While we bounced along the rutted road, the Okinawan, whose name was Takamo, told us, via Matsumoto, that the *sake* we were about to dig up had been buried the day he was born, some forty-three years before. According to an Okinawan tradition, the liquor was set aside for the newborn baby's wedding feast; and, fortunately for us, Takamo had never married. The story, as Matsumoto told it, caused Way to smack his lips. "Nothing like that old prewar stuff," he said, spurring on the jeep.

Shuri had been taken a week before, after an intensive air and naval bombardment, and as we neared the town, or what was left of it, Takamo began uttering little gasps of astonishment and dismay. Some of the houses had been literally pulverized; the rest were heaps of broken rubble. So complete was the destruction that even the pattern of the streets was obliterated, and as soon as we halted in a clearing, Takamo jumped out and began scampering around the ruins looking for some familiar landmark. The rest of us shouldered the shovels, picks and jerrycans and set out after him.

After some ten minutes of zigzagging through the jumble of stone, Takamo seemed to recognize a few fragments of masonry and then the vestige of a doorway. "Ha!" he finally exclaimed, pointing to a pile of scattered bricks. Miles exchanged a few words with him. "This looks like the place," he said and put down his shovel. Takamo began fanning himself with his hat. "Okay, let's get going," said Way impatiently. He took off his fatigue jacket, which was already dark with sweat, picked up a shovel, and started to clear away the debris. We all pitched in except Takamo, who slowly clambered up a pile of stones and squatted down. From there, while we worked, he mournfully surveyed the wreckage of his home.

We had been digging for about a half-hour when I looked up and saw that a truck was parked on the road a hundred yards away and that the driver was leaning out of the cab and peering at us curiously. "We'd better be careful," I remarked to the others, "or we'll have the whole Tenth Army hanging around here pretty soon."

We all straightened up and stared belligerently at the driver, who finally drove off. "I got an idea," said Way. "Miles, tell that gook to come down off that rock pile and stretch out on the ground." Matsumoto relayed the order, and Takamo obediently came down and did as he was told. "Now," said Way, "we can tell those nosy bastards we're on a burial detail. That'll keep them away."

Sure enough, a few moments later, a pair of Marines drove up in a jeep, got out and began sauntering toward us. "What you boys digging after?" one of them asked good-naturedly.

Way jerked his thumb at the rigid, motionless Okinawan and went on digging. The Marines contemplated Takamo. "Jee-zus," said the other one. "What a lousy detail on a hot day."

"Come on," said his companion, "let's get outa here." They went back to their jeep, and I saw them talking to the occupants of a truck who had paused to watch us. Soon, both vehicles drove off and we continued our work undisturbed.

Just as we were beginning to lose confidence in Takamo's integrity, Ross's pick struck something that broke and we heard a splash. Our corpse leaped up, peered down the hole, and nodded excitedly. The pick had apparently pierced the top of the earthenware pot that held the *sake*. Gingerly, we began scraping the dirt away from the sides. Ross dipped a canteen-cup into the opening and brought it up, brimful of a pale liquid, cloudy with silt. He took a sip, grimaced, and passed the cup around. It was warm, bitter, but exceedingly strong. We each swallowed a cupful and jovially ladled and siphoned the rest of it into our two cans.

Thanks to the unaccustomed effect of the *sake*, the drive to Ishikawa was the most enjoyable jeep ride I remember taking in more than five months on Okinawa. We sang, of course, and waved cheerfully to a great number of uncomprehending soldiers who happened to be along the road. An M.P. stopped us on the outskirts of Ishikawa, but I explained, quite forcefully, that I had official business to discuss with the naval commander of the compound; he waved us on.

As soon as we were in the village, Takamo got out, and, in accordance with our agreement, I handed him one of the cans, which he accepted with a deep bow. Way objected strenuously. "The little jerk got his ride, didn't he?" he grumbled. "Ain't that enough? Anyway, drinking liquor is supposed to be against his religion."

"You're thinking of the Moslems, Emerson," said Ross.

"Ah, what the hell's the difference?" Way growled. "Gooks are the same all over the world."

The village was swarming with natives, and we had to move carefully through the narrow lanes. Seemingly endless processions of newly arrived refugees, lugging their few belongings, were plodding in all directions, and the fragile wooden houses bulged with children and old women. Finally, not far from the beach, we spotted the three Nissen huts that housed the Military-Government detachment. I got out and told the others to find a suitable camp site along the shore.

The Military-Government officer in charge of Ishikawa turned out to be a bald, thin-lipped lieutenant commander whom I found at a desk littered with papers. Briefly, I explained my mission: refugees from my division's sector were said to be in this camp, and our G-2 felt that some of them might have information concerning Japanese positions to the south. I tried to sound as grave as possible, but part of my mind was thinking of Way and Ross and the can of *sake*, and under the surface I felt extremely wild, mischievous, and stealthy.

The lieutenant commander looked irritated. "I have received no written request to that effect," he said, riffling the papers before him. "You realize that this is quite i egular." I pointed out that my commanding officer had taken it for granted that Military Government would be glad to co-operate. He grunted. "All right, Lieutenant," he said. "But I'll hold you responsible for the behavior of your men. I don't want them running wild among the natives. We have a strict no-fraternization rule here. And I'll expect you to finish up your work by the end of the week." As I thanked him and rose to leave, he added, gruffly, "Of course, you'll be entitled to use our officer's mess."

I explained that I had brought provisions and could just as well eat with my detachment. He nodded, curtly, as though I had confirmed the conception of the Army as a loose, equalitarian rabble where rank had no privileges and deserved none.

My troops had wisely selected a bivouac out of sight and earshot of head-quarters. I found them in a grove of gnarled pines on the edge of the beach. Ross and Matsumoto were struggling with the tent pole while Way busied him-self with the preparations for the bacchanal. He had placed our four helmets on the ground, and into each was pouring a compost of sake and canned peaches. "The fruit kills the taste of that stuff," he said as I watched him. "It makes a nice punch." Once the tent was up, we all sipped the mixture and agreed that the flavor had improved. The sake was still quite warm, however, so I suggested we put the helmets in the shade to cool while we went swimming. Way offered to guard them. "These woods are full of thirsty gooks," he explained. "I just seen a crowd of them peeking at me through the bushes. You guys swim if you want to. The last time I was in that goddam ocean was when I fell out of a rubber boat at Attu."

We stripped down to our shorts and walked across the hot sand and over the jagged coral, in which the receding tide had left deep rippling pools. Three or four naked children watched from a distance. Miles called to them in Japan-ese, but they wouldn't come into the water. I dived in and swam out beyond the breakers, where I could float gently and watch the quiet sky. There, the faint thunder of the guns, miles away, had an impersonal sound, and you could almost feel the warm salt water washing away the sweat and grime of the past few weeks.

When we came out, finally, the coral pools were tinted with sunset colors, and the shadows of the pines were lengthening on the sand. Way was leaning against a tree, holding a helmet in his lap. Ross sighed contentedly. "This is what I like," he said. "The magic hour before cocktails."

"You got it wrong, chum," said Way. "This is the magic hour *during* cock-tails." He tilted his helmet to his face and took a long, noisy swallow.

Ross and I made ourselves comfortable on the sandy ground and poured some punch into our canteen cups. Miles got dressed; he had some friends among the Military-Government interpreters who had invited him to a sukiyaki dinner in their hut. Before leaving, he divided his sake among the rest of us. "You fellas take it easy now," he said with a smile. Way accepted his share, but after Matsumoto had walked off down the beach, he shook his head. "That Miles is a good boy," he said, "but what he just did don't make sense. Why, this stuff is pure gold." He drank; then he looked at me and his tanned, crinkled face broke into a wide grin. "How you doing, lootenant sir? By God, the last time I felt this good must of been back in Frisco."

"Nobody who lives there says 'Frisco,'" Ross observed, as he gulped down a mouthful of peaches.

I don't remember exactly how the rest of it started. We were sitting quietly, listening to the noises of the stirring village behind us and watching the children who now and then darted from tree to tree around our encampment. Then Way started a long anecdote about a Marine named Fazar he knew in Peiping in 1937. Fazar, according to Way, was the first American casualty in the war against Japan, having been hit in the left buttock by a bullet while posting on horseback near the American compound. A Chinese machine gunner, it seemed, had mistaken him for a Japanese cavalryman as he turned up an alley called Morrison Street. In describing how it happened, Way rose up on his haunches but lost his balance and went sprawling in the sand, tipping over his half-filled helmet. Instantly, the murmuring silence was pierced by a loud chorus of giggles from the surrounding bushes. I looked up and saw at least twenty children, half-hidden in the undergrowth, and all convulsed with laughter.

I remember waving at them, but the memory of what happened next has blurred with the passing years. All I know is that the three of us were suddenly re-enacting the Morrison Street incident, with Way taking the part of the horse and Ross performing as Fazar. My role was that of the Chinese soldier, and as I opened fire with an imaginary machine gun, Way reared up and Ross tumbled over with a howl of anguish. The children screamed delightedly. Giddy with success and *sake*, we repeated the sketch twice more to larger and, if possible, more appreciative audiences. In a matter of minutes, we were in show business.

"What we need is some music," said Way. While he stumbled into the tent, Ross and I did what must have been an excellent parody of Al Jolson's *Sonny Boy*. The front row of children, who had emerged from their hiding places, collapsed with mirth. One roly-poly little boy kept pointing at us and chanting "Shoo Shoo Bei-bee!" a phrase he must have picked up from the G.I.s—so we took him into the act and did a Shoo Shoo Baby routine, with an off-to-Buffalo exit into the tent. There, we found Way adjusting the mouthpiece of his cornet. "Go out there and give 'em hell, Emerson," said Ross. I splashed more *sake* into our helmets. Way returned to the clearing with his instrument, the sight of which set off a great ovation, and began to play *Sweet Georgia Brown*.

The variety show that followed, and the applause it evoked, would have warmed the heart of an old vaudeville trouper. While Way provided the musical accompaniment, Ross told a sure-fire Lapidus story, in dialect and with gestures, and I took it from there with a dead-pan interpretation of a carnival barker, dimly recalled from a Princeton Triangle Show. Together, we then did a scene from *Mutiny on the Bounty*, in which Herb played Laughton's Captain Bligh and I was Fletcher Christian. It went very big. There was also an acrobatic act, mostly leapfrog, with lively audience participation, and a baby parade, with candy-bar prizes for all contestants. But the real boffola was a straight burlesque number in which I covered myself with mosquito netting and did a slow strip tease to Way's muted *Alice Blue Gown*. Ross was the grimacing and sputtering comedian. It was quite probably the corniest public performance ever witnessed on Okinawa, and the most successful. Several small boys who started gasping and choking had to be carried away by their older sisters, while the rest of the squealing audience yelled for more.

We ran through it once again, and then Way put down his horn. "I shot my bolt," he announced thickly. "Can't blow no more." He swallowed what was left in his canteen cup and waved at the circle of children. "All over!" he cried. "Feeneesh!" I sat down heavily on the suddenly swaying ground. I noticed it was twilight. Ross braced himself against a tree. "*Sayonara!*" he shouted. "Good-by!"

The children understood, and came forward shyly. There must have been nearly a hundred in the crowd, the boys half-naked and the girls like so many identical dolls, with their straight black hair and pantaloons. In groups of six or seven, they stepped forward, bowed and said "*Arigato.*"

Then they ran toward the village.

"What the hell are they saying?" Way asked.

"*Arigato* means thank you," said Ross. "They're telling us they liked the show."

I could hear Way chuckling. "Crazy little gooks," he murmured. As the last group bowed to him, he tried to stand up and return the compliment, but he fell back and rolled over, laughing. A little girl tittered. Then they said "*Arigato*" and "*Sayonara*," and vanished into the dusk.

I started to disentangle myself from the mosquito netting, but it seemed like too much trouble. My head was buzzing, and I rested it on the cool, soft ground. The last thing I remember was hearing the splashing of the waves and the sound of someone snoring.

The next day had certain of the characteristics of Don Birnam's Day of Terror in *The Lost Weekend*. For one thing, our eyes would not focus properly, and this, coupled with the most acute symptoms of hang-over that I, at least, had ever experienced, turned our bivouac into a kind of dispensary, with Matsumoto officiating as both orderly and Gray Lady. We rested supinely on the beach, moving as little as possible. "I usually go for a quick slug the morning after," said Way about noon, "but I don't even want to think about what's in that can."

"There's plenty left," said Miles, "in case you want to put on another show." He regretted having missed the performance. When I described it to him, he told me it was probably the first theatrical entertainment of any sort that the children had seen. Okinawa was one of Japan's most backward and neglected provinces, and it was unlikely that any road show from up north had visited the island, at least since the beginning of the war. "No wonder you guys got such a big hand," he said. "They had nothing to compare you with."

Toward the end of the afternoon, we felt well enough to eat a few biscuits and drink some coffee, and afterward Ross and I decided to take a quiet stroll along the beach. Way was not yet up to it. We started off and had walked about fifty yards when a swarm of shouting, laughing youngsters came plunging out of the brush and surrounded us. "Aree Boo Go!" they yelled, pointing at me and mimicking what I vaguely recognized as my *Alice Blue Gown* dance. Wincing, we hastily retreated to the camp site, trailed by cavorting retinue. Way looked up and scowled at the children. "Beat it!" he growled. "Go on, scram! Shoo!"

"*Hai!*" screamed the kids. "Shoo shoo bei-bee!" Two of them pranced around Way, and the others rolled gleefully in the sand. Way appealed to Miles, who sent them away with a few sticks of chewing gum.

"Where did they come from?" Way demanded, lying down again.

"They've been around all day," said Miles. "Didn't you see them looking at you through the bushes? You boys are big celebrities now. You have to get used to it."

We stretched out again and the tranquillity was not broken for several minutes. Then Ross raised himself up on one elbow and peered around curiously. "Do you guys hear noises?" he asked. "Or am I getting the *sake* horrors again?" I listened carefully and became aware of a great rustling and the faint sound of many voices. We stood up and looked through the trees toward the village. "Good God," said Ross. "It looks like a *banzai* charge."

Streaming toward us were hundreds of ragged Okinawans of all ages, with an advance guard of scampering children leading the way. There were many old men, some women carrying babies, a few young girls, and even a scattering of cripples hobbling along with canes and crutches. The mob flowed around our tent, smiling and bowing with great deference, and gathered on the wide, sandy beach, where they proceeded to squat down in a wide semicircle facing the bivouac.

We stared dumbly at the crowd, and then at Miles, who began to laugh and clap his hands. "Do your stuff, boys!" he cried. "The show must go on!" He went into the tent and came out with Way's cornet. "Come on, Emerson! You have a good house tonight!" Then he sat down and guffawed.

At the sight of the horn, the throng started to cheer lustily. There were some more cries of "Aree Boo Go!" and several children pointed me out to the adults. I turned away from the expanse of nodding, grinning faces and glanced at Ross. He was haggard. Way looked at his horn as though he had never seen it before. "Miles," I said, "do something. Go out and tell them to go home. Tell them no show tonight."

"We ain't no USO," said Way.

Still grinning, Miles stepped up, motioned for silence, and began to speak slowly in Japanese. I still don't know what he told them, but they got the impression he was some sort of master of ceremonies. He finished to prolonged applause and came back, shrugging his shoulders. "They won't believe me," he explained.

I asked Way how he felt.

"Lousy," he said. "The horn would kill me."

Ross groaned. "I'll feel like a fool and may collapse," he said, "but we can't disappoint them."

"Emerson," I said, "Herb is right. Go out there and blow."

He gave me a baleful look. "You pulling rank or something?" he muttered.

But he stepped forward. "Okay, you hams," he said, "let's go. Laugh, clown, laugh." He blew a high, brassy note.

Ross and I came out dancing to a roar of delight.

We ran through as much of our repertoire as we could remember, omitting only the more strenuous numbers. The response far exceeded anything we had heard the previous night. A variation of the shell game, in which Way lost track of his cornet, brought down the house completely, and had to be repeated three times. *Sonny Boy*, performed with an Okinawan tot, also got a fine hand. Then, for the finale, I went into the tent, slipped off all my clothes except for my shorts and wrapped myself in the netting. Herb rolled up his pants, picked up Way's helmet liner, which was much too big for him, and put it on backwards. At the first bar of *Alice Blue Gown*, I came stalking out, with Ross, the buffoon, making faces and tossing sand behind my back.

Our appearance provoked a pandemonium of shrieks and howls, but as we went into the act, the din quickly subsided and then ceased altogether. Way suddenly stopped playing half way through a note. I turned around, puzzled, and found myself facing the lieutenant commander in charge of the area, two other naval officers, and three M.P.s.

There was silence for fully five seconds. Then one of the officers motioned to the M.P.s to clear away the crowd. The lieutenant commander addressed me. "Lieutenant," he said icily, "I do not expect you to have an explanation, and if you did, I would not want to hear it." He glanced at his wrist watch. "You will leave this area within one hour. Your commanding officer will be informed through channels."

He turned and began to walk away, but paused and looked back. "I presume that this is what the Army calls interrogation for tactical information," he added, with heavy sarcasm. There was nothing to say, so I nodded.

At the appearance of the M.P.s, the spectators had scrambled up fearfully and quickly dispersed. Now they were all hurrying back toward the village. Many of the children, I noticed, were crying. Ross and I trudged back to the tent and sat down by the jeep and lit cigarettes. The sun had gone down, and the evening air was hushed and cool. Miles came up and began uprooting the tent pegs. "We'd better pack up before it gets too dark," he said. I stood up, wearily.

And then, suddenly it seemed the woods all around us were alive with the crackling of twigs and the rustling murmur of people moving around. Motionless, we listened; and then, from all sides, came the whispering sound of many voices. "*Arigato!*" they softly called. "*Arigato!* Thank you! Thank you!"

JOSEPH WECHSBERG

Honorable Composer Big Click

Without adding my voice to that of the experts who attach great significance to the most trivial Japanese doings, I think there is good news in recent dispatches from neutral sources reporting that very little German music is being played in Japan. The Japs having been ardent devotees of Bach, Beethoven, Wagner, the political implication behind the sudden change in their musical taste seems pretty obvious. Western music in Japan never was art for art's sake as I remember from my own musical experience in Yokohama back in 1929, aboard the Messageries Maritime liner *Porthos*, where I was working as orchestra leader and violinist.

The *Porthos* used to stay eight days in Yokohama, unloading cargo, refueling, taking on food and water for the thirty-eight-day return trip to Marseilles. According to our contract we musicians were supposed to work even in port like the rest of the crew, but the commandant, who was musical and our great friend, never invoked the dreaded "harbor clause." As soon as the last passengers had disembarked we would leave. We returned only at sailing time to play *Kimi-ga-yo* (Reign of My Sovereign), the Jap national anthem, and the *Marseillaise*.

One day in September, 1929, on arrival from France and points east, we were about to go ashore for our Japanese holiday, when the purser, M. le *commissaire* sent for us. It sounded like bad news. Relations between the orchestra and the *commissaire*, our immediate superior, had been strained ever since the red-headed art student from Dallas, travelling alone in Stateroom Number 7, declined the *commissaire's* attentions in favor of Artie, our Yonkers-born pianist.

The *commissaire* had opened the hostilities by making us play overtime in the crushing heat of the Red Sea, when nobody felt like listening to music, much less dancing. In Colombo he forbade us to go ashore, because he knew that the artist was waiting for Artie at the Galle Face Hotel. In Singapore he refused to give us the customary twenty per cent advance on our salaries. Regulations provided for payment only after our return to Marseilles and we had to borrow from the *maître d'hôtel*. Sometimes we borrowed from the barman in First Class or the *chef de cuisine*. All *maîtres d'hôtel*, stewards, cooks, cabin boys hated the *commissaire* for his rigid, un-French attitude. All were on our side.

When the *commissaire* barred us from the swimming pool and the First

Class bar, we retorted by abruptly changing from waltz to fox-trot and back to waltz measure while he danced with our *casus belli*. A man without a sense of rhythm, he stumbled and stepped on the girl's feet. After this had gone on for some time, she left him in the middle of the dance floor and went back to her seat. The *commissaire* ran up to the bridge and informed the *commandant* of our newest crime. The skipper's reprimand, though necessarily firm, was rather perfunctory. The *commissaire* came of a French-Colonial family in Saigon, French Indo-China, and the ship's officers, solid burgeois from the *Midi*, resented his being too friendly with the Japanese passengers. He had three gents from Mitsubishi Co., Ltd. at his table and made it a point never to join the ship's officers at apéritif time. He was a thin-faced, morose man with the anemic complexion and the prematurely aged features of white people in the tropics.

At that trip our orchestra consisted of Artie, an easy-going American pianist, myself—I'm Czechoslovakian—as violinist, and Etienne-Marcel, aged sixty-two, a lovable bass player from Brussels. I'd met him at the *Quat-z-Arts Cafe* on Place Pigalle, unofficial meeting place of Paris musicians. Even among the broke-but-cheerful habitués of the *Quat-z-Arts*, colorful individuals in need of a haircut, Etienne-Marcel was an outstanding character. He carried a bass bow under his arm, sporting it like a riding whip. With his magnificent white beard he looked like a reasonably well done copy of Johannes Brahms. He had visiting cards, "Etienne-Marcel Brahms, *neveu*," which he distributed among unsophisticated audiences. He was a widower, living alone in a small house in one up the steep streets leading up to *Sacré Coeur*. Once a year he went to Japan to visit his only son, a civil engineer in Tokyo, solving the financial problem of ocean travel by taking a job as musician aboard. When the passengers registered surprise at a bass player instead of a cellist working with a three-man-orchestra, Etienne-Marcel would say, "I have a friend at the hiring bureau. Any bass player having a friend there is as good as a cellist."

He was immensely popular with the passengers, especially those under seven years of age, for whom he produced eerie *sul ponticello* effects and imitations of The Roaring Lion, The Growling Leopard and The Howling Tiger on his bass fiddle. But he was a serious-minded fellow when it came to making good music. He played difficult parts directly from cello scores. His great idol was Serge Koussevitsky, a former fellow bass player. "I once heard him do *Zigeunerweisen* on the bull fiddle," Etienne-Marcel said. "I was so excited I couldn't sleep for two nights and I had to get drunk."

Etienne-Marcel was the *commissaire's* arch-enemy. He had his private fights with him. The climax was reached that day in Yokohama when we were called to the *commissaire's* office. The *commissaire* informed us that we were to stay aboard and give a concert of modern music for a party of Japs whom he'd invited. Etienne-Marcel was furious. His son had wired that he was to leave for Hokkaido the next day; could father come to Tokyo at once? As to Artie he had a dinner date with the red-headed artist at Tokyo's Imperial Hotel. I told the *commissaire* that the orchestra never worked in port. If necessary, I added, we'd take the matter to the *commandant*.

"That's too bad," the *commissaire* said, dryly. "The *commandant* went ashore. He won't be back until tomorrow." He glanced over our contract which was on his desk. "Harbor clause, *hein*? Unless you are at the music salon at eight-thirty, I'll have you disembarked for breach of contract. That's all."

We tried to slip away but the *commissaire* had special sentries posted at all gangways. Artie spent the rest of the afternoon vainly trying to get a long distance call through to the redhead. Etienne-Marcel was mad and silent.

There were about twenty Japs at the music salon. From every angle they looked like good material for a cartoonist. We saw tuxedos, morning coats, gaudy tweed suits. A three-hundred pound specimen with the physique of a *Sumo* wrestler had on a tail coat. There was the slightly nauseating odor of fish that always hovers about a Jap crowd. An old man in a ceremonial kimono with protruding underdrawers and bare feet in wooden getas was talking to a naval officer who picked his faulty teeth. The little Annamite cabin boys from Tourist Class were serving trays with Scotch whisky, Cognac brandy, French wine, Jap Kirin beer.

Etienne-Marcel skillfully held up an Annamite and stored a tray behind his bass. The *commissaire* came over for a briefing. "This is an audience of musical experts," he said. "The old gentleman in kimono is Mr. Oshima, editor of *Ongaku-Sekai*, musical monthly. Next to him is Captain Takata of the Musical Section of the Imperial Household Department. Over there is Professor Ikeda, secretary of Dai-Nippon Composers' Association, talking to Mr. Aoki of Ryu-ginsha Publishers. And there are two men from the Osaka Broadcasting Association. I hope you won't disappoint them."

"What is he up to?" Artie said when the *commissaire* had gone back to his guests. "Does he want to become director of the Tokyo School of Music?"

We had two rounds of Cognac behind the bass fiddle and went to work, playing Darius Milhaud's *Three Rag Caprices* and Debussy's *Voiles* and *La fille aux cheveux de lin*, arranged for small orchestra. The listeners showed the half-bored, impatient attitude of boxing fans during the preliminaries. The applause was lukewarm; a subdued restlessness was about the place. We went out on deck to get some fresh air. Artie lighted a cigarette, gazing across the piers and hangars toward where he thought was the Imperial Hotel and a red-head. Nobody spoke a word. Presently we were joined by the *commissaire*. He carried a hand-written score.

"I want you to play this next," he said airily, trying to sound amiable. "A simple thing, composed by a friend in Saigon. You won't have any difficulty playing the composition at sight. The audience will be very interested."

He thrust the music into my hands, leaving me in silent rage. Drawing up the program is the orchestra leader's sacred prerogative. Now a man who scarcely knew the difference between a door-key and a viola-key was giving orders!

The composition was titled *Interlude Indochinoise*, Arrangement for Small Orchestra, by Kanji Ueno. Artie whistled softly. Etienne-Marcel said, "So, we are plugging this piece for his honorable Jap friend, Ueno. *Tiens!* If that isn't the Bolero!"

We looked at the score. Kanji Ueno had done a good enough job of camouflage but the source of his *Interlude Indochinoise* unmistakably was Ravel's *Bolero*. The same repetition of a single theme, in unvarying rhythm, becoming a gradual crescendo. Kanji Ueno even used a similar theme.

"Imitating American fountain pens, French vermouth and Belgian paintings," Etienne-Marcel said with disgust. "And now stealing Ravel!" He took the score, tore up the sheets and threw them across the railing. They were floating on the dark, oil-stained water in an easterly direction, perhaps toward Pearl Harbor.

"Good!" Artie nodded approval. "And what now?" From the Salon the *commissaire* beckoned.

We took up our places on the platform. The *commissaire* stepped in front of the piano and bowed deeply. "Gentlemen! I have the honor of bringing to your attention the work of Mr. Kanji Ueno, the young, promising composer living in Saigon. This is the first performance of his new composition *Interlude Indochinoise*, arranged for small orchestra."

There was loud applause. The listeners leaned forward in their chairs in anticipation of a musical and, above all, patriotic treat. Mr. Oshima, the old man in kimono, slipped off his sandals and pulled up his bare feet under his kimono, playing with his toes in utter concentration.

Etienne-Marcel helped himself to another glass of Cognac and stepped forward. "M. le commissaire will permit me to add a few words of admiration," he said. "The piece we are going to play will give you the thrills of Indo-China's jungles, a musical painting of great suggestive force. This discriminating audience will recognize the ultra-modern harmonies and rhythms of this daring creation of the Japanese genius who only recently emerged from obscurity into the light of the appreciation of connoisseurs. I dedicate this first performance to the memory of my immortal uncle, Johannes Brahms."

There was a moment of stunned silence. Captain Tanaka of the Imperial Household Department stopped picking his teeth and said, "Brahms? Brahms?" Etienne-Marcel stepped down and ceremoniously handed the captain a visiting card. Both men bowed deeply. Mr. Aoki, the music publisher, started writing in a notebook. The *commissaire* seemed flabbergasted. Etienne-Marcel, deadpan, came back to the platform. I had a cold, burning feeling inside as though I'd swallowed the sword of Admiral Togo.

"We are playing in the key of C flat, 2/4 time," Etienne-Marcel whispered. "Let me do a few solo tricks. I'll give you a sign when to come in. From then on it's everybody on his own."

"But what are we going to play?" Artie asked.

"Just improvise. Ultra-modern, and strictly jungle."

Artie nodded in delight. Before I could say a word, Etienne-Marcel launched into a sensational glissando, winding up with The Roaring Lion and The Howling Tiger, and throwing in a brand-new sound effect that may have been The Snoring Rhinoceros.

The listeners were transfixed. Etienne-Marcel gave us an imperceptible nod. I took a deep breath, like a parachutist on his first leap, and attacked the key of C-flat, with Artie producing a series of rhythmical, discordant clashes that would have made the young Stravinsky turn green with envy. It was unmistakable genius, with perhaps a dash of *Alexander's Ragtime Band.* We were careful to emphasize a strong rhythm and made frequent changes, looking deeply concentrated.

After five minutes of this I put down my violin and stole a glance at the audience. Mr. Oshima's toes were wriggling, keeping time with the accentuated rhythms of Artie's bass chords. Captain Tanaka absent-mindedly used his toothpick in his wide-open mouth. The music publisher wrote feverishly in his notebook, and the three-hundred-pounder in tail coat slid down from his uncomfortable western chair and crossed his legs in reverse to his thighs.

Some lesser experts in the rear registered complete bewilderment. This music wasn't to be taken lightly. It was different, ultra-modern and written by a compatriot. To all seeming our weird improvisation, aided by a little mass suggestion, had caught on.

Then I saw the *commissaire* to the left of Captain Tanaka. His wide-open eyes popped out of a bloodless face and his Adam's apple was moving up and down convulsively. He seemed on the verge of collapse. For a moment I was almost sorry for him.

Artie showing signs of exhaustion, I adjusted my instrument and took over. Somehow an old Czechoslovak folk song, *Têce Voda Tece* went through my head—perhaps I'd been thinking of home. Idly improvising on the beautiful melody, I was roused by Artie's whispering, "Are you crazy? Get off that melody!" I changed to the cacophonous sounds of the Indo-Chinese jungle, and just in time, for some listeners seemed to be getting suspicious. Joined by Artie and Etienne-Marcel, I went into a fortissimo climax. We ended with an impressive C major whole tone scale, in unison.

The audience burst into wild applause, Captain Tanaka crying, *"Banzai!"* The fat man on the floor pounded on his chair. I bowed, modestly, and Etienne-Marcel and Artie bowed with me. It was too bad that Kanji Ueno from Saigon wasn't here to enjoy the greatest triumph of his career.

The *commissaire* seized my wrist. "I'll put you into the brig," he muttered. His hands were wet. He seemed to have aged in the past quarter hour. "I'll blacklist you from the entire French Merchant Marine and—"

"Pardon me," Mr. Aoki, the music publisher interrupted. "Congratulations for bringing to our attention most gifted Japanese composer, M. le Commissaire. And to you, gentlemen, for excellent rendition of most difficult composition. Altogether from memory. Truly astounding! May I see score, please?"

"Sorry, we don't have it," Etienne-Marcel said, wiping his forehead. "We studied the piece in manuscript with Mr. Ueno."

"M. le commissaire will undoubtedly be able to get you the score from Mr. Ueno," Artie added politely.

"I shall be deeply obliged," the publisher said to the *commissaire* who snapped for air and nodded, incapable of uttering a syllable.

The old fellow in kimono showered me with a torrent of Japanese words, fanning himself with his derby.

"Mr. Oshima requests humbly you repeat second part," the publisher translated. "Most beautiful melody, he thinks."

"Yes," several voices cried. "Please repeat. Encore, encore."

I explained, regretfully and with truth, that we were completely exhausted. Mr. Oshima's parchment-colored face was twisted in an ugly grimace of disappointment. Two young men pushed forward, hissing through their teeth as they asked Etienne-Marcel for his autograph. He signed Etienne-Marcel Brahms, *neveu*. At last we were able to dodge further enthusiasm and left.

The *commissaire* was waiting outside. "You are confined to your quarters until the *commandant* returns," he said, hoarsely.

I had my answer ready. "Certainly. We'll just go in there for a moment and Etienne-Marcel will make another speech."

He swallowed hard and ran his trembling fingers through his hair. "Go away," he finally said. "Perhaps you'll get run over in Tokyo."

The following day the music-conscious *Jiji Shimpo* carried a two-column story of the "sensational premiere." Reporters called me up at the Imperial asking details about Kanji Ueno. I sent them to the *commissaire*. Mr. Aoki announced that his publishing firm was honored to bring out *Interlude Indochinoise*. The Central Symphony Orchestra was reported interested in the score and the Osaka Broadcasting Association cabled to Kanji Ueno, offering him the job of music director. Captain Tanaka told the *Jiji Shimpo* a Japanese order was to be awarded to the *commissaire*.

On the trip back the *commissaire* never called us into his office. In Marseilles he requested to be transferred to another liner. We never saw him again.

A few months later I met Etienne-Marcel at the *Quat-z-Arts* in Paris. He showed me the newly-published score of *Interlude Indochinoise* by Kanji Ueno which he had just received from his son in Tokyo. There was no trace of Ravel's Bolero. This time the Honorable Ueno's inspiration could clearly be traced back to Claude Debussy's *Afternoon of a Faun*.

BARNABY CONRAD

◄——►

The Greatest Bullfight Ever

I HAD A pretty nice big house in Málaga and I was a friend of Carlos Arruza, the matador, so that's why the Town Council came to me. "*Mira, Señor Vice Consul*," they said. "We are going to present a gorgeous diamond medal to the *torero* who gives the best performance at the bullfights during our annual fair. It is an exquisite thing, made especially in Madrid at a cost of 5000 *pesetas* and we should enjoy the honor of presenting it to your friend Arruza in your house."

"The honor will be mine," I said. "And I shall plan a party for that date. But how can you be sure Arruza will give the best show?"

"He cannot fail," they said. "First he is fighting both Friday and Sunday; if he is out of form or the bulls are bad on Friday, he will have another chance on Sunday. And secondly, Manolete, Arruza's only real competition, has been wounded and will not be able to fight."

"And thirdly," spoke up a member of the Council uneasily, "he *has* to be the best for we already have his name engraved on the medal."

On Friday Carlos arrived for the first fight and Málaga was agog, for he had become the most sensational thing in bullfighting. Most people defended the classic purity of Manolete's style but for sheer brute courage, this young Mexican was unchallenged.

Then too, the señoras and señoritas weren't oblivious to that beautiful physique, and the unruly brown hair that topped his shy handsome face. Arruza had donated the entire proceeds of his first fight of the season, $7000, to the mother of a bullfighter killed in the ring. After that he was the most popular matador in Spain.

This season Arruza was contracted for the staggering number of 140 fights in 180 days! This meant fighting in Madrid one day, Barcelona the next, going to Lisbon, Bilbao, Mallorca, in planes, cars, trains, snatching a meal and a bit of sleep when he could, and every day leaving thousands of people thrilled by his skill and courage.

When I went to see him this afternoon before the fight his face was pale and drawn and I could see that the ninety fights he had already fought under this regime had aged him.

April, 1948

"*Chiquillo*," he said after we'd talked awhile and as he wiggled into the gold brocaded pants, "what's this about a medal?"

I explained.

"*Caracoles!*" exclaimed Carlos. "They have put my name on it already! But anything can happen in a bullfight! How can they know if I feel like fighting? Or what about the wind? Or what about the bulls, eh? That slight detail must be considered—the bulls."

At four o'clock they paraded into the brilliant sun and the band blared forth with the *paso doble*, Carlos Arruzo. Carlos grinned nervously and threw his dress cape up to me.

His first bull was a bad one, but he did pretty well, and the *presidente* let him take a lap around the ring to receive the crowd's applause. The second bull was Estudiante's and he did a very good job, being conceded two ears from the dead animal as an evaluation of his bravery and skill. Morenito de Talavera felt the pressure of the two good fights that had gone before him, and surpassed by far his natural ability, cutting one ear and taking a lap around the ring.

Arruza, seemingly unconcerned by this competition as he waited for his second bull to come out, looked around, hugging his big red and yellow cape to him and smiling his little-boy smile at friends.

His bull skidded out of the *toril* and brought boos from the crowd because it was so small. But the boos switched to "*Oles!*" when Arruza passed the bull closely three times, the lethal horns inches away from his knees. Few people objected when, after he had placed three beautifully executed *banderillas* and one sword thrust, the *presidente* granted him both ears and the tail for his brilliant fight. Women threw down roses to him and men threw cigars, hats, even overcoats. A few people booed, though, saying he didn't deserve the tail since the bull was so small.

However, the medal seemed cinched, especially after Estudiante and Morenito de Talavera were bad on the last two bulls, and I left the plaza jubilantly. The next day the program was Estudiante and Morenito again plus a little Mexican Indian named Cañitas. Nothing to fear, we thought, for the bulls were giants; we had seen what Estudiante and Morenito had to offer and who ever heard of Cañitas?

None of the three fighters was anything but discreet on his first bull. But then—the trumpet sounded for Cañitas' second, and out it came—a black and white monster weighing 750 kilos!

Cañitas went pale when he saw the creature rip part of the wooden barrier apart, but he set his Indian jaw and you could see him telling himself, "If I'm going to die I'll die in a blaze of glory." The bull ran around the empty ring twice looking for something to kill, and then Cañitas stepped out and dropped to his knees, letting it go by with a *whoosh*, as the great horns passed his head. A gasp of surprise went up from the crowd who had expected him to play the bull as safely as possible. Then when he passed the bull even closer, they set up a continuous roar. After numerous fancy passes with the cape, he placed three sets of *banderillas* with the arrogance of a gypsy, with the *muleta* he accomplished a *fuera* that bullfighters dream about, then drew back and dropped the bull with a sword thrust almost to the hilt. The crowd went wild and insisted upon his getting both ears, tails and a hoof, the most you can get. I left the plaza for the day, feeling a little sick.

The next day was Sunday, and the Town Council came to see me with long faces. "Now what do we do?" they asked reproachfully, as though it were my fault. "Order another medal," was all I could suggest.

Arruza arrived at six in the morning after having fought in Cadiz the afternoon before and driving all night to Málaga. I went to the hotel to wake him at three, and the Idol of Spain was a mess; he looked green and staggered as he got up to go to bathe.

"I'm exhausted." The words tumbled out. "I've got a fever of 102, I can't go on like this every day. I never want to fight again. I'm going to go to bed for ten years when the season is over. How was the fight yesterday?" he continued wearily while putting on his frilled shirt. "I haven't seen the papers as yet."

"Cañitas turned in the best fight of the season," I said.

Carlos stopped tying his tie. "Are you joking?"

"No," I said. "He got inspired—fought as he's never fought before—cut ears, tail and a hoof." I cleared my throat. "But—uh—you'll come up to the house for the ceremony anyway, won't you?"

Arruza regarded me quietly and said: "I'll be there, *chiquillo*."

I made the error of taking two women to the last fight. Carlos was first on the program, and when he got to his knees and let the bull pass by him four times so close that it removed part of his embroidered jacket, the girl on my right passed out; the other girl was just about to faint too, but she was too busy reviving her friend. Carlos did every pass in the book plus two of his own invention, and the girls couldn't stand any more; they left just about the time he dropped the bull with one thrust. The crowd went wild, and the *presidente* signalled with his handkerchief for the *banderillero* to cut one ear, two ears, two ears and tail, two ears, tail and hoof, and Arruza circled the ring, triumphantly holding his prizes aloft.

It was a wonderful fight, but we all knew Cañitas had been just a bit more graceful, more daring, more suicidal, the day before.

After Arruza came Parrita and Andaluz, both good bullfighters, but people were still limp from the first fight and didn't pay much attention to them. When Arruza came out and stood waiting for his second bull people applauded wildly, but we really didn't expect him to do anything more; it's rare when a bullfighter puts up a good performance on both bulls.

The bull was a monstrous creature, and Arruza studied it from behind the fence for a few moments. Then he stepped out shakily into the ring and stood there swaying and putting his hand up to his feverish head and pressing his hot temples with his fingers, but as the bull drew near he collected himself, let the cape unfurl in front of the animal's nose and passed it by in a series of classic *verónicas* that drew great "Oles!" from the crowd. Then in a few moments they were yelling "No! No!" as he passed the bull in the graceful butterfly pass, letting it come so close each time it seemed he would be caught and spitted on one of the huge needlelike horns.

Came time for the *banderillas*, and Carlos placed the three pairs of barbed sticks superbly, running at an angle at the bull as it charged, and sticking them in the withers with his arms high and finally spinning to one side to let the bull hurtle by. Then he begged permission from the *presidente* to risk his life in still another pair. It was granted and Carlos picked an impossible way to place them: with his back against the fence, he incited the bull, "Uh-huh Toro! Uh-huh-huh!" and stood there calmly watching it bear down on him. When the enraged animal was two feet away, Carlos raised his arms, dropped the *banderillas* in place, ducked to the side, the left horn grazing his chest as the bull crashed into the fence.

The trumpet blew for the death; with the scarlet rag and the curved sword in his hand, Carlos dedicated the bull, facing the crowd with exhausted, unseeing eyes. Then he went out for the last round.

His first pass with the *muleta* was the "Pass of the Dead One," so called because so many bullfighters have been killed doing it. Carlos called the bull from twenty feet away, and as it whooshed by he remained absolutely motionless and straight, letting the bull choose whether he was going to crash into the cloth or into his legs. Still motionless, he let the bull wheel and charge three times. Then Arruza decided to try a pass of his invention—the "Arrucina." The *muleta* is held behind the back so that only a tiny portion of the deceptive cloth shows, leaving the entire body open as a target for the bull.

When he put the *muleta* in back and people realized what he was going to do they screamed "No! No!" again, but the bull had already charged and somehow the horns missed Carlos by centimeters. But when he tried it again from the other side, the right horn went around Arruza's leg and the bull hurled him high into the air. He somehow spun around on the horn so that when his body slapped the ground he was stretched out under the bull, the length of his body between the animal's front legs, and his head between the wicked horns. People hid their eyes, yet before the needle points could find the inert form, Carlos had reached up and locked his arms around the bull's neck in an iron grip. The bewildered bull spun around and around. Finally he gave his neck a mighty snap, flung the man from him like a rag doll to the ground ten feet away, but before he could charge, Arruza's men were between them and had attracted the bull's attention. Arruza lurched drunkenly to his feet and stood there swaying, bruised and dazed, his uniform in ribbons, but miraculously not wounded. He picked up his sword and the rag.

"*Fuera!*" he yelled at his *banderilleros*. "Get out of the ring."

The amazed men retreated several feet behind him.

Arruza whirled on them and snarled: "*Fuera* I said! Leave me alone with him!"

When they had all left the ring, the matador calmly turned to the bull, who was pawing the ground and studying him ten feet away; got to his knees and inched forward toward the animal. The bull shifted his feet and the crowd gasped, sure that he would charge. But he didn't; it was as though he were hypnotized and cowed by the enormous brute courage of this man-thing on its knees and Arruza kept coming, staring fixedly at the bull until he arrived in its very face.

Then, with the muzzle of the bull almost touching him, he leaned forward and rested his elbow on the bull's forehead!

He turned around and stared up at the crowd with the bull's nose against his back. We were afraid to scream for fear the noise would make the bull charge, but when he faced the bull again and, still on his knees, made it pass by four times, spinning in against the shoulder each time, a great roar burst from our throats. And then suddenly Carlos rose to his feet, and hurling himself on top of the horns, he sank the sword in between the shoulders to the hilt, the bull reeling and its hulk crashing over backwards to the sand.

Delirium took over the plaza, and the *presidente* waved his handkerchief for one ear, again for two ears, again for the tail, again for a hoof—*and still again for another hoof, for the first time in bullfighting's long history!*

So Arruza got the medal and we had the party, but our honored guest left early. He had to hurry to Valencia for a fight the following day.

H. L. MENCKEN

◄───►

Downfall of a Revolutionary

OF ALL the eminent characters who flourished in the West Baltimore of my nonage, the one most venerated by the boys of my generation was Hoggie Unglebower, an uncouth youth whose empire and influence, radiating out from an humble stable in the alley which ran behind our house in Hollins Street, covered altogether an area of at least half a square mile. No storekeeper of that time and place was better known, whether for good or for evil, nor any cop, however heinous, nor any ma'am in the public school up Hollins Street hill, nor bad nigger in Vincent alley, nor blind man in practice at Hollins market. Between the longitude of the market and the wilderness of Steuart's Hill, all through a chunk of territory four or five blocks thick, he was a hero to every boy above the age of seven.

The reader of today, soaked in the Freudian sewage for so many years, will assume at once, I suppose, that Hoggie must have been a Lothario, and his headquarters a seraglio. Nothing could have been further from the truth. He was actually almost a Trappist in his glandular life, and his hormones never gave him any visible trouble until much later on, as I shall show in due course. In the days of his greatest glory his view of all human females was predominantly disdainful, but it never led him to use them wickedly, or even impolitely. When a hired girl issued into the alley to flag a rag-and-bone man or hunt for a lost garbage box he would whistle at her satirically and shout "Ah, there!" but at the same time he always took off his hat. To women of greater age and station he was courteous to an extreme degree, and when he visited a neighboring dwelling with his terriers to purge it of rats he always wiped his feet at the back door, and never failed to address the lady of the house as Ma'am.

No, Hoggie was not carnal in the Catechism sense, and I incline to think that that was one of the reasons all the boys so greatly respected him. The male infantry of today, debauched by Progressive Education and the sex hygiene quackery, are said to be adepts at the art of love before they are more than half house-broken, but that was certainly not true in my time. The boys of that Mousterian generation, until adolescence came down upon them, regarded girls with frank aversion, and had as little truck with them as with cats or cops. It is, of course, a fact that the probable delights of amour were occasionally discussed, but it was always vaguely and with a considerable uneasiness, for any

September, 1940

move to put a concrete project into effect would have involved a close approach
to females, and that was never done if it could be helped. What made Hoggie
a personage was nothing in that line; it was mainly, and perhaps even only, his
successful and notorious resistance to the doctrine that cleanliness is next to
godliness.

In his father's stable he led the life dreamed of as ideal by all normal boys,
then, now, and forever. No one, it appeared, had any authority (at all events,
any authority that he recognized) to make him comb his hair, or brush his
clothes, or shine his shoes, or wash behind the ears. He wallowed there day in
and day out, including especially Sundays, in such slops as every boy longs to
own, but is never permitted to have. Preferring the society of horses and dogs
to that of men, he lived among them freely and unashamedly, sleeping with
them, eating with them, and sharing his confidences with them. He got his hair
cut when he damned well pleased, and it wasn't often. Hating neckties, he
never wore them. When he thirsted, he drank from the end of the stable hose,
and if anyone stopped to gape at him he squeezed the hose (which was old,
soft and full of holes) and sent a fine stream into the gaper's eye.

In brief, a magnificent specimen of Natural Man, somehow surviving un-
scathed every corruption of an effete and pusillanimous civilization. He came
of a conventional family and had been to school, but had fought off successfully
every effort to denaturize him. His days were busy, and full of enterprises that,
to us boys, were important, difficult and excessively romantic. He was the archi-
tect, builder and navigator of the largest and fastest double-decker sleds known
in West Baltimore, and probably the best repairer of boys' wagons ever seen
in Christendom. He knew how to knock a barrel to pieces without splitting
any of the staves, and how to put it together again. He could teach tricks to
horses, and had so far mastered their vocabulary of whinnies and pawings that
he carried on long conversations with them, often laughing heartily at their
pawky humor. He was a dog doctor of great gifts, and kept a large stock of medicines for his patients on a shelf in the stable. To cops, despite all their clubs,
handcuffs and side-arms, he presented a calm and unflickering eye, and they had a
high respect for him, for when he went to the aid of one who was overwhelmed
by a passel of bad niggers, the bad niggers lost consciousness almost instantly,
and awoke in the watch-house with huge bumps on their heads. Hoggie, dis-
daining firearms, did his fighting with clubs, and had an arsenal of them ready
to hand—little ones for light jobs, and thick, warty shillalahs for really earnest
work. When he came down upon a skull something gave way, and it was
never Hoggie or his weapon.

He was the best dog-trainer for miles around, and could transform even the
sorriest mutt into a competent ratter. For this purpose he liked to have them
young; indeed, he preferred to begin on them as soon as their eyes were open. At
that age, of course, they were no match for actual rats, and even the more active
sort of mice had the edge on them. To equalize the odds, Hoggie would catch
infant rats in a trap, pull their teeth with a pair of pliers, and then throw them
into a barrel with a couple of his pupils. As the latter gained in strength and

technique, he would test them with rats of gradually larger growth, retaining at first one tooth each, and then two, and then four or five, and finally a whole set, upper and lower. Now and then a freshman was badly mauled in these exercises, but Hoggie did not despair, for he knew that any sort of educational process was bound to be painful, and he preferred the hard way for dogs as for men. His graduates were all recognized virtuosi. One day he let me go along as he took one to a hay-and-feed warehouse for a final examination. The candidate was only a spindly black-and-tan, but within three minutes by the watch he had unearthed, run down, and killed a whole bucket of rats, some of them of the fearsome sewer variety, with fangs two inches long.

Hoggie admired dogs, and was admired by them in turn, though his medicating of them ran to heroic measures. His usual prescription for the common run of canine malaise was the better part of half a pound of Glauber's salts. The colored quacks who practised a Dahomeyan farriery in Reveille's livery stable down the street hesitated to give so large a dose to anything short of a cart horse, but Hoggie believed that it was foolish to temporize with disease, and proved it by curing most of his patients. He was also adept at surgery, and could point to at least a dozen dogs that he had treated successfully for broken bones.

He sutured the lacerations that followed dog-fights with the thick, black thread used by shoemakers, and always waxed it carefully before setting to work. He was, I believe, the first canine dentist ever in practice in Baltimore; to this day, in fact, they are rare. He pulled the damaged teeth of his patients with the same pair of pliers that he employed to prepare rats for his academy, and sometimes he had to pull very hard.

I heard him say once that most dogs, like most human beings, were born with too many teeth, and that getting rid of half a dozen or so toned up their systems and improved their dispositions.

No one that I ever heard of approached him in the delicate art of trimming puppies' tails. His technique was of the whirlwind variety: the tail was off before the puppy had a chance to be alarmed. In my earliest days he had a formidable rival in Old Julius, an Aframerican *mohel* with headquarters in Reveille's stable, but as the years passed he gobbled all of Julius' practice, and in the end his mastery was admitted by everyone.

In that era the different breeds of dogs in vogue nearly all wore their tails clipped, so Hoggie was kept busy. I have seen him knock off six or eight of an afternoon, with the whole Hollins-Street gang for a gallery. Our own dogs, from the early eighties onward to the middle nineties, all passed through his hands, and every one of them was friendly to him afterward, and wagged its stump whenever it encountered him. He also treated dogs when they took to nibbling grass in the yard or showed other signs of indisposition—always with a massive dose of Glauber's salts as a starter. He had plenty of other medicines, and used them freely on occasion, but he depended mainly on Glauber's salts, just as Dr. Wiley, our family doctor, depended on castor oil.

Hoggie's incurable boyishness was shown by the fact that, for all his fondness for horses and dogs, he hated cats with a blind and implacable hatred, and spent a great deal of his time tracking them down and executing them. There was a time, indeed, when his chronic war upon them aroused some ill-will in the neighborhood—but not, of course, among the boys.

What was done about it I forget, but for a while he locked himself in his stable, and refused to have any truck with human society. Even the cops were given to understand that their room was preferred to their company. But then a stray cat scratched a baby down the block, and under cover of the ensuing uproar Hoggie emerged from his solitude, and resumed his crusade. I well recall the day when, as a gesture of triumph, he threw eight dead cats into the alley in one lot, and got into a row with the street cleaner who had to haul them away.

The street cleaner, it appeared, held that a person engaged in such wholesale slaughters should dispose of his own dead, and not dump them on public officials. He cited the example of the hotels which carted off their own garbage, and that of the candy factory down the alley which kept a wagon to handle its own boiler ashes, but Hoggie refused to allow any weight to the argument. So far as he was concerned, he said, the cats could lie in the alley until the Judgment Day, along with the rats that he heaved out almost daily—the melancholy refuse of his college for puppies. The street cleaner muttered a while longer and threatened several times to submit the whole matter to the jurisprudence of Murphy the cop, but in the end he loaded the cats upon his cart, and during the weeks that followed he loaded many others.

Until a fresh generation of kittens worked its way in from Hollins market, the Union Square neighborhood was almost as bare of *Felidae* as Greenland. A few, of course, survived in houses, but they were kept as closely penned as canary birds.

The boys of the Hollins-Street gang believed, like well-educated American boys everywhere else, that cats had nine lives, but Hoggie dissented. He admitted freely that no cat within his experience ever had so little as one life, but he insisted that his researches indicated that five was the limit. Indeed, it was only battle-scarred old Toms who went even that far: the average free-lance cat, depleted by its wandering, precarious life, was disposed of finally after being killed three or four times.

One day the alley metaphysician, Old Wesley, undertook to point out a possible statistical fallacy in this doctrine. What evidence was there, he demanded, that the Toms which Hoggie killed five times had not been killed four times before by other executioners, thus making up the classical nine? This argument, rather to the astonishment of his listening admirers, floored Hoggie completely. The louder he howled against it, the more he became confused and out of temper, and in the end he was reduced to the sorry expedient of denouncing Wesley as a sassy nigger, and threatening to set the medical students on him. His failure in the debate, and above all his resort to what amounted to forensic blackmail, lowered his stock with the boys of Hollins Street, but not for long. In a little while he recovered face gloriously by staging, in the privacy of his stable, a dogfight that went down into history as the most thrilling ever seen in West Baltimore.

Despite his unhappy encounter with Old Wesley, he was commonly on good terms with the colored people who lived in the alley, and exercised a general jurisdiction over them, milder and more understanding than that of the cops. They had a high respect for him, and went to him in their troubles, though in his practice as dog-doctor and cat-and-rat exterminator he was uncomfortably close to a medical student. He did not hold himself out as skilled at human medicine, but the bottles he kept for dosing dogs were at the disposal of any blackamoor who wanted to try them, and many professed to be benefited. In particular, the liniment he used on dogs run over by carts was said to be very efficacious against rheumatoid afflictions in *Anthropoidea*.

Once he scared off all his Aframerican patients by stuffing a dead cat with oats, and using black shot-buttons for its eyes. This gruesome object, while it remained on exhibition, kept all the colored people out of his stable, though we white boys thought it was very nobby. It didn't last long, for the huge, ferocious rats of Hollins market quickly heard of it, and one night they rushed the stable and devoured it, eyes and all. All that remained of it the next morning was a carriage-bolt that Hoggie had employed to counteract the flaccidity of the oats.

His downfall I can place with reasonable accuracy in the year 1890, when I was ten years old and he must have been about twenty-two or three. One afternoon in summer, on my way to Reveille's livery stable to visit my father's horse, John, who was laid up with epizoötic, I encountered Hoggie at the corner of Baltimore street in such vestments that I stopped dead in my tracks, and gaped at him as if he had been a cop in motley or a two-headed boy.

He had on a brand-new suit of stores clothes, golden brown in color, and wore a pair of the immense yellow shoes then in fashion—as wide, almost, as a streetcar at the ball of the foot, but stretched out to a long point at the toe. On his head was a cart-wheel straw hat with a brim at least six inches deep, and a gorgeous red-and-white ribbon. His collar, which was of fresh celluloid, rose above a boiled shirt that gleamed like snow on the Alps, and around it he wore a bright green four-in-hand tie, with the ends tucked over to expose a stud that glittered like a diamond, but was no doubt something else. He was shaved so closely that his neck and chin were criss-crossed with red gashes, and the rest of his face was a brilliant vermilion. Finally, and most amazing of all, his hair—at least such of it as I could see below his hat—was cropped to its roots according to the best technique of Barber Lehnert. As I passed him, I caught a gust of Jockey Club scent, familiar to me as the special favorite of our current hired girl.

I was so astounded that I passed him without greeting him, staring idiotically. He paid no attention to me, but stalked along painfully, like a man in a barrel. I spread the news all over the neighborhood, and Hoggie's secret quickly leaked out.

He had succumbed at last, after all his years of amiable outlawry, to one of the most conventional of human weaknesses: he had fallen in love. Some inconsiderable slip of a girl, name unknown, had collared him, tamed him, and made of him the dreadful poppinjay that I had seen. The rest of the pathetic story follows classical lines, and is soon told. Hoggie disappeared from his stable, and was reported to be occupying a bedroom in the Unglebower family home, and actually eating at table. In a little while he vanished altogether, and reports came in that he was married to the lady, living in far Northwest Baltimore, and at work as a horse-car driver. That was the last I ever heard of him.

MORRIS MARKEY

Who Killed Joe Elwell?

IF YOU were looking for a boundary marker, as it were, between the Smart Set of the lobster-palace days and the Café Society of our own time, you could find its location easily enough, and indeed you could find the precise hour and minute when the old order passed, giving place to new.

The location is the four-story granite house at No. 244 West 70th Street in the City of New York. The time is thirty-five minutes past eight o'clock on the morning of Friday, June 11, 1920. For Mrs. Marie Larsen went into that house at that moment and discovered her employer, Joseph Bowne Elwell, dying of a bullet wound in the exact center of his forehead.

Elwell was the very last of the men-about-town in the tradition of Van Bibber. The gentlemanly punctilio, the discreet elegance and gallantry that were essential to the role in those days were the very things that delivered a bullet into his brain. And, ironically enough, it was those identical qualities in the wellbred character of Edward Swann, the District Attorney, that made a solution of the puzzle almost impossible. The people involved in the affair were ladies and gentlemen of substance and refinement. Mr. Swann could not bring himself to deal rudely or realistically with them. Indeed, he was so intent upon preventing a smirch on any name that he was deceptive in his dealings with the press to the point of downright dishonesty.

The dashing Elwell (who was forty-four years old when he died) was no Johnny-come-lately. He had put together a quite substantial fortune despite the fact that the only capital he possessed at the beginning was his nimble mind, plus instinctive good taste, plus the manners of a gentleman that he had learned at his mother's knee. On the morning that the bullet found him, he owned about $500,000 worth of real estate. He had about $100,000 worth of personal property. His stable of twenty thoroughbreds was racing at Latonia. He kept his yacht at Palm Beach for his annual winter sojourn there. He owned five automobiles and, of course, the house on 70th Street.

It is true that he laid the foundation of these riches at the card table, where he played bridge for ten dollars a point and, on one occasion at least, gained thirty thousand dollars. Yet, significantly enough, the very friends who lost to him insisted unanimously that he was by no means a professional gambler. "It was a pleasure to play with him," they said, "and it was worth it to have him

October, 1950

beat you, because he had a cool passion for the science of bridge, the philosophy of a card game. He never seemed to give a thought for the money involved, whether he won it or paid it out."

Gambling at cards was not, in short, his weakness.

But he had a weakness. And it seems to have absorbed his time and his thoughts to an almost fantastic degree.

Among the countless distinguished men who were delighted to know him, he was a man of impeccable honor, of fastidious regard for the social conventions. He was generous and considerate, and his nod of assent was better than a signed contract. But among the countless beautiful women who were equally delighted to know him, he was an insatiable voluptuary, a heartless rake who, with neither compunction nor pity, took the full advantage of their frailty. He played upon a whole orchestra of women as a conductor upon the podium bends the fiddles and the woodwinds to his whim.

Elwell lived an odd sort of life in the 70th Street house. It was big, as city houses go, and superbly furnished. Yet he had neither butler nor cook nor maid to keep it for him. He employed a combination secretary and factotum, William Barnes, and a chauffeur, Rhodes, both of whom lived out. Mrs. Larsen, the wife of a butcher, came every morning to prepare his breakfast (two breakfasts if a lady were present) and clean up the house.

It was this aura of secrecy, of a peculiar need for complete privacy which, in a time when expensive entertainment was expected of all prosperous gentlemen, first gave the citizens a hint that here was something rather special in the way of a mystery. "What does he do every night, when he goes home to that silent house and takes off his tail coat and white tie?"

Rhodes, Barnes, and a former chauffeur told the newspaper reporters all about it. If their comments were to be summed up in one statement, it would read like this: "During the four years I've worked for him he's had more than fifty women. Most of them were very high-class-looking dames, and I got the idea most of them were married to somebody else. But I don't know any of them by name, because that's where he was very careful. He'd tell me to go to some street intersection or some restaurant, and then he'd roll up the glass to cut me off from the back of the car. There would be a dame waiting for him, and she'd get in, and I couldn't hear a word they said even if I'd wanted to.

"When we got to the 70th Street house he would take the lady in, and wave me away, and I'd put the car in the garage and go on home.

"There were seven women to my knowledge, though, that had a key to the house. I think there were twelve, but seven to my knowledge. I don't know when they used the keys, because I never was around the place at night. When he drove out at night, he used taxicabs.

"But even all this blueblood didn't seem enough for him. Many a time we would be driving along the street and some woman on the sidewalk would catch his eye and he would signal me to pull up. He would always say to the dame, 'Why! I haven't seen you since Palm Beach!' or something like that. If the woman looked insulted he would apologize for his mistake. But you'd be surprised how many of them didn't act insulted at all."

Now you should understand very clearly that amorous dalliance with the fair was a profoundly different game in the days of the Smart Set—particularly with the wedded fair. In our own time of Café Society, it is catch-as-catch-can, and few holds barred. But in the early Twenties, when an odd affair called the honor of a gentleman was an item in the moral currency, there were rules. Men simply did not take it kindly when their wives slept with other men, and so the most serious of all the rules was called the Unwritten Law. The cuckolded husband was assumed to have (unless some tedious jury failed to get the point) at least some small right to blow the brains out of the scoundrel who had seduced his wife.

The males of the city generally accepted this notion as an explanation of Elwell's sudden end. They made up a jingle which was a favorite at the cocktail hour:

> Who killed Joe Elwell?
> I, said the Banker,
> And now I will spank her.
> I killed Joe Elwell.

The ladies, quick to establish the honor of their sex, countered with their own explanation:

> Who killed Joe Elwell?
> I, said the lady.
> His conduct was shady.
> I killed Joe Elwell.

It was in this Cock Robin mood that an absurdly incompetent investigation of the affair got under way—an investigation that proved one thing: that a cop had better have a course in logic than a closet full of Old School Ties.

Elwell had been born into a respectable and moderately prosperous family in New Jersey. At twenty-five he was advancing steadily toward the top of a Brooklyn hardware firm. He had done well enough to join a club, small but socially correct, and it was there that he learned to play bridge whist. The game fascinated him utterly. He harnessed his mind to it, and before he was thirty he was the leading bridge expert in the country, with two published books on the subject behind him and eleven more to come. He was one of the most active members of the New York Whist Club, and a founder of the Studio Club—which was so exclusive that the membership was limited to twenty men of affairs.

He married and his wife bore him a son, but by 1916 Mrs. Elwell had had enough of a man who drew women to him as a magnet draws needles. She obtained a legal separation, but not a divorce.

On New Year's Day of the year in which he died, Elwell was driven to Palm

Beach by Rhodes, the chauffeur. Nothing seems to have transpired in his
Florida sojourn that could have the least bearing upon his violent end. Late
in May, he sent Rhodes back to New York with the car, and a few days later
took the train for his own return journey. It was reported, after his death, that
as soon as he returned from Palm Beach he called upon his wife and asked her
to give him a divorce, saying that he would like to marry again, and that she
refused. Mrs. Elwell denied this and said that she had wanted a divorce at
the time of their separation, but that Elwell preferred to remain married to
shield himself from getting in too deep with other women.

On the night of June 10, thirteen hours before the fatal shot, Elwell went to
a dinner party at the Ritz-Carlton Hotel. The hosts of the occasion were Mr.
and Mrs. Walter Lewisohn. Octavio Figueroa, a journalist from Buenos Aires,
was a guest. And so was Viola Kraus, Mrs. Lewisohn's sister. Indeed, Viola
Kraus was the guest of honor. Three months before, she had won an interlocutory
decree of divorce in the court at White Plains from her husband, Victor von
Schlegell. On this night, the degree automatically became final, and the party
was by way of celebrating the event.

Unhappily, something occurred to mar the gaiety of the occasion. As the
Lewisohn party settled themselves in their chairs and the waiters scurried about
them, a burst of hearty laughter came from a table only a few feet away. They
turned their heads and saw von Schlegell, in merry humor, seated with a beautiful young woman dressed all in black.

When coffee and brandy were done, the Lewisohn party took the elevator
to the roof to dance a little while, and von Schlegell and his young lady came
to the same elevator. As far as can be determined, only one remark was made
as the car swept upward: von Schlegell's companion said, "It seems we just
can't keep away from each other." Nobody undertook to make reply. A little
later, on the roof, Elwell and Viola Kraus were dancing a waltz when von
Schlegell and his partner drifted close to them. Von Schlegell said, "Hello,
Joe."

Viola Kraus and von Schlegell and the young woman in black all said afterward that Elwell smiled and returned the greeting. Walter Lewisohn disagreed
with them. "I was seated at the table and watching everything closely," he
said. "When Von spoke, Elwell's face did not change expression and he did not
acknowledge the greeting."

At about ten o'clock, von Schlegell took his young lady away. Some half-
hour later, Elwell went off in advance of the others to the New Amsterdam
Theatre to get tickets for the Ziegfeld Midnight Frolics. When the rest of the
party arrived he was waiting for them, tickets in hand. All of them danced, now,
and sipped champagne, and enjoyed the floor show until about one-thirty in
the morning. In the light of subsequent events, it seems almost certain that
there was some misunderstanding within the little group at this period. When all
hands decided to call it a night, and came down from the New Amsterdam roof,
Elwell announced that he would walk home alone. He saw the others into a
taxicab and then went away westward on 42nd Street toward Eighth Avenue.

Nobody knows how he spent the next hour. The telephone records of the Columbia Station showed that two calls were put through from the Elwell house—one at 1:45 and the other at 2:04. Viola Kraus telephoned to him at two-thirty and found him at home, and attempted to patch up whatever unhappiness the evening had produced. He tried without success to get through to his some-time partner in the racing stable, W. H. Pendleton, at Cedarhurst, L. I. The operator later said she rang for some moments, but got no answer.

(It should be said here that Pendleton was at home. The telephone was beside his bed. He said that it never rang at all. The New York *Times* reporter, desperate for news and being constantly misled by the District Attorney's office, made a great deal of this episode and, with elaborate innuendo, predicted the arrest of Pendleton within twenty-four hours. The idea was an absurd one. Pendleton was a staid, family sort of man. He had sold his share of the stable to Elwell, ". . . because I just couldn't keep up with Joe or go out with him. His pace was too fast for me. We had lost touch with each other, but I'll testify that he was a man of honor in all his dealings. I admired him and respected him.")

It was very hot that night. At 3:45, John Isdale, chief engineer of a cargo steamer, got up from his bed in the house two doors away from Elwell's. He had been roused from uncomfortable half-sleep by the loud, popping exhaust of a racing automobile. He went to the window and saw the car drawn up in front of the Elwell house. "I didn't see anybody get out of it," he said, "and I didn't see anybody get in. I don't know the color or the make of the car. In about five minutes it went away, still popping that damned exhaust."

At six-thirty that morning of June 11, Henry Otten, the driver of a dairy wagon, left a quart of milk in the vestibule of No. 244. He said that the glass-paneled entrance door was shut as usual, but the double-wing storm doors were wide open.

At seven-twenty, the postman entered the vestibule, saw the milk, and dropped four or five letters on the tiled flooring. He pushed the bell-button twice, as was his custom. He was never able to remember, afterward, whether he pulled shut the storm doors behind him as he went away.

At eight-thirty, Mrs. Larsen arrived. The storms doors were shut and the latch had caught so that she had to use her key—the same key opening both storm doors and entrance doors beyond the vestibule. The milk was still where Otten had placed it. She saw no letters at all.

Mrs. Larsen hurried back to the kitchen and threw open a couple of windows. She puttered around for a moment or two and went back toward the front of the house. In a small room, the "reception room," just to the right of the main-entrance hall, she saw something that stopped her in her tracks. Joseph Elwell was sitting upright in an upholstered chair, dressed in green silk pajamas and barefoot. His face was faintly streaked with blood. His breathing made a loud sound.

Mrs. Larsen ran out the front door, and her cries brought Patrolman Henry Singer from his traffic post at the corner. When Singer got to the house, he ran back into the street, and found Otten the milkman on his way back through the street making collections. The two of them had Elwell half out of his chair when Singer said, "Hey, wait a minute. This guy's been shot!" Otten looked again and saw that this was, indeed, the truth. They put Elwell back into the chair as they had found him, and Singer called headquarters. He looked about for a pistol, but found none.

The man-about-town was taken in an ambulance to Bellevue, where he died two hours later without recovering consciousness. By the time he drew his last breath, the house on 70th Street was half-filled with detectives under the field command of Captain Arthur Carey of the Homicide Squad. The next day John F. Joyce, an assistant District Attorney, entered the case.

The reception room itself was small. The furniture consisted of two upholstered chairs, a small table, and three pictures on the wall. Elwell's own chair stood with its back to the wall, in the usual place. There was no sign of disturbance whatever, except that the second chair had been moved a few feet from its ordinary position. It faced Elwell's chair, at a slight diagonal, some six feet away. Singer and Otten could not remember whether they had moved this chair when they undertook to put the dying man in a more comfortable position.

The bullet had passed directly through Elwell's head and imbedded itself in the plaster, some four inches above the back of the chair. During the first few minutes of his investigation, Singer had picked up an empty .45-caliber shell which had been ejected from an Army-type Colt automatic. The bullet, dug out of the plaster, matched the shell.

On the floor beside Elwell's chair were some of the letters that the postman had delivered that morning, all unopened. Another letter, a routine report from Lloyd Gentry, the trainer of Elwell's racing stable in Kentucky, was opened and lay stained with blood upon the floor at his left hand. None of the other letters, when opened by the police, proved to be of any significance.

Elwell had his cigarettes especially manufactured: cork tips for himself, gold tips and rose tips for the ladies. He had been smoking one of his own, which lay half burned out on the carpet beside his chair. On the marble mantel shelf there was a half-smoked cigarette of a common brand. It had been smoked from the wrong end and the brand name was burned away.

It was easy to decide that robbery was not the motive for the crime. There were two basement doors, both of them locked and neither tampered with. All of the downstairs windows were protected from intruders by ornamental iron grilles. In Elwell's bedroom on the third floor the clothes he had worn to the Lewisohn party were laid out where he had taken them off. On his bed also there was $400 in cash, and his diamond studs and cuff links, worth about $7000.

He had not slept in his bed (unless, perchance, it had been remade later), though indentations in the pillow indicated that he had lain there a little while on top of the counterpane. Beside the bed on the floor there was a copy of the

Morning Telegraph, a racing paper, and an ash tray filled with his own cigarette ends.

In the closet of Elwell's bedroom the detectives found a pink silk negligee. A little square of the cloth, apparently bearing the embroidered name or initials of its owner, had been cut away with a knife. And that careful attention to the garment was the chief clue to Elwell's character, or at least to his code of behavior. It was a sample of his way of doing things. For, despite the scores of women who were so powerfully drawn to him, who pressed their favors upon him with discretion thrown to the winds, Elwell remained discreet. In his effects there was not found one letter from a woman. He kept no diaries. Rhodes and Barnes and Mrs. Larsen all solemnly swore that they did not know the identity of any of these beautiful and breathless creatures.

The tale of door keys in the hands of special favorites was, unhappily, soon dispelled. The police found a locksmith who had changed the locks to the front doors more than six months earlier and had filed only two keys to fit them, one for Elwell himself and one for Mrs. Larsen. And upon this point Mrs. Elwell had an observation to make: "Joe wasn't a fool. He would never take a chance on two women using their keys the same evening. If he gave out keys at all, it was to people who would come and gamble with him."

Yet there was little evidence that Elwell had held gambling parties in his home. Only a single deck of cards was located—in a desk on the second floor. Part of a faro layout was found in a storeroom.

William Barnes had this to say: "It wasn't a woman who killed him, even if a woman could handle a gun that big. When they found him, he had left upstairs the toupee that covered his little bald spot, and his bridge of false teeth was upstairs too. He never would have sat down with a lady, looking like that. I figure how it happened was this: He brings some fellow home with him or maybe lets the fellow in when he rings the bell. He sits down and the fellow sits facing him, probably holding the gun in his hand and saying what he's going to do. I've seen Mr. Elwell lose $50,000 in an evening at bridge, and never bat an eye about it. He didn't know what it was to be nervous or afraid. He wouldn't have begged or pleaded with this fellow or made any promises. He would have pretended the whole thing was a joke, even if he knew it wasn't a joke. I can see him now, reaching down to the pile of letters the postman delivered, and opening one and commencing to read it, and saying to this fellow, 'Very well, old chap. If you're determined to shoot me, go ahead. While you're waiting, I'd better go over my mail.' And so the fellow shot him. To my mind, he was some woman's husband or maybe brother."

Most of the investigation and the questioning of witnesses was carried on in the house at 70th Street, which for nearly ten days was the scene of feverish comings and goings, of lights that burned all night. Dr. Charles Norris, the Medical Examiner, published his report to the effect that:

"The medical evidence supports the factual evidence, in that Elwell was shot some time between the delivery of the mail and the arrival of Mrs. Larsen.

It seems apparent that the wound was received from ten to fifteen minutes before Mrs. Larsen arrived at the house.

"The circle of powder marks about the bullet wound was three inches in diameter. Tests with a similar weapon show that the muzzle was held not more than three feet from his forehead and probably not more than one foot. Even assuming that the weapon was in the room, and that some misguided person secreted it before the arrival of detectives, it would be an awkward and unusual thing for a man to shoot himself directly through the center of the head. Suicide seems unlikely."

At this point District Attorney Swann, himself a gentleman of the old school, took personal charge of the inquiry. He permitted Joyce to stay with the case and he brought in another assistant named Dooling. Joyce and Dooling immediately began to bicker between themselves, but since the whole investigation turned into a masterpiece of incompetency, their bickerings seem inconsequential now.

A detective made a discovery in the cellar.

It was a hidden package containing a pink silk nightgown, a pink silk robe, and two pink silk slippers. Mrs. Larsen was brought to the mat and finally confessed that she had taken them out of Elwell's bedroom closet (missing the negligee that was found) and tucked them away in the basement before the detectives arrived that fatal morning. "I thought," she explained, "that it wouldn't look nice for them to be found in his bedroom."

Mr. Swann told the press that these articles belonged to a person whom they might call "Miss Wilson." And then, as Mrs. Larsen's composure suffered another breach, it was revealed that "Miss Wilson" had appeared breathless at the Elwell house at almost the hour when he was breathing his last in Bellevue.

Mrs Larsen: "She wanted to run upstairs and get her things. But the upstairs was full of detectives by now, and anyway I told her I had hidden the things. She said, 'Isn't this an awful accident?' And I said yes, it was, and she went away."

At this hour of the day, no newspapers had appeared with reports of the Elwell shooting. There was, of course, no radio. The assumption was that Mrs. Larsen, under the influence of her employer's gallantry, had telephoned the news to "Miss Wilson." She denied that she had been paid for her thoughtfulness or bribed to keep it silent.

More than a week passed before the insistent reporters drove Swann to the admission that "Miss Wilson" was, in reality, Viola Kraus. The District Attorney explained his subterfuge: "We are investigating a murder, not the frailties of womankind. I am loath to mention any lady's name. Was it not a Prince of Wales of whom his friends said, when he was called to testify upon a lady's honor, 'He lied like a gentleman'?"

With Viola Kraus now so intimately involved with Elwell's life, it was inevitable that her divorced husband, von Schlegell, should attract the attention of the authorities. He was questioned in the Elwell home for nearly five hours, and at the end Swann gave the reporters this account of the interview:

Von Schlegell, American-born, was an engineer. He had been educated at the University of Minnesota and was a partner in a New York firm. His meeting with Elwell and the Lewisohn party at the Ritz had been purely accidental. He did not remember the name of his companion of the evening. She was a Minneapolis girl who had got in touch with him when she came to New York.

He had, he said, delivered this young woman to her apartment at ten o'clock, following the Ritz dinner. Business required him to go to Atlantic City the next day, but his car had developed trouble. Late in the night he had taken it to his garage and insisted that it be repaired by morning. He had taken delivery of the car at about ten o'clock the morning of June 11, and started for Atlantic City. At Red Bank, the motor had quit again, and he had left the car there, going to Atlantic City by train. Having concluded his business, he had spent the night in a boardwalk hotel, taken the train to Red Bank, picked up his car, and driven to New York.

Under increasing attack from the press, Swann finally admitted that von Schlegell had not really denied knowing the name of the young woman in black. "I concealed her identity upon my own initiative," he said. "Enough names have been dragged through the mud in this case." He finally got around to saying that the girl was Elly Hope Anderson, the daughter of a prominent merchant in Minneapolis. She had been playing organ and studying voice in the East for some time. Swann accepted the statement she made to the press in Minneapolis:

"Von took me to my apartment at 10, directly from the Ritz. He didn't come in. I was leaving for home the next morning, but he asked me to come to his apartment for breakfast. I did go there, at about 8 o'clock. I left him about 9, to go to the Grand Central for my train."

Swann's people never let Captain Arthur Carey do very much but run errands. The inference was that the Police Department, necessary but a trifle unpolished, might cause embarrassment among the important names involved if given too much rein.

It goes without saying that nobody has ever been arrested and accused of the murder of Joseph Bowne Elwell.

The lens of time, however, brings these affairs into a clean focus. And a theory clamors from the record: Joseph Elwell did, indeed, commit suicide.

So it is possible to pose a hypothetical question:

Did Mrs. Larsen walk into the reception room that morning to discover that her godlike employer had killed himself? Did she see a pistol on the floor beside him? Did this spellbound woman think at that moment as she thought later, when she decided that pink silk things in Elwell's closet "would not look nice"? Did she think that it would be a shameful thing, no less, for the world to know that this paragon of mankind had taken his own life? And did she pick up the pistol and tuck it into her apron—whence it could be taken out again a little later and tucked into a pocketbook and carried away at the end of a dreadful day?

It is easy enough to reach the conclusion that the cigarette on the mantel was tossed there by Otten the milkman when he came into the room and was shaken by the sight of a bloody, dying man.

And it is easy to see how Joseph Elwell shot himself squarely in the middle of the forehead, as awkward and bizarre as that may seem at first thought. The next time you have an empty .45 automatic around the house, try holding it with both hands at arms length, and pointing it at your brow, and pressing the trigger with your thumb.

Be sure it is empty. Because it certainly would work.

HENRY MORTON ROBINSON

The Bird of Mars

You never hear a loud voice at a cock-fight. The sport is carried on in a whisper—a whisper that leaps secretively from the mouth of one cocker to another as they greet each other in the subterranean byways of the sport. Cock-fighting is forbidden by statute in every state in the union, yet there are more than ten thousand fighting-cocks in New York state alone, and approximately five hundred "mains" or tournaments take place in various parts of the country every Saturday night from December to May. Thrivingly, quietly —so quietly that sheriffs, news-hawks and reformers never hear of it—the breeding and fighting of cocks goes on all over the United States, and although a pit is occasionally raided, cock-fighting has attained such an underground momentum that it seems destined eventually to rise to the surface as a legitimate activity—the most colorful and exciting pound-for-pound sport in the world.

The smartest main I ever attended was held on the penthouse roof of a Park Avenue apartment; the host was a steamship magnate who wanted to pit his imported South American birds against an upstate breed of fowl produced by an artist friend of mine. The steamship man had some gorgeous birds, among them a gold and ruby-colored cock that might well have crowned the helmet of Mars himself. But gay plumage and the tense urgings of a dinner-jacketed crowd weren't enough for the South American birds to win on. The homely breed of White Hackles developed by my artist friend swept the penthouse decks in seven straight victories, and incidentally cleaned up more cash for him than he'll ever make in seven years of impressionistic painting.

More typical, perhaps, of American cock-fighting and the atmosphere that surrounds it, was the main I saw in an abandoned root-cellar somewhere in New Jersey. To this day I don't know exactly where that cellar is located. Twenty-four hours prior to the fight I had received a mysterious card informing me that a debate was to be held between Professor Polycarp and Dr. Johnson on a topic as yet unannounced, and that if I really wanted to hear the debate I should take the third left-turn after passing a truck with a blue tail-light parked on a certain road north of Closter. The third left-turn proved to be a dirt road slanting obliquely into the Jersey underbrush; for five miles it twisted and back-tracked, then came to a dead end in the middle of the woods. I doused my

March, 1934

headlights (caution is second-nature among coqueteurs) and in a few moments a young farmer bearing a lantern appeared at the side of the car. "This way to the debate," he grinned, leading me down a narrow path to the cockers' rendezvous. It was a gaunt mansarded house standing on the edge of a dismal field; not a crack of light could be seen through the heavily shuttered windows, not a sound of man or nature pierced the lugubrious silence. My guide led me to the rear of the house, tapped on a bulkhead door. It lifted eerily, I paid the admission fee of three dollars, then descended into the earthy-smelling darkness. Now I began to hear the reassuring murmur of human voices; a bolt scraped in front of me, a door was pushed open, and I could see in the center of a dimly-illuminated cellar a crowd of fifty persons bending intently over a spotlighted pit.

It was an assorted crowd of human beings, all male. A few of the spectators were wearing Chesterfields and imported derby hats, but the majority wore caps and corduroys. Clearly, however, caste counted nothing here. You might be a banker or a burglar the rest of the time, but now you were merely one of the cocking fraternity, interested in nothing except the fight which was about to begin.

I found a place at the rail and gazed down at the sunken pit covered with moist tanbark. Two handlers, both good yokel types, were "gaffing" the birds, that is, fastening bright steel spurs about two inches long to the birds' ankles. These gaffs are made of handforged, surgical steel and must be delicately adjusted by expert fingers if the cock is to wreak maximum havoc upon his adversary. While these adjustments were being made, I heard a quiet-eyed, carefully-barbered gentleman announce in a conversational tone that he was placing $5000 on his purple Grist Grady cock to defeat his opponent's russet-colored Ginger Buck. "Make it seventy-five hundred," sighed the owner of the Ginger Buck, a funereal fellow in a furlined overcoat. "Anything you say," murmured the other. Additional bets ranging from ten to ten hundred dollars were now made by various spectators. Very little actual talking was done. A lift of the finger, a nod of the head, and the bets were made. They paid, too, in cold cash. No checks, no I. O. U's, no welching at a cock-fight. The cocking code is as strict as the Stock Market regulations, and violators never have a second chance. . . .

The birds were now "breasted," that is, given a preliminary peck at each other while their legs and feathers were firmly held by handlers. Wings had already been clipped to a fighting minimum, combs and wattles pared off cleanly, so that the birds were nothing but beak, spur, and sinew, conditioned to steely hardness by long months of exercise and diet. Each bird weighed exactly 5 pounds, 6 ounces at the pitside scales. They were as evenly matched as human ingenuity could contrive, and the decisive factors of victory could be only those deep, mysterious elements that make one man, one horse, or one bird superior to another.

The cocks were now grounded in the center of the ring, and the fight was on. They feinted at each other like boxers, one-two, one-two, then the Ginger-

Buck lunged at his rival with a cunning, cruel stroke, so rapid and invisible that it made an adder's tongue look like an up-grade freight in motion. No human eye has ever seen a gaff strike home; no camera has ever recorded it. It is the fastest movement in the animal world, and you can only judge its speed and power by its effect on the bird that stops it. In this case the purple Grist Grady was knocked backward about two feet, and the Ginger Buck was all over him in a hail of beak and spurs. I thought it was curtains for the under bird, but he came off the ropes with a bounce, and carried the fight to his rival for a full sixty seconds of savage give-and-take. The punishment was terrific on both sides; the thudding impact of gaff on feathers sounded like a carpet-beater at work. I glanced at the chief backer of the Grist Grady cock, and had the strange feeling that he was thinking more about the bird's bravery than the money he was going to lose. For as sure as death he was going to lose it. The Ginger Buck was now playing a pizzicato solo on the purple rooster's breast; for eight mortal minutes the already-defeated Grist Grady took those whistling gaffs in every part of his body, until at last a lightning thrust of steel pierced his head and knocked him dead on the tanbark.

Tension, sharply released, slid out in long breaths from the spectators. A few mumbled words of praise for the dead cock, some congratulatory nods at the winning owner, and a low buzz of expectation as the handlers brought out the next pair of birds. I saw twelve more fights that night (there are generally thirteen fights to a man), but at no time did the tension relax or the combative tempo slacken. Some of the fights were over in a minute, others lasted half an hour, but there wasn't a single minute of stalling or faking during the entire show. The birds were in that pit for a single reason:—to fight till they were dead or victorious. And they apprehended that reason so perfectly that they seemed impatient of the necessary delays imposed upon them by their human handlers.

But all this, you may object, savors rather strongly of cruelty to animals, and suggests more than a hint of brutality among the men who follow the sport of cock-fighting. Well, no matter what your preconceived opinions are on this subject, the charges of cruelty and brutality cannot be sustained. For the simple truth about cocks is this: *they love to fight!* They will leave their mates and food to give battle to any adversary, no matter how formidable. The bravery of the cock is unbelievable; he will fly at a police dog or a condor with equal ferocity, and will shuffle a bull-snake to death in thirty seconds. I have seen a gallant cock rout a fox who thought, quite erroneously, that he was going to have chicken for supper. Many cock-fanciers will tell you that the courage of a fighting-cock is unmatched by anything in the world, and that even the gored bull is inferior to him in point of fearlessness.

It must also be realized that the cock is practically insensible to pain, his nervous system being so constituted that he either doesn't feel it, or is utterly indifferent to its effects. For example, a cock mortally maimed and merely hanging together in a mass of shreds, will eagerly gobble corn as though he expected to live another twenty years. Or he will pull himself together for one last despairing thrust at an opponent just at the moment that his handlers are mercifully dispatching him. A cock is apparently a cross between a chunk of brass and an Iroquois warrior: you can't hurt him, but if you do, he won't let you know anything about it. Gameness is his principal characteristic, the very essence of his being—so closely interwoven with life itself that the one cannot expire until the other is dead. With him, the life force is synonymous with pugnacity, and it would be depriving him of his major function if he were not permitted to fight.

Inevitably, certain types and strains of fighting-cocks are superior to others; these strains, well known to all breeders of the fowl, are carefully crossed and blended to produce the three desirable attributes of speed, courage, and endurance. Not even the breeding of race-horses is more delicately calculated, for no horse now racing has a pedigree as lengthy as some of the more famous breeds of game fowl. A recorded genealogy of three hundred generations is not uncommon; thus the intelligent breeder of gamecocks knows exactly what has gone into his birds, and can prefigure with Mendelian accuracy the results of any given combination. Let us suppose, for instance, that he wishes to add poundage and endurance to a plucky but physically-enfeebled line. He will begin by crossing his stock with the magnificent Asile strain from India, and immediately the offspring will be noticeably heavier and stronger. But, since the Indian cock fights at a much slower tempo than our western birds, this offspring will lack the necessary speed. Therefore it is essential to dilute the Asile blood-content by repeatedly mixing it with occidental stock specially selected for swiftness; probably as little as $\frac{1}{64}$ Asile will give the best results. But as so frequently happens with the plans of men, Nature sometimes take a mysterious hand, and whole flocks of expensively-bred birds go to seed overnight. No one knows why, yet suddenly you have a tribe of heavy-moving, dull-spirited birds on your hands. The best thing to do then is to give away your stock and start all over.

The dream of every breeder is, of course, to produce a super-cock—one that fuses all the known virtues into a single invincible line. Many breeders have almost succeeded; the Shawlnecks, the Roundheads, and the Irish Reds can always be depended upon to slash away until they have beaten everything in sight—sometime including their own handlers. For every now and then a "man-fighter" is developed—a bird so ornery that it will try to cripple its handler with a wicked cut at his wrist or ankles. These cocks are comparable to the one lion in a thousand that cannot be trained by man, or to the temperamental filly who slings her hoofs at the stable-boy from sheer perversity.

The cocking gentry are great gamblers, and there is something about a cockfight that inflames the coolest blood to a betting fever. There are reasons for this, of course. For one thing the game is absolutely on the level. It is impossible to dope a cock or bribe a handler, for in either instance the knavery would be apparent to the most stupid observer Furthermore, the cock cannot take instructions, and would not if he could. It is his single-tracked idea to get out there and fight till he hasn't a beak to peck with: double-crossing his backers isn't in his line. Lastly—and this is true of every cocker I know—the men who breed, own, and handle the birds are personally *fond* of them. They have such affectionate confidence in their feathered charges that they gladly throw the whole weight of their private fortune, whether it's ten dollars or ten thousand, into the pit with them. It's gambling, sure enough, but it's not like throwing inanimate dice or spinning a mechanical wheel. You have no personal emotion about these devices, but when you've raised a plucky cock from chickenhood, you get attached to the brave little beggar, and want to back him with everything you own. Sometimes, to your sorrow, you do. But then again, a single five-pound gamecock may bring plenty of new dollars home to roost. There is a breed of fowl known as Mortgage-Lifters, much honored in the Southern States for the cash they have won for owners who backed them with a deed to the old plantation.

As long as men admire stamina, beauty, and bravery in the creatures they breed, the Bird of Mars will be an undying favorite. Cocks are feathered fighting machines, so brilliantly colored and so marvelously constructed, that they fascinate the eye and charm the spirit of all who behold them. At present there is a vast reservoir of mawkish and misplaced sentimentality impounded in the American mind concerning the cruelty of cock-fighting, but along with other mistaken notions of morality, this prejudice is bound to evaporate. And as for the brutalizing effect upon the spectators. I can only point out that the grit and invincibility displayed by any cock, in any pit, might well be used as a model by almost any human being especially in these trying days when tenacity and courage are most needed and most rare.

FRANKLIN P. ADAMS

Proposition: Am I a Good Father?

Am I a good father? No. Corollary: Is my wife a good mother? No.

Including parents, there are six in our family, so I took a poll, asking the question posed in the title.

Yes, four: No, one: Undecided, one.

I was the undecided one. The one who voted No in the poll was Mrs. A., though I can imagine her saying, if she reads this, "Leave me out of this." She won't read it, for she reads only Edna St. Vincent Millay and the radio section of the Sunday New York *Herald Tribune*. And books on psychoanalysis. I should venture that she is a better authority on her Jung than on her young.

There are so many varieties of goodness that I beg leave to revise, as they say in Congress, my opening speech. In many ways, I am a good father. I have four children, and in at least one way that is better than most fathers are doing. And I certainly spend more time with my children than the usual father who leaves the house before they're up and comes home when they're in bed. Or, if they are grown, and at home, he leaves before they're awake, and when he comes home they've gone out.

I am not like that at all. For one thing, we live in the country, and of my Gainful Occupations only one requires my physical presence in New York. So I'm at home, keeping—since fuel-oil rationing—the grate fires burning.

Considerable water has flowed over the dam, thanks to the Bridgeport Hydraulic Company, since King Lear (a rotten papa if I ever read of one) made his celebrated observation about the acuteness of a serpent's tooth and the ingratitude of offspring. For nowadays the gratitude is on the other foot. It is Papa who is grateful to the kids for their very existence.

By the way, I don't know how it is in other homes, but my children have two antipathies. They dislike the apellation Dad or Daddy; and they don't like to be called by their given names. In fact, one of my boys has discovered that boys who always are called by their given names are more likely to be unloved, both at home and in school. Nor is it just because my children have polysyllabic names: Anthony, Timothy, Persephone and Jonathan. They sign even their school papers with their diminutives or nicknames. Anthony is Tat, Timothy is Tim, Persephone is Puffy and Jonathan is Jacky. Technically and potentially delinquent, and practically and kinetically lovable, all of them.

July, 1945

I do not delude myself with the notion that a good father has the complete confidence of his children. My father, who probably had the reputation of paternal goodness, as I have, used to tell me to tell him my troubles. And I know now that nobody knew the trouble I seen. Nobody knew but me. Why, I never dreamed of telling him the tragedies of my adolescence; the jealousies, envies, loves, fears and hatreds that fester in school and college. And thereby I learned a lesson.

And this is where, it seems to me, I am a good father. I never ask, or have asked them to tell me the woes that beset them—daily woes and those they consider permanent. I tell them mine, and let the nature of children take its course. Eventually they tell me a lot; with one of my boys we exchange what he calls p's. of l.—problems of life. Of course, I am no fool. I know that words mean different things to fathers than to children. Even Theatre. To me a theatre was, and is, a place where a play is performed. To them, as to the vast majority of Americans, a theatre is a movie house. What we call a play, they call a stage play, and few children—and comparatively few adults—ever have seen a stage play. Me, I'd rather see a third-rate play than what is known as a good movie. And when it comes to *Life with Father* or *Oklahoma!*, no movie could match them. Nothing in a movie can compare with the thrill of a rising curtain. Three of my children have seen a good many stage plays. During the first year of *Life with Father* I saw it with my two aged children, then thirteen and twelve. As Mr. Day stormed about, objecting to the coffee, making the waitress cry and calling his guests "those damn gypsies," my son whispered, "Papa, he's just like you." And added, "And he's right, too."

There are externalities that divide fathers and sons. Two days after my first son was born, I observed that it was strange to be born at a time when he will never know what life was like before there were tabloid newspapers, radios and airplanes—things taken for granted. When I first saw the Woods electric horseless carriage speed up Grand Boulevard, Chicago, we all knew that Nothing Would Come of It. And though I got A in Physics, I do not yet understand the telephone, the radio, or even why a motorcar goes.

Once, when the boys were little, and I was reading to them about George Washington, one of them asked, "Did you know him?" And while that gap tends to close up, it never heals, and the father who says that he and his son are chums, lies. Friendly, joyous and happy in each other's society—yes. But Pals, Buddies, etc? No.

In that my children never have Cried for Bread, or Gone about in Rags, I have been a good father, or rather a good provider. When the boys emerged from public grammar school, they went to New England prep schools which insist on payment in tender legaler than hay. It may have been better for them if life had been less easy for them, though each of them probably has a notion that he has the toughest lot of all his young acquaintances. And that is one of the ways wherein I don't know whether I am being a good or a bad father. I probably never shall know. I doubt that Poverty is a Blessing or that Plenty is a Curse; or vice versa.

I do not lie to my children, and I doubt that they lie, or at any rate, fail to tell the truth. They do not, like some persons of any age, give the answer they think the querist wants. Never shall I forget when I left them, boys of five and four, in Gramercy Park for an hour. They were indignant because they had heard the attendant tell a little boy that the goldfish would bite the boy's hands off. There only comment was, "That is *not* true."

Early in my fatherhood I learned that it is wise not to laugh at a child who says something comical; for one thing it makes him self-conscious; and for another he then tries, in order to win parental approbation, to be comical. For example, in the early days of *Show Boat* my oldest boy, then five, heard the Hammerstein-Kern song about the Mississippi so frequently that it was Old Man Mama, Old Man Papa, Old Man Delia and Old Man everything. And one day, watching the grass being cut, he sang:

> Ol' man mower,
> He don't know nothing,
> He just keeps mowing a lawn.

My second boy, who at four had watched a calving and a foal, was lying on the bed beside his mother about a month after the birth of his brother Jacky. He heard the baby crying, upstairs. "Ma," he said, "are we going to have any more children?" "I don't know, Timmy," she said. "Well," he said, tapping her on the abdomen, "is anybody in there now?" . . . I was a good father not to laugh; and Mrs. A did a good dead-pan act. When the boys use profanity or obscenities, I do not rebuke them with a "Never say that again." My theory is that prohibition glorifies such things in the adolescent mind.

In their early schooldays there were parents' meetings about what should be done with children and the radio. It seems that the school children listened to Dick Tracy and Junior G-Men and other bang-bang programs whose names I have forgotten. My theory was to let them alone; that (a) it soon would bore them, and (b) it would do them no harm. For I think that parents tend to exaggerate the harm—or even the good—of anything children hear on the air, see in the movies, or read. My parents were exercised because some of us went every Saturday afternoon to see the melodramas (twenty-five cents) at Havlin's Theatre. Soon they palled, and we all began going to the Olympic Theatre (Continuous Vaudeville—10-20-30). It seems to me that I learned a lot at those variety shows, though it now runs to the ability to sing the songs I heard there, and I learned nothing at Sam T. Jack's Madison Street Opera House, a burlesque house where the knee was considered uptown. Those shows were tiresome, but I still think that Ward and Vokes, Weber and Fields, and Matthews and Bulger at the Olympic were great things to have seen.

In my early days I read the Alger books. I took seriously their lesson—that Industry and Thrift would lead to Wealth and Happiness. Well, I have been industrious, unthrifty, debtful and happy at least fifty-one per cent of the time. But I brought all the Alger books home one day—and the older boys read ten or twelve and let the rest go. "They're all alike," was their criticism. That never occurred to me when I read them. My youngest son now has read *Ragged Dick* three time.

I grew up after the Frank Merriwell era, and I never have read one; but I read Nick Carter, five cents, erroneously referred to as Dime Novels. I don't remember them, but I recall being frightened at the pictures of Injun Joe and of Tom Sawyer and Becky Thatcher in the cave. And my greatest and most fascinating fright was to look at the Doré pictures in our *The Rime of the Ancient Mariner*. Especially the ones, "Yea, slimy things did crawl with legs upon the slimy sea," and "the Albatross about my neck was hung." And my children, who wouldn't give those pictures a tumble, were frightened when the Shadow, according to them, said, "The weed of crime bears bittah fruit! Ha!" The young ones now hear *Bulldog Drummond* and *The Thin Man*. Harm? Nuts! —a catchword the tough boys of the 90's never said.

There is a popular impression to the effect the son and the mother, and the daughter and the father, are the affinities. My daughter, thirteen, while she tells me her secrets, tells most of them also to the girls in the school bus. Her allowance, twenty-five cents per week, goes for movie magazines and for postage to write to stars for photographs. She has a deskful of such trumperies— trumperies to me, romantic triumphs to her. *Et ego in Arcadia!*

For did I not have a signed photograph of Fritzi Scheff in *Babette*? Did I not have one of May Irwin, and forge her signature? Did I not cut, from *Munsey's Magazine*, the pictures of Maxine Elliott, Mary Mannering, Virginia Harned, and—a hot number—Cissy Fitzgerald? Who is Papa to tell Puffy that she is foolish about movie stars?

Incidentally, I am a good father in that I have liked to see my children grow up—two of them, at fifteen, already were taller than my five feet ten; and now they are well over six feet. I am told that most parents try, unconsciously perhaps, to keep the children babies as long as possible, thinking—any psychiatrist will tell you—thereby to arrest their own inevitable senescence. And while it seems not so long ago that the feet of those boys could not touch the floor of a car, it is a joy to have them now drive me—each of them knowing more about the inside of a car than I know or ever shall know. My darling, they are growing old, and though their mother has no silver threads among the gold, I've, alas, alas, alack! silver threads among the black.

When the orison to the dice is accompanied by, "My baby needs a pair of shoes," the prayer is simple to answer. My children need four pairs of shoes at a time. And, with rationing, this good father hasn't had a new pair since 1937. ... By the time this appears, my oldest boy will be wearing shoes bestowed upon him by a grateful government.

Now, none of my children is the student their Old Man was. It happened that I attended a preparatory school in which you did well or got out. My offspring, it seems to me, barely hang on. I wish I cared more than I do. I care, but I do not worry. And while I know that all boys who do badly won't be U. S. Grant, and all boys who get fired won't be Poe or Whistler, I still do not worry. All our kids have one negative trait: they have no meannesses.

Among the few times that I felt like a good father was one evening when they had come down to the train to meet me. I detrained with an old newspaper friend, Mr. Herbert L. Jones. The boys threw their arms around me, almost knocking me down. "What's the idea?" asked Jones. "We like him," they justified. . . . I felt good for two days.

My attitude toward them, and their education, may be shown by a poem addressed to my boys:

> Gentlemen, I love and like you,
> Caring little for your I.Q.

◄───►

Attorney for the Defense

EDITOR'S NOTE: *The late Clarence Darrow was 79 when this achieved print. Active practice was definitely over for the lawyer who never, in more than fifty years at the bar, appeared on the side of the prosecution, who never, in scores of capital cases, had a client executed. We gave him a fairly pedestrian assignment, asking him to write a piece giving a few pointers on jury-picking. It was greater luck than we merited to receive in return this winged answer to profounder questions than we had the wit to ask. For here is no less a thing than a golden epitome of all the wisdom that has accrued to an ever-youthful spirit in the late evening of a well spent life. Far more than a mere footnote to the tricks of his trade, it is a philosophic summation of the practical answers to any present day Pilate who might jesting ask "What is Justice?" It is an answer wise though witty, compassionate though cynical, the answer of the man who said of the great Governor Altgeld what might equally well be said of himself: "Even admirers have seldom understood the real character of this great human man. It was not a callous heart that so often led him to brave the most violent and malicious hate: it was not a callous heart, it was a devoted soul . . . that spoke for the poor, the oppressed, the captive and the weak."*

THE audience that storms the box-office of the theater to gain entrance to a sensational show is small and sleepy compared with the throng that crashes the court house door when something concerning real life and death is to be laid bare to the public.

Everyone knows that the best portrayals of life are tame and sickly when matched with the realities. For this reason, the sophisticated Romans were wont to gather at the Colosseum to feast their eyes and other senses on fountains of real blood and await breathlessly the final thrust. The court room is a modern arena in which the greatest thrills follow closely on each other. If the combat concerns human life it presents an atmosphere and setting not unlike those cruel and bloody scenes of ancient Rome. The judge wears the same flowing robe with all of the dignity and superiority he can command. This sets him apart from his fellowmen and is designed to awe and intimidate and to impress the audience with seeming wisdom oftener than with kindliness and compassion.

May, 1936

One cannot help wondering what happens to the pomp and pretense of the wearer while the cloak is in the wash, or while changing into a maturer, more monarchical mantle, as his bench becomes a throne, or when he strolls along the street in file with the "plain clothes" people.

When court opens, the bailiff intones some voodoo singsong words in ominous voice that carries fear and respect at the opening of the rite. The court room is full of staring men and women shut within closed doors, guarded by officials wearing uniforms to confound the simple inside the sacred precinct. This dispels all hope of mercy to the unlettered, the poor and helpless, who scarcely dare express themselves above a whisper in any such forbidding place.

The stage, the arena, the court, are alike in that each has its audience thirsting to drink deeply of the passing show. Those playing the parts vie for success and use whatever skill and talent they possess. An actor may fumble his lines, but a lawyer needs to be letter-perfect, at least, he has to use his wits, and he may forget himself, and often does, but never for a moment can he lose sight of his client.

Small wonder that ambitious, imaginative youths crowd the profession of law. Here, they feel, they, themselves, will find the opportunity to play a real part in the comedies as well as the tragedies of life. Everyone, no matter how small his chance may be, tries to hold the center of some stage where the multitude will scan his every move. To most lads it seems as though the courts were organized to furnish them a chance to bask in the public eye. In this field the adventure of life will never pall, but prove interesting, exciting and changeful to the end. Not only will he have the destinies of men to protect and preserve, but his own standing and success to create.

Chancery cases are not especially interesting nor exciting, however. These are supposed to be heard by a judge. He listens long enough to feel satisfied that the case promises to consume considerable time and work and interfere with many hours of leisure, so he refers it to a "Master in Chancery," a lawyer-friend of his own appointment, who is paid by fees that come directly from the litigants; the Master in Chancery employs a court reporter who takes the evidence in shorthand while the Master may take a nap in an adjoining office. After the client's resources are exhausted by the court reporters and Masters in Chancery, the documents are locked up in a safe to await the blowing of Gabriel's horn.

If it is a real case, criminal or civil, it usually is tried by a jury with the assistance and direction of the judge. In that event, every moment counts, and neither the lawyers nor the audience, or even the court, goes to sleep. If it is a criminal case, or even a civil one, it is not the law alone or the facts themselves that determine the result. Always the element of luck and chance looms large. A jury of twelve men is watching not only the evidence but the attitude of each lawyer, and the parties involved, in all their moves. Every step is fraught with doubt, if not mystery.

Selecting a jury is of the utmost importance. So far as possible, the lawyer should know both sides of the case. If the client is a landlord, a banker, or a manufacturer, or one of that type, then jurors sympathetic to that class will be wanted in the box; a man who looks neat, and trim and smug. He will be sure to guard your interests as he would his own. His entire environment has taught him that all real values are measured in cash, and he knows no other worth. Every knowing lawyer seeks for a jury of the same sort of men as his client; men who will be able to imagine themselves in the same situation and realize what verdict the client wants.

Lawyers are just as carefully concerned about the likes and dislikes, the opinions and fads of judges as of jurors. All property rights are much safer in the hands of courts than of jurors. Every lawyer who represents the poor avoids a trial by the court.

Choosing jurors is always a delicate task. The more a lawyer knows of life, human nature, psychology, and the reactions of the human emotions, the better he is equipped for the subtle selection of his so-called "twelve men, good and true." In this undertaking, everything pertaining to the prospective juror needs be questioned and weighed; his nationality, his business, religion, politics, social standing, family ties, friends, habits of life and thought; the books and newspapers he likes and reads, and many more matters that combine to make a man; all of these qualities and experiences have left their effect on ideas, beliefs and fancies that inhabit his mind. Understanding of all this cannot be obtained too bluntly. It usually requires finesse, subtlety and guesswork. Involved in it all is the juror's method of speech, the kind of clothes he wears, the style of haircut, and above all, his business associates, residence and origin.

To the ordinary observer, a man is just a man. To the student of life and human beings, every pose and movement is a part of the personality and the man. There is no sure rule by which one can gauge any person. A man may seem to be of a certain mold, but, a wife, a friend, or an enemy, entering into his life, may change his most vital views, desires and attitudes, so that he will hardly recognize himself as the man he once seemed to be.

It is obvious that if a litigant discovered one of his dearest friends in the jury panel he could make a close guess as to how certain facts, surrounding circumstances, and suppositions, would affect his mind and action; but as he has no such acquaintance with the stranger before him, he must weigh the prospective juror's words, manner of speech and, in fact, hastily and cautiously "size him up" as best he can. The litigants and their lawyers are supposed to want justice, but, in reality, there is no such thing as justice, either in or out of court. In fact, the word cannot be defined. So, for lack of proof, let us assume that the word "justice" has a meaning, and that the common idea of the definition is correct, without even seeking to find out what is the common meaning. Then, how do we reach justice through the courts? The lawyer's idea of justice is a verdict for his client, and really this is the sole end for which he aims.

In spite of the power that the courts exercise over the verdict of a jury, still the finding of the twelve men is very important, sometimes conclusive. It goes without saying that lawyers always do their utmost to get men on the jury who are apt to decide in favor of their clients. It is not the experience of jurors, neither is it their brain power, that is the potent influence in their decisions. A skillful lawyer does not tire himself hunting for learning or intelligence in the box; if he knows much about man and his making, he knows that all beings act from emotions and instincts, and that reason is not a motive factor. If deliberation counts for anything, it is to retard decision. The nature of the man himself is the element that determines the juror's bias for or against his fellowman. Assuming that a juror is not a half-wit, his intellect can always furnish fairly good reasons for following his instincts and emotions. Many irrelevant issues in choosing jurors are not so silly as they seem. Matters that apparently have nothing to do with the discussion of a case often are of the greatest significance.

In the last analysis, most jury trials are contests between the rich and poor. If the case concerns money, it is apt to be a case of damages for injuries of some sort claimed to have been inflicted by some one. These cases are usually defended by insurance companies, railroads, or factories. If a criminal case, it is practically always the poor who are on trial.

The most important point to learn is whether the prospective juror is humane. This must be discovered in more or less devious ways. As soon as "the court" sees what you want, he almost always blocks the game. Next to this, in having more or less bearing on the question, is the nationality, politics, and religion, of the person examined for the jury. If you do not discover this, all your plans may go awry. Whether you are handling a damage suit, or your client is charged with the violation of law, his attorney will try to get the same sort of juror.

Let us assume that we represent one of "the underdogs" because of injuries received, or, because of an indictment brought by what the prosecutors name themselves, "the state." Then what sort of men will we seek? An Irishman is called into the box for examination. There is no reason for asking about his religion; he is Irish; that is enough. We may not agree with his religion, but it matters not; his feelings go deeper than any religion. You should be aware that he is emotional, kindly and sympathetic. If he is chosen as a juror, his imagination will place him in the dock; really, he is trying himself. You would be guilty of malpractice if you got rid of him, except for the strongest reasons.

An Englishman is not so good as an Irishman, but still, he has come through a long tradition of individual rights, and is not afraid to stand alone; in fact, he is never sure that he is right unless the great majority is against him. The German is not so keen about individual rights except where they concern his own way of life; liberty is not a theory, it is a way of living. Still, he wants to do what is right, and he is not afraid. He has not been among us long, his ways are fixed by his race, his habits are still in the making. We need inquire no further. If he is a Catholic, then he loves music and art; he must be emotional, and will want to help you; give him a chance.

If a Presbyterian enters the jury box and carefully rolls up his umbrella, and calmly and critically sits down, let him go. He is cold as the grave; he knows right from wrong, although he seldom finds anything right. He believes in John Calvin and eternal punishment. Get rid of him with the fewest possible words before he contaminates the others; unless you and your clients are Presbyterians you probably are a bad lot, and even though you may be a Presbyterian, your client most likely is guilty.

If possible, the Baptists are more hopeless than the Presbyterians. They, too, are apt to think that the real home of all outsiders is Sheol, and you do not want them on the jury, and the sooner they leave the better.

The Methodists are worth considering; they are nearer the soil. Their religious emotions can be transmuted into love and charity. They are not half bad, even though they will not take a drink; they really do not need it so much as some of their competitors for the seat next to the throne. If chance sets you down between a Methodist and a Baptist, you will move toward the Methodist to keep warm.

Beware of the Lutherans, especially the Scandinavians; they are almost always sure to convict. Either a Lutheran or Scandinavian is unsafe, but if both-in-one, plead your client guilty and go down the docket. He learns about sinning and punishing from the preacher, and dares not doubt. A person who disobeys must be sent to Hell; he has God's word for that.

As to Unitarians, Universalists, Congregationalists, Jews and other agnostics, don't ask them too many questions; keep them anyhow; especially Jews and agnostics. It is best to inspect a Unitarian, or a Universalist, or a Congregationalist, with some care, for they may be prohibitionists; but never the Jews and the real agnostics! And, do not, please, accept a prohibitionist: he is too solemn and holy and dyspeptic. He knows your client would not have been indicted unless he were a drinking man, and any one who drinks is guilty of something probably much worse than he is charged with, although it is not set out in the indictment. Neither would he have employed you as his lawyer had he not been guilty.

I have never experimented much with Christian Scientists; they are too serious for me. Somehow, solemn people seem to think that pleasure is wicked. Only the gloomy and dyspeptic can be trusted to convict. Shakespeare knew: "Yond' Cassius has a lean and hungry look; he thinks too much; such men are dangerous." You may defy all the rest of the rules if you can get a man who laughs. Few things in this world are of enough importance to warrant considering them seriously. So, by all means, choose a man who laughs. A juror who laughs hates to find anyone guilty.

Never take a wealthy man on a jury. He will convict, unless the defendant is accused of violating the anti-trust law, selling worthless stocks or bonds, or something of that kind. Next to the Board of Trade, for him, the Penitentiary is the most important of all public buildings. These imposing structures stand for Capitalism. Civilization could not possibly exist without them. Don't take a man because he is a "good" man; this means nothing. You should find out what he is good for. Neither should a man be accepted because he is a bad sort. There are too many ways of being good or bad. If you are defending, you want imaginative individuals. You are not interested in the morals of the juror. If a man is instinctively kind and sympathetic, take him.

Then, too, there are the women. These are now in the jury box. A new broom sweeps clean. It leaves no speck on the floor or under the bed, or in the darkest corners of life. To these new jurors, the welfare of the state depends on the verdict. It will be so for many years to come. The chances are that it would not have made the slightest difference to the state if all cases had been decided the other way. It might, however make a vast difference to the unfortunates facing cruel, narrow-minded jurors who pass judgment on their fellowmen. To the defendants it might have meant the fate of life rather than death.

But, what is one life more or less in the general spawning? It may float away on the tide, or drop to the depths of oblivion, broken, crushed and dead. The great sea is full of embryo lives ready to take the places of those who have gone before. One more unfortunate lives and dies as the endless stream flows on, and little it matters to the wise judges who coldly pronounce long strings of words in droning cadence; the victims are removed, they come and go and the judges keep on chanting senseless phrases laden with doom upon the bowed heads of those before them. The judge is as unconcerned about the actual meaning of it all as the soughing wind rustling the leaves of a tree just outside the court house door.

Women still take their new privilege seriously. They are all puffed up with the importance of the part they feel they play, and are sure they represent a great step forward in the world. They believe that the sex is co-operating in a great cause. Like the rest of us, they do not know which way is forward and which is backward, or whether either one is any way at all. Luckily, as I feel, my services were almost over when women invaded the jury box.

A few years ago I became interested in a man charged with selling some brand of intoxicant in a denatured land that needed cheering. I do not know whether he sold it or not. I forgot to ask him. I viewed the case with mixed feelings of pity and contempt, for, as Omar philosophized, "I wonder often what the vintners buy one-half so precious as the stuff they sell?" When I arrived on the scene, the court room looked ominous with women jurors. I managed to get rid of all but two, while the dismissed women lingered around in the big room waiting for the victory, wearing solemn faces and white ribbons. The jury disagreed. In the second trial there were four women who would not budge from their seats, or their verdict. Once more I went back to the case with distrust and apprehension. The number of women in the jury box had grown to six. All of them were unprejudiced. They said so. But everyone connected with the case was growing tired and skeptical, so we concluded to call it a draw. This was my last experience with women jurors. I formed a fixed opinion that they were absolutely dependable, but I did not want them.

Whether a jury is a good one or a bad one depends on the point of view. I have always been an attorney for the defense. I can think of nothing, not even war, that has brought so much misery to the human race as prisons. And all of it is so futile!

I once spent a winter on the shores of the Mediterranean Sea. In front of my windows, four fishermen were often wearily trudging back and forth, and slowly dragging a long net across the sand. When it was safely landed, a few small, flop-ping fish disclosed the results of their labors. These were scattered dying on the beach, while the really worthwhile fishes were left in the sea, which somehow reminded me of our courts and juries, and other aims and efforts of optimistic men and their idle undertakings, and disheartening results.

Judges and jurors are like the rest of humans. Now and then some outstanding figures will roll up their sleeves, as it were, and vigorously set to work to reform the courts and get an efficient administration of justice. This will be ably seconded by the newspapers, lashing courts and jurors, past, present and prospective, into a spasm of virtue that brings down the innocent and guilty together, assuming always that there are innocent and guilty. Then, for a time, every defendant is convicted; and soon the campaign reaches the courts; after ruining a few lives and reputations, the frenzy is over, and life goes on smoothly and tranquilly as before.

When I was a boy in the country, one of the standard occupations was whittling. It became as mechanical as breathing. Since then I have decided that this is as good a way to live as any other. Life depends on the automatic taking in and letting out of breath, but in no way is it lengthened or made happier by deep thinking or wise acting. The one big word that stands over courts and other human activities is FUTILITY.

The courts may be unavailing, lawyers stupid, and both as dry as dust, but the combination makes for something interesting and exciting, and it opens avenues that seem to lead somewhere. Liberty, lives, fortunes, often are at stake, and appeal for assistance and mercy rend the air for those who care to hear. In an effort to help, often a casual remark may determine a seemingly vital situation, when perhaps the remark, of all the palaver, was the least important one breathed forth. In all questions men are frequently influenced by some statement which, spoken at the eventful time, determines fate. The most unforeseen, accidental meetings sometimes result in seemingly new and strangely fateful family lines. In fact, all that occurs in life is an endless sequence of events resulting from the wildest chance.

Amongst the twelve in a jury box, are all degrees of alertness, all sorts of ideas, and a variety of emotions; and the lawyers, too, are important factors in the outcome. They are closely observed by the jurors. They are liked, or disliked. Mayhap because of what they say, or how they speak, or pronounce their words, or part their hair. It may be that a lawyer is disliked because he talks too little, or too much; more often the latter. But a lawyer of subtlety should know when to stop, and when to go on, and how far to go. As a rule, he must not seem to be above the juror, nor below him. He must not too obviously strive for effect. He often meets baffling situations not easily explained. Sometimes it is better for him to talk of something else. Explanations must not be too fantastic, or ridiculous. It does no harm to admit the difficulty of the situation, to acknowledge that this circumstance or that seems against him. Many facts point to guilt, but in another light these facts may appear harmless.

Lawyers are apt to interpret deeds and motives as they wish them to appear. As a matter of fact, most actions are subject to various inferences, sometimes quite improbable, but nonetheless true. Identifications show common examples of mistakes. Many men are in prison and some are sent to death through mistaken identifications. One needs but recall the countless errors he, himself, has made. How many have met some person whom they believed to be an old-time friend, and have found themselves greeting a total stranger? This is a common mistake made in restaurants and other public places. Many identifications in court are made from having seen a person but once, and under conditions not critical. Many are made from descriptions and photographs, and urged on by detectives, lawyers, and others vitally interested in the results. From all of this it is easy to see that many are convicted who are guiltless of crime. In situations of strong agitation, acquittals are rare, and sentences made long and barbarous and inhuman.

The judge is, of course, an important part of the machinery and administration of the court. Like carpenters, and lawyers, bricklayers, and saloon-keepers, they are not all alike. No two of them have the same fitness for their positions. No two have the same education; no two have the same natural understanding of themselves and their fellowman, or are gifted with the same discernment and balance. Not that judges are lacking in knowledge of law. The ordinary rules for the administration of law are rather simple and not difficult to follow. But judges should be students of life, even more than of law. Biology and psychology, which form the basis of understanding human conduct, should be taken into account. Without a fair knowledge of the mechanism of man, and the motives and urges that govern his life, it is idle to venture to fathom a situation; but, with some knowledge, officers and the public can be most useful in preserving and protecting those who most need such help. The life of almost any unfortunate, if rightly understood, can be readjusted to some plan of order and system, instead of left to drift on to ruin, the victim of ignorance, hatred and chance.

If the physician so completely ignored natural causes as the lawyers and judges, the treatment of disease would be relegated to witchcraft and magic, and the dungeon and rack would once more hold high carnival in driving devils out of the sick and afflicted. Many of the incurable victims of crime are like those who once were incurable victims of disease; they are the product of vicious and incompetent soothsayers who control their destinies. Every human being, whether parent, teacher, physician, or prosecutor, should make the comfort and happiness of their dependents their first concern. Now and then some learned courts take a big view of life, but scarcely do they make an impression until some public brainstorm drives them back in their treatment of crime to the methods of sorcery and conjury.

No scientific attitude toward crime can be adopted until lawyers, like physicians and scientists, recognize that cause and effect determine the conduct of men.

When lawyers and courts, and laymen, accept the scientific theory which the physicians forced upon the world long years ago, then men will examine each so-called delinquency until they discover its cause, and then learn how to remove the cause. This requires sympathy, humanity, love of one's fellowman, and a strong faith in the power of knowledge and experience to conquer the maladies of men. The Forum of the lawyers may then grow smaller, the court house may lose its spell, but the world will profit a thousandfold by a kindlier and more understanding relation toward all humankind.

JIMMY CANNON

◄──►

This Prize-Fight Racket

THE fight racket is the swill barrel of sports. It is a suburb of the underworld and the money handlers of this foul game are often despicable scoundrels who will do anything that brings in a buck. There is a similarity between some managers of fighters and those gentlemen who supervise the working schedules of prostitutes. They both profit from another's agony and the one with the talent who does the work is frequently shortchanged. Getting caught is the only violation of ethics recognized by many in either of these branches of the amusement business. But a big difference is a guy can go to jail for arranging the appointments of a streetwalker while a pug's guardian is licensed by the state to practice a calling which is legitimate in the opinion of the law. But if what happens in a ring occurs in a saloon it is a crime and those connected with it can be booked for assault. It seldom happens due to the souvenirs customarily given away free of charge to policemen who attend brawls in taverns. The double sawbuck is the customary memento presented to patrolmen present at such functions, although many bar and grill owners insist a fin has been added to this since all this talk about inflation.

I do not agree with those philosophers of the muscle who claim prize fighting is a healthy form of exercise which strengthens young bodies and creates character in the hearts of the innocent participants. It is a filthy enterprise and if you stay in it long enough your mind will become a concert hall where Chinese music never stops playing. Old fighters who do not go insane are considered fortunate and those who leave the ring with breakfast money are exceptional. Smart ex-fighters are those who do not have to check into the almshouse when they are through and have managed to remain sane enough to do a night watchman's job. It is a wonderful pastime and if I had a son who wanted to be a prize fighter I would beg him to go into a nice respectable business such as safeblowing or purse-grabbing.

The law permits a manager to cut a third out of his fighter's purses for himself. It is an immense clip when you compare it to the ten per cent a theatrical agent takes out of an actor's salary. I have yet to hear a ham admit there was an agent who earned his end of the deal. But it is seldom that a fighter is able to escape with two-thirds of the money he bleeds for as the fifty per-cent slice is the grab most managers demand. Very few of them operate alone because they give away pieces of their guys in exchange for mysterious favors which the fighter never appreciates. The manager usually deals in politicians, gangsters and, in some instances, sports writers. Matchmakers in most clubs are offended and believe they have been swindled if a manager does not kick back to them a gift of cash. Promoters dig in for their share of fighters they start out and many a time the fellow who takes the lickings finishes up with the smallest chunk after the money has been assorted and dispensed.

The code of fair play which rules most games is not apparent in the boxing racket. The bribing of referees and judges happens as often as a certain type of manager can get to them. It is not considered wrong to scream for justice and accuse honest officials of being crooks when your man has lost on the square. The reputations of honest officials are often damaged by managers even when they give a true verdict against a fighter. Most managers who do not holler consider themselves to be slackers and the shrieking of lies is supposed to signify love of your fighter. Seconds figure ways to evade the rules. Many instruct young fighters how to jab with the thumbs as a blind opponent is not considered to be as formidable as one who has ordinary vision. Low blows are valid in the minds of such handlers as long as a fighter is not penalized for them. Dirty fighters are those who do not draw large money.

It is only natural that the public is suspicious of fights and the journalists are forever searching for evidence of larceny. But in all the time that Joe Louis has been fighting I have never heard one of his contests denounced as a frame-up although many of them have appeared strange due to the curious deportment of his opponents. In the days of his greatness Louis inspired his straight men with a fear which caused them to fall in clammy ecstasy as soon as the first punch grazed their chins. It was an authentic happiness and they were eager to get out of his way before his cobblestone fists damaged them beyond reconstruction. Many of them resigned with joyous cowardice after being slapped a cuff which would not disturb the senses of a high-school girl. They ran from him in disgraceful retreats after panic looted them of their dignity. Some of them sweated in the dressing room as though they imagined he would use a baseball bat on them instead of his fists. There were some who began to lose weight the day they signed the contract and there were others who never pretended they were engaged as prize fighters and acted as though they were clowns employed to make the audience laugh at their shameful tactics to avoid being struck. Great fortunes were bet on the results of these fights. But it is a tribute to Louis that the public always believed he was an honest man in a league of burglars and rewarded him with a faith which is amazing in this cynical age of the breaking atom. As Louis comes to the end of his term as heavyweight champion we must consider what happened in his last fight with Jersey Joe Walcott in order to appreciate the purity of this great athlete. It was first made as an exhibition match. So mediocre was Walcott's history as a heavyweight that the promoters believed the public would not accept him as a contender. He was a cautious man with little respect for his own ability. He had resigned from the ring many times to work as a handy man because doing odd jobs paid him more than he would make with his fists. He was a fair puncher and what the fight racket calls a cutie.

His style consisted of no style at all. He would run and hide, skip and loiter, occasionally punch with a right hand, pausing timidly in his constant flight. The State Athletic Commission of New York jostled the promoters into changing the billing for the bout and when the time came it was advertised as a fight for the heavyweight championship of the world. It was considered a swindle and a humorless joke on the people who pay to watch fights. But I can't recall a fight which blew up more action among the gamblers. Only a few bet on the result because this is what they call proposition gambling. They bet that Walcott would or wouldn't last a round and spread their money down to the 15th, the odds changing with the rounds selected. At the end of the fight the majority of the people in Madison Square Garden thought Walcott had won the decision. I was one of them and I scored eight rounds for the challenger, seven for Louis. The referee gave it to Walcott, but the two judges overruled him and saved Louis' title. An inspection of their score cards showed that Walcott had won the fight on points, which is a system the New York Commission installed to prevent draws although not many understand it and I have not the space to go into it here. The verdict was heckled and all over the town people complained that Walcott should have won. But there was no sense of injustice among those who were steady patrons of fights in New York. They believe in the old tradition of the ring that a title can't be won by a man who runs away. They figured the judges had made an honest error and they let it go at that. If any other fighter had fallen heir to such an unexpected legacy of bad judgment the District Attorney probably would have had detectives out putting the sleeve on everyone mixed up with it. But this was a Louis fight and he is a special guy. All of them believe he was never party to a crooked fight and they respect him as a good man in a business dominated by thieves. Even a decision which they considered wrong could not molest their conception of him. They are absolutely right.

It is Louis alone without the aid of anyone else who made himself immune from the disease of greed which infects almost every other guy in the fight racket. The guys who do his business are all right in their way and up to now they have never made a wrong move in boxing. But it's Louis himself who has acted as though prize fighting was a sacred calling and not the ugly graft it is. Not once in the time Joe has been champion has he abused the office. In all the fights I have seen him make I can't recall him striking a foul blow. There were times when Joe could have used illegal tactics without any criticism. They tried everything against him, but it never agitated him out of his stately and always honorable fury. Max Baer hit him after the bell and this would have provoked the average fighter into retaliation. But Joe looked at Baer with disgust and shambled back to his corner, the contemptuous glance the only indication that he knew he had been fouled. He made Baer quit that night and I suppose that is the classic revenge.

The commercial anger of brutality does not recommend a man anywhere outside the ring unless you are looking for a guy to break a strike or roll a lush. It must make you wary of a man because if you are a good fighter you must inflict pain on another man and the chances are you may enjoy it. But Louis is more than a prize fighter and he is a promise that the equality promised all men in the basic documents of our freedoms may be achieved by all of us. Lena Horne, the great torch singer, said it better than I can. She is a sensitive girl who understands what is going on in the world. I met her when she was working the Copacabana and one night she asked: "When is Joe going to quit?"

"Two more fights," I said, because this was before they had made the Walcott match.

"I wish he'd quit now," Miss Horne said. "He means so much to so many people. I'd hate to see him beaten."

There are those who will tell you that Louis was an ordinary heavyweight who was erroneously accused of greatness because of the ineptness of his opposition. But you don't believe them. There were few as good in any age and that goes for all of them. You can start with John L. Sullivan and come right down to Jimmy Braddock, the one before Louis. There never was a heavyweight champion who took the chances Louis did. They were all alike to him and he fought them all. He never ducked anyone. There were nights when he was slovenly and could not solve the moves of his opponents, but always he went at them and tried to compel them to fight. The only plan he ever had was to go for a guy and stick with him until he could catch him. It will be remembered when a lot of things are forgotten that Walcott knocked him down twice. But Louis was always the aggressor. He never backed up. Walcott ran and hid and Louis pursued him even when he was rickety-legged and his left eye was a blood-flecked crevice in a lump of discolored flesh. If you looked at the course of the fight you would have believed that Walcott was the one who had been injured early and was trying to protect himself from further punishment. There is no doubt that Louis is done as a fighter of greatness. But it is my opinion he will have enough left in him to beat the likes of Walcott when they fight again this summer. I squandered no time in making this prophecy. On the day after the Walcott fight I picked Louis to win by a knockout next time around. I have no reason to change my opinion.

What happened with Walcott humiliated Joe and irritated his pride. He hid himself out in an apartment in uptown Manhattan and sat there with Manny Seamon, the trainer, dourly listening to jazz records. The telephone rang and no one bothered to answer it and the doorman in the apartment house denied there was any tenant by the name of Joe Louis. I was the first newspaperman to interview him after this fight. On a wind-cleansed day we stood at the window of his apartment and looked down at the Harlem River through the weather-stripped trees. Joe pointed to a small frame building.

"George Washington slept there," Louis said.

"He slept in a lot of joints," Seamon said.

"Sleep all the time," Joe said. "Must of had some second lieutenant run the army for him."

We discussed jazz and then he told me what he thought had made him slow and tired-looking in the Walcott fight.

"I made the fight for myself," he explained. "He didn't make it tough for me. He did so many wrong things. I saw every opening. But I couldn't go get him. It was such a lousy fight. I saw him when he made the mistakes. It's like a guy running. You can't make a sprint at the end. Your legs feel you can go, but you feel bad in the pit of your stomach."

I said this sounded like a rundown of the symptoms of old age.

"Diet and drying out," said Louis who came in at 211 for Walcott. "I wanted to weigh '12. I should have weighed '14 for the fight. I dried it out of me. I killed myself taking off the four pounds. But that ain't no excuse. It was a real lousy fight."

The first time I ever saw him was with Primo Carnera and he was a myth already. They said he was the best to come up since Gene Tunney, but a lot of us were careful and waited until we saw him. If you saw him that night and still doubt his claim to greatness then you are afflicted with amnesia or you are a liar.

Primo Carnera was a big but harmless man. At one time he was moved around by a syndicate of gangsters and they pushed guys off the raft in dives which many thought were square fights. Primo was agile in a big-footed way, but his arms were impotent when they laced the gloves on his hands. He could not punch and what he knew had been taught to him because he had none of the instincts a fighter must have to survive. But they had protected him and some of the opponents had been bribed not to hit him and there were still some who believed this grotesque man with the picket-fence smile could take a punch. Louis had a stately manner beyond his years when he came into the ring that night. He was blank-faced and quiet as he sat in his corner and he appeared to be a concentrated man. The first left hook Louis hit him was a solid one. It smeared Carnera's spit-wet lips and the mouth seemed to open and swallow his face as the blood spread like a grimace he could not control. The punch amazed Carnera. Never before had he been hit that hard. The terror seemed to wither his gross features because his eyes became large with astonishment. They had guarded him from beatings, but this one was on the level and the guy who was hitting him was the best puncher of his time. Louis was fast then. It was not the speed of body and feet. It was a swiftness of the arms. He would jab, hook and then suddenly the punches started and they didn't stop until you fell. He knew you were hurt before you did and that is when he commenced to let them go with a reckless accuracy that reminded you of Dempsey. In those days they were shaken up with the first punch and frapped with the flurry that followed. There were some who were in there to stay and they did. They did not try to win, but wanted the dubious honor of going the limit. They disgraced themselves, but this made them attractions because a guy who went fifteen rounds with Louis was accused of being a hell of a fighter. They fooled him once, but never twice and the next time around he caught up with them and they finished on their backs.

When the Max Schmeling match was rigged I was a reporter on the New York *American*. There was a young fellow named Joe DiMaggio in his first year as a big-leaguer and I liked to travel with the Yankees because this was a great team and your story figured to lead the sports section every day of the baseball season. Schmeling had retired. They had run out of opponents for Louis and they sent for Schmeling because he had been heavyweight champion of the world and this would give the match the appearance of a contest. The *American's* sports editor was the late Ed Frayne and he asked me if I wanted to hang around for the Louis-Schmeling fight or go West with the Yankees. I figured Louis would take Schmeling when he wanted to and I wanted to see what Di Mag would do against Western pitching. So I went out of town with the Yanks. We were in Detroit when Schmeling knocked him out. So I have never seen Louis beaten. But I was there the next time they fought and that night Louis was the greatest fighter I have ever seen. I wasn't there when Dempsey knocked out Jess Willard in Toledo. But I have seen the movies of that fight and this is the only other heavyweight I would have made an even-money shot with Louis on the night he destroyed Schmeling in one round.

There is little malice in Louis. The only men he fought whom he truly hated are Schmeling and Walcott. Schmeling degraded him by declaring that Louis had quit in the first fight. Walcott insisted that he had knocked down Louis while working as his sparring partner and had been fired for what he did. I remember sitting with Louis and talking about Schmeling on the night before the second fight.

"Why he say I quit?" Joe asked. "He looked to quit hisself in the seventh round. I hit him in the belly and I seen 'quit' looking out at me. Why he say I quit?"

"He's trying to steam you up," I said.

"Who you pick?" he asked.

"You," I answered. "By a knockout."

"How many?" he asked.

"Six," I replied.

"One," Joe said. "It go one."

"Why one?" I asked.

"That's all it go," Joe said. "It go one."

The first punches Louis reached him with were jabs. They made Schmeling's neck jerk as though he had run into an invisible wire. Louis never paused after that. Schmeling screamed and turned his back to Joe, holding onto the ropes. Louis had a fury which is seldom seen in the ring. It was a calculated rage and one controlled by intelligence. If ever a fighter made a perfect fight Joe did that night.

It always has been Joe's theory that a champion does not defend his title. He puts it there for them to take. They never have to search for him. Always he comes at them and he tried to get them out of there as fast as he could. There never was any stalling to make the other guy look good. If he caught you he nailed you and his pursuit was always hurried. In the first fight with Billy

Conn many thought Louis was too far behind and only a knockout saved him from defeat. On my score card it was even, although the officials had Conn out in front. The truth was deformed because it made a better story, but never in this fight was Louis in any real trouble. But if you read the memoirs of some sports observers you would think that Joe was on the border of insensibility all evening. Conn was not a powerful puncher and his skill as a boxer was exaggerated. Billy was a fast fighter. He got around with a wise nimbleness. But Conn couldn't force you out of your style with false moves as a good boxer is supposed to do. He depended on quickness and this scheme took him into the 13th round. It is the popular conception that Conn made the decision which got him knocked out. Some insist he broke his diagram of movement and decided to knock Louis out instead of jabbing and running. But that is not true. Conn made a mistake. Louis caught up with him. Those were the years of Louis' greatness and you were only entitled to one error. Joe stepped in and the next thing you knew a guy had smelling salts under your nose.

There have been a lot of guys who could fight better than Jimmy Braddock. But there were few who came into the ring the way he did. He approached a fight the way a clerk goes to his desk every morning. It was the job he worked at to make a living for his family and he did the best he knew how. It was his philosophy that a fighter goes as far as he can. It is the referee's job to count you out and you are supposed to get up if you can. The night Louis took the title from him Braddock fought with the calmness of a man with great pride in himself. In the first round Braddock knocked Louis down. It wasn't much of a punch, a right uppercut, and Louis ran into it. It sat Joe down, but it didn't hurt him. After that it was obvious that Braddock didn't have a chance. The people in his corner demanded that Jimmy quit. But Braddock said no and Louis took care of him and gave him a terrible beating. He lay in the ring with the blood running all over him and there were many in the ball park who believed he was fatally hurt. I was supposed to have filed a humorous story of the fight, but I asked them to let me out of it because I could locate no comedy in the butchery of a guy who was brave according to the rules of his profession. I tell you this because Braddock was better than the record in the book. I doubt if Jimmy ever considered himself a valorous man, but he was when you compare him with some of those who made more money by running and holding. So you must take his opinion of Louis seriously and appraise the champion by what he says.

"Nobody hits like Louis," Braddock said.

"What about Max Baer?" I said.

"A joke compared to that Louis," Braddock insisted. "A punch is a punch. But that Louis. Take the first jab he nails you. You know what it's like? It's like someone jammed an electric bulb in your face and busted it."

"What about the right hand?" I asked.

"It ain't like a punch," Braddock said. "It's like someone nailed you with a crowbar. I thought half my head was blowed off. I figured he caved it in. I felt it after he hit me and I couldn't even feel if it was there."

I talked with Louis about Braddock after the fight. "I like to fight old Jim again," Joe said.

"I thought you liked him," I said. "You want to murder him?"

"He make me the money," Joe said. "I like to make old Jim the money."

The second Conn fight confused the authorities. The years had begun to rot Louis, but we believed he was as good as ever. They watched him hunt down Conn in a desperate chase. But Conn was so bad that night it was impossible to detect what time had done to Louis.

"Billy not even half the fighter he was," Joe said. "I knock him out any time after the first round. I feel him out and come back and say I can get him. But Manny Seamon say to take it easy. Manny say I punch myself out and lose him. Manny say I may have to go fifteen. Billy wasn't like a heavyweight."

The one after that was with Tami Mauriello. On the morning of the fight they weighed in at the Garden and again Louis asked me the old question.

"What you pick?" he asked because I had called the round in the second Conn fight. "How long I fighting tonight?"

"Three," I answered.

"You must be in a mood for a long fight," Joe said.

It went only one, but Joe was fortunate to get by. Tami Mauriello was never much. He is a fat man and that makes it difficult for him to train. But Tami hit him and the punch jostled Louis into the ropes. Mauriello was amazed by what had happened. He took a tourist's look at the champion hanging on the ropes and that cost him any chance he had of winning. Mauriello went down with the first hook Louis hit him and he never was able to get going again. Then came the Walcott fight and when you saw it you realized Louis had come to the end of the line. Jersey Joe is a guy who had one good night and it almost made him champion of the world. But Louis was the greatest champion that ever held the title. No one ever fought more. Not one of them ever had his grace as a guy. When I say Joe is the best I am not defending my generation. The book will tell you how good he is and all the fights were won without the edge most fighters need to build a reputation. But if Louis doesn't quit after this one he will be beaten by the first young guy who conquers his fear and stands up to him.

WILLIAM MOULTON MARSTON

◄――――――――――――――――――――――――――――――――►

Is the Jury Ever Right?

IF YOU, though innocent of crime, were identified positively by a dying man as his murderer, and if the District Attorney swore to hang you unless you confessed, would you dare to let your case go before a jury? Perhaps you would, if you had money to hire the best criminal lawyer in town. And perhaps, even so, you'd be making the last important mistake of your life.

But suppose you had no money to hire jury-bamboozling counsel? Edward McGrath of New York, in such a situation, declined to accept a prison sentence for second-degree murder. A jury promptly sent him to Sing Sing's death house. But Louis De More, in St. Louis, Missouri, entertained a less naive faith in the fact-finding ability of juries. He confessed a murder which he had never committed and cheerfully accepted a life sentence which he had done nothing to deserve. That's one way of snatching your fate from a jury's hands if you have courage and a sufficiently compliant philosophy.

De More's story is an interesting one. At 11 o'clock of a Sunday evening, motorman Fisher, operator of a one-man car, was held up by a thug wearing a blue suit and a gray hat. The hold-up man was chased by patrolman Siko. Suddenly the fugitive turned, took Siko's gun away from him, and brutally pumped five bullets into the officer's body. The murderer escaped. Two hours later a police sergeant picked up De More, who was wearing a blue suit and a gray hat and who had no alibi. Siko, dying at a hospital, identified De More as the man who had shot him. Motorman Fisher also identified De More as the car robber. Through forty-eight hours of continuous questioning by police the victim maintained his innocence. Then the prosecutor promised De More certain hanging if he went before a jury and life imprisonment if he confessed. The defendant confessed, as he afterward stated, for the sole purpose of remaining alive until the real killer was found.

By strange good chance this happened two weeks after De More entered prison. The murdered policeman's revolver was found in the possession of an ex-convict. Motorman Fisher identified the real robber just as positively as he had identified De More. A jury accepted this identification without question, despite Fisher's initial mistake, and convicted the real killer. When De More was granted a pardon he was asked what he intended to do now. "Get out of this state inside 15 minutes," he replied. "And believe me, if I ever have to get to

July, 1935

another state west, I'm going around Missouri!" De More had the right idea. There are some troubles it is better to go around than to face—among them trial by jury.

The startling fact that a jury is never right has been proved beyond doubt by my work in the psycho-legal laboratory. No jury can be right—or anywhere near it—in its total reconstruction of facts. Experimental analysis of a jury's best efforts demonstrates clearly that finding any high percentage of facts accurately under our present legal procedure is psychologically impossible. Of course, reconstructing the facts correctly may not be necessary to effect justice in a given case. Even though facts were completely discarded, flipping a coin would produce a just decision in one case out of two according to the law of chance. But we need not be as cynical as that. Juries, on the average, may find about one-third of the actual facts correctly, while adding only about one-fifth fiction in their total findings.

What's the trouble with juries—why are they such wretchedly poor fact-finders? Because, in the first place, the witnesses who testify before them observe so little of what actually happened and make so many mistakes in reporting it. Psychologists discovered this fact by means of Aussage tests. An incident is performed in the class-room and student witnesses are asked to write down everything they observed. Results vary. But the incompleteness of the reports and the mistakes made are always amazing.

In Kansas University experiments, for instance, the correct statements made by witnesses were much fewer than the incorrect ones. An unarmed person in the incident performed, who made no offensive remarks, was described by three witnesses as carrying a revolver, snapping it several times at another man and yelling, "Stop or I'll shoot!" Another actor who did carry a revolver was little noticed by any of the witnesses. In Northwestern University Aussage tests, where several actors yelled insults at each other angrily, many witnesses testified that "No one spoke," or "I heard nothing." These unbelievable errors in testimony are typical.

I adapted the Aussage tests to duplicate court procedure. In court, a witness may give three different types of testimony. He may tell his own story freely with little prompting. He may answer non-leading questions by friendly counsel, called direct examination. And he may undergo cross-examination where leading, or suggestive questions by opposing counsel are permitted. In my experiments witnesses had to testify in all three ways.

I staged a simple incident before 18 witnesses, most of them lawyers. A young Texan entered the room where I was lecturing and handed me a yellow envelope. Then he drew from his pocket a large, green-handled knife with a six-inch blade. He opened the knife with one hand and scraped at his gloved thumb, facing the audience as he did so. I read a message, meanwhile, which looked like a telegram.

Not one of those 18 witnesses noticed the Texan's knife! Their attention was on the supposed telegram. When asked in direct examination about the knife, they all denied seeing it. During cross-examination they became still more vehement in their denials—they suspected the cross-examiner was trying to trick them into making false statements. Yet the knife had been held in full view for approximately three minutes. In a real case, what chance would the jury have had to learn from those 18 witnesses that this defendant was carrying the murder weapon?

Including the knife, there were 147 points to be observed in this experimental incident. The average witness reported 41 of them, making his testimony only 28% complete. Witnesses on the average supplied 8 false points, an error of 20%. Put yourself on the jury. How would you go about separating the 8 mistakes each witness made from the 41 correct statements? If two or more witnesses made the same mistake you'd be pretty likely to accept it as truth. Of course, you wouldn't have to wonder continually whether the witnesses were lying, as some of them undoubtedly would be in court. But still your fact-finding job would prove impossibly difficult—two-thirds of the real facts would remain a mystery because none of the witnesses observed them.

Free narration, which is kept down to a minimum in court, is by far the most reliable form of testimony. Direct examination is slightly more complete than free narration, but also contains more errors. Cross-examination, while furnishing the most entertainment for the jury, is practically worthless as an aid to fact-finding. But juries, instead of discounting the tricks of cross-examining lawyers, are likely to remember the answers thus obtained as high spots in an otherwise dull and boresome proceeding.

"Isn't it true," asked cross-examining counsel in a hotly contested divorce case, "that you were found unclothed in the co-respondent's apartment, by your husband and his detectives, and that the co-respondent was found there also in a similar condition? Answer yes or no."

"Yes," stammered the blameless wife, whose husband had told her that he had rented the apartment for her, "no! That is to say—I wasn't there, ah—*he wasn't there.*"

The jury snickered. Cross-examining counsel had practically won his case with that one question. The real facts were that divorce evidence had been framed. The co-respondent had come into the apartment without the woman's knowledge, while she was taking a bath, and had removed his clothes in another room. If she had answered "yes" to the cross-examination question, the jury would have understood her answer as an admission that she and the co-respondent had disrobed together in an apartment she knew to be his. If she had answered "no" her answer would have seemed like a defiant lie, since she had already admitted going to the apartment which she really thought was her own, and undressing there to take a bath.

The jury found the girl guilty of misconduct with the co-respondent and awarded her husband a divorce. It was the "professional" co-respondent who later suffered an attack of conscience and gave the show away.

Most members of the legal profession will admit that human testimony is fallible. But they support the jury system on the theory that mistakes made by one witness will be corrected by another. The jury's finding of fact is supposed, for this reason, to be more accurate and more complete than the testimony of any one witness.

But it isn't. I had the testimony of 30 witnesses—24 of them lawyers—considered and passed upon by 6 juries, 3 juries of men and 3 of women. The jury findings were then compared with the reliability of the witnesses' testimony. Four of the six juries proved less complete and less accurate in their findings than the average witness whose testimony they had considered. Two of the juries were more efficient than the average witness, though less reliable than the best witnesses. The average jury was just about as dependable in its findings as the average witness was in his testimony. A large number of witnesses to the same incident do not boost the jury's batting average—it still remains about one-third complete and one-fifth wrong regardless of the number of witnesses called.

And if such be the rating of six highly educated and intelligent juries, with all witnesses also above the general level of intelligence and telling the truth to the best of their beliefs and abilities, what will be the rating of an ordinary jury listening to average witnesses in court? What do you think—can such a jury ever be right enough in its total reconstruction of facts to support a just and logical verdict?

In my jury experiments psychological observers were planted in the jury-room to find out how errors in fact-finding were made. They discovered that jurors of both sexes gave much greater weight to the testimony of witnesses who were very positive in their statements than to those who were hesitant and cautious. The jurors should have followed precisely the opposite rule. Analysis of testimony actually shows that witnesses who think carefully before answering questions and in general exercise the greatest caution, give by far the most accurate and complete evidence.

In one instance, jurors ignored 11 reasonably cautious witnesses and believed a single witness who threw both caution and reason to the winds. The reasonable eleven described the Texan as wearing ordinary clothes.

These witnesses were not very certain, nor were they in agreement as to the exact colors of his suit, overcoat and hat, but no extraordinary colors were mentioned. Came, then, the dawn of fantasy. The twelfth witness swore positively that the young man had worn one high shoe and one low one; that one shoe was black and the other tan; that his necktie was bright scarlet, tied in a flowing bow, with a red coat to match. This witness' manner was self-assertive as Napoleon's.

He had believed utterly what he was saying—having been kidded into it by friends who knew he was hypersuggestible—and he resisted all attacks upon his reliability, fighting back aggressively at his cross-examiner like Dr. Condon in the Hauptmann case.

As a result of his certainty, both juries, male and female, found facts in accordance with this fantastic testimony! They believed the freak witness, my observers reported, because they thought nobody would make up such a wild tale—he must have seen the crazy clothes he told about or he would never have thought of describing them. Then, too, he was so sure of himself, so confident, and he made such a fool of the cross-examiner!

But if juries are prone to accept without question anything a confidence-inspiring witness says, they are just as likely to reject in total the story of a witness whom they regard as untrustworthy, no matter how strong the evidence supporting his story may be. A special jury of eleven, sophisticated New York business men recently awarded the charming Mrs. Wilma E. Gould a verdict of $25,000 against her brother-in-law and his detectives for framing divorce evidence against her and so damaging her character. This despite the fact that a well-known call-house *madame* testified that the pretty plaintiff was one of her girls up to the very night before her marriage. Bruce Reynolds, foreman of the jury, explained their verdict by saying, "Had it been any other man with whom she went to the so-called love-nest, we might not have felt as we did." In brief, the jury discarded all defense evidence because they distrusted "Prince Mike Romanoff," the amusing scapegrace whose story the evidence tended to corroborate. Psychologically, the very fact that Mrs. Gould believed this convincing imposter to be a prince was evidence that she went with him voluntarily. As one of her former girl-friends explained to those unheeding jurors, "Some men might have had to use drugs on Wilma—but not a Prince!"

Another pet juristic theory which the jury-test experiments exploded was the traditional notion that seeing a witness on the stand and hearing him testify helps the jury greatly in finding the real facts. Hearing oral testimony is more entertaining but less fact-producing than is the reading of typewritten testimony taken outside the jury's presence.

The findings of juries who never saw the witnesses proved superior both in completeness and accuracy to the findings of juries who heard testimony in the usual way. Jurors are not trained psychologists—why should we expect them to avoid personal prejudice for or against witnesses who appear before them under artificial conditions? Their judgment is far more reliable when based upon logical analysis of typed statements.

But suppose, after all, you had to risk your life at the hands of twelve good men or true women. Suppose the law put you on a spot and left it up to a jury to find the facts which would send you to your home or your hereafter? Many quite innocent people have faced this situation. Would you prefer to be tried by men or by women? No, the answer does not depend upon your sex— unless you happen to be an especially alluring female. The answer depends upon whether the true facts will convict or acquit you. If you want the best fact-finders, pick a jury of women.

Female juries excel male juries, on the average, both in completeness of findings and in accuracy of report. Women are more painstaking than men, and far more patient in working out detailed facts. My women jurors went over their notes again and again, searching for details which had escaped them. Two of the three female juries prepared exhaustive charts, comparing the testimony of all witnesses on every point in issue. No male jury did this. Men become quickly impatient with details. They want to get through with the job and get it over with.

Each man has his own ideas of "how it must have been," and is more interested in defending his own acumen than in sifting out the evidence objectively. Women jurors are frequently stubborn-minded, but usually because they have misunderstood some disputed point. Once a woman juror understands what the other woman is talking about she will discuss the issue on its merits. Men juries do relatively better on logical analysis of typed testimony. Women show the greatest margin of superiority in psychological analysis of the witnesses themselves during oral testimony.

But if you are being tried by women jurors, look out for handsome, self-assertive men witnesses. Several errors of fact were written into my female juries' findings because a good-looking young Irish lawyer insisted that his observations were right and those of all other witnesses were wrong on certain points. Male jurors invariably threw out the Irishman's statements. Or if, by chance, you are a personable male and are being tried by women jurors by all means take the stand in your own defense. Even if you are guilty of robbing or kidnapping a woman, you may very likely enlist her sympathies in your behalf. Mary McElroy, who was kidnapped from her bathtub by the McGee boys and kept chained to a farmhouse wall for 39 hours, is having a nervous breakdown because her kidnappers have been convicted and Walter McGee is under sentence of death for the crime. "All kidnappers but mine," says Miss McElroy, "should hang." They gave her roses and showed her how a machine-gun worked to wile away her captive hours. "I didn't mind being chained," she said, "after all they couldn't have me running around." Though McGee is uneducated, uncouth and has a criminal record for bank-robbery, the kidnapped girl described him as "nice, well-educated, and not of the criminal class." Which goes to show how strictly any woman may be expected to adhere to fact-finding when there's a dominant male in the case.

The best possible fact-finder under our present law is a judge. Three judges— two men and a woman—decisively proved their superiority over juries in my experiments. A judge, for one thing, doesn't have anybody to argue with and so devotes his full attention to the evidence.

The judge who was kind enough to compete with my first set of male and female juries was no less distinguished a person than Dr. John Henry Wigmore, Dean of the law school at Northwestern University and one of America's foremost authorities on the law of evidence. Dean Wigmore, as might have been expected, excelled both juries by a wide margin in the reliability of his findings.

The other two judges who took part in my experiments were not lawyers though both were professional fact-finders in other fields. One was a reporter, the other an historian. Dr. C. C. Tansill, professor of American history, proved remarkably accurate in his findings, but less complete than Dr. Wigmore. Miss Emily Davis, reporter for *Science Service*, surpassed both her male competitors. With the juries' average score taken as zero, the net score for the three judges was as follows: woman reporter, 16.5; man lawyer, 12.3 man historian, 5.3. The fact-finding abilities of reporter and lawyer, according to these results, seem to lie fairly close together. But history suffers sadly from the contrast—only one-third as reliable as it would have been if written by a newspaper woman! It is surely a pity that the law forbids trying cases before a female reporter with the jury thrown out of court.

But if, when all is said, juries cannot find the facts, there is one consolation for those who like to see wonders performed in strange ways. Justice may rise triumphant over fact-finding, and over logic as well. Many a verdict, based upon totally wrong facts, has produced substantial justice—either by destroying a dangerous enemy of society or by freeing a man not guilty as charged.

Consider, for example, the Twichell case, tried before a jury in Philadelphia. A maid in the Twichell house was in the habit of unbolting a gate in the high wall surrounding the back yard every morning. One morning she found her mistress, Mrs. Twichell, dead in the back yard, her skull smashed in with a poker which lay beside her. The maid ran out through the back gate to the street and called the police. She told the officers that she had found the gate locked and had unbolted it herself. Since this gate was the only means by which an outsider could have entered the yard where the body was found, and since Twichell himself was the only insider with a motive for killing the woman, he was indicted on the maid's testimony for his wife's murder.

At the trial the maid repeated her story about the gate being locked. The jury believed her and convicted Twichell. Later the prisoner confessed to his lawyer that he was guilty. But he had been convicted on false facts. He had killed his wife upstairs, inside the house, and had carried her body down to the yard. Then he had gone to great pains to unlock the back gate and leave it ajar, thus planting evidence which pointed to some outsider entering the yard and killing Mrs. Twichell.

The mistaken maid had testified from habit and not from real memory at all —she honestly believed she had unlocked the gate because she had done so every morning for many years. Twichell was rightly convicted on fallacious testimony, wrongly accepted as fact by the jury. Perhaps they didn't like his face or the way he combed his hair. But if the jury hadn't found the wrong facts the law would not have permitted them to declare this murderer guilty beyond a reasonable doubt.

Or take the recent case of Albert H. Fish, one of the most dangerous and re-pulsive maniacs in criminal annals. He confessed to the murder of a little girl and pleaded insanity. He had killed at least three children in ghastly ways, eat-ing the flesh of his victims. Evidence showed that this old man had been suf-fering all his life from the worst possible combination of abnormalities, masochism and sadism. Reputable and unprejudiced alienists testified that Fish was legally insane.

He had played whipping games with his own children in an abnormal way. He had tortured both his victims and himself. He had thrust 29 steel needles into his abdomen, suffering constant pain as a result. While in prison he twice carved his own body with improvised instruments, enjoying the pain, and matter-of-factly reported the visits of angels who talked to him. In discussing his own possible execution, Fish smiled in ecstasy, saying that to burn in the chair would be the final supreme thrill of his warped life.

Could any rational person doubt that this man was insane? But the law says that insane people can't be executed. The jury wanted to kill him. So they found that he was sane.

This jury obviously did not concern itself with facts but only with its own, preconceived idea of justice. And this justice could not have been carried out had the facts been found correctly. Theirs not to reason why but to avenge horribly murdered children. Fish himself will doubtless be grateful to them for their decision as the death hour approaches, thus furnishing the final conclusive proof of that fact which the jury denied.

It is difficult to escape the conclusion that complete or accurate fact-finding can never be accomplished by juries under our present judicial system. It is equally certain that competent fact-finding is the only possible foundation for justice. Law itself is valueless until facts are found which enable the authorities to apply the law justly to individuals concerned. Because the more important facts cannot be established in the minds of a jury, our leading racketeer-murderers like Capone are not sent to prison for murder but for failing to pay an income tax on the profits of murder. To permit juries to take the law into their own hands regardless of facts, as in the Fish case, is to sanction legal lynching. What must be done is to improve our fact-finding process.

A few practical suggestions may be made without waiting for Utopia. Women can be impaneled on trial juries increasingly, without change of present law. With very slight alteration in our legal machinery, provision might be made for taking depositions of witnesses—free from cross-examination—immediately after the occurrence witnessed, or as soon as legal action started. The fact-finding value of such freshly remembered, written testimony is probably a hundred times as great as the value of oral testimony taken under present court conditions.

Juries may be encouraged, or even required, within the discretion of a trial judge, to read written testimony before reaching a decision. This would counteract personal prejudice against witnesses in the jurors' minds to a surprising degree. In many types of cases fair-minded litigants who seek genuine justice may waive trial by jury and have the facts found by a judge. Experts in detecting deception may be called to the stand and deception tests permitted under proper psychological conditions for getting at the real truth. Psychological experts in the interpretation of testimony may be asked to sit as "friend of the court" by judges who are willing to admit that there is still something for a judge to learn in analyzing humans.

Some of these suggested improvements in the fact-finding process are already in the throes of practical development. But until science finds the facts in law as it does the germs in medicine, justice must be based on guess-work as was pill-peddling in the Middle Ages.

WILLIAM J. LEDERER

◀ ———————————————————— ▶

Them Marines!

EVERYONE asks, "How the hell do the Marines get that way? What makes them such good troops?"

I tried to find the answer in military textbooks. No luck. So I went into the field and started asking around.

When the 1st Provisional Marine Brigade was getting ready to embark for Korea, I put the question bluntly to a group of them in front of a recruiting station. "Hey, how come you guys've got such a good reputation?"

The veterans in the crowd didn't answer. But a beardless kid without any ribbons spoke up. "Mister," he said crisply, "we're respected because we're professionals."

"What do you mean?"

"I'll show you," he said, leading me inside.

On the Army bulletin board hung a clipping from a recent magazine, "Join the New U. S. Army and Be Treated Like a Gentleman."

"So?" I asked, "what has that to do with the Marines?"

The kid winked and dragged me to the Navy section of the recruiting station. Here a poster showed a destroyer cutting through the waves. It said, "Join the Navy and See the World."

Next he took me to an Air Force recruiting ad. A handsome aviator, with medals gleaming from his belly-button to his clavicle, smiled from the wall. The caption said something about joining the Air Force for a career and promotion.

"Now," said the young Marine, "look at the Marine posters."

At the Marine office there hung no printed matter at all. But there was a crudely painted picture of a red, hairy, doubled-up fist. Under it were splashed these words: "You're not good enough to be a Marine!"

"See," said the fuzzy-faced private, "we don't fool around with mama's boys or kids who need their noses wiped or guys looking for a home or a cheap vacation. The Marines are professional fighters. If the recruit can't take it and dish it out, he won't make the grade."

I've heard this talk of "being pros" on posts all over the world. And the longer a Marine stays in the service, the more firmly he seems to believe that either you're a professional fighter or a dead one. There's no place for amateurs.

After World War II the Marines came into the debate about how Germany should be occupied. Duty in a conquered country offers many temptations to troops; the unsettled conditions often taint the men and make them soft.

John McCloy suggested to Congressman Vinson that it might be a good idea to expand the Marines and have them act as occupation troops. Vinson, in turn, sent for General Vandegrift, then Commandant of the Marine Corps.

"Well, General," said Congressman Vinson, explaining the proposition, "how would the Corps like to be expanded to 750,000 men?"

"Sir," replied the general, "that's impossible."

"Oh, I believe Congress would enact the legislation."

"But, sir," said General Vandegrift, "that has nothing to do with it. There aren't 750,000 men in the United States good enough to be Marines."

The Marines don't advertise that they're unique or tough or well trained; still, they have an uncanny way of demonstrating it to anyone who may have doubts.

In Korea, some British Commandos, who aren't exactly sissies, joined up with the Marines. There had been a lot of talk about which group was the most rugged.

One night two Commandos and two Marines were isolated in a foxhole forward of the main lines. At dawn one of the Commandos said, "We're surrounded by a couple of hundred enemy in the hills. Are you blokes ready to attack?"

The other Commando replied, "I'm ready, matey, but what about these Yankee Marines? Think they can keep up the pace?"

One of the Marines stuck his head out of the foxhole to look around. An enemy bullet at the end of its trajectory landed in his mouth, knocking out two teeth.

"Blimey!" said a Commando. "You caught it with your teeth!"

The Marine casually removed the bullet from his mouth.

"Don't make a practice of it," he said, "but it's a quick way of estimating range. The gooks is about five hundred yards off. Let's wait till they get closer before attacking. Then we can use bayonets."

The other Marine looked disgusted. "You clumsy dope," he growled, "if you'da rolled with it like they taught us at Parris Island, you wouldn't've lost those teeth."

When I was in Pusan I put the question to a Marine major. "Why are the Marines so good?"

"We get along okay," he replied, "because we got discipline!"

"What do you mean, discipline?"

"Well," he said, "there's a story about the Marine lieutenant who operates a rest camp and a company of battle-weary Marines who came down from up North for a couple of days of relaxing.

"That night, about two a.m., it was cold, and the lieutenant sat in his jeep smoking and just keeping an eye on things. Suddenly he heard a woman scream. A girl with no clothes on ran from one of the houses with a Marine right behind

her. The Marine wasn't in full uniform either. The girl flew past the jeep. The
Marine was gaining on her, but when he got to the lieutenant's jeep he stopped
and saluted.

"That," said the major, "is discipline."

When I stopped laughing I said, "What did the lieutenant do?"

"Do?" said the major, surprised. "I don't know. But I'm sure he did what any
self-respecting officer would do; he returned the salute and said, "Hey, Marine.
That babe's got a head start on you. You better take the jeep!"

A correspondent said, "The story's apocryphal, all right."

"Probably," said the major, "but Marines are all nuts; anything can happen
in the Corps."

The Marines in their long service have learned that it's not the Fancy Dans
who make the best fighters. Many a lad who is termed a screwball in normal
society has just the restlessness and energy required by a professional fighting
outfit. As long as the screwballs perform their military duties according to the
high Marine standards and reflect credit on the Corps in public, they get along
fine.

The greatness of the Corps comes partly from the fact that most of the men
are "characters." The Corps probably is the last stronghold of individualism. No
military organization but the Leathernecks could enjoy telling the legend of
Lucy Brewer who, after plying the oldest profession in Boston for quite a while,
got run out of town and joined the Marines in disguise. She served for three years
with distinction aboard the frigate *Constitution*. The Marines still brag about
their legendary Lucy. "As far as we know, she did her duty and fought like a
tiger," a Marine told me. "Could you ask any more of a rifleman?"

Despite their hilarious antics, the Marines sometimes try to give the impression of being a mousy little outfit entirely devoid of the color for which they
are so famous.

One of their greats was Gunnery Sergeant Dan Daly. As an enlisted man he
won two Medals of Honor, the Navy Cross, the Distinguished Service Cross,
and three French decorations—and all these while he was still alive!

Gunnery Sergeant Daly was the firebrand who led his platoon into a haz-
ardous position in Belleau Wood shouting, "C'mon you crazy sons-of-bitches!
Do you want to live forever!"

The battle cry was repeated all over the world, and when Daly arrived in
Paris, the press beseiged him.

"How," asked a reporter, "did you think up your wonderful command?"

"What command?" said Daly.

" 'C'mon you crazy sons-of-bitches! Do you want to live forever!' "

Daly's face lighted with what is known as baby-faced disdain, then, very
earnestly, he said, "Do you think that a Marine non-commissioned officer would
use such bad language to the men under him? What I said was, 'For goodness'
sake, you chaps, let us advance against the foe!' "

And he stuck to his story.

John Zimmerman, a *Marine officer*, told me this (I repeat, this came from a Marine officer): "The United States Marine Corps is a bewitched, bedeviled, nutty collection of the most determined individualists that this country can boast. The attitude of this conglomeration of knuckleheads, geniuses, and plain unvarnished s.o.b.s is toward itself one of amazed and delighted tolerance. They have made the Corps into an organization which is constantly bubbling within and leaking at the seams from the internal pressures generated by its colorful personalities."

Being an organization of individualists, the Marines have an internal loyalty unknown to other normal units, but loyalty is something they never discuss. Marines usually speak of other Marines in terms of cynical contempt. Not long ago I heard two sergeants discussing a colonel who was on the staff of the Secretary of the Navy.

"Him?" said one of the sergeants. "I know that slopehead."

"Yeh?"

"We were at Peleliu together."

"What'd he do?"

"Oh, the joker got the idea that a wounded guy laying in front of a Nip cave oughta be rescued. And the dumb buzzard felt he was the only guy in the outfit could do the job. They just don't come any dumber than the colonel."

"What happened?"

"The knucklehead runs out to rescue the wounded guy. About every Jap in the island was shooting at him. But he made it by luck. After dark he dragged me back to safety."

"It was you he rescued?"

"Yeh, the dumb cluck."

"My God! How dopey can a colonel get? They should've given him a court."

But just let an outsider presume to criticize the Marines! Not even the President of the United States could get away with that.

Army recruiting ads say that twenty-five noncombatant soldiers are needed behind the lines to back up every man at the front. In the Marines there isn't any such thing as a noncombatant. All Marines, regardless of specialty, are *constantly* trained for combat. Normal assignment may call for a Leatherneck to be a cook, baker, truck driver, or even tree surgeon, but he's still a fighter. When the Marines lost their few planes at the battle of Wake Island, the pilots and ground crews reached for their rifles and fought to the end as infantry.

All enlisted Marines, including generals' orderlies, are armed at least with M-1 rifles or carbines and full combat packs, bayonets, shelter halves, mess kits and helmets.

Last winter the Chinese Reds ambushed a UN convoy on the road from Koto-Ri to Hagaru-ri; the *Assistant Public Information Officer* of the Marine First Division took combat command. All through the subzero night his small convoy, consisting of ROK soldiers, American soldiers, and Marine troops, fought off three enemy regiments.

When General MacArthur entered Seoul, there was no Marine band to give him honors. The Leatherneck musicians had stowed their horns and were up fighting the North Koreans.

Then there's the front-line cook who collared a friend at baking time and yelled, "Hey, Bill, watch the bread for an hour. I'm going on a short patrol and give a buddy a breather."

Even the lady Marines catch the spirit. (And never say "lady Marine" when they're around. "Don't call me that," one told me, "I'm just a plain ornery Marine.") After the normal indoctrination, a group of Marines (female) were recently sent out to watch combat troops in maneuvers. One of the Leathernecks (female) was handed a flame thrower. She strapped it on and let loose an arc of terrible flame. Then she said, "Isn't there any place on this gadget to fix a bayonet?"

The practice of making every Marine primarily a combat man (and a specialist only as a sideline) is fundamental to Leatherneck thinking. The officer's insignia or enlisted men's rating badges tell that the wearer is qualified to command troops. A Marine may be temporarily specializing in aviation, public information, engineering, or legal work; but that has nothing to do with his rank. Commanding troops is the basic qualification for promotion. In the Marines being a lieutenant colonel means that the officer is qualified to take a battalion composed of over a thousand men into combat. A Marine colonel may run an air group, but he can take over a regiment at any time.

The Marines have enlisted men piloting all types of planes. In the Leatherneck's opinion, jockeying a plane is not a specialty which requires officer's rank. Only command of troops deserves that.

This fact may explain the excellence of Marine tactical air training for troops in Korea. They know troop capabilities and what the men do under all conditions. There is direct communication between the field and the plane. The fliers' primary mission is to work with the men on the ground, so everything—including the planes and their armament—is designed for that purpose.

Marine flyers attend schools with troops and often sleep in the same barracks. They know the ground personnel. They are as close to the infantry as are the Marine artillery or tankmen.

At the Battle of the Naktong Bulge the Marines were taking a hard time from North Korean troops. The commander radioed for air support. In a short time Marine planes arrived from a carrier which had been steaming offshore not many miles away.

As the planes came in low over the Marines' heads, the Army observer ducked and said, "They're attacking us by mistake."

A Leatherneck grinned.

The planes strafed about sixty yards in front of the Marines and moved the spray of lead up to the enemy positions.

"That's Two-gun Murphy's outfit," said the rifleman. "He knows us. When we start advancing there'll be a hail of lead in front of us all the time. Boy, I'll never forget the time Two-gun backed his jeep into the general's new limousine and then convinced the Old Man it was his fault."

Marine officers generally are regarded as guys who have had more experience and know more soldiering than enlisted men. As of today, 87.5 per cent of the officers on active duty in the Marine Corps have served as enlisted men. Last winter they promoted three Leathernecks—Gregon Williams, Dustin Colley, and Chesty Puller—to general. All three were originally commissioned from the ranks.

The Marine brass doesn't go in for quickie inspections of the front lines—with a photographer along for home consumption. They're up there all the time, mucking with the combat troops. This tradition was already old back in 1836 when the Marines were ordered to frontier duty on the Georgia-Florida border. The Commandant of the Marines, Colonel Henderson, went out to take personal command of his troops. Before he left he tacked a sign on the door of his Washington office:

"*Gone to Florida to fight the Indians. Will be back when the war is over.*"

When Congressmen Hugh Scott and Henry Latham visited the Marines at the Naktong Bulge front, they found Brigadier General Craig, the senior Marine officer in Korea, sleeping on the ground and eating the same food as his men.

"Have you a headquarters with a bunk and mess table and orderlies?" asked the Congressmen.

General Craig said, "When the rest of the Marine troops get bunks and tables, then we'll think about giving them to the officers, too."

I told a colonel, "It's marvelous the way you look after your men."

"Bah!" he said. "Nothing of the sort. But we do make them look out for themselves. Every Marine is a one-man regiment; he constantly bears in mind that food, arms, training, health, and recreation are his responsibility."

The Corps always tries to give equal creature comforts to officers and men. At Quantico, a visitor can drive all over the station and unless he reads the name plates, he'll never know which houses belong to officers and which to enlisted men.

When I visited the Marines at Quantico, I saw a magnificent red brick building and wondered what it was. The inside was lush, with beautiful hardwood floors, lovely murals, a fine band and bar. Marines sat about drinking beer with some of the best-looking and best-dressed girls I had seen for some time. I mention the good-looking, well-dressed girls, not to be funny, but to impress on you the dignity and pleasantness of the place.

I thought, "What are enlisted men doing in the Officer's Club?"

A Leatherneck approached me. "I beg your pardon, sir, this club is for Marine enlisted men only."

"Hey!" I said. "I just heard that funds for enlisted recreational projects were being reduced. How did you Marines wangle Congress out of the appropriations for this club? It must have cost $200,000."

"Wangle Congress out of it, my foot," said the Marine. "We raised the money and built the place ourselves."

"Is it legal to build private buildings of this nature on Government Reservations?"

"In the Marine Corps, anything which improves the fighting qualities and morale of the men is legitimate."

A fighting man must use extreme initiative to get along. If the idea appears too radical, he tests it by two questions: (1) Will it help win battles? (2) Will it help the Corps' morale and efficiency?

The story goes that in Korea a company of Marines was temporarily assigned to the Army Quartermaster Corps. The Leathernecks were griping because they didn't like Army food and they didn't like the idea of carrying stores. They wanted to go to the front.

One day a carton they were carrying broke open. Onto the ground spilled pieces of clothing equipment assigned to a Philippine army general.

The Leathernecks had an idea. They debated whether or not it would help win battles or improve Marine morale and efficiency. They decided that it would be legitimate under the latter. They dressed one of their South Korean helpers in the uniform of a Philippine army general, and named him General Gonzales. Taking him over to the Army quartermaster depot, the Marines told the Army that the Filipino general, who came from Zamboanga and spoke only Chabacano, was observing the Marines, and that he desired a jeep of his own and a flag officer's mess.

The Marines enjoyed their "general's" food for about a week. Then a note came over from the Army. "Lieutenant General ——, USA, will visit here in a couple of days. He has spent many years in Zamboanga and speaks Chabacano fluently. He would enjoy very much having lunch with General Gonzales."

General Gonzales suddenly decided to observe the Marines at the front.

Because of their continued success in battle and out, the Leathernecks have developed considerable self-confidence. Recently a social-relations professor, trying an experiment in morale for the Navy, went to interview a group of Marines. His first contact was a rifleman just off watch.

"I'd like to ask you a question," said the professor, "about Marine officers."

"Be happy to help you, sir."

"Suppose a Marine officer gave you an order, and then left the immediate area. Later, the officer realized he had made a mistake. What would most Marine officers do in such a case? Would they say nothing and let you carry out a wrong order—or would they admit to an enlisted man that they had made a mistake?"

"Sir," replied the private, "what you asked me is what you might call a hypothetical question."

"How so?" said the professor.

"Well, sir, no s.o.b. of a Marine officer ever makes a mistake."

Then there was the Army three-star general who made a courtesy inspection of a Marine artillery battery in Korea. Inspecting down the ranks, he found a private who was a shell passer.

"Private," the general said, "suppose you were in a cold climate and the hydraulic recoil mechanism on your howitzer froze. How would you fire the piece?"

"Why, General, sir, a Marine would never let his equipment freeze. That's impossible."

"But suppose you were way north and it *did* freeze. How would you then fire your weapon?"

"General," said the private, shaking his head. "You just don't understand Marines. That mechanism wouldn't dare freeze—unless all of us was dead first."

Not so long ago, in the march back from the freezing Changjin Reservoir area in Korea, the Marines illustrated this point well. Their food froze, but their equipment got back in perfect order. And when the troops were back on Navy ships and rested, their officers inspected their equipment—including some tropical gear. Someone remarked that it was zero outside, and asked why the Marines had tropical gear.

"Why, hell, we got to stay ready for anything," a private said. "Who knows where we'll land next?"

Less than 300 of the Leathernecks are "missing in action" in Korea, though the total for all UN ground units is about 20,000. The Devil Dogs bring back their wounded, even their dead. Their morale is not made up by "girlie" shows, Coca-Cola and moving pictures; it comes from a raging pride in their units and the Corps itself. The terrors of the march back from the Changjin Reservoir probably won't be fully realized until some cantankerous Marine has time to lay down his rifle and write his memoirs. But throughout that freezing hell the Marines took care of their wounded.

They were in a mountainous area with no air strips, and they knew that if the badly wounded didn't get air evacuation they might not get out at all. Military experts were pessimistic. Perhaps they didn't realize that all Marine aviators are qualified to make carrier-deck landings.

The Leathernecks found a small piece of stony ground about the size of a couple of tennis courts. A carrier flight-officer got down there with his flags and wig-wagged the Marine planes to their landings. The wounded were crammed in the rear of the TBMs. The planes' wings were held until the props had revved up—and then released for the high-speed take-off.

A newspaperman said that it was a heroic performance.

"Nuts," said a Marine. "It was routine. The only guy really on the ball was O'Malley. He flew in eight five-gallon gasoline cans."

"You needed gas on the march?"

"And how! It was the best damned drinking gasoline you ever got a lip around. It's remembering such things that makes a guy a professional. But O'Malley's had a lot of practice."

The Leathernecks try to be prepared for all emergencies and practice for them. During the peacetime years there was a Marine general who had put on too much weight. So he took up riding. He would drive his car from his quarters to the stables outside the post. Here he changed to riding clothes, got on a horse and cantered home. After a drink he rode back to the stables, showered and came home by car.

One afternoon as he rode into the post a Marine private, with his carbine at the ready position, stepped out from behind a hedge.

"Dismount, advance, and be recognized," he ordered.

The general smiled. "I'm General——"

The sentry cocked his rifle. "Show your identification card!"

The general didn't have it. It was back at the stables.

"Then you can't enter here."

The general didn't argue; he mounted his horse and returned to the stable. Picking up his identification card he rode back to the same entrance. Once more the sentry stepped out.

"Dismount, advance, and be recognized."

The general dismounted, advanced and respectfully displayed his identification card.

"Proceed in, sir."

Mounting, the general entered the post. Then he stopped.

"Sentry."

"Yes, sir."

"This is peacetime. Who gave you orders to challenge everyone coming through this gate?"

"No one, sir. I was just practising. My sergeant says that's the only way to become a professional."

That word professional comes up all the time. A Corps news release tells of a company of Marines which had lost its light machine gun to the Reds in a night raid. "Let's get it back," a squad leader told his men. They moved out with the sergeant, away from the defense perimeter, and soon sighted twenty-five Reds lugging the weapon along.

"I'll throw a grenade," volunteered one rifleman.

"No! You might damage the gun!" replied the sergeant. "Pick 'em off with your rifles."

Such stories are not unusual. A sergeant on a combat patrol told this one:

"When our ammunition ran out, one of the men would race ahead of the lines, strip the weapons and ammunition from several dead Chinese, and dash back. Then the outfit would resume firing."

A while back an isolated company was surrounded by Reds in the mountains near Koto-Ri. UN planes dropped them supplies. One of the drops, containing most of the food, was caught in an air current as the parachutes opened, and the packets dropped slowly into Communist-held territory.

The next day the troops returned to the lines, and the drop crew met one of the riflemen.

"Jeez, we were sorry to see that food drop go to the Reds," the sergeant said. "I guess you went hungry last night."

"We did like hell. The company commander broke us out of our holes and made us get the chow back. We all ate!"

Marines usually manage to win. When the Panama Canal was opened, the ships of the United States Fleet were lined up to be the first vessels to steam through the world's newest wonder.

As the fleet entered the channel, the sailors learned that two Marines had already paddled the length of the canal in a dugout.

Leathernecks in general feel that a Marine rifleman is the most effective military man alive. In the Marines the rifleman is king. He gets the honors and the privileges. The officers feel the same way about it. Colonel Sam Moore, a Marine aviator, described himself as "a rifleman who at present is flying a plane."

The Marine witchery has been boiling for 176 years of United States history. The Marines accept it as normal procedure. It's like the sergeant who won a Medal of Honor in the Pacific for single-handedly holding back a Japanese attack all night.

"Hell's fires!" he said. "If I'd been on the ball and hadn't lost my pistol in the lagoon, I'd have brought back the whole damn company of them Japs as prisoners. The colonel must be crazy recommending me for a Medal of Honor. The dumb knucklehead should have me court-martialed for losing my equipment!"

The Time of Ruby Robert

I saw Bob Fitzsimmons a good many times, both in action, and when he was ambling on the streets of Chicago, sometimes leading his pet lion. His hair was reddish, but he wasn't so very ruby after all, and as for freckles, though he was cartooned with a great back covered with freckles the size of a quarter, he wasn't very freckled either. Sports writers must have something sensational. When it isn't at hand they make it up, and often out of scant material. Fitz's clothes always seemed too tight for him, too tight in the shoulders. He dressed rather flashily, not in taste like "Gentleman" Jim Corbett. He talked like a Cockney, pronouncing "half," "arf," and the like. As he walked along you could see that his legs were not of the same giant proportions as his shoulders. The latter were simply huge.

You will find in the twenty-third book of the *Iliad* old Homer's description of the fight between the boxer Epeius and the boxer Euryalus, in which Epeius smote Euryalus, so that his legs sank beneath him. They fought in those days with thongs of ox-hide fitted about their hands. There may have been critics of the game, but they did not indulge for years in comparative analyses, and in fanciful reasons for the defeat of one or the other. The Homeric fight reminds one of the contests of Fitz, for when he smote an antagonist the latter's "glorious limbs" sank beneath him.

I have been interested in pugilism all my life. I have seen many of the greatest of the pugilists. The reports of fights have a strange fascination for me, and I have always studied them, as later I have followed the explanations and criticisms and guesses of the men who follow the sport for the newspapers. If you will consider that many of them were not born when Corbett defeated Sullivan in 1892, or even when Fitzsimmons defeated Corbett in 1897, you will see that when these judges of the sport indulge in comparisons, and say that Louis is a greater puncher than Jeffries was, or that Peter Maher was a harder hitter than Louis, they are manifestly venturing an opinion without the facts having been gathered by the eyes. One thing that stands out is the constant cry that Louis was knocked down by Schmeling, and later by Galento, and that shows that he is not all that he is cracked up to be. They don't take into account that many of the greatest boxers were knocked down somewhere along the path of their career. The great Sullivan was knocked down by Charley Mitchell, who was a middleweight. Jack Johnson was knocked down by Stanley Ketchell, a middleweight. Fitzsimmons was knocked down many times. Corbett was knocked down and knocked out. Dempsey was knocked out of the ring by Firpo. Tunney was knocked down for a long count by Dempsey. The list could be amplified. This is enough to prove that the most skilled boxer can get it and that it does not speak much one way or the other as to his standing. Certainly and plainly Sullivan was a better man than Mitchell; Jack Johnson was a better man than Ketchell, and Fitzsimmons was a better man than the men who floored him. Dempsey demonstrated his superiority over Firpo on the spot. And Tunney, though knocked down, got the decision, and I have never heard any great howl that he did so. The case against Louis passes out when the facts are considered which should enter into a judgment of him as a champion. No one who knows anything would say that Galento is a better man than Louis. A big awkward fighter can get in a blow sometimes, and for that matter, an ordinary man could knock Louis down, or Sullivan in his best days, if he got the right sock on the right spot. I have a memory of Sullivan being knocked down in barroom scraps. I am surprised to see experts give so much attention to the knockdown that Louis received at the hands of Schmeling. Schmeling is a big man and when he got in the right blow on Louis, Louis had to go down, as great fighters did before him. There is nothing to this.

I could put up a good argument to the effect that Fitzsimmons, all things considered, was the greatest fighter who ever lived, but it would be a long argument and intricate with comparisons back and forth. Along the way I'd have to get Dempsey out of the way, who at Toledo in his fight with Willard was a whirlwind of power and skill. I have felt that Fitz could have defeated Sullivan. But I'll not indulge in such speculations. I'll only say that Fitz never had a superior, and rest the case upon some salient facts. In this connection I might mention first the matter of his age when he won battles, this as bearing upon his strength and vitality. He was never anything more than a light heavyweight, a class created in 1903 when George Gardner defeated Jack Root. Fitz defeated Gardner in the fall of 1903. So that when he defeated Corbett in 1897 he was only the middleweight champion.

Sullivan called Fitz a fighting machine on stilts, in reference to his spindling legs and his enormous shoulders and arms. But be it observed I don't recall an instance where Fitz's legs gave out on him. They seemed to have the endurance of steel. As to age he was thirty-five when he won the championship of the world over Corbett; he was forty-one when he gave the giant Jeffries with his 220 pounds of bone and muscle a terrible beating, and conceivably might have won the fight if his hands had not been turned to pulp by hammering the bronze head and jaws of Jeffries. On the other hand Corbett was towards thirty-one when he lost to Fitzsimmons; Dempsey was thirty-one when he lost to Tunney; Sullivan was thirty-four when he lost to Corbett. I differ from experts on fighting as to this age matter. A man at thirty-one or thirty-four is good enough for any man of any age. It may be that dissipation will lower a fighter's effective strength, but the mere matter of years, which have not advanced beyond thirty or so, will not do so. The case of Fitzsimmons proves this, and I stress it to make the point in favor of the Cornishman as a fighter with no superior. He had what no one can explain: he had strength, as Sullivan had, strength that can endure, that can rush and deliver great blows, strength that can stand up when beaten and bloody and fight on, as Sullivan did in his fight with Corbett. There was a report about that Sullivan was drunk the night before that fight. It is likely true, for Sullivan had been drinking heavily for years. And they say that is bad for the muscles and the wind—but look at Sullivan lasting for 21 rounds, chasing Corbett around the ring, and at last sinking in exhaustion in his corner. The standard reports of this fight say that Corbett defeated Sullivan; they do not say that Sullivan was knocked out.

Corbett was a boxer. He cut his foes to pieces, and as for himself he was hard to hit. He cut Fitzsimmons to ribbons, but it did not avail him, as it did in his fight with Sullivan. Fitz stayed on, though several years older than Corbett, and older than Sullivan was when Corbett defeated him. These points are well to remember.

I saw Fitzsimmons in action several times, first with a fighter named Ed Dunkhorst, who was called the "Human Freight Car." He was the Carnera of his day. When the two stepped into the ring it looked like a fight between a grasshopper and a rat. You can well suppose that if Dunkhorst's weight had sent a blow to Fitz's jaw that Fitz would have gone down. Why not? Dunkhorst must have weighed towards three hundred. But Fitz almost murdered this huge slugger, as he waltzed around Dunkhorst planting terrible punches that made Dunkhorst grunt and double up. Before this time Fitz had defeated Peter Maher, and the first Jack Dempsey and a long list of fighters of all weights. He took them all on, saying that the bigger they were the harder they fell.

Then I saw the fight between Fitzsimmons and the champion of South Africa, a heavyweight named Jeff Thorne, or Jim Thorne, the name is differently reported. Thorne greatly outweighed Fitz, perhaps by twenty pounds anyway. Thorne was not to be despised. There had been so much talk by this time of Fitz's short punch, a kind of corkscrew it was, that I was very glad of the chance to see him use it on this Jeff Thorne. I wanted to see how it was that Fitz could put a man down so that he could not get up. In this connection you must admit that many champions didn't put their men down so that they could not get up; they wore them out, or cut them to pieces, or covered them with blood and bruises, or put them down as Dempsey put down Tunney—who got up. Fitz put them down for good. He did it with Corbett, and many others.

Malachy Hogan, a referee long remembered as an honest man and a good fellow, met me on the street one day in Chicago and gave me a ringside seat to this fight between Fitz and Thorne. It was held at Tattersall's, and I was there on time, sitting within a few feet of the ring, waiting to see Fitz do the trick.

Pretty soon the fighters entered the ring amid great applause. Fitz in a manner ambled into the ring, though he was quick and nimble enough. His indifference was laughable: He looked about as if he knew what the result was going to be, as if he wanted to get at the business and have it over. His legs were slender, but not too much so, not as much so as the cartoons of the time led one to believe that they were. He was bald, but what hair he had was not so ruby after all. The arresting thing about him was his shoulders, which were huge, with no ridges of muscles, but as it seemed with long thin muscles slipping and gliding smoothly and easily beneath his skin, not so freckled after all. His arms were the most powerful to look at that I ever saw, and without bulges. They were long symmetrical cables of muscle, like a python's body, like the legs of a large man. He probably weighed about 160, a good deal less than Thorne, that was clear.

Fitz sat in his corner unconcerned, waiting for the bell, while Malachy Hogan stepped about getting ready to judge the fight. At last the bell! Fitz ambled over to the center of the ring, and there met Thorne coming on fast, full of fight, and striking out viciously over and over. He tried for Fitz's jaw. Fitz lifted up one of those huge shoulders, and sent the blow harmlessly to one side. He tried for Fitz's stomach. Fitz just drew in his stomach, and the blow fanned the air. Meantime Fitz did not strike a blow; and meantime I was watching every movement with concentrated eyes. The round ended with no damage. Thorne had not hit Fitz, Fitz had not tried to hit Thorne. I was wondering what cunning plan Fitz was nursing in that small bald head of his, I was watching to see the famous corkscrew.

Well, the second round, with Thorne after Fitz as in the first round, to no result! Then they got close together, and I looked and watched. Then this is what I saw: Fitz twisted a short blow to Thorne which caught him on the chin. The blow was not over six inches in delivery—but what a sock! You could tell that from the way that Thorne crumpled. He sank down to the resin. Malachy counted him out. He did not get up. He lay there limp and helpless. Malachy with the help of some others carried him to his corner. When he was put into his chair his head fell over on his breast. They rubbed him with ammonia. They sprayed champagne upon him. Still he did not come to. He was dead to the world. I wish I had held a watch on all this. But it was a good deal more than 18 seconds. It seemed to me several minutes before Thorne awoke to the realities. He had received one of Fitz's twists from one of those python-like arms. Can you think of another fighter who did the like, or did what Fitz did at Carson City to Corbett? Does this count in measuring what Fitz was when compared to other fighters?

No championship should be decided on ten rounds. I indulge that judgment based upon what I have seen, for outside of Fitz and others, Choynski included, and Jack Johnson in a sparring match, I saw Young Griffo, Terry McGovern, Tommy West, Benny Leonard, Harry Wills, Firpo, and in the old days Joe Goddard, Jim Hall, a marvelous boxer, whom Fitz defeated with some difficulty, and once a few years before Sullivan died I saw him spar with Jake Kilrain. A fighter can be very bad off in the tenth round, or even in the fifteenth round, and then come on and score the victory. That's what it means to have strength, that enigmatic X. That's what it means to fight 75 rounds, as Sullivan did with Jake Kilrain. That's what it means to be bleeding and reeling, as Fitz was in the

13th round at Carson City, and then in the 14th round to score a terrible knockout. Which shows that a man's strength and punching power can be on tap when he is bleeding. In these days a technical knockout is awarded when a man is blind and bleeding. Not in the old days, not in the days of Homer, nor in the days when Jeffries was blind from Fitz's blows at Coney Island.

One time in a conversation with Corbett, not many years before his death, I asked him how it was that he had fought sixty rounds, and others had fought as many in former days, and then in these later days 15 rounds were considered a long fight, long enough to test the superiority of one of the contestants. His reply was that fighters grew to be trained for speed and terrific strength, quickly exerted; while formerly they were trained for endurance, trained by running and other exercises that make for wind. There is something to this, but it doesn't quite convince. Later than this I read a statement by Tunney in which he said that ten rounds were not enough upon which a championship should pass. And I believe that in the second fight between him and Dempsey, Dempsey might have scored a knockout if the fight had gone to fifteen rounds. The matter comes back to that enigmatic thing called strength, to which I have already referred. In this talk I furnish material for experts to argue, but I am an expert myself, since I have done for years what experts do, namely, I have watched fights, read the reports of fights, and talked to experts who have seen fights that I did not see.

Fitz's fight with Corbett at Carson City helps to prove my point. I didn't see this fight, but I have talked by the hour about it with Bob Davis, who was in Fitz's corner there, representing the *New York Journal*, and as a coach to Fitz. You will find descriptions of this fight in plenty, but none so vivid as that Bob Davis can give at the luncheon table. It was a fierce fight, animated by hate on Corbett's part, and by cool ambition on Fitz's. Corbett kept dancing about jabbing and cutting Fitz, and dodging Fitz's blows. He hit Fitz enough. He covered him with blood. In the sixth round Fitz was down. It seemed that Fitz was through. In the thirteenth round Fitz presented a spectacle as terrible as Galento did in his recent fight with Louis. But the fight was not stopped. It had to go on to a finish.

Bob Davis told me that Fitz came back to his corner at the end of the thirteenth round with his chest streaming with blood, with his face covered with blood, with his eyes half-blinded. He sat down and his seconds began to sponge him off, to work on him. Then Fitz said coolly and as a matter of fact that he would get Corbett in the next round and to put up money on it, to tell the boys to bet. Think of that! When Bob heard Fitz say this he turned to his fellows and told them to put their money on Fitz. That was the amount of confidence that Bob Davis had in Fitz, sitting there covered with blood. More than that he sent a wire to his paper, saying that Fitz had won in the fourteenth round. This before the round was fought! But it was soon fought. Fitz worked what was called "the fatal shift," some kind of a placing and bracing of his feet in which all his bulk and strength were put into leverage, and he delivered the solar plexus, a blow to the midriff, which sent Corbett writhing and helpless, defeated and counted out. Everybody knows what it is to get a blow in the pit of the stomach. That was what Fitz gave Corbett. He had studied it out, and it did the trick. That made Fitz heavyweight champion of the world, at thirty-five years of age, weighing about 160 pounds. He began then to tour the country heralded as the champion of champions. He was thus heralded, but his name lacked magic somehow. He didn't clean up. He was not a gentleman, a Shakespearean amateur; he was a fighter. Six years after this time he won the light heavyweight championship. He was only the world's middleweight champion when he defeated Corbett.

In 1898 Jeffries after a bruising fight in San Francisco with Tom Sharkey, gaining the decision in the 20th round, was after Fitz. Fitz told him to go and get a reputation. Finally when the match was made Jeffries took on Tommy Ryan as a trainer, a very foxy and able fighter. He trained Jeffries so that Fitz would have difficulty in hitting him. That is he trained him to a kind of crouch, with the head down and one fist thrust forward. The great hulk, Jeffries with his 220 pounds of bronze-like flesh, did not want to be hit by a fist with only 160 pounds back of it, seeing that those pounds were Fitz's. Fitz gave Jeffries everything he had. He was then thirty-seven years of age. Jeffries was twenty-four. In the 11th round Jeffries knocked old Fitz out.

Fitz turned forty and challenged Jeffries. In the meantime Jeffries had fought Tom Sharkey 25 rounds and had won the decision. There was no knockdown. For the first time that I know anything about, pictures were made of the fight. I saw them and studied them, watching the short Sharkey and the tall bear-like Jeffries fight toe to toe, round after round. You couldn't tell from the pictures that either one had any advantage. They toed the mark and slugged. Often Jeffries' head went back, often Jeffries soaked Sharkey with terrific blows. But it turned out that Sharkey's ribs were smashed. The fight looked like a draw. But after observation at the hospital it was not difficult for doctors to say that Sharkey was badly punished, even if not knocked out.

At this time there was a huge fellow named Gus Ruhlin, called the giant grip-man, as he had run a grip-car. In the week before Fitz fought Jeffries the second fight, Fitz took on this Ruhlin, defeating him handily in a few rounds. Also in this week he took on Sharkey, knocking him out in two rounds, as I remember the facts. True, Sharkey had been badly macerated in that fight with Jeffries, but what do you think of the trick that Fitz turned in actually knocking out the tough Tom Sharkey? Then came Fitz's second fight with Jeffries. It took place at San Francisco.

As I am writing this article a magazine is on my desk with a piece in it by Hype Igoe, in which he says that Fitz gave Jeffries the most awful beating that he ever saw a man take in the ring, and that Dempsey's destruction of Willard or Firpo cannot be compared to it. I have heard the same thing from men who were on the ground, from Louis Houseman, a sports writer for Chicago papers, from Malachy Hogan already mentioned. Fitz was over forty, and Jeffries twenty-six. Fitz was a light heavyweight, Jeffries was one of the heaviest of the heavyweights.

Houseman told me that Jeffries at the last was nothing but bloody pulp, he was blinded, reeling. In these days the fight might have been stopped to save the life of Jeffries. Fitz had the fight won by a large margin until the strange end of things in the eighth round. Then suddenly Jeffries, out of his blindness, delivered a blow which sent Fitz sprawling to the mat. It turned out that what happened was this: Fitz walked close to Jeff, saying, "Hit me, Jeff." That's what he told Houseman, and Houseman told this to me. Spectators did not realize at the time that Fitz had nothing on which to continue the fight. His hands were just mush, bloody mush. That's why he said to Jeffries, "Hit me, Jeff," and exposed himself so that Jeffries could do it. When Fitz was in his dressing room they had to cut the gloves from his hands. His endurance had not deserted him, he was simply without weapons. Can any fight by Sullivan, by Dempsey, by anyone be compared to this? To me it puts Fitz at the top. For courage, for power, for skill, for fighting will, there is nothing in the record of Sullivan down to Joe Louis that holds a candle to it.

After this fight Fitz drifted around, sometimes fighting, but not notably. He got to be fifty and wanted to fight. The authorities would not let him. His purse was thin, and finally it came out that he had died in Chicago, aged fifty-six. Like other men he had to leave it to posterity to judge of him, to decide how good he was; and as in the case of other men, experts argue about him, and lie about him, and misvalue his record. So far as I am concerned I think he was a wonder in every way.

JAMES W. POLING

◄──►

Brotherly Love

THE gentle art of torture is one of the most venerable and least recognized of mankind's accomplishments. Like sex, it has reared its ugly head through all the pages of recorded history. The tortures of the Spanish Inquisition, the Middle Ages, the French Revolution and other notable eras are commonplaces accepted by everyone. But few realize that torture is one of the essential, even if minor tools of our present day boasted civilization. There is today one nation whose torturers would make even the experts of the Inquisition blush for their own ineptitude. However, this is not generally true and the fact is that the noble and ancient art of torture has for the most part fallen on meager days.

The survival of torture to the present was, as has always been the case, accomplished with the connivance of various religions and through the not always openly admitted assistance of criminal law. Also, torture even more than ever before has become an invaluable weapon of politics.

In the Western world the cultural centers of torture are, in the order named, Russia, Germany and Italy, and our own, our native land. If my rating is at all unjust I can only blame the exceedingly efficient censorship bureaus of the countries I have slighted.

The methods of torture most highly favored are in the main classical in their conception. True, a few innovations have been introduced but none of them are very startling and we can only conclude that our ancestors knew their stuff.

The Nazis and the Facisti, while they may not be blood brothers politically, show a strange and unimaginative kinship in the realm of torture. Both specialize almost solely in castor oil and in prolonged beatings.

That castor oil can be an instrument of torture is obvious to anyone who, as a child, over-indulged his appetite for green apples. The favorite dose is from one pint to one quart and the immediate results are what you might expect. The true beauty of this form of torture lies in the fact that such a dose will cause an internal rupture and hemorrhage that will bring about a death within three or four days which can neatly be written off as "death from natural causes."

The really serious business of torture, in both countries, occurs in the concentration camps (prisons for political offenders). Regrettably enough little artistry or variety is displayed. Solitary confinement and starvation, the ever-

November, 1936

491

present castor oil, and beatings in various forms constitute the larger part of the program.

While these beatings may lack the refinement we might logically expect to find in a civilized nation the following quotations from the lips of Wolfgang Langhof, who spent thirteen months in a concentration camp, prove that the treatment is not ineffective:

"Their faces were battered all over, their ears torn, their lips split, their eyes bloodshot and discolored. . . . Their truncheons rained on me, blood ran in streams from my body, nose and mouth. I was unable to move, my neck and arms were swollen, all my front teeth were gone, my whole body was purple, blue, black, green and red, and all swollen . . ."

That should give you the general idea.

My most ironical torture story from out of Germany concerns the fate of a young Jewess who made the grave mistake of having sexual relations with an Aryan. The Nazi council in her city learned of this and was quick to recognize the monstrous nature of her crime: she was threatening the purity of the whole race, her flesh was a blight on the very flower of German manhood! Five of these flowers were ordered to teach the young lady the error of her ways.

A ritual of torture is specified for this particularly horrible offence. The victim is first stripped and then flogged; her head is shaven and she is forced to drink a pint of castor oil and, finally, obscene phrases are painted on her bare flesh in an indelible fluid. The naked girl is then left to her own devices.

Our five avenging angels of the swastika called on the young Jewess in question and escorted her to a secluded woodland dell. She was stripped—and it was at this point, I assume, that inspiration came to the ring-leader. He had a hurried and whispered conference with his colleagues. They agreed that his was a splendid idea. And so, with Teutonic precision and thoroughness, the five men, in turn, soundly raped the girl. They then proceeded with the rest of the ritual and, having done their duty and having fought the good fight for the Fatherland, departed, complacent in the thought that they had taught this Jewess that her body was anathema to every brown-shirted and right-thinking man. Leaving behind them, I don't doubt, a slightly bewildered young lady.

The Italians are responsible for only one notable advance in the technic of pounding a man to pieces. They have evolved *Bastonatura in stile*, a highly specialized school of bludgeoning. The weapon is a specially made cudgel, weighted in the end and rather flexible. Those who wield it are trained in barracks where they first practice on dummies.

Blows from the bastinado are inflicted on the lower part of the face. Care is taken not to fracture the skull, in order to avoid death, and great artistry is displayed in shattering the jaws; thus laying the victim up for months and in such a shape that he can't conveniently speak harshly of his benevolent dictator.

Considering the crudity generally encountered in Germany and Italy it is encouraging to find this isolated proof that there still exist in those countries people who are endeavoring to restore torture to the dignified and artistic position it once occupied.

In turning to the land of the free I am forced to admit, unpatriotic though it may sound, that we in America have not taken advantage of our opportunities. In the realm of torture we are a backward nation, more notable for our vim and vigor than for our finesse.

Torture in America might never have made even the meager strides it has, had not the early scientists in the field found a convenient guinea pig for use in their laboratories—the American Negro. One of the most zealous scientists was one Southern gentleman who used to pass a dull afternoon lashing naked slave girls. When this bored him he would seal the gashes he had made with blazing sealing wax and then see how many strokes of the lash it took him to knock the hardened wax out again. His daughters were always interested and appreciative onlookers.

Intensive torture of this nature has decreased but the Southern Negro is still in a far from enviable position. Lynching, tar and feathering and even burning at the stake are not unheard of.

Full credit for the preservation of the art of torture in America is not the exclusive property of the Southern gentleman. Credit must also be given to prison authorities, gangsters, strike-breakers, chain-gang supervisors and last, but certainly not least, that guardian of the law—the common or garden variety of policeman.

Two Negroes recently chopped off their own feet to escape from the sweat box, floggings and other little devices which keep life from growing monotonous on a chain gang. Six policemen in Tampa were charged with the first degree murder of a man they suspected of communistic activities; after flogging him they tarred and feathered him and as a result he "did languish and did die." The Supreme Court recently set aside the death sentences imposed on three Mississippi Negroes because "it would be difficult to conceive of methods more revolting than those taken to procure the confessions of these petitioners." The men were hanged from trees and stripped and lashed with belts, buckles attached, until their backs were laid bare and until they confessed. The idealistic judges in Washington asserted that "the rack and torture chamber may not be substituted for the witness stand."

The gangster and strike-breaker specialize in beatings and in murders preceded by the slicing off of the ears and tongue; pins and toothpicks thrust under the nails; and cigarette lighters applied to the tenderer parts of the body. To them must also go the credit for the discovery of the cement keg. What could be more pleasant than to thrust your bound enemy up to his neck in a keg of wet cement and spend the hours while the cement hardens pointing out to him the error of his ways? Also, once the cement has hardened you have a very convenient package; a package heavy enough, when thrown into a river, to sink into the slime and disappear.

The cement keg may possibly survive in history, but only as a novelty. However, we have made one contribution to the noble art of torture which the future historian must inevitably note with care and admiration. I give you, gentlemen, the Third Degree.

Would you like to get kicked in the groin? Have you an overpowering desire to be questioned, without having food, water or sleep, by relays of detectives for ninety-two hours on end? Would you like to be blinded by being forced to stare into a terrifically high powered light for hours on end? Have you a desire to be put in a dentist's chair and held there while the dentist grinds down a good molar with a rough burr? Or would you prefer to have your Adam's apple pounded by a blackjack until blood spurted from your mouth?

All the little pleasantries I've enumerated can probably be had at your nearest police station, provided you are suspected of a major crime and are reluctant to confess your guilt. If the crime is major enough you may be provided with even more varied entertainment.

"Taps" is a form of indoor sports particularly popular with the boys in the back room of the police station. In playing "Taps" the prisoner is first strapped to a chair. After he has been made comfortable he is pounded on the side of the head with a piece of rubber hose, or "goldfish." He must not be knocked unconscious but must be struck hard enough to experience jolting pain. If the game is to be played expertly the blows must be delivered with machine-like regularity. Timing, as in tennis and other games, is essential and the perfect stroke is one delivered at regular thirty second intervals. The one drawback to the game is its lack of variety. The prisoner in the chair is always "It." To compensate for this "Taps" has a distinct advantage over most station house games; the rubber hose causes no scar and the red welt it raises won't be visible on the witness stand the next morning. The joke of this is that the prisoner's head will be damned sensitive for weeks or even months.

Kicking a suspect in the abdomen, bouncing his head off a cement floor, the dental burr and Adam's apple treatments, baseball bats, pool cues, burning with cigarette ends and other divertissements all have their loyal adherents and any policeman who advocates a specific form of "exercise" can quote you many cases to prove its effectiveness. Fortunately, most policemen are open-minded and quite willing to listen to a fellow officer representing an opposing school of thought. This leads to a widespread knowledge of the art of torture as practised within the law and makes for versatility.

If you are considering a life of crime you had better bear in mind one important piece of advice I have for you: never shoot a cop. His brother officers are so apt to resent it. And their resentment is liable to make you very uncomfortable.

Emanuel Lavine reports a typical case. Patrolman Charles Reilly was murdered by a Peter Heslin during a hold-up. In trying to return his .45 to the holster strapped across his abdomen Heslin shot himself in the upper part of the thigh, near the groin. Blood from the wounds led police to his hide-out. He was hauled out of bed in his night-shirt, thrown down two flights of stairs, dragged by his legs down the lower floor hallway and dumped on the street. Until the patrol wagon arrived and during the ride to the station he was kicked and beaten, in a sort of warming up process, by the officers who had captured him. At the station he was carried into a rear room where Reilly's body rested on an army cot and dumped on the floor. An Executive officer looked into the room long enough to say, "Be careful, boys. Don't touch his face, the marks will show."

The nearly naked man asked for a blanket, because he was cold. The blood-soaked canvas which had been used to cover Reilly's body was wrapped around him. When Heslin asked for a drink, the contents of a full cuspidor were dumped in his face. Then a detective selected the largest and heaviest nightstick available, took a good grip, and with all of his force struck Heslin on the wound near the groin where the .45 slug had entered his body. This fresh opening of the wound caused the blood to spurt like a small fountain. A brother detective next scraped up all the dirt he could find on the floor and rubbed it into the wounds made as the bullet passed through the man's leg, hoping, as he said, that the son-of-a-bitch would die of infection. The following man ground out the lighted end of a fat cigar in Heslin's navel. Other men applied lighted cigarettes to the more sensitive parts of his body. After this palled on them they gave the gunman a farewell going over with nightsticks and sent him off to Bellevue. Heslin was eventually electrocuted. Cop killers always are . . . if they live that long. My final bit of advice to those of you contemplating a life of crime is this: if you do shoot a cop don't be as dumb as Heslin. Just stick your gun to your head and let go as soon as you hear his brother officers pounding at your door. It'll save you a lot of trouble.

Yes, everything considered, I think it is safe to say that the cop has been the most potent force in keeping the art of torture alive in modern American life. I appreciate the work he is doing in carrying on a long and honorable pro-fession and I hope I won't sound hypercritical when I complain of his lack of finesse. As one who takes great pride in his country it pains me grievously to see other nations forge ahead of us in this field. This should not be.

I have a suggestion which, if followed, will remedy this distressing situation. I suggest we select from each metropolitan police force its most sadistic member. He shall then be sent to Russia to take a post-graduate course in torture. On his return he will take over the Chair of Torture in the local Police College. To make this plan as effective as possible gangsters, Southern gentlemen, strike-breakers, prison wardens, chain-gang supervisors, people with a race or color complex and all other interested parties will be admitted to the course free of charge.

My plan, I am sure, would bring new life, talent and artistry into American torture and it would only be a question of time until we assumed world leader-ship.

The reason I feel so certain of the success of my plan is that I have very carefully specified Russian training for our research students. Russia's artistry in torture is as advanced as her political theories. Her accomplishments put the rest of the world to shame. All honor to the Hammer and Sickle, a government de-signed to give the common man a break and a government that has established a new record for all time in both the quantity and the quality of her torture.

It is easy to assign credit for the Soviet's exceptionally meritorious performance. In the beginning there was Lenin, who said, "Do you think we can remain in power without having recourse to the most brutal methods?" There was a man who clearly understood how to retain office.

Lenin's attitude led, indirectly, to the formation of "The Extraordinary Commission for Combating Counter-Revolution, Sabotage, and the Dereliction of Duty," more commonly known as the *Cheka* and unquestionably the most murderous and bloodthirsty organization in the history of the modern world. With its informers, secret police, torturers, executioners, and charnel-houses located in every district of Russia the *Cheka* was a marvel of efficiency, as any organization which can torture and execute 1,761,065 people in the course of eight years must be. The *Cheka* never missed a bet. It had an executive known as the Director of Corpse Transportation and never threw away a body before making sure that the gold teeth had been extracted.

Such an organization must have a capable leader. The outstanding success of the *Cheka* in its chosen field was undeniably due to the genius of Felix Dzerzhinsky, the twentieth century Torquemada.

But Dzerzhinsky, no matter how willing, couldn't carry out the work of the *Cheka* singlehanded. He was supported by a huge organization, employing thousands of men. The *Commissars of Death*, as the official torturers and executioners were known, were the backbone of the *Cheka*. There were only a couple of hundred of these desirable and much sought after posts and some of the incumbents achieved their own especial brand of fame.

Peasant Pankratov, for example, with thousands of victims to his credit, was a punctual, quiet man who went about his work as meticulously as a bank clerk. He even kept a record of the number of bullets issued to him each day and the number used. Before killing his victims he used to flog them unmercifully, beat them in the face with his revolver butt until they were unrecognizable and then, when the fun was over, shoot them. At the end of his day's work he would go quietly home to his mistress, a former prostitute. When he was promoted to a well-paid job in the government he left his whore behind for his successor.

Maga was one of the highest scoring of all the executioners, with 11,000 victims to his credit. His scoring ability was abruptly cut short on the day he went haywire and, pulling his gun, ordered some of his fellow executioners to the wall.

Zayenko, a mousy young man from Kharkov, disdained killing his victims with his own hands. He had a knack for artistic flogging and would end his part of the performance by skinning his victim's hands. The actual killing was left to his assistant, Eduard, who made it a point of honor never to shoot before telling the practically dead man a funny story.

Odessa was honored by the presence of a gargantuan Negro by the name of Johnson who had been one of the better Parisian pimps before he became "Comrade"-conscious. Johnson had a way with a knife and, with a few adroit strokes, could cut away the flesh and lay bare the sinews, which he ripped out by hand—to the extreme discomfiture of his living victim. He was noted for the broad smile that played over his features during the course of this operation and reckoned to be a man with a devilish sense of humor.

The girls of Russia weren't ones to shirk their duty and some of them, too, rose to the front ranks. The blonde Vera Grebenniukova was probably the most famous. This young lady got her early training under Johnson but soon developed her own technic, which consisted of literally shredding her victims. With a feminine eye to the preservation of her clothes she frequently worked in the nude; bloodstains being notably difficult to remove. Vera may have been lacking in modesty, but not in energy. During one period of six weeks she accounted for seven hundred people at the rate of about fifteen a day.

Rosa Schwartz, of Kiev, also was a disciple of nudism. She always visited her victim's cell in the raw, smoking a cigarette and carrying a gun. After a chat and a smoke she would extinguish the cigarette in her victim's eyes and then start shooting. Essad-Bey, who has written the best account in English of the work of the *Cheka*, encountered another young lady in Moscow who loved dearly to go visiting the infirmaries, where the sick prisoners were, with a stout whip in her hand.

But for really thorough workmanship the Pole Achikine, of Simforopol, was the most noteworthy executioner of them all. He had a romantic preference for women prisoners. After stripping them he would first emulate the goat, and then, taking up a sword, cut off their ears, hands and breasts. Having warmed up to his work he would burn or pierce the eyes out and, in the end, cut off the head.

With such talented boys and girls in his employment it is easy to understand why Dzerzhinsky had little trouble in making the *Cheka* a household word in all Russia.

Nor were the operatives of the *Cheka* completely lacking in finesse and subtlety. A good many prisoners of the *Cheka* came out of prison with whole bodies. These fortunate ones had only to spend an unlimited number of weeks in solitary confinement in extremely hot or freezing cold dungeons. I shouldn't have said "solitary" confinement since they could enjoy the company of the large rats who dwelt with them. Others were shut up for extended periods of time in cells with raving maniacs or sexual lunatics. Some were prevented from sleeping for days on end and some fed nothing but salt herring while a water tap flowed constantly outside their cell door. And a few were left to philosophize for weeks, in brightly lighted cells, the walls, ceilings and floors of which were constructed of distortion mirrors. These were the fortunate ones that came out of jail, as I said, with whole bodies. Whether, after the loss of their minds, their bodies were of much use to them during the remainder of their days in the insane asylums of Russia is something I leave you to judge.

Some of you may have felt that in assigning supremacy in torture to Russia I was overstating the case. I trust that the following quotations, as recorded by Maître Aubert and Essad-Bey, will convince you that I was speaking the simple truth:

"In the city of Taganrog, in southern Russia, fifty young officers were bound hand and foot and flung alive into red hot blast furnaces. In Blagoveshchensk, corpses of officers and soldiers were found with gramophone needles under their nails, with their nails torn from their fingers, and with shoulder straps nailed to their flesh. In the Ussuri district Czech prisoners were found whose skulls had been smashed in, their genitalia amputated, their eyes put out and their tongues torn out.

"At Kharkov the butcher Saenko was celebrated for his skill in skinning heads and hands. He plunged the hands of the accused into boiling water, then tore off the skin to make human gloves. His abattoir was known as the Glove Factory.

"At Odessa officers were taken on board the steamer *Sinope*, fastened to beams with chains, put in front of the oven and slowly roasted. Others were cooked in boilers, then plunged into the icy sea, and thrown again into the oven. Still others were burnt alive, fastened to planks which were slowly pushed into ovens bit by bit, a few inches at a time."

If you still refuse to recognize, with me, the supreme genius of the Russian people I can only make one last, despairing gesture and quote to you, from Nilostonski's *Der Blutraush des Bolschewismus*, this official description of the condition of the abattoirs on the day of the evacuation of Kiev.

"The whole of the concrete floor of the huge garage was covered with blood which, owing to the heat, had already coagulated; it was mixed with bits of brain, cranial bones, wisps of hair and other human remains, the whole resulting in a horrible mess several inches deep. Close by this gruesome scene, in the garden of the same house, there lay a hundred and twenty-seven bodies. The heads of all the corpses were battered in, some of the skulls being quite flat. They had probably been killed by having their heads flattened out by some sort of block. Others had no heads at all, but the latter had not been cut off; they had been torn away. In a far corner of the garden we discovered another common grave containing about eighty bodies. No one can have any idea of the wounds and mutilations we found upon them. Some had their bellies slit open, some had no limbs, some had been cut to pieces, some had their eyes put out and many had no tongues. We discovered a number of bodies which showed no signs of having met with violent death. But when they were examined by the doctors, the trachea and aesophagus of each victim was found to be full of earth. The wretched creatures had evidently been buried alive and had swallowed the earth as they tried to breathe. Among them were old men, young men, women and children. One woman was bound by a rope to her daughter, a child apparently of about eight years of age."

I rest my case.

It is reassuring to know that in this mad, chaotic world of ours there is at least one nation carrying on the brave old traditions of the past in this glorious fashion. Torquemada and the Holy Fathers of the Inquisition can rest peacefully in the knowledge that they did not live in vain. Still, I must be fair and not pay all my homage to a nation. While thrones collapse, society reels, and civilization goes on apace man, in his godlike image, remains eternally the same—at least in the exquisite pleasure he derives from doing unto others what he'd damn well not like to have done to himself.

The following sentence is quoted from a Bolshevik paper fittingly entitled *The Voice of Truth:*

"It is time to clear the streets of human bodies as the dogs, which have tasted human flesh, become dangerous."

It isn't only the dog that becomes dangerous, after tasting human flesh.

The end, thank God.

ROBERT C. RUARK

◄───►

The First Time I Saw God

I<small>T WAS</small> about 5:15 p.m., 108 miles northeast of Oran, I remember, when the starboard gunners shouted, "Torpedo off the bow!" The helmsman tried to swing her so the thing would run parallel to us, but the old bucket was bottom-heavy with about nine thousand tons of high explosive and she was sluggish as a sleepy sloth. Whatever it was took a long time coming, but not long enough to dodge it. As I recall, I didn't pray, even though I had seen that afternoon, and on other days, what happens to a ship that gets smacked with a crawful of high ex. I felt a vague regret over the fact that getting blown up at the age of twenty-seven left a lot of pleasant things undone, and that was about all. Whatever it was hit us with a dreadful crash. The deck plates popped and spouted flame. The ship took a list, and was knocked heavily off her course. The feeling then was impatience that she didn't blow and get it over with. But no last-minute consignments of soul, no death-brink stammers of apology for what had been a short but gaudy life amongst the shattered Commandments. She didn't blow. And I uttered no prayer of thankfulness. I just figured that if there wasn't enough sincerity in me to pray ahead of it, there wasn't much point in praying behind it. The Lord and I did little business together in those days. It was more or less as if we had been introduced by the wrong folks.

If we can flash forward about nine years, now, I will tell you about a wordless prayer I said. I said it through my pores, sitting in a grove of trees in Tanganyika, East Africa, hard by a crocodile-infested river called The Little Ruaha. There wasn't anybody around at the time but the Lord and me and some wild animals. I didn't make any sort of formal speech out of it. Just told Him thank You very kindly for not blowing up the ship that day in the Mediterranean, and for letting me live till this day. It was a little late coming, this thank-you note, but I never meant anything more vehemently. And so far as formal religion goes I am a very irreligious fellow, who smokes, swears, drinks whiskey, ogles girls and at that very moment was paradoxically interested in killing things.

I was very grateful to be alive, at that moment, for I was alone in the nearest thing to the Garden of Eden I ever expect to see. We had stumbled, while on safari, onto a piece of land which had largely been untrammeled by human feet, and uncontaminated by human presence. The exact location remains a secret. The place was too good for man to louse up. Its keynote was perfect peace.

March, 1952

We were out after kudu—greater kudu—one of the more elusive and possibly the most beautiful of all African game. He is as big as a horse, and as dainty as his tiny cousin, the dik-dik. He has enormous backswept upcurling horns that completely spiral twice, ending four or five feet from his skull in shining ivory tips. His coat is delicate grey, barred in white, and there is a chevron on his nose, and his heavy neck wears a long dark mane. Also he is ordinarily twice as wild as any animal, save possibly the bongo. A man is lucky to see one kudu in many months of hunting.

Here the kudu were comparatively as tame as the little Thomson gazelle. I suppose we saw 60 or more in two weeks, and might have shot 20 if we counted the immature bulls. The cow was as tame as domestic cattle, nearly. I shot one kudu bull, because I wanted the trophy badly. The rest of the time we just looked around.

We marveled. Here was country as the first man saw it. We were camped on the river's edge, beneath a vast grove of acacias. It was like living in a natural cathedral, to look upward in the cool, created by the flat tops of the giant trees, with the sun dappling here and there to remove the dank darkness of moist forests. It reminded you of sunrays streaming in through the stained glass of a church window. The straw beneath the trees had been trampled flat by all the generations of elephants since the first elephant. The silence was unshattered by traffic sounds, by the squawk of radios, by the presence of people. All the noises were animal noises: The elephants bugled and crashed in the bush across the little river. The hippos grunted and the lions roared. The ordinarily elusive leopards came to within 50 yards of the camp, and coughed from curiosity. The hyenas came to call and lounged around the tents like dogs. Even the baboons, usually shy, trotted through the camp as if they'd paid taxes on it.

The eland is a timid antelope, a giant creature who'll weigh up to 2000 pounds, and who almost never stops moving. He is as spooky as a banshee, and unless you chase him on the plains in a car, a couple thousand yards away is as close as you're apt to get. Here the eland came in herds, walking inquiringly toward you. The same applied to the big Cape Buffalo, who ordinarily snatch one whiff of man-scent and shove off. The buffalo walked up to us here, their noses stretched and their eyes placid and unafraid. We watched one herd of a hundred or so for half an hour, and finally shooed them into the bush.

The impala, lovely, golden antelope with delicate, lyrelike horns, are usually pretty cheeky little cusses, but here they were downright presumptuous. As we drove along the trails in the jeep, we would have to stop the car and drive them off the path. They leaped high above the earth for sheer fun, not from fear, and one little joker actually jumped completely over the car—just to see if he could, I suppose.

Even the crocodiles seemed unafraid. They slept quietly on the banks, and didn't bother to slide into the water at our approach. The guinea fowl, usually scary birds, were as tame as domesticated chicken. We must have seen at least 3000 one morning, and they neither flew nor ran to the nearest exit. They walked with dignity.

This place had been seen only by one other safari, and was not despoiled by natives. The locals lived 18 hard miles away, and they were not a tribe of hunters. They grew crops and grazed cattle, and robbed wild beehives for honey, and generally did not even tote the customary spear, which is as much a part of native equipment as the umbrella is to the Londoner. One grizzled grandsire, 18 miles away on The Big Ruaha, told us solemnly that he had lived there all his life and had never seen a kudu. We saw 14 that day.

You felt that here was a capsuling of creation, unsoiled, unspoiled, untouched by greed or selfishness or cruelty or suspicion. The white hunter, Harry Selby, whose life has been spent among animals, out of doors, gasped continually at the confidence and trust displayed by the profusions of game. We didn't want to shoot; we didn't even want to talk loud. Here you could see tangible peace, here you could see the hand of God as He possibly intended things to be. We left the place largely as we found it. We felt unworthy of the clean, soft blue sky, of the animals and birds and trees.

It was not until we found this camp that I became aware of what had happened to me in Africa. It had been happening daily, but my perceptions had been so blunted by civilized living that I had somewhere lost an appreciation of simplicity, had dulled my sensitivity by a glut of sensation and the rush of modern existence. All of a sudden I was seeing skies and noticing mountains and appreciating animals and cataloguing the flowers that dot the yellowed, grassy plains of Africa. I was tabulating birdcalls and marveling over the sheer drop of the Rift and feeling good. I was conscious of the taste of food and of the sharp impact of whiskey on a tired man, and the warmth of water in the canvas bathtub, and the wonder of dreamless sleep. I was getting up before dawn and loving it. I was desperately anxious to win the approval of the blacks who made up my safari—me who never gave much of a damn about Presidents and kings. I was feeling *kind*, and acutely alive, and very conscious of sun and moon, sky and breeze and hot and cold.

This has to be a paradox, because my primary business in Africa was killing. I was there to shoot. And I shot. I shot lions and a leopard and a buffalo and all the edible antelopes and all the good trophies I could rustle up. But I never shot needlessly and I never killed anything for the sake of seeing it die. We killed for good trophies, and we killed to feed 16 hungry people. Killing does not seem wrong in Africa, because the entire scheme of living is based on death. The death of one thing complements the life of another thing. The African economy is erected on violence, and so there is no guilt to shooting a zebra that the lions will have tomorrow, or a lion that will eventually be a hyena's breakfast when he is too old to defend himself against an ignoble enemy.

This is a hell of a way to write, for a professional cynic, but you see I'm not really cynical any more. What has wrapped us all in a protective armor, an insulation against honest stimulation, has been an artificiality of living that contrived civilization has thrust upon us to the detriment of decency.

Things are very simple in the African veld. You is or you ain't. You are a courageous man or you are a coward, and it takes a very short time to decide, and for everyone you know to detect it. You can learn more about people in three days on safari than you might run down in a lifetime of polite association under "civilized" circumstances. That is why very few foreign visitors are speaking to each other when they finish a long trip into the bush.

There is no room for selfishness. A safari is as intricate as a watch. It is pared down to the essentials of good living—which is to say food, transport, cleanliness, self-protection and relaxation, or fun. It has a heavy quotient of hard work, in which everyone has a share. It is like a ship, on a long cruise, in that respect. There is a thing for every man to do, and if he fouls off his duty the failure affects everybody, to everybody's hurt. A sloppy gunbearer, who lags behind, can get you killed. Indecision on your part or the part of any vital member of your party can get you killed. Cowardice can get you killed. Lack of caution can get you killed. You shake your shoes each morning on the off chance a scorpion has nested in your boot. . . .

When you live among phonies long enough, when your life is a vast and complicated cocktail party of communication, pose, frustration, confusion, pressure, refinement, and threat of indistinct doom, you can forget that the human body is a very simple organism with very simple demands. It does not take much to amuse a monkey, but we have seemingly overendowed ourselves with playthings, with extraneous fripperies we call necessities, with gimmicks, gadgets, gizmos, and distractions that completely obscure the basic truth that a night's sleep, a day's work, a full belly, and a healthy elimination is about all a human organism needs for satisfactory existence. The refinements come later, of themselves.

I find today, to my dismay, that while I live in New York in an approximate palace—freshly decorated, at God knows what cost in blood, sweat, and money—I was happier in a tent. It kept the rain off me, needed no lease, was easily movable and did not require air-conditioning. The bed was a cot, and tired as I was nightly it could have been upholstered in spikes without disturbing my rest.

Now I'm back on my old routine of toying with a chop, and spending eight thousand dollars for a dinner I don't want, but I don't like it. I recall a fellow by the same name who used to pick up a whole guinea fowl and devour it with great enthusiasm, and who never cared too much whether the Tommy chops had been cooked sufficiently or not. Cold spaghetti tastes great out of a can. Beer is never better than when warmed by the sun, due to no refrigeration. I read a lot of mishmash about diet—in the words of my friend Selby, the hunter: *Gimme meat, and skip the extras.* In Tanganyika I ate like a starved cannibal, and lost weight. There I was eating to live—not to sell books, not to be entrancing, not to be stylish. I was eating because I was hungry, and was burning up enough of what I ate to keep me thin enough to climb a mountain or crawl through a swamp.

You realize that a man who earns a living with two fingers on a typewriter has always accepted the A & P, the local supermarket, the utilities company, the waterworks, the central heating, and the highway department as part of his life. All of a sudden, save for a few conveniences, I was right back with the early man.

If we wanted light we either built a fire or turned on a very primitive lamp. Fire we always needed, if only to fend the hyenas off tomorrow's dinner, and always in the starkly chill nights to keep from freezing. So we had to pitch camp where dry wood was. And close to where water was. And where dry wood was, and water was, and wood was, and food was, you had to travel. In the absence of a highway department you have to take a panga and cut your own roads through dense growth, or build your own bridge, or pave the bottom of a stream with rocks you have painstakingly gathered.

I had accepted light, heat, water, roads, and food. Especially food. You flicked a switch, screamed at a janitor, started the car and let her ramble, or picked up the phone and called the grocer. The most intimate contact with food I ever had was when I ate it and when I paid the bill. Now I was for the first time in the bacon-bringing business, which is to say that 16 people eat or don't eat according to what I could do with the business aperture of a rifle. Not that my wife, the hunter, or I would starve, of course. But there were 13 hungry black mouths, used to consuming 10 to 12 pounds of meat a day—*each*—wondering what goodies *Bwana* was going to fetch home that day to plug the aching void. By goodies they meant *nyama*—meat. Zebra meat, eland meat, buffalo meat, any kind of meat. I was the Chicago stockyards, the slaughter pens, the corner delicatessen, in their simple and direct minds. This was a new thing. I hunted for it, and I found it, and I shot it, and we butchered it, and then we ate it. What we didn't eat was made into *biltong*, dried meat or jerky. The hyenas, the jackals, the vultures and the marabou storks cleaned up on the odds and ends.

There is a neatness to Africa that needs no sanitation corps, no street-cleaning department, no wash-down trucks. What the hyenas and jackals don't get the buzzards get. What they don't get the marabou storks get. What else is left around the ants get. There is no garbage—no waste.

Maybe that's one of the things that hit me hard. No waste. Back home I seem surrounded by waste—waste of money, waste of time, waste of life, waste of leisure, mostly waste of effort. Away out yonder, under the cleanly laundered skies, there seems to be a scheme that works better than what we have devised here. There is a dignity we have not achieved by acquiring vice-presidencies and a $50,000 bonus and planned economies and the purposeful directorship of the world.

The happiest man I ever knew is named Katunga. He is an old Wa-Kamba, whose filed front teeth have dropped out. His possessions are four wives, a passel of old children, young children, and grandchildren. And *pride*. Katunga is known as *Bwana* Katunga to white and black alike, because Katunga is the best skinner of animals in the whole world. He achieved his title because he once approached Philip Percival, the now retired dean of all white hunters, and spake thusly:

"*Bwana*, I see that all white men are called *Bwana*. *Bwana* means Lord, or Master. Now I, Katunga, am an atheist, because my father was good enough for me. But to be called *Bwana* means that a man is master of something, and I am master of my knife. I am the best skinner in the world. Why cannot I too be called *Bwana Katunga?*"

"*Jambo, Bwana Katunga,*" Mr. Percival said, and *Bwana Katunga* he has remained. He sings as he skins. He is a happy man, with a sense of humor, and he has never seen Dagmar or Milton Berle, and he disdains a gun as an unworthy weapon compared to a knife. Nor does he pay a tax or fret his soul about extinction. Death holds no horror for him.

One day just before I left East Africa I heard Katunga speaking more or less to himself, as he flensed a Grant gazelle I had shot. He was surrounded by his usual clique of admirers, for Africans are great listeners.

"I am an old man," Katunga said. "I am not so very long for safaris. Someday soon I will die. But when I die—when I, who am now called *Bwana Katunga,* die—I will have left my mark. The safaris will pass my *boma*. They will see my houses, and my maize fields. They will see my wives and my children and my grandchildren. They will see what Katunga has left behind him, and they will say: '*King-i* Katunga lived there!' "

And true enough, *Bwana* Katunga will have become King, since he realizes his worth and anticipates it before time awards it to him. Not many captains of our industry can say as much.

The best man I ever met, white, black, or varicolored, is named Kidogo. Kidogo is a Nandi boy, about twenty-eight years old, who was my gunbearer. He is rich according to his standards. He has wives and children and herds of cattle and grainfields. He has been to English-talking school and it has neither made him a scornful African nor a wishful Englishman. He will work harder, give more of himself to the problem at hand, sleep less, complain less, be more humble, more tolerant, and more efficient than any "civilized" person I know. With it he retains a sense of humor, too, and a vast pride in himself as a man. He hunts as a gunbearer for the best hunter in the business only because he loves the hunt and he loves the hunter and he loves the business of being with *Mungu,* which is God, no matter how you spell it or conceive of it. I feared the scorn of Kidogo more than ever I feared the wrath of God or man, and it pleased me that finally he approved sufficiently to make jokes with me. A joke from Kidogo was accolade enough to make my year. It told me I was a fairly decent fellow, worthy of association with a superlatively brave man, a tolerant man, a good man. Apart from the joking compliment, he showed no surprise when his bossman casually assumed that I would join them in a happy little adventure called "pulling the wounded buffalo out of the bush." Kidogo tracked the blood spoor for me, with his life on the line ahead of me. He seemed confident that his life was in good hands, since he had no gun. Adam, the other tracker, showed the same sort of confidence in Selby, and to be accorded a similar consideration as Selby was the deepest bow to my ego I ever experienced. Because Selby is the all-time pro at standing off charging buffalo at four feet.

I still thrill, from time to time, about the dedication to danger that was given me by three relative strangers. "Clients" are generally told to wait in the jeep until the dirty business of finishing off a wounded, dangerous animal is com-

plete. If they are "good," or nonabrasive clients, they might be asked if they care
to join in the dubious fun of extracting a sick, sore, and angry animal from his
bastion in the thorn. We hit a buffalo hard. Twice he went to his knees, but
nevertheless recovered and took off with the herd.

"Let's smoke a cigarette and give him time to stiffen," Selby said. We smoked
the cigarette, Selby, Adam, and I. Kidogo doesn't smoke.

"Well," Selby said, directly to me, crushing out his smoke, "let's go and
collect the old boy." No ultimatum to wait in safety. No request as to whether
I wished to play. It was assumed by Harry Selby, who is half buffalo and half
elephant, and two lean blacks who live by danger, that I was naturally going to
tag along. No Pulitzer Prize, no Congressional Medal of Honor, would ever
give me the thrill I got that day out of casual acceptance as an equal.

You see there is a thing about the buffalo. He is a very naughty creature, as
Selby might understate it. He is so bloody awful, horridly, vindictively naughty,
after he has been hurt that he is almost impossible to kill. He will soak up bullets that would stop elephants cold, and still keep coming. He can run faster
than you can. He can turn faster than you can. He will hide if possible and take
you from the rear, and he can hide in bush that wouldn't cover a cat. He weighs
in the neighborhood of 2500 pounds. He will hook you with his razor horns—he
charges with his head straight out and his eyes open—and then he will go and
pick you up from where he has thrown you and he will throw you again.
When you cannot move he will jump up and down on you with feet as big as
flatirons and as sharp as axes. He will butt you and kneel on you and if you
climb a tree he will stretch that big snout up and lick the flesh off your feet
with a tongue with a rasp. When he is wounded and you are up against him
there is only one logical development. You die, or he dies, because he will not
run away. He just comes, and comes, and the brain shot sometimes won't stop
him. Most wounded buffalo are killed within a hand's reach. The starkest fear
I have every known was given me by buffalo, until the fear became a fascination,
and the fascination an addiction, until I was almost able to observe myself as
another creature, and became bemused by my own reactions. I finally courted
buffalo as a hair shirt to my own conscience, and almost would have been interested objectively to see how many possible ways there are to be killed by one.

In this trip to Africa, and in my association with Selby, Kidogo, Adam, and
a few lions, leopards, buffalo and other vindictive insects, I had the opportunity
to find out about courage, which is something I never acquired from the late
war. I know now that I am a complete coward, which is something I never
would admit before. I am the kid with the dry mouth and the revolving stomach,
the sweaty palms and the brilliant visions of disaster.

But cowardice has its points, too. There are all gradations of fear, and the
greatest gradation is the fear of being known to be afraid. I felt it one day after
a lengthy stalk through awful grass after a wounded buffalo. When I finally
looked at him, and he looked at me, and there wasn't any tree to climb and
no place to hide, I was the local expert on fear. At less than fifty yards a buffalo
looks into your soul.

I unlimbered my Westley-Richards double-barreled .470, and let him have it where it hurt. Then I went off and was sick. And then for the next sick and several weeks, I had to force myself to inspect his relatives at close quarters. I was frightened of embarrassing Harry and Kidogo and Adam by my own cowardice, so my cowardice conquered the minor cowardice, which only involved dying, and so we went and sought the buffalo. Ditto lion, leopard, rhino. Likewise snakes. A small cobra is very large to a man who fears caterpillars.

I learned, on this expedition, about such things as grass, and its relation to rain, and its relation to game, and game's relation to people, and people's relation to staying alive. There is a simple ABC here: When it rains too much, the grass grows too high. Also trucks get stuck, but the main point is that when the grass grows too high you can't get there from here. You stay where you are, and all the frantic cables from home can't reach you.

Also when the grass is too high the game is in the hills, and you can't get to the hills, and furthermore the carnivore which live off the game are out of sight, too, because there ain't no carnivore where there ain't no game. The lions and leopards and cheetah can't operate in the high grass because the Tommies and Grant and zebra and wildebeeste know that the carnivore can't operate in the high grass. And it is an amazing thing that all the hoofed animals drop their young when it is raining so hard that nothing predatory can move much, which gives the young a short chance to stay alive. Me, I always thought pregnant animals went to hospitals when their time came on.

I learned something of females on this trip, too. Such as how the male lion seldom kills. What he does is stand upwind and let his scent drift down. Once in a while he roars. While he is creating a commotion the old lady sneaks along against the wind and grabs what she is sneaking after and then she breaks its neck. And brings home to father the spoils of her effort. We have reversed this technique in this country.

The emphasis on sex is very simple in Africa, having little to do with the citified voodoo with which we have endowed it. Sex is not really a symbol, nor is it hidden, psychiatry-ridden or obscure. There are two sexes—doumi, the bulls, and manamouki, the cows. They work and they breed and they die. There is no such thing as a sterile man, because the woman shops around amongst the village until she breeds. Breeding is thought to be highly important, since it begets Mtotos, and children of both sexes are highly regarded as both nice to have around the hut and valuable in an economic sense. Neither sex of animal nor human group seems overworried about morality as we know it, or the implications of sexual jealousy as we know it. They got sex, and are content, and do not need a Kinsey lecture to impress its importance on each other. They also have sun and rain and seasons, and if they take the sheep and goats into the huts at night it is to keep the sheep and goats from harm while simultaneously keeping warm. It makes as much sense as tethering a poodle to a restaurant radiator.

What I have been driving at all along is an explanation of why I want to go back to Africa, again and again and again, and why I think Kidogo the gunbearer is more important to life than Einstein or Dean Acheson. It is because I discovered in Africa my own true importance, which is largely nothing. Except as a very tiny wedge in the never-ending cycle that God or *Mungu* or somebody has figured out. The Swahili say: "*Shauri Mungu*" meaning "God's business," when they can't figure out an explanation for why it rains or they lost the way to camp or there aren't any lions where there should be lions.

In Africa you learn finally that death is as necessary to life as the other way around. You learn from watching the ants rebuild a shattered hill that nothing is so terribly important as to make any single aspect of it important beyond the concept of your participation in it. You are impressed with the tininess of your own role in a grand scheme that has been going on since before anybody wrote books about it, and from that starting point you know true humility for the first time.

I believe today I am an humble man, because I have seen a hyena eat a lion carcass, and I have seen the buzzards eat the hyena that ate the lion, and I saw the ants eat one buzzard that ate the hyena that ate the lion. It appeared to me that *Mungu* had this one figured out, because if kings fall before knaves, and they both contribute to the richness of tomorrow's fertile soil, then who am I to make a big thing out of *me*?

It was not so much that I was a stranger to the vastnesses of Tanganyika, which are not dark but joyous. It was not that I was lost in a jungle so much as if I had finally come home, home to a place of serenity, with a million pets to play with, without complication, with full appreciation of the momentary luxury of being alive, without pettiness, and finally, with a full knowledge of what a small ant I was in the hill of life.

I belonged there all the time, I figured, and that's why I say I had to go to Africa to meet God.

MARTIN MAYER

Wall Street: Men and Money

WALL STREET is a street six blocks long, running from Broadway to the East River; on its path it dips and widens and bends to the north, hiding the low, ugly, old buildings by the river from the high, ugly, old buildings on the hill. It has a working population of thirty thousand men and women, most of them producing and consuming money. With another seventy thousand who work in the surrounding canyons, laborers in the Wall Street vineyards handled in 1951 more than twice as much money as the Federal government. What happens every day in its buildings and on its pavements affects half the population of the world.

Wall Streeters get their incomes by taking a little piece out of every dollar that comes by. The Street is first of all a big commission house. Whenever anybody buys a stock or a bond—except in rare and isolated cases—Wall Street makes a dollar. More than fifteen per cent of all bank loans pay interest, or a discount profit, to a New York house. Practically all the financial arrangements of the insurance companies and the pension funds produce money for a Wall Street specialist and his staff.

The Street's prosperity depends almost entirely on the amount of money that floods past, and this reliance on public whim puts everybody on a ferris wheel that rolls even more rapidly than the market itself. Right now, though 1952 will not be so fat as 1951 or 1950, the boys are doing pretty well. The telephone switchboards, mechanical calculators and IBM machines are humming happily in the old offices (except for a huge, shiny, one-story Chock Full O' Nuts eatery nothing has been built on Wall Street for twenty years). On the grey streets, where the sun rarely shines, well-dressed audiences (Brooks Brothers has its only New York branch store a block away on Broadway) listen tolerantly to the ragged itinerant preachers who still descend daily on the financial market to cast the money-changers from the temple. Idle-hour conversation is usually about some expensive hobby—the current favorite is high-fidelity audio equipment— and fine cigars move fast in the tobacco shops. Nobody minds even the Wall Street smell, which in good weather comes from the coffee roasters to the south, and in bad weather from the Fulton Fish Market to the north.

Every weekday crowds fill the exclusive downtown luncheon and professional clubs that occupy the top floors of the skyscrapers, charging from fifteen dollars

September, 1952

to five hundred dollars a year in dues (which usually go up as the member gets older), and from a dollar and a quarter to four dollars for lunch. (The Stock Exchange Luncheon Club, though strictly professional, is pretty exclusive, too: it has an individual little cigar holder waist-high in every booth in the men's room.) The quick-order broker's express lunch places near the exchanges get five and six diners to a seat between twelve and two and there is almost always a wait for a table at such fine financial restaurants as Whyte's and Ye Olde Chop House.

In the financial papers cheerful advertisements announce the greatest flotations of stocks and bonds in the history of the world; at the Stock Exchange prices bounce up and down near a 21-year peak; in the offices there are rumors of high and mighty Christmas bonuses. Almost everybody is making money.

And almost everybody earns it. American industry is expanding at a fantastic rate—23 billion dollars of new investment last year alone. Some of the money comes from past or present profits and some from the government; but industry must get the great bulk of its new cash in four ways: by selling pieces of itself (stocks) or IOU's (debentures) or mortgages (bonds), or by borrowing from banks and insurance companies. All that money comes from the public, either directly or through insurance policies and bank accounts. By the operation of a relatively free market the savings of Main Street filter through Wall Street to the companies that will pay the most rent for the money and use it most profitably.

And without the men who work on Wall Street the job couldn't possibly be done.

The New York Stock Exchange and its subsidiary corporations occupy an oblong block bounded on the long sides by Broad Street and New Street, on the short sides by Wall Street and Exchange Place. The block looks like an off-center football goal, with 19-story and 23-story office buildings at the ends and in the middle an eight-story building with fancy renaissance façade. Behind the façade is an enormous room, 115 by 140 feet and five stories high. It calls itself "The Nation's Market Place."

Large open telephone booths—ten phones to a booth—line the floor; each member of the Exchange (price of a membership: $40-50,000) who has business from the outside rents one or more phones and stations clerks to take care of them. When a call comes in from the home office the clerk notes the order and calls his floor member by pushing a button to clap the member's number on a big annunciator board high on the walls at both ends of the room. The member walks rapidly to the phone (running is forbidden by the laws of the Exchange), then plunges back toward the center of the floor to do business.

He trudges ankle deep in every imaginable kind of paper (except cigarette paper—smoking is forbidden) to the post at which the ordered stock is traded. There are eighteen of these posts, twelve on the central trading floor, six in an annex on the ground floor of the north office building. Each post is a horseshoe counter with a horseshoe board running above at hair level. On the outside the board gives the names of the stocks traded at this particular post; on the inside it is a hatrack for the clerks who stand behind the counter, keeping track of the market.

No stocks are bought or sold over that counter; all the trading occurs outside, along the edges of the horseshoe. The Stock Exchange, the Curb Exchange and the regional exchanges outside New York are all auction markets—that is, nobody sets a price. The price results from competitive bidding on both the buying and the selling sides. It works when the bid (the price somebody is willing to pay for a stock) approaches the offer (the price at which somebody is willing to sell). At the exchanges it works well, because the stocks traded are all owned by so many people that somebody usually wants to buy and somebody usually wants to sell, because the corporations represented are so widely publicized that everybody has a good idea of what he thinks the stuff is worth, and because certain brokers—called specialists—keep the market steady by buying or selling for their own accounts.

The specialists do other work. Most customers tell their brokers to buy or sell "at the market" (at the best price available when the order hits the floor), but many order at specific prices which are below or above the current bid or offer. No order is ever killed until the customer kills it; if a man wants to order RCA at ten dollars a share his broker will handle it for him. But the broker can't stand around the post waiting for RCA to drop fifteen points, so he leaves the order with the specialist, who will execute it when and if it comes "in line" with the market. For this service the specialist, who never does business with the public, gets a cut of the broker's commission when the transaction comes through. On the New York Stock Exchange there are 350 specialists, handling an average of four stocks apiece.

Specialists are not the only members who have no direct contact with the public. All bidding in the auction is in terms of "round lots"—hundred-share units for most stocks, ten-share units for some less active issues. A broker with an order to buy fifteen shares of RCA will go to an "odd-lot" dealer, who will fill the order at the price of the next round-lot sale, plus 12½¢ a share (25¢ if the price is over 40) for himself. There are a hundred members of the New York Stock Exchange whose entire business is the purchase and sale of odd lots. Also on the floor are 150 free-lance brokers who execute orders for other brokers when business is heavy or when a member is too busy elsewhere to come to the Exchange.

Almost a thousand brokers—and an equal number of clerks, reporters and runners—work five and a half days a week (they get Saturdays off in the summer) on the dimly lit floor of the Stock Exchange. The morning sun is kept out by forty-foot damask curtains that are apparently never washed; the afternoon sun is blocked by the fifty-story bulk of 1 Wall Street. Most of the denizens work in ordinary business suits, but some wear the cream-colored cotton jackets of the cigar-store clerk; all have pinned to their jackets oval badges which tell everybody who they are and where they come from. They keep in touch with the market through the ticker tape, which is flashed on large screens in all four corners of the main room, announcing by symbols all sales, the stocks involved, the number of round lots in each transaction and the price. They haven't much time for lunch, but will usually dart across New Street for an artless ten-minute meal at Eberlin's Restaurant or the Hargus Cafe. During the course of a year each member will buy and sell, by oral agreements, tens of millions of dollars worth of securities, almost all of it representing other people's money —a fearful responsibility.

They carry their burdens gracefully, however, and do business with a charming informality. Large, beefy broker comes striding toward a post, one hand at his side holding a rolled-up newspaper, the other hand aloft waving a slip of blue paper. As he nears the post he shouts to the clerk.

"How's Monkey?" (What are the bid and offer prices on Montgomery Ward?)

"Sixty-two—one-quarter," says the clerk. (Somebody is willing to buy at 62; somebody else is willing to sell at 62¼.)

Broker strides on into a *Kaffeeklatsch* where assorted other brokers are debating the merits of the Giants and the Dodgers. He shouts again.

"I have six Monkey at one-eighth!" (I will sell six hundred shares of Montgomery Ward at $62.12½ a share.)

"I'll take two!" one broker announces.

"I'll take one," says another broker.

"Okay, you're making life tough," the seller says grimly.

There is a moment's pause. Then: "And I'll take the other three at sixty-two," says the specialist.

"Sold!" says the beefy broker, and a man who once owned six hundred shares of stock is now the proud possessor of nearly $40,000 cash.

At the Curb Exchange, a few blocks away across Trinity Church graveyard, the procedure is slightly different. For many years the Curb was an outdoor market with members trading on the sidewalk and in the gutter of Broad Street, and a complicated code of hand signals was developed so that brokers on the ground could get messages to and from their clerks, who hung out the windows of the surrounding office buildings. Much of this system has been kept in the modern Curb Exchange Building. The clerks sit at telephone desks that rise in seven tiers on the east and west walls (the higher the desk, the lower the rent) and signal orders to the 499 members (going price for a membership: $10,000 to $15,000). The building is 25 years newer than the Stock Exchange, the posts are octagons instead of horseshoes, the specialists handle odd lots as well as deferred orders, the floor is larger and better lit and a little more efficient. Business is a lot lighter, too, though the Curb has been going up. (Partly because its new management is bright as a taxable dollar—this summer it is pioneering a three-thirty closing time to free its members from Saturday work and give investors in the Western time zones a longer run for their money.) On the whole, however, the stocks traded on the Curb represent corporations smaller than those on the "big board."

Big board and little board, both are amazingly efficient, honest and open markets. No transaction can be concealed from the public; at both exchanges special employees make sure that every sale gets on the ticker. Both run large and expensive quotation services (nearly 22,000,000 calls in 1951); if a man wants to know the latest bid and offer before he orders, his broker can call the quote room and a telephone girl will give him both sides of the spread. No member of either exchange is permitted to deal in listed stocks off the trading floor (except in the case of exceptionally large—and exceptionally well-publicized—sales that might swamp the market), so that the public knows at all times the price of every stock and the number of shares that are traded. Both exchanges maintain a considerable police force of accountants, who see that the members' books are always in order; and a paid president—not a member with friends—enforces the rules at both. If a man loses his money in the market it is almost always his own greed, stupidity or gullibility. It is certainly never the fault of the exchanges, and it is very rarely the fault of his broker.

It couldn't be. There have been unscrupulous men on the floors (one of them actually got to be president of the Stock Exchange in the very bad old days directly after the crash), but today the government keeps out the nice-guy and the heavy-socialite "operators"—and the members themselves have always kept out the others. They have a heavy stake in honesty. Last year alone some $20,000,000,000 in stocks and bonds were traded on the Stock Exchange and the Curb, all on the basis of verbal promises to deliver or pay. Such promises must be kept: a dishonest man would have as much chance on either floor as an atom in a bomb.

Winthrop Smith is a short, stocky man of 59 with a cheerful moon face, a fringe of greying hair and neat, rimless glasses. Behind the glasses his eyes sparkle in a subdued, dignified way, and behind the eyes his quick mind probes constantly—in the office and after hours—at the facts and theories and never-ending problems of finance. He has one of the biggest jobs on Wall Street; he is managing partner of Merrill Lynch, Pierce, Fenner and Beane.

Of the $20,000,000,000 in stocks and bonds traded last year on the New York exchanges, MLPFB (known familiarly as We the People) handled the buy or the sell orders on more than $3,500,000,000. Some brokers have two employees: a telephone clerk at the exchange and a girl to relay calls from the office. MLPFB has about 4,000. More than six hundred teletype machines, using 65,000 miles of leased wire with a yearly rent of a million dollars, connect the home office (three blocks from the Stock Exchange, occupying the bottom five floors, and half of the sixth floor, of the world's third tallest building) with 105 branch offices in 36 states, Canada and Cuba. The firm has 95 partners who own 96 seats on 42 exchanges; it is the largest securities broker on all the big exchanges, the largest commission broker in every commodity futures market, the largest dealer in unlisted securities. In 1951, before taxes but after their own salaries and distribution of more than $3,000,000 in bonuses to their employees, the partners split up profits of $9,481,359.

Nobody at Merrill Lynch waits for an elevator: escalators connect all six floors, carrying a constant weight of busy employees. Music by Muzak can occasionally be heard above the racket of telephones, typewriters, mechanical quotation boards, teletypes, IBM machines and running feet. In the research department a hundred men and women check the past performances of stocks and bonds; last year they answered thirty-five thousand letters requesting advice on investments. In the billing division another hundred girls send out 150,000 statements a month; in the home-office board room sixty account executives and five partners handle about a million dollars of business every day. Eleven partners are members of the Stock Exchange, and six of them work regularly on the floor, but they can't do all the volume—in 1951 MLPFB paid $1,394,020 to 24 floor brokers who handled orders from We the People.

The heart of the business is in the wire room and the adjoining IBM room, which occupy more than half the third floor and handle about ten times as many orders as the downstairs board room. On an average day eight thousand buy or sell orders come in on the wires, giving the stock, the number of shares involved, the limit prices (if any), and the customer's account number. The teletype girls rip off the messages, paste them on small sheets of colored paper, then put each order on one of five conveyor belts. The order jogs along the belt to the appropriate telephone operator, who calls the appropriate trading floor. When the order has been executed she writes the final price on the sheet of paper and sends it back to the teletype, which confirms the transaction to the client. A customer in Denver who ordered two hundred shares of Montgomery Ward "at the market" at 11:15 knew by 11:17 that he had bought two hundred shares of Montgomery Ward at $62.12½ a share.

And, in the most remarkable operation of all, he got his bill the next day. The teletype operator dropped the confirmed order into a box beside her machine, and a messenger picked it up. She took it to a girl in the IBM room, who reached into a library of punch-cards and pulled out a card already punched for Montgomery Ward. She handed this card and the order slip to a girl at a punch machine, who quickly punched the card with the customer's account number. Another girl took the card, reached into another library and got another card, this one already punched for two hundred shares at $62.12½. Another messenger took the two cards to an IBM machine which produced a master card with all the information, and a copy of the master.

Still another messenger took the copy to still another IBM machine, which chewed at it briefly, punched its contents on a long, pink tape, and fed the tape into a teletype machine at the close of business. The corresponding teletype at the other end printed the customer's bill, and the Denver office had nothing to do but stencil the envelope and mail it.

Two IBM repairmen are on constant duty at MLPFB, watching the 130 business machines. They also keep an eye on the electronic calculator, which

Merrill Lynch rents from IBM for two hundred dollars a day. The calculator sits at one end of the long room, its tubes blinking incomprehensibly from nine to five. It has one job: it figures out the day's business at Merrill Lynch, Pierce, Fenner & Beane.

Corn doesn't grow in Chicago, and money doesn't grow on the Stock Exchange. At one time corporations raised a good deal of new capital simply by throwing new issues onto the floor of the Exchange, but successful selling under these circumstances required sleight-of-hand manipulation of the market, now banned by good taste and good law. A few corporations still raise new money through the Exchange by issuing "stock rights," which give current stockholders the right to buy additional shares at a price substantially under the market; but nearly all new issues are sold to the public direct.

In theory these new issues are sold the way coffeepots are sold: the corporation puts out the stock, a group of wholesalers buy it and pass it on to retail dealers, who sell it to the public. In practice it is a hell of a complicated operation, because somebody always needs a coffeepot while nobody ever needs stocks, and because a company that makes coffeepots knows which pots will sell while a corporation can't possibly know which stocks and bonds will sell.

So a corporation, or city, or port authority that wants to issue new securities has a choice of two courses: it may hire an expert to design the issue, then send around a circular announcing that it will put out certain securities at certain terms, and that bids from underwriters (stock-and-bond wholesalers) will be opened on a certain date; or it can go to an underwriter and say, "This is my problem—what can you do for me?"

The underwriter, whether he gets the securities by competitive bidding or by negotiation, buys the entire issue; the corporation now has its money and is ready to go. Then the underwriter sells the securities, setting a price that will, he hopes, get rid of them quickly at a profit. A successful underwriting job should be completed within a week or so from the date of issue; if it takes longer it is a failure—the underwriter has been "locked in," his money is stuck where he can't get at it, and the amount of new securities he can underwrite has been decreased. If the underwriter is stuck with the stock forever he is "frozen in"; such a catastrophe, in a large issue, may put him out of business.

To split the risk and get more salesmen an underwriter will usually invite other underwriters to come in on the deal, organizing a "syndicate." (In competitive situations he gets his syndicate together before he bids.) Each member of the syndicate buys an agreed portion of the issue and sells retail to its clients and people who walk in through the front door, wholesale to dealers and other friends. The business is held together by continuing informal relationships between various underwriters, and between each underwriter and his customers.

For many years the personal relationship was the way to get underwriting business as well as the way to manage it. Large corporations did all their financing through one underwriting house, which advised them on all financial matters, to the point where a partner in the house often sat on the corporation's board of directors. Whether or not these relationships add to the cost of financing is an enormously complicated question (Congress and many states have decided that they do, ordering railroads and public utilities to put their issues up for competitive bidding instead of negotiating the terms with old friends); whether they violate the antitrust laws is a matter now being decided by Judge Harold Medina and a few thousand lawyers in the greatest legal beano since the Bourbon Restoration.

Many Wall Street houses, singing old songs with old friends, were caught off key by the quick growth of competitive bidding, and in the years immediately after the war midwestern firms such as Halsey, Stuart & Co. and Otis & Co. took over a large part of the business. Recently, however, Wall Street has bounced back; in 1951 the largest of the underwriters was The First Boston Corporation, with headquarters, oddly enough, in New York. And the old established house of Kuhn, Loeb & Co.—a partnership, not a corporation—was high up on the list.

Kuhn, Loeb occupies the bottom four floors of an old, dark office building one block from Wall Street on William Street. A visitor to the executive offices can take the elevator one flight up, or walk on an ancient, black marble staircase that winds around one of the beams, over the cashiers' windows and the accounting department, where some clerks still sit on high stools at high tables. On the second floor the guard is Donald Beaton, an elderly, kindly man who was Mrs. Otto Kahn's private chauffeur for 29 years and knew senior partner John Schiff when John was a boy. Schiff, now 48, tall, thin and whitehaired, the handsomest man on Wall Street, runs the business in the same graceful, personal, conservative way his grandfather ran it sixty years ago. Kuhn, Loeb is one of the few places in New York where the boss will come out himself to usher the visitor in. With these friendly small-town banking habits Kuhn, Loeb in 1951 managed financing to a total of $603,938,053.

Most of these issues will never see a trading floor—of half a million American corporations less than three thousand are traded on the nation's sixteen exchanges. Stocks in the others, most of them too small or owned by too few people to produce the constant bids and offers necessary to an auction market, are bought and sold "over the counter" by more than thirty thousand salesmen and dealers scattered throughout the country. Nobody has any exact idea of how many shares are traded by these dealers, but the general estimate seems to be that over-the-counter dealings—excluding government bonds but including securities also listed on an exchange—account for substantially more trading, and slightly more money, than the New York Stock Exchange.

Though he will sometimes act as a broker and work for a broker's commission, the over-the-counter dealer usually makes profits the way a storekeeper makes profits—he buys cheap and sells dear. He will "take a position" in a stock (buy a quantity of shares), and then offer the stock for sale to the public or other brokers at a price higher than his purchase price. He works through the medium of "The Sheets"—a high, narrow, thick book with pink pages, issued daily by the National Quotation Bureau and containing bids and offers on thousands of unlisted securities from dealers all over the country. If a customer asks a dealer for a stock he doesn't own, the dealer will look in The Sheets, find the offer price, and quote a slightly higher figure. The Sheets are not available to the public; they are the "inside" prices, to dealers only; the "outside" prices printed by financial newspapers always give the dealer a profit on the deal.

This part of the securities business has a few giants—Blyth & Co., The First Boston Corporation, MLPFB, and so forth—but most of the trading is done by small firms. Joseph J. Lann Securities, Inc., employs only Joe Lann, one trader, and a few telephone girls, but it ranks fairly high in the profession. Lann himself is a large man in his early fifties, with a fine, greying mustache, a fine, greying head of hair, a conservative yet flamboyant pin-stripe suit and the general look of a movie heavy. (Since almost all his business is done by telephone, on hot summer days when he doesn't expect visitors he will shed his pin-stripe suit and strip to slacks and a polo shirt; others, less formal, strip to shorts and sneakers.) He sits at a walnut desk cluttered with telephones, looking away from his window, which faces over a small building onto a large building. The telephone never shuts its yap, but Lann is used to it: he has been on The Street since childhood. Like most over-the-counter dealers, he thinks fast.

Any stockbroker can predict with great accuracy which fifty of the fifteen hundred stocks on the Stock Exchange will be most actively traded in the next year—the corporations are large, their activities are well publicized, investors know about them. But the over-the-counter dealer must work with corporations almost unknown to the mass of the investing public. Since he makes his living by the turnover of his capital, he must be even more careful than the underwriter never to get frozen in. He must pick over the hundreds of thousands of corporate issues and find a few which he can promote into activity.

He will often "make a market" for a stock where no market was before. He hears, for example, about a proposed bank merger in Maine, gets hold of the balance sheets and after looking them over finds the proposition interesting. He telephones Maine, speaks to the presidents of the banks, to any local stock dealer, possibly to a few large stockholders. He buys a few shares of one bank or both, makes sure he can get more, then puts an announcement in The Sheets to the effect that he maintains an interest in these stocks, will buy at a certain price or sell at another, higher price. He has made a market.

Before this burst of creative activity, a man who owned shares in these banks and needed money instead would have had to hunt for a buyer, and accept an arbitrary price. Now he has a place to sell them—and he can buy them with the knowledge that if he ever needs cash the shares will sell for cash.

These activities are the important part of Wall Street, but with all that batter in the icebox there's bound to be an assortment of cake, and in the financial market sidelines are sometimes tastier than the main chance. Three of the big underwriting partnerships have rich specialties that turn up juicy in the year-end balance sheets. Lehman Brothers runs the nation's most important investment-advisory service, telling clients with more than $400,000 (Lehman won't touch anybody with less than $400,000) where to put their money; the yearly fee is about one-half of one per cent of the total invested. Goldman Sachs employs a group of experts to play domestic arbitrage, cashing in on the minute differences between the prices and market values of stock rights, merger bonds and reorganization bonds, throwing a million dollars into the hopper to make an instantaneous, absolutely certain five hundred. Wertheim & Co. takes deep plunges in the market with its own cash, and is generally considered the smartest smart money in The Street. Usually, Wertheim & Co. works with the low-priced, profitless stocks on the exchanges; its bright young researchers and wise old partners are trained to smell a growth situation at two years' distance. If necessary, they will buy a controlling interest in a sagging corporation and give it financial advice to put it on the road to profits and send the stock a-climbing. Wertheim's most spectacular deal was in the capital stock of Nedick's, Inc., a New York chain of hot-dog and orange-drink stands, which it bought for $60,000, including lawyer's fees, in 1934 and—after taking dividends of more than $2,000,000—sold for nearly $4,000,000 in 1951.

Many other firms do all their business on the fringe of the market. Carl Marks & Co., for example, works solely with stocks and bonds of foreign corporations and governments. Marks himself is a short, round, soft-spoken New Yorker with a fringe of black hair over his ears, a thousand theories about Life and Business, and a million facts about the foreign securities market. He has a private teletype to London to keep him in touch with developments on the English market but his business, too, is mostly by telephone. He employs ten traders, each an expert on one part of the world; they sit at a row of switchboards in a room glassed off from the rest of the office, buying and selling over the telephone, yelling questions at each other or—most often—at Marks, referring constantly to scrawled memoranda on top of their switchboards or a blackboard at one end of the room listing the latest prices of active foreign issues.

Closer to the market, and further away from corporate finance, is the options business—Puts, Calls and Straddles. In plain language, options are a way to play the market—or to hedge against the market—on fairly little money. A man who believes that Montgomery Ward is going up can either buy the stock or buy a Call—an option to buy the stock at the present market price at some future time. One hundred shares of the stock will cost him, at this writing, around $6200; a Call, giving him the right to buy one hundred shares for $6200 at any time within the next ninety days, will cost him about $400. He is not obliged to buy; his maximum risk is $400. If the stock goes down, he simply drops his option; if it goes up, say from 62 to 70, he takes up the option, buys his one hundred shares for $6200, takes them to his stockbroker, and sells them on the Market for $7000—netting, after the cost of the option, $400. A Put is the opposite of a Call—it gives the customer the right to *sell* at the present market price, whatever happens to the market during the time the option is in force.

A Straddle, which costs more, gives its owner the right to buy, to sell or *to do both at different times* during the life of the contract. In a rapidly fluctuating market the Straddle may pay both ways.

Twenty-five brokers, all in New York, handle the nation's Put & Call business, which in 1951 involved about $100,000,000 worth of stocks. The brokers do not themselves issue Puts or Calls—they buy the options from one set of people and sell them, at a higher price, to another. Buying them is a cinch, but selling is not so easy. Two of the bigger brokers—Filer, Schmidt & Co. and Thomas, Haab & Botts—put ads into the New York newspapers almost every day, offering options for sale. The standard minimum price, for some reason hidden in the European origins of the business, is $137.50 for a thirty-day one-way option; the longer the option runs—six months is about the maximum—the higher the price. Sometimes, to make the option more attractive, the fixed price of the stock will be above (for Calls) or below (for Puts) the current market price, and the price of the option will be correspondingly lower.

The largest and most important of these fringe operations is the investment-fund business, which gives the small investor professional management of his money and a share in a widely diversified portfolio of stocks. The funds are corporations which sell shares in themselves, then invest the proceeds in stocks and bonds; they pay dividends to their stockholders on the dividends they receive and on their capital gains. They come in two varieties: the open-end fund, which stands ready at all times to buy its stocks back from its stockholders at their net worth, and sell to new stockholders at net worth plus the cost of selling; and the closed-end fund, which is like an ordinary corporation—its stock issue is pretty much fixed, and shares are bought and sold in the market.

Today the funds have assets of about $3,000,000,000, and hundreds of thousands of stockholders, most of them $100-to-$1000 investors. Brokers, who used to believe that the funds were stealing their business, now recommend them to many small customers; of seven brokers whose "free advice" ads were recently answered by an editor of *Forbes* Magazine, three (not including Merrill Lynch, Pierce, Fenner & Beane) advised mutual funds.

All these people are watched by some federal agency, usually the Securities and Exchange Commission. The SEC makes big medicine, but the ingredients are almost wholly preventive. The agency exists to protect people from fraud, not from themselves. It has three main functions: to keep crooks and adventurers out of the securities business, to prevent manipulation of any security, in any market, and to guarantee that all relevant facts about new securities—and all securities listed on the exchanges—are available to the public before it is asked to buy.

A corporation that wants to sell to the public any large issue of new securities must file a registration statement with the Commission at least twenty days before the date of issue. The statement must contain a complete analysis of the corporation's administration, financial structure and current business, an announcement of the purpose for which the new money is to be used, and an exact explanation of the terms of the security. The SEC will investigate the statement and certify that it is complete—*not* that it is accurate or that the security is worth a penny (if the statements are false, however, the buyer can sue). If a man wants to organize himself into a corporation to mine uranium on the moon, and sell a million dollars' worth of stock to keep himself in steaks until he gets there, the SEC will not stop him. But it will insist that these facts be given to a prospective purchaser.

To stop manipulation the SEC keeps a careful eye on The Sheets and the volume of trading in each stock at the exchanges. Any sudden burst of activity will send SEC investigators to the brokers to find out who bought or sold the stock, how and why. To keep crooks away from the securities business, the SEC registers every interstate stockbroker, stock dealer and investment fund; and SEC auditors descend unannounced at irregular intervals to examine the books.

On the whole, however, the SEC regulates through associations of the regulated—the exchanges and the National Association of Securities Dealers. Each of these organizations is registered with the Commission, and only members of an association can work in the richer mines of the securities business. The constitution and by-laws of each association must be submitted to the SEC for approval; if the Commission doesn't approve, it can, after appropriate hearings, make changes. The SEC can expel members or officers from any of these associations, and the associations may, of course, expel their own. Any expelled member can appeal to the Commissioners and to the courts.

They always appeal. Where there is government regulation, by Thumb's rule, there will be lawyers. Nearly a thousand law firms have offices in the financial district, and a score of them are giants—"factories," the boys call them—employing fifty or more lawyers. They spread over two, three and even four stories of the more important office buildings, with law libraries on every floor; they are genteel as git-out and often serve four-o'clock tea to everyone in a large conference room or some partner's splendid office. They work their young lawyers hard (sixty hours a week is not uncommon) but pay them well (the usual starting salary is eighty dollars a week), give them bonuses, month-long summer vacations in their first year and an unusually good chance of working up to a partnership.

These Wall Street firms work all over the country; the average member, after some experience, will spend nearly a month out of town every year. They do every kind of corporation law, property law, labor law, tax law, estate law and administrative law, and a good deal of ordinary law to boot. A new and highly profitable part of their business is private placement—the sale of an entire issue of new securities to an insurance company or some other institution. The corporations like private placement because it eliminates the costs of underwriting and registration statements (the securities are not offered to the public, so the SEC never enters); the law firms like it because it gives them a firmer grip on their clients; but the men who must actually draw up the hundreds of pages of dull contract think it stinks. They call it "boilerplate work."

When necessary, the lawyers sue: contracts are usually sacred on Wall Street, but sometimes they're hellish. The best case in recent years involved Kaiser-Frazer Corporation and the Cleveland underwriting house of Otis & Co. It began on February 3, 1948, when Otis and two other companies agreed to underwrite 900,000 shares of new K-F stock, buying the shares from K-F at $11.50 to sell to the public at $13—a twelve per cent, or very good profit. The offering date was to be February 9, 1948; but during those six days, even though K-F bought 186,200 shares on the open market to hold it up, the price of the old K-F stock dropped. Cyrus Eaton, majority stockholder in Otis, decided that the stuff was weak, and went looking for a way out.

Shortly before noon on the offering date, a lawyer connected to Otis by many mysterious telephone calls entered a stockholder's suit against K-F in Wayne County Court, Detroit. The lawsuit, by endangering K-F's assets, changed the whole picture and gave Otis a chance to back away; and Eaton cheerfully sent the bad news to his good friend Henry Kaiser. Henry bellowed like a smitten buffalo, called his lawyers and promptly filed suit, charging conspiracy to welsh. On July 10, 1951, a New York Federal Court awarded K-F $3,120,743.51 in damages. Otis appealed, and in April, 1952, the Circuit Court threw out the judgment on the grounds that K-F's prospectus—the sales pitch for the new issue—had been misleading, and that K-F therefore couldn't enforce its contract. K-F is now appealing to the Supreme Court with the argument that Otis & Co. knew all the details of the prospectus, including anything in it that might be misleading to outsiders, and therefore can't claim it as a defense.

For these and other services K-F in 1951 paid the Wall Street firm of Willkie, Owen, Farr, Gallagher & Walton some $208,400. The fee was by no means extreme—last year RCA paid $375,000 for legal services from Cahill, Gordon, Zachry & Reindel; and AT&T, sharing the wealth, paid $193,900 to Root, Ballentine, Harlan, Bushby & Palmer and $137,750 to Davis, Polk, Wardwell, Sunderland & Kiendl.

They used to tell a story about a small businessman, broke and friendless through no fault of his own, who came to Baron Rothschild and told the Baron his estimable tale of circumstance. Rothschild listened and said he would like to help, and then he thought for a moment. "I won't lend you any money," he said. "I'll do something better." He led the trembling businessman from the office and walked with him, arm in arm, across the floor of the London Exchange.

Today no individual can make a man's fortune simply by calling him a friend, but the Federal government, by walking across the floor with the financial market or throwing spitballs at it, can make or break the fortunes of almost everyone on Wall Street. Its agent is the Federal Reserve System, which by various means controls the nation's money supply; on Wall Street its representative is the Federal Reserve Bank of New York, which in addition to its mechanical and discretionary jobs keeps six billion dollars in shiny gold bars watched by plump, balding guards who never talk to visitors or take their hands out of their pockets, in a vault five stories below the sidewalk on the bedrock of Manhattan Island.

The Federal Reserve System influences the financial market directly by setting up margin requirements—telling brokers how much they may lend their customers—to prevent artificial inflation on the stock market; but its greatest power over Wall Street comes from its control of the money supply. Bank deposits are money just as dollar bills are money, and at the end of 1951 there was $160,000,000,000 of bank money in the nation. To assure that this supply matches the nation's need for cash the Federal Reserve has a bludgeon, a whip and a bridle—the bludgeon is its power to tell the banks what proportion of their funds they may lend, and what proportion they must keep in reserve; the whip is its ability to lend money, or refuse to lend money, to the banks themselves; the bridle is its operations in the government-bond market (by buying bonds the Federal Reserve puts money into the economy, increasing the money in the banks; by selling bonds it takes money out).

All these matters are as important to the financial market as wings to a bird. Wall Street lives by the interest rate, which is the rent for money, and as a rough rule the rent will go up when the supply goes down, and down when the supply goes up. People buy stocks and bonds, rather than simply socking their money in a savings bank, because stocks and bonds pay more rent; and when the interest rate goes up stocks and bonds must give a greater return or give up the ghost.

The banks themselves are constantly busy in the securities market, though their activities are strictly regulated by law. They use their unloaned desposits to buy and underwrite high-grade municipal and state bonds, manage trusts and estates which own stocks and bonds, lend money to brokers and underwriters to finance operations, and lend long-term money to industry itself in direct competition with the bond market.

The long-term loan business—which accounted for about five billion dollars out of 67 billion on loan from the banks at the end of 1951—is a new one for bankers, who used to restrict their lending pretty much to bakers who needed money to buy flour and would pay it back when they sold the bread. But the banks have gone into all sorts of business recently—automobile loans, personal loans, installment-buying loans—changing banking from the deadest of professions to one of the liveliest.

Even the giant Chase National Bank—third largest in the country, with total resources of nearly five and a half billion dollars—has gone after the small-loans business in newspaper, magazine, radio and television ads. Chase has its headquarters one block from the Stock Exchange in a 38-story building, a fancy, stone-front affair completed in 1927. The stonework extends to the inside, but except for the air-conditioned fourth floor, where the executives hang out, Chase is a pretty businesslike place, featuring large bull pens and few private offices. Since bank salaries do not compare well with other salaries (any other salaries) Chase coddles its employees with free lunches, free life insurance, free education, and an extensive free medical department. To get young blood into the banking field it runs a large-scale executive-training program and takes it officers from the ranks.

A large bank must be as far above Caesar's wife as Caesar's wife is above suspicion; dignity is the password. Winthrop Aldrich, chairman of the board at Chase, is so dignified that despite his vigor he looks fifteen years older than his 66 years, and he is surrounded by soft-spoken, carefully groomed, absolutely polite assistants. Elsewhere on The Street the Brooks look is cherished; at Chase it is a point of order. Nevertheless, some of the dignity has gone out of the old business. When Chase advertises its uses two slogans—"Why don't you talk to the people at Chase?" and "It pays to do business with Chase." For 75 years it was, to everybody connected with the bank, "The Chase." Now it's just "Chase."

In most western towns with fairly modern newspaper plants a visitor can stop by a first-floor plate-glass window and watch the presses roll. He can get the same entertainment right off Wall Street, on the New Street side of the Dow Jones building, and the press he sees is a monster that can handle eighty full-size newspaper pages at a time and runs every night but Saturday night from seven o'clock to well after midnight. It prints the eastern edition of *The Wall Street Journal*.

Business is generally good on Wall Street, but at the *Journal* it's spectacular. Even in the boomiest days of the Great Boom the *Journal's* circulation never touched sixty thousand; today it has passed 235,000. Though it is still *The Wall Street Journal*, less than half the circulation is printed on the New Street press (the rest rolls off the rubber in Chicago, San Francisco and Dallas, with local news added on the spot), and less than half the average issue goes to financial matters. To increase its general-business circulation, the *Journal* spends more money for advertising than any other newspaper in the nation.

And the *Journal* is only one part of the Dow Jones organization, which includes *Barron's*, a weekly financial magazine, and the Dow Jones tickers, the nation's third or fourth largest news service (they never tell anybody how many customers they have), running into 386 cities, maintaining some nineteen offices and 250 reporters to gather news for all three operations.

Printing and publishing is a big business on Wall Street. *The Wall Street Journal* has a serious rival in the *Journal of Commerce of New York*; most of the large brokerage houses and banks print up regular reports on the state of the nation and various industries; the Stock Exchange puts out a pocket-size magazine, *The Exchange*, with a circulation of seventy thousand; the law firms spew countless briefs at the courts; and almost every one of the many financial professions has a trade journal all its own. Specialized research organizations such as Dun & Bradstreet and Moody's Investor's Service issue reports analyzing the strength of people's credit and the riskiness of people's securities. On a far less responsible level there are a number of quickie sheets, charging as much as fifty dollars an issue, giving their special customers "10 Stocks Absolutely Sure

To Go Up," resembling in attitude, accuracy and phraseology the little green cards sold at the entrances to race tracks.

For straight news coverage Wall Street is second only to Washington. Five news services, eight newspapers and ten magazines are represented among the more than a hundred members of the New York Financial Writers' Association, and nothing that happens on Wall Street can get by all of them. Contrary to both popular and professional opinion, they are not rich, and they do not get invaluable inside tips about the market; many of them are members of a labor union—the Newspaper Guild.

In one way they have a far easier life than the ordinary reporter—they don't have to work at night—but to do their job well they must dig around in some spectacularly dull places. And since they are dealing with important executives, not grief-struck widows, they have a private, particularly galling problem. They described it in a song last year at their annual show, *The Financial Follies:*

> *In all financial writing you are sure to meet this guy.*
> *And in his own opinion he stands supremely high.*
> *He knows the big shots everywhere, the President calls him "sir."*
> *He's a very important sonofabitch, he knows your publisher.*
> *He is important, tra la, la, la, la, la, la,*
> *Very important, tra la, la, la, la, la, la,*
> *He'll have you know his shirt is stuffed with real chinchilla fur,*
> *He's a very important sonofabitch, he knows your publisher.*

Times have changed, and all for the better. Today the financial market polices itself well, and the Federal police find each year few if any signs of corruption. Resistance to government regulation has just about disappeared—last year one of the once-hated revenooers, Commissioner Edward McCormick, was hired away from the SEC to become president of the Curb Exchange. The private-club notion has gone to the bottom like a stone: Merrill Lynch alone spends $1,500,-000 a year on advertising and publishing. The Stock Exchange is persuading corporations with high-priced stock to split it, giving stockholders two shares for one, to cut prices and bring more people into the market.

But there's a limit to how many people should come in. Stocks give a greater return than savings accounts because they give less safety; and over a period of a few months they're extremely risky. A man who may have to pull out his cash to pay a doctor's bill shouldn't put it into stocks in the first place—ten or fifteen or twenty per cent of it may not be there when he needs it.

"Only those who can afford to risk," G. Keith Funston, the president of the Stock Exchange, told a gathering of brokers last year, "people with government bonds and savings in the banks, people with life insurance, people with emergency reserves in one form or another—should be encouraged to become shareholders." And everybody with such reserves should as a matter of common sense invest the rest of his money.

In June most Wall Street expert opinion believed that stock prices were going down. But the opinion was not unanimous (Wall Street is unanimous only in believing that the nation will sink if the Republicans lose, a belief it has held in all weathers since 1868), expert opinion is usually wrong—and the short-term movements of stock prices ought not to interest an investor. There is such a thing as a secular trend, and it is upward—which means that over a period of thirty years or so stock prices in general will tend to rise, so that a man who doesn't have to cash in tomorrow doesn't have to watch the ticker. The man who goes to invest his money on a long-term basis gains an income and a hedge against inflation that far overbalance his long-term risk.

He also makes Wall Street very happy.

↤————————————————————————————————↦

The Post Office Case

Wɪᴛʜ the exception of footnotes and one passage from the record of the original hearing, omitted for lack of space, the following is the complete text of the decision of the U. S. Court of Appeals for the District of Columbia, handed down on June 4, 1945, written by Justice Thurman Arnold, expressing the unanimous opinion of Justices Miller, Edgerton and Arnold who heard the case:

Esquire is a well known magazine of general discretion. It contains stories, articles, literary and dramatic reviews. Its contributors include distinguished authors, clergymen, and professors in our best educational institutions.

The Postmaster General revoked the second-class mailing privileges of this magazine, not on the ground of obscenity but because he thought its dominant purpose was to publish writings and pictures described in his order as being "in that obscure and treacherous borderland zone where the average person hesitates to find them technically obscene, but still may see ample proof that they are morally improper and not for the public welfare and the public good". The revocation order would cost Esquire about $500,000 a year and put it in such a disadvantageous competitive position that it probably could not continue as a current magazine of general circulation.

The theory of the ruling depriving Esquire of second-class mailing privileges, while at the same time permitting it to be mailed at higher rates, is stated by the Postmaster General as follows: "A publication to enjoy these *unique mail privileges* (emphasis added) . . . is bound to do more than refrain from disseminating material which is obscene or bordering on the obscene. It is under a positive duty to contribute to the public good and the public welfare."

No doubt such a duty exists. But it does not follow that an administrative official may be delegated the power first to determine what is good for the public to read and then to force compliance with his ideas by putting editors who do not follow them at a competitive disadvantage. It is inconceivable that Congress intended to delegate such power to an administrative official or that the exercise of such power, if delegated, could be held constitutional. Congress established the second-class mailing privileges because it believed that periodicals which disseminated public information, literature, art or science deserved to be en-

August, 1945

couraged on account of their contribution as a class to the public good. But the American way of obtaining that kind of contribution is by giving competitive opportunity to men of different tastes and different ideas, not by compelling conformity to the taste or ideas of any government official. This basic idea has nowhere been more eloquently expressed than in the famous quotation from Mr. Justice Holmes, dissenting in *Abrams* v. *United States.*

"But when men have realized that time has upset many fighting faiths, they may come to believe even more than they believe the very foundations of their own conduct that the ultimate good desired is better reached by free trade in ideas,—that the best test of truth is the power of the thought to get itself accepted in the competition of the market; and that truth is the only ground upon which their wishes safely can be carried out. That, at any rate, is the theory of our Constitution."

What the Government appears to assert is that the power to charge Esquire an additional $500,000 a year for use of the mails, unless it conforms to the Postmaster General's notions of the public good, is not a power to censor because the magazine may be mailed at the higher rate. The key to an understanding of this extraordinary contention is found in the Postmaster General's reference to second-class mailing rates as "unique privileges". He appears to think of his duty under the statute, not as administration of nondiscriminatory rates for a public service, but as analogous to the award of the Navy E for industrial contributions to the war. The Navy E is an award for exceptional merit. The second-class mailing rate is conceived by the Post Office to be an award for resisting the temptation to publish material which offends persons of refinement.

But mail service is not a special privilege. It is a highway over which all business must travel. The rates charged on this highway must not discriminate between competing businesses of the same kind. If the Interstate Commerce Commission were delegated the power to give lower rates to such manufacturers as in its judgment were contributing to the public good the exercise of that power would be clearly unconstitutional. Such a situation would involve freedom of competitive enterprise. The case before us involves freedom of speech as well.

Little more need be said to decide this case. Nevertheless, since we hope that this is the last time that a government agency will attempt to compel the acceptance of its literary or moral standards relating to material admittedly not obscene, the voluminous record may serve as a useful reminder of the kind of mental confusion which always accompanies such censorship.

The first source of that confusion is, of course, the age old question when a scantily clad lady is art, and when she is highly improper. Some refined persons are hopeful that an answer to this vexing riddle may some day be found. Others are pessimistic. But whichever school eventually proves correct it is clear that the problem had not yet been solved when the record in this case went to press.

A second source of confusion in determining what kind of literature furthers public welfare is the dividing line between refined humor and low comedy. To illustrate the difficulty inherent in this problem we cite the following colloquy between counsel for the Post Office and counsel for Esquire. It is typical of hundreds of similar instances.

Mr. Bromley: I would like to know, Mr. Hassell, if you don't mind telling me now, just what it is in that article you don't like. I can't find it.

Mr. Hassell: I would be glad to read it to counsel.

Mr. Bromley: Thank you.

Mr. Hassell: Third column at the bottom of page 144. "He noticed how large the uniform made her behind look."

It may be that the above encourages the use of unscientific terms. Or it may be that it is in the public interest to omit all comment on the part of the lady referred to. Yet it is difficult to make such judgment with the feeling of certainty which one should have when the result of one's decision is to cost a publication $500,000 annually.

This same kind of uncertainty appears in a third problem which must be faced whenever this censorship is exercised. How far will this reform of periodical literature go if the Postmaster General is given a free hand. For example, recently the New York Times (on Sunday, of all days!) carried the following quip by Mayor LaGuardia on the front page where few churchgoers could fail to see it:

"Sorry. Racing does no one any good. It has nothing to do with horses. It has as much bearing on improving the breed of horses as a bawdy house has on eugenics."

Does this mean that the New York Times will lose its second-class mailing privileges if it does not stop that sort of thing?

The Postmaster General gives serious consideration to this aspect of the problem. His conclusion is that occasional indifference to the public welfare may be indulged by an editor provided that it is not so frequent as to be classed as a habit. His opinion puts it in this way:

"When such writings or pictures occur in isolated instances their dangerous tendencies and malignant qualities may be considered of lesser importance.

"When, however, they become a dominant and systematic feature they most certainly cannot be said to be for the public good, and a publication which uses them in that manner is not making the 'special contribution to the public welfare' which Congress intended by the Fourth condition."

The Postmaster General appears to think that the improper dominant motive which he suspects from reading Esquire is corroborated by its editor's statement. He quotes the editor as follows:

"The editor of this publication admits that from its origin 'our humor and our articles and our fiction all stressed a man alone angle—you might call it a stag party type of treatment,' and testified 'we called it the smoking room type of humor.' "

Now it is well known that when men gather together without the companionship of women an unrefined atmosphere is apt to spread over the entire gathering like a fog. And so the Post Office argues that only an editor indifferent to the public welfare would permit an atmosphere of this kind to dominate his magazine.

Unfortunately this still leaves the dividing line between an occasional vulgar lapse and a vulgar dominant purpose in a good deal of obscurity. It also leaves unsettled the question who is finally to decide what the dominant purpose is. For example, when we turn to the record we find that the weight of the evidence is that the magazine as a whole is unobjectionable. Far more witnesses testified against the Postmaster General's conclusion, than for it. They included men of national distinction as writers, scientists and educators. They also included the vigilant New England Watch and Ward Society. The Postmaster General is supported only by five clergymen, a psychiatrist, a lady prominent in women's organizations, and an assistant superintendent of schools. In this situation, assuming the existence of the power to censor, may a court review the issue of dominant vulgarity on its merits?

The answer of the Government is an unqualified no. It contends with some reason that this court has no right to review the Postmaster General's notions of dominant vulgarity if they are supported by substantial evidence. It argues even more persuasively that no right minded man can brush aside as insubstantial the opinions of five clergymen (among whom is a bishop) on what is good for the public.

We think the Government is clearly right in its contention once the power claimed by the Post Office is assumed to exist. There is a practical reason, apart from respect for the testimony of clergymen, why the administrative imposition of literary and artistic standards cannot be reviewed by a court on its merits. Opinions on such matters differ so widely that if the evidence in the record before the Post Office were to be weighed each side would have to continue calling witnesses indefinitely in order not to be outweighed by the other. We have no doubt that thousands of reputable experts on the public good could have been obtained by each side in this case. We know of no way a court can evaluate the comparative expert qualifications of persons who hold opinions on what the public should read. Once we admit the power claimed here we see no room for effective judicial review of its exercise. And so in practical effect it amounts to a power in the Postmaster General to impose the standards of any reputable minority group on the whole nation.

In addition, the record suggests that the power claimed here would be used by sincere and conscientious officials to bind modern periodical literature to the standards of a former generation. This is dramatically illustrated by the cross examination of H. L. Mencken, who appeared as a witness for Esquire. No one today would question either Mr. Mencken's eminence or his complete respectability. Yet counsel for the Post Office attempts to impeach his testimony because about twenty years ago an issue of the American Mercury was refused all mailing privileges. It would be difficult to find anyone today who could with reason object to this issue of the magazine. The attempt to impeach Mr. Mencken on this account reads as follows:

Q. Mr. Mencken, you are the author of a story called "Hat-Rack," aren't you? A. I am not, sir.

Q. You published it in your magazine? A. I did, sir.

Q. That story had to deal with some sexual activity in a box-car or freight car? A. Not specifically. It dealt with people who engaged in sexual activity, but there was no scene of sexual activity in the story.

Q. Was "Hat-Rack" the name of the woman who did that? A. Nickname. Did you ask who wrote it?

Q. No, sir; I did not. A. I will tell you if you want to know. It was written by Herbert Asbury, the great grand-nephew of Bishop Asbury, the first American Methodist bishop.

Chairman Myers: For whom De Pauw University was originally named.

The witness: I didn't know that. There was a report that Asbury was the great-grandson of the Bishop, but the Bishop actually was a bachelor. He is a great-grandson of the Bishop's brother.

By Mr. Hassell:

Q. Mr. Mencken, was the issue of your magazine containing that story declared non-mailable by the Post Office Department? A. Yes, sir. I think you ought to let me explain what happened, if you care to.

Q. Yes, sir; go right ahead. A. The Post Office entered that case rather late. An effort was made in Boston to suppress the magazine as a measure of revenge by the Boston Watch and Ward Society, which we had been denouncing. They proceeded by threatening a newsdealer. The poor newsdealer had no stake in the thing and was willing to subside and withdraw the magazine, so I went to Boston and sold the magazine myself on Boston Common and insisted on the Watch and Ward Society arresting me.

I was arrested, tried and acquitted.

Meanwhile, subsequent to my arrest, and four or five weeks subsequent to the time the magazine had gone through the mails, the Post Office Department issued an order barring it from the mails. It was a purely imaginary order. There were no more to be mailed.

So I went to court on that and I had injunctions against the Post Office by two Federal judges, both of whom denounced the Post Office as obscene, indecent, unfair and ignominious.

I agreed with the verdict thoroughly and believe it was just to this minute.

The Post Office tried to hit me in the back when I was fighting with the filthy Comstocks in Boston. I fought the Comstocks and I fought the Post Office, and I put my magazine back in the mails and they have never molested me since.

Q. Didn't the Federal Court in New York refuse to issue an injunction as the case was moot? A. That is not precisely what happened. I had my injunction in the district courts of Boston and in New York, and the Post Office, pursuing its filthy course of trying to persecute me, appealed to the Circuit and the Circuit after two years decided that the case was completely moot because we were in point of fact through the mails. They decided I could not get relief because the Post Office barring me from the mails was completely dishonest—I wasn't an applicant to the mails.

The three examples cited above effectively illustrate the intellectual standards required for the kind of censorship exercised in this case.

We intend no criticism of counsel for the Post Office. They were faced with an impossible task. They undertook it with sincerity. But their very sincerity makes the record useful as a memorial to commemorate the utter confusion and lack of intelligible standards which can never be escaped when that task is attempted. We believe that the Post Office officials should experience a feeling of relief if they are limited to the more prosaic function of seeing to it that "Neither snow nor rain nor heat nor gloom of night stays these couriers from the swift completion of their appointed rounds."

PAUL GALLICO

◀ ─── ▶

The Melee of the Mages

So NOW I'm writing a story. What can happen to me? All right, so I don't got much education from getting tossed out of grade 8A of P. S. 191 which is just a couple of blocks east of Delancey Street where I was born, for clipping that big, dumb Jake Rosenzweig, so he goes to a hospital.

Maybe if I don't take that poke at Jake ten years ago for giving me the business, when the teacher ain't looking, I go a lot further, though I guess I ain't done so bad, have I? Ask any sporting writer about Goldie. Who is writing all the press releases for Hymie Korngold's stable of Fighters that Fight, so they go in the papers sometimes with only a couple of words changed? Who takes care of the sportswriters around the training camps when we got a boy working out, and runs errands for them? Who is even allowed by Hymie Korngold sometimes I should handle a boy for him out of town when we got a fight that ain't too important? Little Irving Goldstein. But everybody calls me just Goldie.

So I guess I ain't sorry I put the slug on that big Rosenzweig, he should gradually waste away from a fatal sickness, for what the lug done to me and them other kids, the bully. A supply of small buckshot he used to keep in his cheek, and then "zip!" he'd snap one out with his teeth and sting you in the ear or the back of the neck. So one day I let him have it. There shouldn't a been no trouble only I busted his jawr and made him swallow some of the buckshot, it couldn't happen to him better. But he goes to the hospital and they give me the heave-o out of P. S. 191 and I hadda go to work.

But education ain't everything, especially when you got natural ability like I have which comes by me naturally, and Joe Parkhurst who is the sports columnist for the *Morning Democrat* says it's even better if you are going to write stories you don't have too much education or the editors will not know what you are trying to say.

Joe shows me a check for one hundred bucks he got one day for writing a story for a magazine out of his head, so I says—"Boy, what a racket. How long has this been going on? I'll bet I could write a story. Gimme the angle will ya, Joe?"

So Joe says—"Sure, Goldie. It's a cinch. All you do is sit down at a typewriter with a lotta paper and just tell what happens to somebody."

January, 1941

I says—"And they give ya dough for that?"

Joe just flashes the pay paper again. You gotta admit it's a convincer, ain't it?

So that's why I'm writing now the story of how we come to win the middle-weight championship of the world with Packy McSween at the Yankee Stadium last June from Joe Falone, the champion and holder of the world crown, before eighty-nine thousand people in what the sportswriters called *The Melee of the Mages*, also the *Combat of the Conjurors* and the *War of the Wizards*.

Maybe if you was there you are saying to yourself, what is the story in that, because after the hocus-pocus between Hex-Eye Lipschitz and Professor Swammi the Wabadaba of Waaf is over, all you see was Packy slide out from our corner and park his right alongside Falone's kisser after which the call for the stiff-wagon is in order.

Chum, I'm telling you that that part of it was just wrapping up the package and delivering it C.O.D. What I got is the stuff that goes inside the bundle before we hand it to Joe Falone, the inside dope that don't get into the papers on account of what Hymie Korngold calls it secrets of the trade.

It begins maybe six months ago when Hymie Korngold gets a mad with Hex-Eye Lipschitz who has been working for us regular, and tosses him out of the office over the matter of a couple of bucks. Maybe it is a foolish thing to do, but Hymie is very fond of a buck as everybody knows and if a guy is not entitled to be peculiar about something, what is it worth?

Also since we make the surprise win with Packy McSween over K. O. Hogan in the Garden in three rounds last winter with Hex-Eye putting the double whammy on Hogan, so it gradually comes a weakness over him and he doesn't duck Packy's right, Lipschitz—he should getting in both knees eventually enough water to floating the Queen Mary—is becoming so swelled up he is not only raising his prices double but he is also demanding a piece of the fighter which is something Hymie will part with his right leg sooner than.

I guess you read about Hex-Eye Lipschitz who is a curious character around the fight racket who has the wonderful gift endowed by nature to put the hex on a fighter so he loses, just by sitting in the opposite corner and giving him the eye. He is a little Yiddle, who you would not notice in a crowd except he's got bug eyes with a very funny look in them sort of creepy-like, and when he gives them to you good, you feel like one good slap on the elbow would knock you out for a week.

Hymie picked him up in Detroit where he was making cakes and coffee putting the zing on prelim boys for two slugs apiece, brought him to New York and put him on the big time working for our stable, and I gotta hand it to him, he done pretty good, because we don't lose a fight since he joined up.

He got a regular price scale of twenty-five bucks for the left eye only where the fight ain't so important or you feel pretty sure your boy he win anyway, fifty bucks for the right eye only which is a lot more powerful and is good for a semi-windup, and one hundred smackers cash for the double whammy, which is both eyes full strength, where you are in the main event and gotta win.

So right after we stiffen Hogan, Hex-Eye is around saying that he is underpaid for his services and that he will take ten per cent of Packy McSween from now on, along with double price since nobody expects Hogan will be knocked out and he alone is responsible for this glorious victory.

Naturally Hymie is sore and says Hex-Eye should gradually die first, and he is nothing but a banjo-eyed faker what he picked up when he was starving in Detroit and made him a national character in the newspapers and that the whole thing was only a lot of cykology anyway, and that he would expose him and would he now get the Hell out of the office. So Hex-Eye Lipschitz quick gives Hymie both eyes, making Hymie duck, and then takes the air. An itching should it be by him in the nose all day long but he shouldn't be able to sneeze yet.

But I am thinking that is maybe a very wrong thing Hymie says to a guy with as powerful an eye as Lipschitz, and I am wishing maybe he has not done it, because we are going very good with the stable and especially Packy McSween. I guess maybe Hymie figures he has done wrong too, for he cools off the next day and sends around word to Hex-Eye that he was only kidding and he will pay him more money but he should forget about a piece of Packy because Packy is already cut up like a jig-saw puzzle and there are not enough pieces left to go round.

We wait three days and nothing happens and I am getting very nervous when Hex-Eye sends word back what Hymie should do with his money because he has insulted him and that from now on he will have no part of him any more and besides which he has signed up with Big Augie Schonblum's stable which is the manager of Joe Falone, the middleweight titleholder of the world, and when he meets up with any of Hymie's fighters in the opposite corner, he will not only give them the double whammy with both eyes, but also the lip which he has been working on with some good klulases, which is Jewish curses, for good measure.

Well, that is bad, but not so bad, because we don't fight many of Big Augie's boys on account of him and Hymie don't get along very well together, and we figure we are at least a year away with Packy for a shot at the middleweight crown of the world.

But that just goes to show you how things happen in the fight racket and that you can't never tell. Angelo Da Spoldi, who is next in line for the summer crack at Joe Louis, goes and breaks his arm falling off one of them electric horses in Steeplechase Park and Mike Jacobs is out at the big ball park match.

He gotta have something to throw in there, so Uncle Mike gets busy and promises Big Augie the Mint, ten shares of U. S. Steel and a piece of the Empire State Building if he will sign for Joe Falone to defend his middleweight title of the world in the Yankee Stadium against Packy McSween.

Big Augie signs, and we're in. We get the crack at the middleweight championship crown of the world, one of the prized bubbles of Fistiana. It is true, there is a side arrangement where Big Augie will wind up with practically all the dough with Packy in there just for the healthful exercise in the open air, but nothing worse should happen to us then we get a chance to lift that title a year sooner.

So trouble starts. Right away we find out why Big Augie is so eager to put the John Patrick Henry on the dotted line. He figures he got the difference. We are so excited about getting the match we forget all about Hex-Eye Lipschitz. He should slowly become so crippled in the spine he can't even sitting in a wheel chair yet.

The night of the afternoon we sign up the match for the photogafers, he calls Packy up on the telephone at his home and says—"Listen, Irisher, you tell that cheap goniff of a manager of yours that there ain't no use of your even going in the ring against Joe Falone, because I will be sitting in his corner and I am putting on you the left, the right, and the double whammy and you will be stiffen so quick the customers don't even get a chance to take off their coats and sit down," and he hangs up.

So Packy is around the office the next day, all broke up and doesn't want to go through with the fight because he says he knows that Lipschitz will put the zing on him and he seen how it worked on K. O. Hogan.

This Packy is not like the rest of them bums, he is a good kid, when you get to know him, but being a Irisher goy he is terrible sensitive and superstitious about the Evil Eye and hexes. He is a clean living boy that come outa the Golden Gloves with a good left and a short right that reminded you of the one Jack Delaney used to throw.

Hymie developed him good and brought him along easy, and we are no worse than even to lift the world diadem from the brow of Falone, if Packy will just forget about Hex-Eye and go in there and spear with his left until he can find a spot to drop the payoff with the right.

So Hymie has to go to work on him and says—"Aw, now Packy, that's all a lot of hooey. Anyway, Hex-Eye is a Jewisher and it's a Jewisher curse so it don't do no good against Irishers."

"O yeah?" says Packy. "That looked more like a Harp to me than a Star of David on Hogan's bathrobe. He was a Mick, but he dropped his hands when Hex-Eye put the $100 whammy on him and gimme a clip at his jaw."

Well, Hymie I guess had forgotten that.

Miss Mitnick who is Hymie's seccatery and a cute trick that I could go for myself, with big brown eyes, lets out a sigh, and says—"Oh, Packy, I'm just knowing you can beat Mr. Falone. He got nothing that you haven't got."

By which I am having an idea that maybe Miss Mitnick is a little sweet on Packy, for which I don't blame her for like I said, he is a nice clean-looking kid with red hair. But Packy just groans and says—

"Oh yeah? He's got Hex-Eye Lipschitz."

So finally Hymie has to tell me to go out and square it with Hex-Eye.

I beat it up Broadway a couple of blocks and go over to outside the Garden where I hang around until pretty soon Hex-Eye comes along alone and I grab him and get a finger in his buttonhole.

"It's O. K., Hex-Eye," I says. "Hymie says you're to come back to work for him. And to show there's no hard feelings he's giving you five per cent of Packy McSween after we win the world's title. Now what do ya say?"

What do I get? I get a look outa them awful bug-eyes so it's coming in my legs a weakness already.

"Amscray, bum," he says. "You go back and tell Hymie Goldkorn I wouldn't have no fifty per cent of what's gonna be with Packy McSween after I and Joe Falone get through with him. I wouldn't take no hundred and fifty per cent. He called me a banjo-eyed faker, me what is responsible for his success. You tell Hymie next time I am seeing him I am putting a klula on him, down a open manhole he should fall and break both ankles. And anyway, I am sign up with Big Augie, and am very busy. I am putting the whammy on a big dinge we are fighting in Philadelphia tonight and I must go home and practice before the mirror until it is time to take the train."

I give him a good klula when we walked away. His teeth should all gradually fall out down his throat so he should choke to death yet. But it don't look so good for our side, what I have to go back and tell Hymie, does it?

So there we are, and time goes by like it does and all of a sudden it is only three days away from when we are packing up to go to Madam Bey's camp at Summit, N. J. for six weeks of outdoor training so we can get a little steam-up for the fight in the papers which is not going so good right then because all the boys were kind of set for the Da Spoldi-Louis match, and we are very low in our minds.

Packy has not been working out good in the gym at all, and Hex-Eye has announced in the newspapers that he is going along to Gus Wilson's camp at Orangeburg, N. J. where Joe Falone, the champion of the world, will train for his title defense and Hex-Eye said that he will also go into training and work out both eyes every day so that they will be extra-special sharp and full of the old zing when it comes time to slapping the whammy on Packy McSween.

Hymie is sitting at his desk, all slumped down with his hands in his pockets shaking his head and moaning—"We gotta do something, we gotta do something. That kid he lose the fight already. A flyweight near tipped him over in the gym today. We gotta do something against Hex-Eye."

All of a sudden he looks up at the ceiling like he was going to bust with a sneeze. Then he starts chewing on his lip and bangs the desk with his fist and yells—"I got it, Goldie! I got it! Gimme that phone."

He grabs the phone by the neck and gives the number in Yiddish first he is so excited, and while he is waiting for it he says to me—

"Goldie, beat it over to the Garden and round up them boxing writers. Tell 'em to be down here at five o'clock this afternoon. Tell 'em I'm gonna have a statement of the utmost importance for them. That always gets 'em. See if ya can get some of those columnists too, anybody that's around there."

So I go over to the Garden and dig 'em up like he says.

I am back in the office at five o'clock with all of the sportswriters and columnists I can round up which all are very curious about what kind of an important statement Hymie is giving out but I can't tell 'em nothing because I don't know nothing what is in Hymie's mind.

I gotta hand it to Hymie, it was good. He keeps us waiting in the outside room about five minutes. Then he throws open the door and says with plenty of the old schmaltz in his voice—"O.K., boys, you can come."

And when we go in, what's standing there? Such a thing shouldn't happen in a nightmare.

It's a tall guy, over six feet with a big black beard so long he shouldn't ever have to wear a necktie. He is wearing a black cloak like a Rabbi only on his head he got a white turband wound around like them pictures of snake charmers. Also he got a mustache like a Turk wrassler from Jake Pfeffer's stable. He stand there grinning with white teeth like a horse.

"Boys," says Hymie—"I'm introducing to you Professor Swammi, the Wabadaba of Waaf, from India. That's in Asia." Then he turns to the guy and says—"Go ahead, Professor, give it to 'em just like you give it to me."

So the Professor gives a bow and touches two fingers to his noggin and then his beard and says like this in a deep voice like in *Schule*—

"I am introducing myself, I am Abadullah Swammi, Great Wabadaba of Waaf, Seer and Prophet of Tetragramatan, delver into the eighth, ninth and thirteenth mysteries of Asch Mezareph and Sepher Jetzirah, Seeker after the Golden Egg of Bramah, Interpreter of the Nuctemeron, the Zahun and the Mizkun. I read the past in the crystal ball, the present in the Sacred Mirror of Cahor, and the future in the Secret Scrolls of the Seven Butatars of Pharzuph, for one dollar. I am the Alph, the Eph, the Zizuph and the Toglas . . ."

I hear one of the boys in the back row make the crack—

"Not to mention the Phonus and the Balonus!"

But Hymie he don't hear anything he is so excited, although I gotta say it sounds more like out of the Talmud than from Indians, but Hymie just slaps his side and says—"Ain't it a spiel, boys, ain't it? Has he got it? I'm asking you?"

Joe Parkhurst says—"He sure is a pip, Hymie. Whadaya gonna do with him?"

"What am I gonna do with him? That's what I'm telling you. He's a genuine Indian magic. He is joining up with the camp of Packy McSween challenger of the middleweight crown of the world when we are going to Madam Bey's. He is the reply of Hymie Korngold Ink to that cheap, lowlife faker Hex-Eye Lipschitz who is giving out statements already from the camp of Joe Falone, about what he should do when Packy gets in the ring. One look from them lamps of the Professor and Hex-Eye should drop dead."

"You mean he's going away to camp with you?" says Parkhurst.

"Absolutely and positively! He's in strict training like Packy. He's got to exercising his eye again because he ain't used it since the last time in the desert in India when he gives it to a wild helephant so he's gradually falling down from convulsions."

The same guy who makes the other crack says—"Who, the helephant or the Professor?" but nobody pays him no attention, because them guys know a terrific story when they see it, and after they ask a couple more questions they all beat it away to get it into the paper and the Professor goes home to pack for Madam Bey's.

Hymie says to me—"Ain't he terrific, Goldie? But terrific? He got a studio in the Bronx. Everybody in high society on the Grand Concourse goes to him. It comes to me like a flash. My sister is telling me about him. Two weeks ago he is saying to her she is going on a trip. And now unexpectedly already she is packing to go up to Grossinger's in the Catskills on the invitation of Yella Weintraub. Like a flash it comes to me we get the Professor. So he joins the camp for five C's if we win the title, three C's if something happens."

I gotta admit the Professor has a terrific make-up, but I'm not going so good for the Professor yet, why I do not know, so I say—"Can he give the eye?"

"Can he give the eye?" Hymie yells. "You're asking me can he give the eye? How the Hell do I know can he give the eye? He looks like it, don't he? He says he can. We gotta do something, don't we? So all right, we take him to camp with us. When them photographs come out of the Professor in his turband, that Lipschitz should bust from jealousy."

Well, I'm telling you it's wonderful. Do we get publicity? Two hours each morning I gotta spend just pasting up clippings in Hymie's press book.

What looks like starting off may be a crowd of twenty-five thousand with a eighty grand gate, is selling already so many tickets, Mike Jacobs got to increase the ringside seats and print more.

We got one gang of writers in our camp covering Packy's workout and another bunch that do nothing but just cover Professor Swammi when he trains in the ring, putting the eye, after Packy is finished working out. And it's the same over in Joe Falone's camp where Hex-Eye is training first one eye, then the other and then both and issuing statements what he will do to Professor Swammi and Packy McSween.

You can't read nothing else in the newspapers except about what they call the "Combat of the Conjurors," the "Battle of the Enchanted Optics," and the "Tournament of the Thaumaturgs."

We are up and down with Packy, who works out good one day and lousy the next according to what the reports are coming out of Falone's camp, on Hex-Eye. Like the day the story comes out of Orangeburg that Hex-Eye puts the zing on a bottle of Grade A in the middle of the ring in front of everybody, giving it only the right eye alone and when they open it afterwards, it's buttermilk.

"Boy," Hymie says to me, "that's bad. I tried to keep the papers away from Packy, but he heard it over the radio and now he don't feel so good no more. We gotta have Professor Swammi pull one that'll throw a scare into them. Maybe he should work out this afternoon wilting some flowers, or something."

But I says—"Leave it to me, I got a better idea."

So I fix it up with George Lawson, a big shine sparring partner for ten bucks extra he should get bewitched, but good. So while him and Packy are working a fast round, Professor Swammi climbs up the side of the ring, mumbling something and giving George both eyes. I gotta hand it to him, the dinge earns his ten. Right in the middle he drops his hands and starts to moan—

"O Lawdy, Lawdy, de eye is on me. I feels the strength a-oozin from mah bones."

So of course Packy stiffens him with the right, and we get a lot of fine publicity in the papers and Packy starts to work good again until we get word the next day that Big Augie has got Clyde Beatty to bring a trick lion over from the circus for Hex-Eye to practice putting the whammy on, and now the circus is going to use Big Augie because the same night the lion got sick of the stomach and died in great agony.

A couple of days later Joe Parkhurst comes out with a big column in the *Morning Democrat* which is an exclusive interview with Hex-Eye Lipschitz himself in which he says—

"Who did this so-called Professor Swammi ever Hex? What's his record? Let him go out and get a reputation before he tries to climb in the same ring with a man who has put the whammy on some of the best boys in fistendom. I say let him name one guy he has give the eye to. What goes on?"

And then comes in the interview a long list of all the boys Hex-Eye has put the peepers to so that they are either knock out or lose the dezision, ending up with K. O. Hogan.

Well, Packy is pretty sick again when he reads that one, and Hymie has to think fast so he says maybe it is a good idea if we give the Prof. an out-of-town try out to see if we can't build him up a little before we throw him into the ring against Hex-Eye in the main event.

We have a good lightweight, Sammy Levin, going in Scranton in a special eight against Rocky Bazone, a couple of nights later and Hymie, who is too busy to leave, sends me with the kid to handle him and tells me to bring the Professor along he should take a workout on Rocky who is all washed up and can't punch any more so Sammy is a sure thing to win. Otherwise why should we be in there fighting him?

That ain't a trip I'm gonna forget. First they musta had a plage of gnats down there in Scranton because I never get stung so many times in my life, I am busy all the time slapping at them. And second is, the Professor he don't go so good.

It is a sell-out house because word has been printed that the Professor will be there, and so we are in our corners after the introductions, waiting for the bell with me telling Sammy how to use his left, and the Professor wearing his white turband is hanging over the ropes in the corner with me.

So the bell rings and the Professor fixes his lamps on Rocky who is coming out of his corner winding up his right, and says— "Mene! Mene Tekel Upharsin!" which Sammy thinks I am giving him some last minute instructions in Yiddish so he turns his head and asks—"*Vos hoste gezugt Goldie?*"

So he is not looking at all when Rocky comes over and parks that right square on his potato, and Sammy is out like a light.

Well, I am telling you that if the knockdown timekeeper is not a personal friend of Hymie's and does not give Sammy one of those—"One—one and a half, two—two and three quarters," counts for about eighteen seconds, he will never get up except I have the presents of mind to kick over the water bucket right where Sammy is laying so it goes over his head and he makes it, otherwise

the timekeeper is going to have to say, "Nineteen, twenty, you're out!" no
matter how good friends he is with Hymie.

It takes Sammy four rounds to know what town he's in, but he comes around
and we get the nod, but just. It's a good thing Hymie got friends among them
judges too. And all the way home on the train them gnats is with us.

Well, it's all right, and Hymie give out the story how Sammy Levin is foully
butted by Rocky Bazone, but that the power of the Professor's eye holds off
Rocky until Sammy can come back and dezision him.

But I am beginning to be a little uneasy by this time and am wishing that
Big Augie has the Professor and we have Hex-Eye Lipschitz, when it comes up
the fight. I will like it better.

So it's coming on close to the big show, and nobody don't write no more
whether Packy McSween is sweating good, and works four fast rounds with his
spar mates, or whether Joe Falone's lightning left is as fast as it was two years ago.
All that's in the papers is what Hex-Eye will do to the Prof. when he gets him in
the ring and how Professor Swammi will put the Egyptian Blast on Hex-Eye
before Hex-Eye he even gets one look at Packy.

The *Morning Scimitar* comes out with the life story of Hex-Eye Lipschitz,
and puts on a hundred thousand circulation, so Hymie counters right away with
a series of signed articles by Professor Swammi in the *Morning Democrat* which
is spooked by Joe Parkhurst. A couple of guys in Tin Pan Alley even write a
song—*With the Swammi on that Swannee River Shore*. I'm telling you the
build-up is terrific.

So it's coming closer all the time to the fight. Hex-Eye goes on *We, The
People* on the radio in which he says with his left eye alone he will not only put
the snore on the Swammi but he will cripple all his relatives too.

Hymie comes right back and gets the Professor on *Information Please*, where
he turns out an awful dope what don't know any of the answers to the questions,
but Hymie explains quick to the press that that is because on account of the
radio he cannot use the power of his eyes which is what he is going to give
to Hex-Eye and Joe Falone the night of the fight so it will be coming to them
both the St. Vitus dance for a month.

It is fix up with the Commission that both Hex-Eye and the Professor are
issued seconds' licenses so they can walk to the center of the ring with the two
boys, because that is where the big event is going to take place where they will
go to work with their whammies and try to put it on each other and the two
fighters, just before they ring the bell.

Hymie and Big Augie reach an agreement in Mike Jacobs' office that neither
Hex-Eye nor Professor Swammi are to show up at the weighing-in, because
Uncle Mike points out that when 79,000 people have bought tickets, with the
unreserved sections still to go, they are entitled to a gander at the big doings, or
as one sportswriter called it the Duel of the Demons.

So finally comes the day of the fight which is scheduled for ten o'clock at
night in the Yankee Stadium, and you couldn't buy a ticket for it no matter who
you knew. Everybody is going to be there to see what happens when the famous

Hex-Eye Lipschitz meets Professor Abadulla Swammi, the Wabadaba of Waaf, face to face. The whole Bronx has a special section to cheer on the Professor while the Lower East Side and the Grand Street Boys have bought two thousand seats together to yell for Hex-Eye.

And I am feeling not so good. That afternoon, I am up in our office which is closed, to get a block of tickets Hymie left in his desk. No one is supposed to be there so when I hear a sort of funny sound from the inside office, I am surprised. I go in, and there is Miss Mitnick, and she has her head down on her arms over her typewriter and is crying. She ain't a very big dame, and she got them soft dark eyes that look even better when they're leaking.

So I says—"Well, well, sister. Something wrong? What's eating ya?"

She looks up at me so I feel I'm gonna melt and says—"O Goldie, Goldie, I'm so unhappy. I'm so afraid Packy isn't going to win and will be hurt. I saw Packy last night. He thinks he's going to lose. He doesn't believe in the Professor, and I don't either. A friend wrote to him from Scranton that the Professor was a big flop as a hexer and Levin would have been knocked out except they gave him a Chicago count. So now Packy is sure that Lipschitz will put the eye on him and he will be knocked out too. O Goldie! Can the Professor do anything?"

"Sister," I said—"I'll betcha the Professor couldn't put a cat to sleep if he had a can of chloroform in both hands. That Hex-Eye's got the goods, because I seen it work on Hogan. It looks bad, don't it? A congestion should slowly come to both his lungs and it shouldn't be handy an oxygen tent."

Miss Mitnick put her head down and is sobbing harder, so I'm putting my arm around and saying—"Don't cry so, sister. Maybe Packy's gonna win yet because he's got a good punch. You're pretty sweet on him, ain'tcha?"

She says—"Y-yes, Goldie, I am. He loves me too. He said so."

"Ya known him long?"

"Y-yes," she says. "We were sweethearts when we went to public school together on the Lower East Side, but we had a quarrel and I didn't see him again until I came to work for Hymie. It's all made up now, and now he isn't going to win and will get hurt . . ."

It come to me like a lightning!

I'm telling you, I should live so, it comes on me just like a lightning out of the sky. I musta hit poor Miss Mitnick an awful clout on the back I got so excited because she jumped up with a scream, but I said—

"Sister, I got it. I'm tellin' ya I got it. You just leave it to Little Goldie. We're gonna see who puts what whammy on who. An Packy's gonna be the new champion of the world. G'bye now, and don't you worry no more."

I beat it over to the Hotel Edison where we had our headquarters. But fast. They were all back from the weighing-in and sitting around the room looking sick, Packy, and Hymie, and Doc who works in the corner with Hymie.

I says to Hymie—"Where's the Professor?"

Hymie answers—"He's in his room. He don't feel so good, he says. Maybe he wants to take a run-out powder."

"He's gonna feel worse before he feels better." The next minute I'm in his room. He ain't got his turband on and is sitting on the sofa looking sort of green because he is scared to death of meeting Hex-Eye Lipschitz and he got a just-opened bottle of whiskey on the table and a glass, which I knock onto the floor.

"Professor Swammi," I says—"You and me are going to have a little talk."

So we have a little talk.

So now I'm gonna tell ya about the fight because maybe you ain't a ex-bootlegger, or night-club owner, or gangster or a actor or a politician, in which case you wasn't sitting close up enough to that ring to really see what happened.

Boy, if I'm living to be a hundred I ain't never gonna forget the noise that crowd makes when me and Packy and Hymie and Doc and the Professor come down the aisle to go into the corner. Wow!

The Professor has on a new white turband with a silver star sticking up in the front of it and a new cloak that Hymie got made up at Brooks Brothers Cos-tumers for him with silver stars and moons on it. Did we get a hand with every-body yelling—"Attaboy, Swammi old boy! Stick it on him! We're with you!"

Then Joe Falone, the middleweight world's championship titleholder comes in with his gang with Hex-Eye Lipschitz wearing a dress suit they rented for him somewhere over on Second Avenue, with a red band across his shirt front like a diplomat, puffed up like a politician and wearing a pair of blue goggles over his eyes so as not to strain them until he is ready to let go the big whammy, and the crowd goes wild.

"Come on, Hex-Eye," they yell—"Show up that big phony! Make him like it!"

Harry Balogh was using the loudspeaker for the interductions, but you couldn't even hear them with those because of the noise the crowd is making. It seemed like the whole city is split up over who is going to win between Hex-Eye and the Professor.

So the moment comes at last when the referee calls the two boys to the center of the ring. I am crouched down at the ringside in our corner, and don't think I wasn't sweating. I am so excited I can't even think of a good klula to say at Hex-Eye.

There they are in the center of the ring, Joe Falone and Packy shaking hands and I can see Packy's knees shivering, and Big Augie and Hymie and Hex-Eye Lipschitz and Professor Abadullah Swammi, the Wabadaba of Waaf.

Everybody in the park is standing on their feet, screaming and yelling—"Give it to him, Hex-Eye! Let him have it Swammi! Both eyes, Hex-Eye! Put the Indian sign on him, Swammi! He'll lay down, Swammi! Show him up for a phony, Hex-Eye!"

So while the instructions are going on, the Professor is just standing there quietly grinning at Hex-Eye and showing his teeth, and they sure were nice, white strong teeth, and I can see that Hex-Eye is beginning to get a little nervous because the Professor is just standing there grinning at him like a dope without saying anything. So the referee finishes his instructions and there comes a sort of a lull for a second in which I hear Hex-Eye say to the Professor—

"What are you grinning at, you big *schmock*? You can starting to wipe that grin offn your big ugly face, because I'm gonna give you the eye, and I'm gonna give it to you *now*," and he puts his hand up to his glasses.

That crowd stops yelling just like one big hand had shut it off with a choke.

You coulda heard a dime drop as Hex-Eye slowly removes his glasses and sticks his puss right up close to the Professor's who is still grinning and says—"I am giving you the eye now! I am giving you BOTH eyes!"

And the next thing you know Hex-Eye is clapping his hands to his face and letting out a yell you coulda heard in Weehawken—

"Ow! Ow, my eyes! I'm blind! Help, I'm blind! I can't see!" and starts to stagger around the ring, pawing with one hand and keeping the other over his glims.

Wow! What a yell went up from that crowd! It sounded like eight million people all screaming "Swammi! Swammi! Swammi!"

The ring is full of confusion. Packy is jigging around with a look on his face like he got a reprieve from the Governor. Big Augie doesn't know what to make of it and is trying to catch Hex-Eye to keep him from falling out of the ring. The Professor is taking bows to all four sides, putting his fingers to his bean and his whiskers and the referee is looking confused as though he does not know just what to do.

So I yell up at him—"Throw that bum out of there and start the fight," at just the right moment because it helps him make up his mind. He goes over and grabs Hex-Eye by the arm and hustles him to his corner and out through the ropes while Hymie snatches the Professor who would be in there taking bows all night otherwise and gives him the toss.

"Bong!" The timekeeper yanks the bell, and they're off.

Joe Falone comes out of his corner, and because he is a little dazed by what has happened to Hex-Eye he don't carry his left hand as high as he ought, and BLOWIE! Packy is in there and drops the sweetheart right smack on Joe's china-ware, and the referee he don't even bother enough to count.

We got the new middleweight champion titleholder of the world's crown.

Joe Falone is still snoring in his corner when Hex-Eye starts yelling—"It's all right now. I can see again! Where is that Goniff so I will put the eye on him now. Show him to me!" So when he finds out that his boy has been chilled so he will not be up in time maybe to see next Sunday's funny papers, he is around the ringside yelling—"We was robbed! I got shot! I want another chance!"

But everybody is just giving him the horse laugh, and Hymie is in the ring, hugging and kissing Packy and the Professor, and talking into the radio, and Miss Mitnick comes up and throws her arms around and kisses me and says—

"O Goldie, isn't it wonderful! I'm the happiest girl in the world. And you said it would be all right. But O Goldie, I'm so ashamed of the things I said about Professor Swammi. Wasn't he just too wonderful the way he stood there and put a spell on that awful Hex-Eye?"

So I don't say nothing, and soon she is in the ring with her arms around Packy and the photogafers are taking pictures and also a picture of her kissing the Professor in the middle of his whiskers.

And I am laughing, because there are 89,000 people in that park, but I am the only one that knows that Professor Abadulla Swammi ain't no professor at all, and he ain't from India either. He is Jake Rosenzweig from P.S. 191 whose jawr I busted for giving us kids the business with them little backshot out of his teeth.

If I wasn't so dumb I should of known him right away except it is ten years since I see him and then he is hiding behind all that spinach he grows to play the part of Professor Swammi so he can tell fortunes to the suckers in the Bronx.

And if I got any brains I shoulda known it wasn't gnats that night in Scranton but that big bum still giving me the business with them buckshot. It don't come back to me until I am talking with Miss Mitnick in the office the day of the fight and she says public school on the Lower East Side and a quarrel, and then all of a sudden, like I say, it comes on me like a lightning, where I seen Professor Swammi before, the lug.

So when I'm in his room the day of the fight I tell him what he should do with Hex-Eye when he meets him in the ring and he says he ain't gonna go in the ring because he is afraid of Hex-Eye, so I tell him if he takes a powder I will tell everyone he ain't no Professor Swammi but just plain Jake Rosenzweig, and he is more afraid of that than he is of Hex-Eye.

When Hex-Eye sticks his puss right up into his in the ring, Jake has a half a mouthful of buckshot ready for him and lets him have it right in the eyeballs. He never made two better shots, even in P.S. 191.

All right, is it a story, or is it? I'm asking you. If it don't thinking so the editors I am getting ready for them a good klula. It should come by them gradually a *geschwulst* on the larynx so they shouldn't be able to talking for eight months, except with the hands, where they should getting eventually a roomatism.

FREDERICK HAZLITT BRENNAN

◄————————————————————————————►

The Hole in Mr. Dorsett's Head

MR. DORSETT who I pack for regular at the Hidden Valley Club is a 2-handicap man and a good guy. They said he should take an older caddy to the state amateur but Mr. Dorsett said no, I will stick with Harold, he keeps reminding me that golf is real and golf is earnest. Furthermore, Harold reads a green like he is reading a death sentence to my opponent, Mr. Dorsett said, and one look at Harold's face in a clutch will put the whammy on my opponent.

This was a joke meaning I am serious about caddying, I am a killer-type that always wants Mr. Dorsett to beat their brains out. Mr. Dorsett is built like Sam Snead, only younger, and he swings like Snead, only he is smarter and does not leave himself so many downhill putts. Mr. Dorsett has no flaw in his game, except he is a little too happy and likes his laughs and will now and then goof a shot by not having mental concentration on it. It is not a fatal fault. Jimmy Demaret is the same kind of a joker, he does okay. Besides, there is only one thing that could really ruin Mr. Dorsett—girls or women, they are poison, but up to the state amateur he did not look at one.

Now I will describe Dr. Pruink that done his best to louse up me and Mr. Dorsett. He is a medium-old guy about thirty. He is a siketical analysist doctor that claims to know if you have a hole in your head. He looks and talks like Humphrey Bogart in the movies, he says all golfers show theirself up if they are loopy by the way they act on a golf course. Dr. Pruink should be barred off every course in the United States, he is a stinker.

Next I will describe Mr. Alex Balbriggan, the founder and president of Hidden Valley. He stands six-four and weighs only about 150, but it is all grit and gristle. Mr. Balbriggan is seventy-three years old, he can still break 80, he has hairy ears and a white mustache. In the year 1901 Mr. Balbriggan took lessons from Harry Vardon, he won the state amateur in 1911 and 1913 and was runner-up to Chick Evans in the 1916 Open. He is the killer-type like me and does not allow girls or women on the Hidden Valley course, not even to walk on it.

I guess I will now have to describe Miss Leila. She is a girl about twenty-two. She is almost as pretty as Alice Bauer, but she cannot hit her hat with a golf stick. She does not respect golf. A girl that disrespects golf can ruin you, she is worse than Dr. Pruink, she will add 10 or 11 strokes at least, she thinks she is more important than shooting good golf, she thinks she is better than a 69. Miss

Leila has brown eyes and black hair, wavy with a white streak above her left eye. She is five-foot-three, weighs 119, has a bad temper and is well-stacked.

Now I will tell you what happened.

Just before the state amateur, Mr. Alex Balbriggan sent for me to have a conference with him on the practice green. Mr. Balbriggan putts for an hour after his regular morning foursome.

"Dammit, Harold," Mr. Balbriggan said, "walk over here on the green. Don't be so dignified."

"Yes, sir," I said.

"Humph, humph," Mr. Balbriggan said. "I understand you are going to caddy for young Dorsett in the state amateur. It is an honor and a responsibility for a boy your age, but I have watched you work up from a Class B caddy, you seem to have the right mental attitude, just how important is golf to you, Harold?"

"It's the only thing in life, it's the best, sir," I said. "I am just like you, I guess, I do not think about anything but it."

Mr. Balbriggan nodded his head. "Very good, Harold, you talk like a golfer, I find to my surprise that you are the best under-16 caddy player at this club, that is gratifying, and what do you think of Mr. Dorsett's chance in the state amateur?"

"He has all the shots, Mr. Balbriggan," I said, "and he is due. I figure he can win this one and maybe knock off the national amateur in a couple of years."

"My estimate exactly, Harold," he said. "Don't tell young Dorsett, but I have set my heart on him bringing a national championship to Hidden Valley, I missed it myself by one putt in '16, hell and dammit, but before I die Dorsett must win a national trophy, and nothing must stand in his way, nothing dammit."

"Don't worry about it, sir," I said. "Mr. Dorsett is on his stick and I can tour that Lakeside course with my eyes shut. I will club Mr. Dorsett right and read the greens and steady him in the clutch."

"Yes, Harold, I believe you will," Mr. Balbriggan said. "I understand now why Mel insisted on having you caddy for him, you are in dead earnest, your eyes would haunt a man if he did some damn fool thing like missing a three-foot putt, I wish you could have been with me in '16 in Minikahda, I like your spirit. Tell Joe to give you a dollar and a new ball, present from me."

"Yessir, thanks," I said.

I did not tell Mr. Dorsett about the conference with Mr. Balbriggan. It would of put too much pressure on him. Mr. Dorsett works for Mr. Balbriggan in the hotel business and is paid fifteen or twenty thousand dollars a year. You tell a guy his boss is betting on him, like expecting him to win the state amateur, it is not good.

Anyway, Mr. Balbriggan didn't need to of worried. Mr. Dorsett burned up that Lakeside course four days straight. He beat Mr. Tom Cravens, Jr., in the finals, three-and-two.

"Ha ha ha, Harold, wipe that corpsey look off your face and give me a smile,"

Mr. Dorsett said. "I only won just to see you smile, Harold. Look at this, kid, it is money, it is fifty bucks, it is yours, but first you got to smile."

"Okay," I said, "I'm smiling." Mr. Dorsett was so happy he mussed up my hair and poked the money in my shirt pocket, then he made me go with him to talk to the newspaper guys.

"The name is Harold McClurn," Mr. Dorsett said. "Spell it right, I couldn't have won without this boy, he is almost as smart as Ben Hogan!"

I was afraid they might quote Mr. Dorsett in the papers, so I said, "Mr. Dorsett is kidding. They ain't nobody even almost as smart as Ben Hogan."

Mr. Dorsett laughed and Mr. Lew Johnson of the *Tribune* said he wanted to ask me a question.

"It is this, Harold, what in your opinion is the strongest part of Mr. Dorsett's game?"

"He's a bachelor and does not have nothing to do with girls."

The newspaper guys thought it was funny. Mr. Dorsett got red in the face. "Whoa, now, don't print that!" he said. "Tell 'em you're ribbing me, Harold."

I said oh, sure, I am kidding, because Mr. Dorsett looked so fussed and he is my pal, and you cannot explain about golf to newspaper guys, they think it is just a game like tennis, when the statistics prove that girls or women have ruined more top-flight amateurs and pros than booze, even.

"Ha ha ha, watch yourself, Harold, never crack jokes in front of newspaper guys," Mr. Dorsett said. "They have no sense of humor, they will print it straight. Look, Harold, better put the clubs in my car, I have to collect that brass cup for Mr. Alex, run along and I will meet you at the car."

It took Mr. Dorsett almost an hour to get to the car, but I did not think nothing of it, a guy has to shower and dress and say thanks for the congratulations and talk to Hidden Valley members that drove over the last day to watch Mr. Dorsett win.

On July 26, three days after the state amateur, Mr. Dorsett developed a fade. His practice-round score was 73. On July 27 he was overcorrecting the fade and had a hook, it cost him a 78. On July 28 the fade came back, we had two sliced drives out of bounds, and coming up to No. 11 green Mr. Dorsett shanked a pitching-wedge.

"An 87 is just plain murder, Harold," Mr. Dorsett said, walking in from 18. "I am overgolfed, I am stale, these irons are throwing me, I will go back to the Tommy Armours, this is awful, don't turn in the card, hide my shame."

"I would never admit to nobody that you took an 87," I said. "But we cannot hide the slump very long. They watch you across the fairway."

Mr. Dorsett tried to laugh it off.

"I'm sorry you had to see me in this condition, Harold," he said. "An innocent growing boy should not be subjected to an 87."

"You'll snap out of the slump tomorrow, Mr. Dorsett," I said.

On July 29 we was two under par for the front side, but on No. 10 Mr. Dorsett sliced his drive, topped a 4-wood, shanked a 7-iron, shanked another 7, shanked a niblick, shanked a pitching-wedge.

Mr. Dorsett looked awful, not only his golf but his face. To a good golfer a shank is disgracefuller than being dead drunk or in jail. A dub can cure a shank easy, he does not know how awful a shank is, but a good golfer knows he is really in for it, a shank means you are fed up with golf, you have nothing to live for and want to commit suicide.

He still tried to laugh it off. "Don't stare like that, Harold," Mr. Dorsett said. "I have shanked, but I will repent and shank no more. I will live this down, kid. I am not utterly bad."

"You look like you got the headache and fever," I said. "They is a lot of polio around, it could be polio, how do you feel?"

Mr. Dorsett lost his temper.

"That's enough, Harold, that does it, I am fed up with your obsession on golf, it is just a game. So I am shanking, so what? It does not mean polio, I am not a leper, I haven't murdered anyone, you are to blame for this, Harold, you and Mr. Alex; I can live without golf, damn golf."

Mr. Dorsett threw his driver into some bushes off No. 12 tee, and said, "I'm walking in."

By the time I reached the golf shop Mr. Dorsett had gone home.

Joe McDonald, our pro, called me. "Hey, Harold," he said, "Mr. Balbriggan wants to see you on the east terrace."

He said it like they was a lot going on I did not know about. Tex, the caddy master, winked at Joe, the big wisehead.

Mr. Balbriggan was sitting under an umbrella on the terrace and pulling at his mustache. "Step up, Harold, step up like a man, don't skulk!" he said.

"Yes, sir," I said.

Mr. Balbriggan looked like he had just three-putted 18 greens, like all his friends had died and the clubhouse had burned down.

"Now, Harold, I have an important and confidential matter to discuss with you," he said. "It is a delicate matter, it is between us. Do I make myself clear? Now, then—have you noticed anything wrong with Mr. Dorsett's game since the state amateur?"

"Well, he was two under par for nine holes—"

"Dammit, Harold, don't stare at me like a dead fish," Mr. Balbriggan said, "and if you are going to tell a lie, Harold, put some guts and spirit and manhood into it, but you know damn well young Dorsett has not been himself out there, and I must remind you that a boy who hopes to be a golf professional must be truthful."

"Well, I don't know exactly what you mean Mr. Dorsett not acting like himself, what do you mean, sir?" I said.

"Mentally unbalanced, dammit," Mr. Balbriggan sort of growled. "Has he cracked jokes? Is he the same man you knew before the state amateur?"

"Well, not exactly," I said.

I could not stall around any longer. Mr. Balbriggan said if I did not tell the truth, he would take me off the caddy list at Hidden Valley, I would be branded a liar, I would be marked for life and could not never be a golf pro.

So I had to tell Mr. Balbriggan everything—the whole works. It was rugged. I felt bad. Mr. Balbriggan felt bad too. When I got to the part where Mr. Dorsett shanked, tears come to Mr. Balbriggan's eyes, he stood up and shook his head and walked into the clubhouse, real tottery.

I went straight back to Tex, the caddy master. "What is this?" I said. "What is this I don't know about my guy? What's wrong?"

Tex laughed. "Ha ha ha ha, calm down, kid, it is just a laugh," Tex said. "Dorsett didn't do nothin', the Old Man just found out he's been dating a gal, that's all."

"You're a dirty liar," I said.

"Whoa, Harold, don't call me no liar, I'm a Texan," he said. "I know her name, it's Leila Graham, he met her at the state amateur, he's been dating her on the sly. The Old Man acts like Dorsett is a bank robber, the latest is the Old Man thinks Dorsett must have a hole in his head, that is very funny, poor Dorsett dates a girl and the Old Man decides he must be a Section 8, a psycho."

I looked at Tex hard. In two more years I will be big enough to lick him, but I am already big enough to bash in his head with a niblick, he knows it.

"You're still a liar for my dough," I said, "but if Mr. Dorsett done it, if he went with a girl, Mr. Balbriggan is right. The poor guy does have a hole in his head."

"Ha ha, maybe you got a hole in your head," Tex said. "Beat it, Harold. No caddies allowed in the golf shop."

That evening I was practice-chipping in the back yard when Benny, the kid next door, came running. "Hey, Harold, they's a lady in a big Cadillac out front, she wants to see you."

It was a 1950 Cad, green with the top down.

"Are you Harold McClurn?" the girl said.

"Yes'm," I said.

"I'm Leila Graham, Harold," she said. "Mr. Dorsett sent me over to apologize to you for the way he behaved this afternoon. He would have come himself, but he had a business meeting. Here—he sent you this—it's a peace offering, Harold."

She held out Mr. Dorsett's best putter, a special built off-set job that cost $18.50. I am deadly with it, but I did not want to take it.

"I got no beef against Mr. Dorsett," I said. "We are pals, he don't need to gimme this."

"Now, now, Harold, I know boys, I have a little brother, do not be bashful, Mr. Dorsett wants you to have the shinny stick," Miss Leila said. "Mr. Dorsett is very much attached to you, he is sorry he blamed you, it is all the fault of that horrid old man Balbriggan, making Mr. Dorsett a slave to that silly game."

I took the putter.

Then I said, "Mr. Balbriggan is a fine old guy. He knows all about poor Mr. Dorsett's condition, and you better leave Mr. Dorsett alone. In his right mind Mr. Dorsett does not shank or lose his temper or have dates. You better go with some guy that don't play golf and is in his right mind."

Miss Leilia turned red, she could hardly get her breath to talk with.

"Why, Harold," she said, "you don't actually—you can't really—it's preposterous—why, you poor child—to think such a thing—so that old man thinks Mel is—oh, pardon me for laughing."

"A swell guy like Mr. Dorsett losing his chance at the national amateur— so that's funny," I said.

"Stop staring at me that way, Harold," she said.

"He'll lose a good job, too," I said.

That did it, she could not say anything, she opened her mouth, but no words came out, she just kind of nodded, put the Cad in the hydromatic, and drove off.

You have got to blow a fast whistle on girls or women, you cannot reason with them. They do not care if you shank, if you shoot an 87.

Next morning, when I got out to the club, Joe said I was to report to Mr. Balbriggan in the Founder's Room. It is his office, he never goes downtown, he runs the Balbriggan hotels from it.

"Hell and dammit, Harold, don't cough and don't sidle," he said. "March in here. A boy who can shoot a 71 belongs to the nobility."

"Yessir, good morning," I said.

"Humph, humph, sit down, Harold, I have decided to take immediate action, I refer to Mel Dorsett, he is like a son to me, I must determine just how sick he is, did you ever hear of a siketical analysist, Harold?"

"Yes, sir—like in the *Snake Pit* movie, a mind doctor like they had for Mr. Todd Jennings when he saw snakes in the rough on No. 5."

"Exactly, Harold, children seem to know everything nowadays, not that you are a child," Mr. Balbriggan said, "your maturity is appalling. But here is my plan. I have invited a Dr. Pruink to play golf with Mel and me. Dr. Pruink says he can judge a man's mental condition by watching him in a round of golf."

"I saw Miss Leila," I said.

Mr. Balbriggan gave a sort of jump. "Here? She's dared to come here?" he said.

"No, sir. Last night I saw her."

"Dammit, so you know, so the whole golf district knows. I blame myself, I blame you, Harold," Mr. Balbriggan said, "we should have watched Mel more closely, we should have seen this coming on, it is madness, madness, he had such a beautiful swing, hell and dammit, a swing like that happens once in a generation, Bobby Jones and Mcl Dorsctt, he has more power than Jones, kicks off from his right foot better, like this, where was I, Harold?"

"The mind doctor," I said.

"Oh, yes," Mr. Balbriggan said. "I am going to introduce Dr. Pruink as a friend of a friend from California. Mel mustn't know Dr. Pruink's specialty. I will describe Dr. Pruink as a dentist."

"It's a good idea," I said.

"And the reason I had to confide in you—humph—of course," Mr. Balbriggan said, "Dr. Pruink said he might want to question you, Harold. So you are not to warn Mel or tell anyone."

"I won't tell nobody," I said.

Mr. Balbriggan gave me a dollar and two new golf balls. Then he patted me on the shoulder. "Dammit, Harold, let us hope, for golf's sake, young Dorsett is not in his right mind, as I suspect, otherwise I will disown him, kick him out, by God, I will."

"Don't worry," I said. "Mr. Dorsett is momentarily a sex maniac or something."

An hour and ten minutes later, Mr. Dorsett showed on the practice green. He looked awful nuts, goofed-off, Section 8 for sure. His head was down and he was chewing the corner of a handkerchief.

"Thanks for the putter," I said.

"Huh? Oh—not at all, Harold," he said. "I've got to play with Mr. Alex and a guest—some dentist from California."

Mr. Balbriggan and Dr. Pruink were waiting on No. 1.

Mr. Balbriggan had on his plus-fours and white silk shirt. "Dr. Pruink, I want you to know Mel Dorsett," he said. "Mel is our state amateur champion."

Mr. Dorsett and Dr. Pruink shook hands. Mr. Dorsett did not say anything much or pay attention, but I looked at Dr. Pruink careful. Besides his Humphrey Bogart face, he was not much. He wore pickup clothes, just a T-shirt and old slacks. He was going to use one of Mr. Balbriggan's extry sets of clubs, Ducky was caddying for him, and Jocko always packs for Mr. Balbriggan.

"We should make up a game," Mr. Balbriggan said. "What do you shoot, Doctor?"

Dr. Pruink give a shrug. "I haven't a handicap, Mr. Balbriggan," he said. "I mastered the game some years ago and then lost interest in it."

"You mastered it, huh?" Mr. Dorsett said in a funny voice.

"Oh, yes," Dr. Pruink said. "I might be a little rusty, perhaps you'd better give me a couple of strokes."

Everybody looked at Dr. Pruink, you do not ask a scratch golfer for just a couple of strokes. But Mr. Balbriggan said, "Mel, I told him you are a little off your game, he is a guest and does not want to take advantage."

"I'll play Mr. Dorsett even," Dr. Pruink said. "We'll adjust for the back nine."

Mr. Dorsett started to say something, but Dr. Pruink said he would give Mr. Balbriggan five strokes and adjust, then he said he would play for ten-ten-ten or whatever was agreeable.

Everybody looked at Dr. Pruink, waiting for the gag, but no, he meant it. Ducky winked at me. I did not know what to think, neither did Mr. Balbriggan.

"Guest has the honor," Mr. Dorsett said.

Dr. Pruink teed up his ball. He took a driver from Ducky without looking at it or hefting it. He put his left thumb in his mouth.

"Got a splinter?" Mr. Balbriggan said.

He shook his head, still sucking his thumb. Then he gave a little gurgling sound, pulled out his thumb, then he belched. Then he screwed up his face like a baby about to bawl.

Our No. 1 at Hidden Valley is a par-five dog-leg to the left. It is a 225-yard carry to the turn.

Dr. Pruink waddled up to the ball, like he was a two-year-old just learning to walk, he did not practice-swing or waggle or nothing. He just cut loose with a perfect-form swing.

The ball went 275 down the center.

"Want a mulligan?" Mr. Dorsett said, sarcastic.

Dr. Pruink nodded his head dead pan. "That wasn't too good," he said. "I am rusty. I should have put a slight hook on it and really turned the corner."

He sucked his thumb again, he waddled up to the ball and took another cut without even a waggle.

The drive carried 240 straight, then turned the corner and rolled about 40 more.

Mr. Balbriggan pulled at the hair in his left ear, he looked at Mr. Dorsett, he teed up his ball and drove it his usual straight 200. Dr. Pruink watched him close, but did not say anything.

Then Mr. Dorsett was on the tee. I knew he felt terrible. When Mr. Dorsett is nervous, his neck gets red underneath the sunburn.

Mr. Dorsett pushed a long drive, about 260, and was in the woods beyond the turn to the right.

Dr. Pruink looked at him dead pan. "Ever try sucking your thumb, Dorsett?" he said.

"No," Mr. Dorsett said.

"I find it essential," Dr. Pruink said. "It takes me back to infancy."

Jocko and Ducky laughed, but Mr. Dorsett gave Dr. Pruink a dirty look. Mr. Balbriggan said, "Are you serious, Dr. Pruink?"

"Yes, Mr. Balbriggan," Dr. Pruink said. "Golf is a childish game. The impulse to strike a small object with a crooked stick starts in the cradle. I find that by sucking my thumb I travel back, subconsciously, to childhood."

"Oh—ah—I see," Mr. Balbriggan said.

We all started off the tee. Mr. Dorsett was now definitely sore at Dr. Pruink. He had him pegged as a practical joker someone had wished on Mr. Balbriggan, I guess, because he said, "Mr. Balbriggan, I'm afraid we've been had. I appreciate Dr. Pruink's act, but we'd better look out now for exploding golf balls, ha ha, that thumb-sucking was not bad, I will admit."

Mr. Balbriggan didn't know what to say, but Dr. Pruink took Mr. Dorsett right up on it.

"My dear Dorsett, all golfers would suck their thumbs if they dared," he said, "but they are bound by convention, they chew gum, they chew matches or grass, they suck pipes, cigars, cigarettes. A moment's reflection will make you see, I'm sure, that thumb-sucking is more honest and infantile, I do not wish to be personal but were you not chewing the corner of a handkerchief as you approached the tee?"

"Why, yes, believe I was," Mr. Dorsett said, "but that's a good ways from thumb-sucking. And I will be personal too, your performance on the tee looked damn silly."

Dr. Pruink did not bat an eye. "Golf is a damn silly game," he said. "That's why golfers disguise it with ritual."

Mr. Balbriggan thought up something to say. "I suggest we continue this discussion after we have taken our second shots."

"You see, Dorsett? Ritual enters at once to prevent any intelligent talk on a golf course."

"What goes on here, Harold?" Mr. Dorsett said.

"What do you think?" I said.

"He's a screwball. He's got a hole in his head," Mr. Dorsett said.

We had to hunt for Mr. Dorsett's ball on the edge of the woods. Dr. Pruink and Ducky come over to help us. Dr. Pruink found it in a clump of sumac.

"Little fellow was gleaming at me like a clean tooth," he said.

"Thanks, maybe I should take up dentistry," Mr. Dorsett said.

I hoped Mr. Dorsett would not shank the niblick. But he did. Then he grabbed a putter and batted the ball to the fairway. Dr. Pruink was watching close.

"Do you shank often?" he said.

"Quite often lately," Mr. Dorsett said.

"That's a good sign," Dr. Pruink said.

"Of what?" Mr. Dorsett said.

"Maturation, fella, you are growing up. You want to put away childish things."

"Oh?" Mr. Dorsett said.

"Look here, old boy, did you ever really face the truth about a niblick?" Dr. Pruink said. "It is the classic example of the pre-adolescent tool, a fantasy derived from a bent porridge spoon. The truly adult mind recoils from a niblick, the super-Ego rejects it as a travesty of rational engineering, when you shank with a niblick you are simply affirming that you will no longer tolerate the thing, you give it back to the savages, to the idiot brats in plus-fours who will spend their lives trying to make it knock a rubber ball."

Mr. Dorsett looked really interested in what Dr. Pruink was saying; he even grinned a little.

"You may have a point, Doc," he said.

Then Mr. Dorsett hit a sweet brassie almost to the carpet of No. 1 green. Then I and Mr. Dorsett walked with Dr. Pruink to his ball. Mr. Balbriggan was waiting there for them.

Dr. Pruink sucked his thumb, then took out a No. 4 iron.

"It's farther than that, sir," Ducky said. "It's a full spoon."

"Right, my lad, but I want to show Mr. Dorsett how to cure a shank," Dr. Pruink said. "A shank is entirely mental, it is a rebellion against golf, so do not fight it, old boy, just take this 4-iron and hum a nursery tune to yourself, I get best results with *Rock-a-bye Baby*, then take a couple of long pulls at your thumb."

"To cure a shank I will try anything," Mr. Dorsett said.

He followed Dr. Pruink's instruction and belted a perfect 4-iron right down the middle. "Holy cats," Mr. Dorsett said, and he hit two more sweet 4-irons.

I looked at Mr. Balbriggan. He was staring at Mr. Dorsett and Dr. Pruink, I knew why. Hell and dammit, he was thinking, they both have holes in their heads.

"One moment, Doctor," Mr. Balbriggan said.

"Yes, Mr. Balbriggan?" Dr. Pruink said.

"For our purposes you have talked enough damn nonsense," Mr. Balbriggan said. "There are three young lads present, our caddies. We do not speak lightly of golf at Hidden Valley, sir. On this course golf is still the royal and ancient game, sir."

Poor Mr. Dorsett still had enough of his right mind to look ashamed. "Well, Doc did cure my shank, Mr. Alex," he said.

Mr. Balbriggan shook his head. "You are not yourself, Mel. I am waiting for Dr. Pruink to hit his second shot. All this delay on the fairway is bad manners. Shoot, Doctor."

Dr. Pruink dropped a ball. Ducky handed him a spoon.

"I must beg to differ with you, Mr. Balbriggan, I do not talk damn nonsense, it is the royal and ancient game that is nonsense. Look at me as I stand here with a lump of wood attached to an iron stick, I am required to think it is important for me to propel a ball to an illogically small patch of lawn called a green. Indeed, a golfer has been defined as a man who takes a ball from a hole in his head and transfers it to a hole in the ground, the whole process is too difficult to be amusing and too trivial to be tragic, yet thousands of men have cursed and fumed, wasted their energies and driven themselves to essential hypertension and coronary occlusion, all for the sake of getting on a green in two."

Dr. Pruink still had some breath left. He belted a swell spoon, it was on a line for the pin all the way.

"It's in, Doc," Mr. Dorsett said, "in for a double eagle."

Dr. Pruink was not paying any attention to the shot. He had kept his head down and now he was watching Mr. Balbriggan's feet. "What a foot pattern," he said. "Stand right where you are, Mr. Balbriggan, I must draw it."

He took out his score card and pencil, he got down on his knees and looked at the marks Mr. Balbriggan had made with his feet on the fairway, he copied them down with the pencil.

Mr. Balbriggan was getting sore.

"Dammit, fellow, what is the meaning of this?" Mr. Balbriggan said. "I gave the land for this club, I am permitted to scuffle my feet, stop acting like a fool."

"H'mn," Dr. Pruink said, "a rare pattern, the Chillon group, very significant. Mr. Balbriggan, have you ever wanted to keep slaves?"

Mr. Dorsett grinned, wiped it off quick and said, "Come on, Doc, they're yelling at us from the tee."

Mr. Dorsett hurried off and I went after him.

"Who is that guy, Harold?" Mr. Dorsett said.

"What do you think?" I said.

"He may be a dentist," Mr. Dorsett said, "but he's read a lot of psychology, he is a whizz. Any guy who can cure a shank like he cured mine is wasting his genius pulling teeth."

"He didn't cure you, Mr. Dorsett," I said.

"Why, Harold, you saw me hit three perfect irons."

"You had to suck your thumb to do it," I said. "What good is that? They would all laugh at you in a tournament. If you was to hum *Rock-a-bye Baby* and suck your thumb, they would make you resign from Hidden Valley."

Poor Mr. Dorsett did not realize they would do worse than that to him, they would put him in a booby hatch. "I think I'll resign anyway, Harold," he said.

I felt too bad to say anything.

Mr. Balbriggan was short of the green with his third shot. Mr. Dorsett joined him and Dr. Pruink at the ball.

I was scared the way Mr. Balbriggan looked, his face was brick red, he bit his mustache, his chin quivered.

Dr. Pruink was still Humphrey Bogart dead pan, he did not fear Mr. Balbriggan, his voice was tough and mean. "You should take Harold for your caddy, Mr. B.," Dr. Pruink said. "He hero-worships Dorsett and that's bad for a mature man."

Poor Mr. Dorsett looked worried. "Hey, hey," he said, "what's all this about Harold? Mr. Alex can't have Harold, you must be kidding, Doc."

"Far from it, old boy, I have been studying Harold, he is the eternal juvenile, he will never mature, he will grow up to be a golf professional, he is bad medicine for you, Dorsett, he believes in golf, he followed those 4-irons you hit with more than his eyes, his infantile little soul soared with them. No, old boy, I beg you to give Harold to Mr. Balbriggan."

"Silence!" Mr. Balbriggan yelled. "I am going to shoot!"

It was an easy 7-iron chip from ten feet off the green. Mr. Balbriggan was so sore he stubbed it, the ball rolled two feet. Then Mr. Balbriggan lost his temper and whacked the ball into a trap.

"I knew you'd do that, Mr. B.," Dr. Pruink said.

Mr. Balbriggan looked at him. "You did, eh?" he said.

"I can't miss when I find a Chillon pattern in a golfer's foot tracks, Mr. B. The Chillon pattern is from the Prisoner of Chillon, you are rather a naughty child, Mr. B., in another time you would have kept slaves on your estate, now you have the Hidden Valley Club, and Harold is your slave, and Dorsett was your slave, but he started to mature, he had found something more important than golf, he found a girl, I would guess. It threw you into an pre-adolescent tantrum, and when you hit that ball into the trap, that was the big pay-off, Mr. B. It was not a ball you drove into the trap or dungeon, it was the head of Mr. Dorsett's girl, you are afraid of women, you cannot stand their adult attitude toward golf, you fear a woman will kick over your prison and spank you."

"I do, eh?" Mr. Balbriggan said, and conked Dr. Pruink with his 7-iron. Dr. Pruink fell down. He was out cold.

Then Miss Leila come rushing out of nowhere.

"No women on this course!" Mr. Balbriggan said. "Get off!"

"Just try to put me off, you nasty old man, I saw you hit him, you hit him in cold blood. Shut up, Mel, I am handling this, I will put him in jail, I will help that poor fellow sue him for damages, and you shut up, Mr. Alex Balbriggan, I am going to marry Mel and he will resign from the club and get another job. And Harold, if you don't stop staring at me, I will slap you."

Then Miss Leila saw the blood on Dr. Pruink's head and sort of fainted. Then Mr. Dorsett held her in his arms and mushed her.

That was what happened.

Poor Mr. Dorsett still has a hole in his head, but Mr. Balbriggan cannot do nothing about it. He is scared of Miss Leila. She says if Mr. Balbriggan does not do what she says Dr. Pruink will declare him nuts and will sue him for $200,000 damages. Poor Mr. Dorsett says he will win the national amateur if he feels like it, if not no, golf is just a game, Doc Pruink is a wonderful guy, *Rock-a-bye Baby*, he cured my shank.

Mr. Balbriggan is so scared of Miss Leila he is going to let Mr. Dorsett marry her, he gave Mr. Dorsett a raise in the hotel business, he said, "Harold, hell and dammit, stop staring at me, you and I are the last of the true golfers, but we are hemmed in, we have no choice, we must obey Miss Leila, we are licked, Harold."

I guess we are. Tomorrow is Ladies' Day at Hidden Valley.

FRANK SCULLY

◄ ──────────────────────────────────── ►

The Beaut from Montana

STRIPPED—her favorite pose, incidentally—she was a featherweight, and a fraction under five feet tall. But nobody ever measured her s.a.—in Hollywood or anywhere else.

In Butte, Montana, where she was born and raised, she was known as Sadie Ostomar, but a press agent in Hollywood gave her the nice New England name of Sally Alden. The story was she had seduced her first male in Butte before she was out of pinafores. And whether that's true or not, it's a laughable fact that after she got in pictures every man in Hollywood was scared to death of her. Her five husbands swore to a man that she was *insatiable*, and unfaithful to boot. It is difficult to say which appalled them the more.

While still in Butte, when she was fifteen in fact, she was assigned to the best house in town. No procurer enticed her there. She got in on her own merits. But she was an absolute failure in the business.

When you realize that she was even prettier then than she is now, the thing becomes fantastic. Where now she has a trace of double chin, at that time her features were gently chiseled in Elgin marble. Where now she has to wear an uplift *soutien gorge* to affect a youthful bosom, at that time her body was as firm as an August apple. Today even the cleverest cameramen can't streamline completely her matronly hips, but in those days she was as slender as a birch tree.

From those good old days, however, only her gorgeously slender ankles remain. They're as perfect today as they were twenty years ago. Well, maybe you could add the mass of lovely yellow hair, big blue eyes, uptilted nose and peach-like complexion to her ankles as still being about what they were in Butte.

And yet with all that in her favor she simply couldn't wait to be asked to say yes. The original of the Dorothy Parker girl, "who could speak fourteen languages and couldn't say no in any of them," has always been believed to have been Sally Alden. Nothing could be a greater libel on the Casanova of her sex. It was her impatience and that alone, which caused her to be thrown out of Montana's bawdy houses and into California's picture studios.

From the beginning in Hollywood whenever she came on a set she looked the crew over, and no one from prop-man to producer was safe.

By the time she was forty you'd have expected that sex as a subject would have begun to lose its interest for her, but no victim of Sally's rapacity ever

December, 1934

testified privately to that effect. Any of them could show you permanent scars as proof that they had fought for their honor—and lost.

It would not be portraying her fairly at all to call her "vampire," or a "gold-digger," or simply as her discarded lovers did, a "glamorous bitch in ermine." She openly bragged that she had made them all and any man who said anything else was a fairly transparent liar. And you'd be further from truth if you imagined she liked girls. No, her sex-life was conventional enough, except for the *force* behind it.

In the light of all this can you imagine anything funnier than the story that after the cleanup campaign had driven her out of pictures (she was beginning to skid anyway) and she had decided to try Broadway for a new build-up, she had entered a producer's office and with the terrified eyes of a deer at bay had fought for what the old-fashioned girls used to call something dearer than life?

Why do press agents circulate such yarns? It was, if anything, the producer who put up that old-fashioned fight. I can understand such stories where an old *madame* essays *Little Eva* or *Peter Pan* or the *White Sister*, but Sally was going to play the bag slinger in a revival of *Rain* and it wouldn't have hurt to let the public know that she had plenty of what it takes, especially since it was true.

It happened in Arch Banton's office. Most chorines who have worked for the oversexed Arch de Triumph will admit that they never were hired without at least a mauling, and any extras waiting in the outer office knew he was through casting when the couch was carried out of his inner office and put back among the props in the wings downstairs.

But in Sally's case they carried Arch out on his own couch like a wounded Spartan warrior being carried home from battle on his shield. Anyway you figured it, the scene must have been a howl.

Imagine Arch leering at the sight of a buxom blonde entering his office, licking his thick, loose lips, slyly getting up from his desk so that he could get between her and the door, and then imagine that lecherous look of his turning to terror as he faced a female look more lecherous than his own!

If a bigger belly-laugh could come from mortal man than from the person who might have been privileged to watch Arch hypnotized into a corner—the couch corner—gripping his clothes around him, while Sally, the super-sex sensation, started coiling around him like a cobra, I'd like to hear it.

After she had run Arch through the wringer she decided she ought to get a divorce from Stetson Handler, her fifth husband. She decided to do it quietly in Paris if Stetson would take an outright settlement of $25,000 instead of a monthly alimony. Being no fool, Stetson signed for the settlement.

Sally decided she wasn't going to be bothered with husbands any more. As "fronts" they had cost her too much money. Henceforth, she said, she'd live with her men till she tired of them, and then, like a Henrietta the Eighth, toss them aside. Her mother, who had old-fashioned ideas, said that would be her undoing.

"I'll be damned," cried Sally, "if I'll be trapped into marriage any more."

When pressed about "consequences" she replied, "I've had five, and the little bastards can become bank presidents for all I care. I'm through with marrying with an eye to 'consequences'."

When her mother suggested that might be all right for sons, but daughters need society's protection, Sally glared.

"Nuts," was all she would say.

It was really a sore spot with her. Though she was feminine to a fault, it burned her ego to a cinders that she couldn't produce a daughter. The one she claimed as her own was a phoney. It was really her maid's. They had gone abroad together, entered a Swiss *clinique*, Sally registering as the maid and the maid as Mme. Sally Alden, and when the baby was born it was officially registered as: *Saline Alden, fille de Mme. Sally Alden de Butte, Montana; père inconnu.* Daughter of Mrs. Sally Alden, father unknown! What malarkey! All hooey, even protected by the official records of a friendly republic.

That, in brief, was Sally's real career up to the time she arrived in Paris to divorce Stetson Handler, America's best-kept gigolo, as the newspaper boys privately called him. Then she learned about Lady Mary Fitton, one of Queen Elizabeth's ladies in waiting, the harlot poor Shakespeare fell for. Somebody talked her into making a picture around the black-eyed "lady" of Shakespeare's sonnets, while waiting for her divorce, and she leaped at the chance. I don't know why. Just to show off her French, probably.

But that was the thing that licked her at last. She brought over a skeleton crew from Hollywood to Joinville, just outside of Paris, and hired some frogs to fill in the frame.

Among these French workers was Henri Dupont. He would have been a Marquis if the Second Empire had survived, and he actually did so title himself, though France had been a republic for years before he was born. His name oddly, was Dupont, though in France that has become a gag name like Jones in America.

Fortunately Sally didn't know that. She didn't even know he was a Marquis. In fact she didn't know anything about him until she walked on the set and saw him moving a "nigger," a sort of black screen they use in studios, further away from the camera on the orders of the cameraman; one of her discarded lovers, incidentally.

"Who's that guy?"

"What?" asked the cameraman.

"Who's that guy?" she asked again.

"Just one of the prop-men."

"Make him take my make-up kit to my dressing-room after we knock off for the morning, will you?"

The cameraman saw immediately what was going to happen to Dupont, and though he was an old hand in the picture business and pretty cynical about virtue and all that, something came over him and he decided he had to protect this youth at all costs.

When they had finished shooting the scene and in the general chaos of moving the troupe outdoors for an exterior shot, he told Dupont what he was in for.

"But don't let her do it," he said. "Fight her off. Use every device you can think of and in the end if she has to marry you to get you she'll do it. Whatever you do, don't go in her dressing room. Knock, leave her kit at the door, and scram! That's your only hope. If she gets you as quickly as she wants you, she'll throw you aside in a month like a worn-out glove. I *know!*"

Dupont turned white when he learned the plight he was in, but he had a Frenchman's instinct for self-preservation, and for making money too. For days he played with her and kept slipping in and out of situations that would have hooked even a Cabinet Minister.

It was his cunning against hers, and hers was fortified by a thousand conquests. She was quick enough to see that she could have had him if she proposed marriage, but she was determined not to marry again, and she didn't see why a frog, of all persons, should be so fussy. Wasn't France the "home," if you could call it that, of the *mésalliance?* Why did this kid have to go back on such an established tradition? If she were willing to take up the manners of his country, there was no reason for his going early New England. She said as much to the cameraman, but he only shrugged his shoulders. He had been through all that with her himself.

Oddly, the thing that finally hooked her was a cock-and-bull story the cameraman told Dupont to pass on to her when the occasion arose. The third day on the set she got her first chance to talk to Henri while they were waiting for lights.

"Were you born in Paris, Hank?" she asked familiarly, and with an innocence born of cunning.

"Yes," he said briefly.

"Are you the only child?"

"No."

"I thought the French never had more than one or two children."

"I have five sisters," he said.

That was his cue. The cameraman had told him to say that, and it worked like a charm.

"That's a lot of girls," said Sally.

"Yes, *alors*, girls run in our family."

She wanted him now more than ever. That subterfuge by which she got her other daughter may have fooled the world but in her heart it didn't fool her. If this youth, besides being handsome and of good family, could produce a daughter, that would round out her life in the way she wanted it rounded out. And if she couldn't get the guy any other way than by marrying him, well, one more didn't make much difference in her life, she decided. She could get divorced in a couple of months if she tired of him.

She told her mother she was marrying again, "a Marquee this time."

"My God," cried her mother, "not one of those things they hang outside theatres!"

"No, no, a sort of Count," explained Sally.

"Oh," said the mother.

"I can get a divorce in a couple of months if I tire of him."

But she didn't know France as well as she knew men, for France is the easiest country to get a divorce in and the hardest to get married in, and before she was through she realized that anybody who got married there meant it.

"I can understand now," she said, "why all those artists on the left bank live in sin. They haven't the time or money to go through with this ceremony."

She had to get affidavits from the Consul General of the United States, documents from lawyers which the Consul endorsed, certificates of residence from the Chief of Police of Paris, and the manager of the hotel where she stayed and so on. Document on document piled up and even then she was only to first base.

"You now have to stay in the hotel for thirty days," the Chief of the Bureau of Vital Statistics told her, "and then we will have to publish the banns, and after that you can get married."

"How long will that take?" she asked.

"Forty days, Madame."

"Forty days?"

He assured her politely it would take forty days.

"Unless," he added with a pause, "you can get a letter from the Procurer of the Republic waiving the banns, which are not compulsory in your country. As you are a foreigner he might do that for you, but as your fiancé is a Frenchman I doubt it."

"Who is this Procurer of the Republic? Does he get Folies Bergère girls for Cabinet Members?"

The Chief of the Bureau of Vital Statistics was visibly shocked.

"No, Madame, he is an officer of the Republic—and a very important one."

"Would 5,000 francs make him forget that ten-day clause?"

The Chief shrugged his shoulders. Since the Stavisky case all of them were wary of bribes.

"You might try, Madame."

But even in this she was unsuccessful and in the end had to wait forty days after Dupont said "Yes" before she could officially cash in on his acquiescence.

What torture she went through during that time even one of the old Amazons never equalled.

She tried to get Dupont to go off on trips, but his mother always went along, and spoiled that.

"How do you know we'll be suited for each other?" she once argued with him. "On principle I never marry a man I haven't slept with before marriage."

"I'm sorry, Sally," he said softly, "but I have my principles, too."

"You're the strangest man I ever met," she said, frustrated, annoyed, but still determined to get him.

In the end she did, of course, but not until they were on their honeymoon, and by then all the fight had been taken out of her and she was a licked woman.

To all outward appearances they were a happily married couple, but knowing Sally as you do now, you know that by being brought from the open range of life into its harness room she has been chastened, subdued, defeated.

There was an ironic chuckle in the subdued laughter of her ex-hubands, her ex-lovers and even those who only satisfied her for one night, but to those of us who believe that motherhood is woman's highest purpose in life it would have been a shame if Sally hadn't got her legitimate daughter, and, personally, I was rooting for her.

I don't know if even Sally could have had a greater thrill than I did when the news came from the Montpelier Mountain Lying Inn that an eight-pound daughter had been born to the Marquise Henri Dupont, and that father and child were doing well.

The hospital was proud, too, the Chief Obstetrician saying, "We wanted to keep our record clear. After all, we never lost a father yet."

"Nor an uncle, either," added his assistant.

Sally settled three million francs on Henri for his part in the affair.

"What will you call the baby?" the Bureau of Vital Statistics wanted to know.

"The Beaut of Montana," said Sally, gagging in her ribald way.

"*C'est un joli nom*," the chief said.

"A nice name! You're telling me!" Sally laughed, half pulling him into her bed.

The man wriggled himself free. "*Quelle dame!*" he cried. "In labor pains, even!"

But it really was her last try. After that, she settled down in a château on the Riviera, curbed her roving eye and soon that look of lust disappeared altogether.

I violate no confidence when I say that once that happened she and Henri and the Little Beaut from Montana lived happily ever after.

COREY FORD

◄──►

The Office Party

THERE are several ways of getting through the Christmas holidays. One is to board a ship in San Francisco and sail for the Orient, arranging to cross the International Dateline at midnight on December 24. As a result, the next day on your calendar will be December 26, and Christmas will have been a total blank. Another way to make your Christmas a total blank is to attend an Office Party the day before. . . .

The annual Office Party starts at noon on Christmas Eve, and ends two or three months later, depending on how long it takes the boss to find out who set fire to his wastebasket, threw the water cooler out of the window, and betrayed Miss O'Malley in the men's washroom. By the time the entire accounting department has been dismissed, and the painters have finished doing over the two floors which were ruined when somebody turned on the sprinkler system at the festivities' height, the moment has arrived to start planning next year's party, which everyone vows will be even more hilarious than the last one. Next year all the guests will be supplied with shin guards and hockey sticks.

Usually the merrymaking begins in a modest way, with some paper cups and a bottle of Pretty Good Stuff that Mr. Freem, in office supplies, received from a salesman who was anxious to land the roller-towel concession for the following year. While a few associates drop by to wish Mr. Freem a merry Yule, and sample his P.G.S., Mr. Freem's secretary receives her annual Christmas remembrance from Mr. Freem. She accepts this gift in stony silence, owing to the fact that her employer forgot all about getting her anything until the last minute, as usual, and hastily sent her out an hour ago with $5 and the coy order to buy herself something she likes but not to look at it because it's supposed to be a surprise. (Mr. Freem's secretary has settled on a particularly virulent perfume, which she knows Mr. Freem can't stand.)

Precisely at noon a sound of sleigh bells is heard, and Mr. Twitchard, the boss, emerges from his sanctum in an ill-fitting Santa Claus suit, a white beard, and a jovial smile that fools no one. Mr. Twitchard is a great believer in cementing employer-staff relationships, and as an example of co-operation between the brass and the underlings he has not only supplied refreshments for the occasion, but has deducted ten per cent from everyone's paycheck to cover the cost so they'll all feel that this is *their* party, too. After a few opening remarks, in which

Mr. Twitchard puts everybody in the proper holiday mood by explaining that production has slumped so badly there won't be any Christmas bonus this year, he waves his arm toward the door, and two boys enter with trays of drugstore pimento cheese sandwiches. Mr. Twitchard beams and lights a cigar, inadvertently setting fire to his false beard and thus supplying the only genuine laugh of the day.

The next hour or so is devoted to shaking hands and getting acquainted. After all, the main idea of an Office Party is for the different branches of the organization to get to know each other better, because the L. C. Twitchard Company is really just one big happy family, and the sooner we all forget our inhibitions and get on a first-name basis with each other, the better time we'll have or Mr. Twitchard will know the reason why. The only trouble is that each branch of the organization has the private conviction that all the other branches are manned by imbeciles and crooks, and conversation between them is limited to such expressions of Yuletide cheer as, "Well, you fellows in promotion must have quite a drag, getting that new air-conditioning outfit for your floor," or, "I hear a lot of heads are going to roll in Personnel the first of the year." To make matters worse, nobody is quite sure who anybody else is, and that stranger to whom you have just confided that the organization's weak link is the Front Office will turn out to be none other than Mr. Furbish, second vice-president and a brother-in-law of the boss.

The only thing to do, under these circumstances, is to get good and loaded as fast as possible. After sufficient champagne has been mixed with sufficient rye, the ice is broken, and the celebrants are not only calling each other by their first names, but are adding certain endearing epithets which they have kept bottled up all year. For example, that mild, soft-spoken Mr. Murgatroyd of the accounting department has just backed his immediate superior into a corner, and is telling him in a loud voice that he ought to know for his own good what people are saying about him, they all think he is nothing but a stuffed shirt and why doesn't he try and act like a human being for a change? (Mr. Murgatroyd will awaken in a cold sweat next morning, and try to remember what he said.)

Little Miss Meeker, who isn't used to cocktails, is contributing to the general merriment by paddling barefoot in the drinking fountain. Mr. Trench of Sales, having pursued his secretary around the desks with a sprig of mistletoe, has cornered her behind the filing cabinet and is assuring her in maudlin tones that his wife doesn't understand him. As a result of these confidences, his secretary will be transferred to the Chicago branch Monday morning.

By midafternoon the party is a shambles. Paper cups, parts of sandwiches, and an occasional girdle litter the floor. Four shirt-sleeved individuals from the traffic department, perspiring freely, have organized a quartet and are rendering such nostalgic Christmas carols as *Jack, Jack, Jack, the Sailor Chap* and *O'Reilly's Daughter*. Miss Meeker has passed out cold, with her head in a wastebasket, and the upright members of the staff are drawing lots to see which one will get her back home to Staten Island. (Miss Meeker will be discovered in Van Cortlandt Park two days later, wandering around in a dazed condition.) Several fist fights have broken out in the men's room, and a first-aid station has been set up in the reception hall for the treatment of abrasions, minor contusions, and black-and-blue marks on stenographers' thighs. Mr. Twitchard remains cold sober, observing the celebrants through his pince-nez glasses and jotting down their names grimly in his little black book. Tomorrow will be Christmas, and maybe Santa Claus will leave a little pink slip in your stocking.

By the time the affair breaks up along toward midnight, at the request of the building superintendent and a squadron of police, so much ill will has been generated among the staff that it will take at least twelve months for the organization to get back to normal, and then it will be time for next year's Office Party.

The only solution I know is to stage an Office Party of your own on December 23rd, two days before Christmas. If you get sufficiently fried, you may wander by mistake into the wrong Office Party the following noon. Not only will the proceedings be about the same as the Party in your own office, but you won't get fired.

And a Merry Christmas to you, courtesy of the L. C. Twitchard Company.

MAX SHULMAN

◄──►

Spanish Spoken Here

Sam Mashoulam, coming home from his barber shop one night with his customers' global opinions on his lips, delivered a short oration to his wife, Nettie, on the duplicity of Argentine politics. Nettie was sure that what Sam said was true, but she cared little for politics. Sam's mention of the Argentine, however, was of interest to her.

"Sam," she said, "thirty years already you didn't write to Meyer your own brother. I'm so ashamed I can't show my face on the street."

"Whatsa matter maybe people on the street are stopping you looking in your face saying whatsa matter your husband the barber thirty years already he didn't write his brother in Argentina?"

Irving, their sixteen-year-old son, took his mother's side. He was entirely in favor of resuming long neglected relations with Uncle Meyer. In Irving's mind, Meyer in the far Argentine was The Rich Uncle. Uncle Meyer had green rolling acres upon which grazed herds of prize beef cattle and fast, nervous ponies. Each night to Uncle Meyer's hacienda came bands of gaily dressed vaqueros to sing and play the sinuous ballads of the pampas. Irving had had a short fling at Spanish in high school, and he knew a thing or two about our neighbors to the south.

Actually there was little likelihood of Uncle Meyer being anything like Irving imagined. In 1912 Meyer and Sam Mashoulam had left the Russian village of their birth and sailed to America to earn their living as barbers, in which trade they had newly completed their apprenticeships. On the crossing they had become friendly with a fellow steerage passenger, a glib Slovene who spoke glowingly of big money and high life in South America. North America, poohed the Slovene, was overrated, enormously overrated. In North America a man must work like a horse and still he starves to death. South America, on the other hand, ah, South America—he did a Balkan version of the rumba to show what he meant. Meyer, a mercurial type, was persuaded.

Ignoring Sam's vehement entreaties, he did not disembark at New York but continued southward with the Slovene. A few months later a letter came to Sam, by this time employed and married to a young immigrant he had caught on the rebound from a second comic of the Yiddish Art Theatre. The letter was from Meyer and confessed sadly that the Slovene had stolen his wicker trunk and left him stranded in Buenos Aires. Send money.

Sam sent. The following year Meyer wrote that he was now working in a high type barber shop and Sam could soon expect repayment. That was the last communication from Meyer.

The years passed. Sam forgave Meyer, as a brother should. In fact, he began to like Meyer better than he ever had when they were together. Meyer's impetuosity took on a gallant aspect in Sam's mind. Dear, brave, foolish Meyer far beyond the seas, he thought, and he spoke very tenderly of him to Nettie and Irving.

Irving was enchanted. Nettie, too, developed an affection for her venturesome brother-in-law, but she took a conventional outlook. "Why," she kept asking Sam, "if you like him so much you don't write him a letter your own flesh and blood, huh?"

Sam, however, had a shrewd notion that Meyer as a memory was likely a more lovable fellow than Meyer as a correspondent. So he steadfastly rejected Nettie's persistent suggestions. After a while the subject became painful, and Sam carefully avoided all mention of Uncle Meyer.

Now this night Sam's dissertation on Argentine politics had reopened the argument. Nettie and imaginative Irving loudly reminded him that blood was thicker than water; they appealed to his sense of propriety; they pointed fingers of scorn at him.

Sam answered that the whole day he cut hair until the eyes and fingers were ready to fall off, his arches Hitler should have, and he comes home at night for a little supper and what does he get? Aggravation. Instead, he charged, of having supper on the table he shouldn't be late to the lodge meeting (tonight, as they well knew, was lodge meeting night) he gets what? Aggravation.

"To the lodge he can go," said Nettie. "For the lodge okay he's got plenty time. But for the brother thirty years already he didn't see in Argentina to write a letter is no time. For the lodge to go play poker lose the money is time. For the brother, no."

"Listen," said Sam, "you think maybe I don't want to write my brother my own flesh and blood in Argentina? Of course I want."

"So why you don't?" asked Nettie.

"Listen," said Sam, "I'm a barber not maybe a letter writer. I can cut hair give shaves massages anything you want it but writing letters it's not my line. Look how many years already I didn't write nobody a letter. A man forgets. Haircuts yes shaves yes massage yes. Letters no. Kill me, I can't do it."

"Why don't you call?" asked Irving.

"Call!" Sam roared. "I'll go in the street and holler yoo-hoo Meyer look it's Sam how are you?"

"On the telephone," Irving said. "You can call the whole world over the telephone."

But Sam brought up the expense of such a project, and even Nettie was forced to agree with him. The argument petered out, and they sat down to dinner.

"I'm late," Sam said quickly as he finished his last spoonful of dessert, and he escaped to the lodge meeting.

At the poker game that followed a token business meeting Sam had fantastic luck. In spite of the twenty-five-cent limit and the fact that half the table played shy all the time and filched what they withdrew from the pot, Sam won eighty dollars.

It took him until four a.m. to do it, which gave Nettie ample time to prepare and polish a tirade to deliver upon his homecoming. She was wound up and ready to let fly when Sam walked in the door.

"Shut up already," said Sam before she could begin. "What's so terrible? I won forty dollars." Then he got three quiet hours of sleep and went to work.

He came home from the shop that night very tired, too tired to notice the sly glances that passed between his wife and son. He was grateful for the silence and attention to his needs at dinner. After the meal he rose wearily and said, "To bed. I'm dead."

"Wait, Sam," said Nettie mysteriously, "you're expecting a call."

Then they told him that before he had come home they had called the long distance operator and that she was now trying to locate Uncle Meyer in Argentina.

"It only costs ten dollars to try to find him," said Irving.

"Ten dollars!" screamed Sam.

"So didn't you make forty dollars by the poker last night like finding money in the street?" asked Nettie. "It's the same maybe like haircut shave money you work for it?"

"Ten dollars to find him!" wailed Sam. "How much costs to talk to him if they do find him?"

"So another twenty, thirty dollars," said Nettie lightly.

Sam sank into a chair and clasped his head with both hands. He cursed himself for reporting so much of his poker winnings.

The phone rang.

Irving grabbed it. "Hello. Yes. Yes. You did! When? Now? Now? Pa, come here quick! They found Uncle Meyer. He's waiting on the phone."

Sam trembled to the telephone. Nettie and Irving quivered close beside him. "Hello, hello," said Sam.

"Mr. Sam Mashoulam?" asked the operator.

"Yes, yes."

"Hold the wire, please. We are ready with your call to Mr. Meyer Mashoulam in Buenos Aires."

There was a pause while the operator notified the bilingual operator in Miami that Sam was waiting. The Miami operator reported in Spanish to the Buenos Aires operator. There was a little discussion between Miami and Buenos Aires.

The sweat rolled off Sam as he stood waiting. Nettie tugged at his sleeve, whispering, "Whatsa matter, whatsa matter?" Sam shook his head fiercely and tore his sleeve out of her grasp.

"Go ahead," said the operator.

"Hello, hello," Sam yelled. "Meyer? Meyer?"

"Sam!" came a voice from South America.

Then Sam burst into a torrent of Yiddish. "Meyer, my dear brother. Meyer, how are you? Meyer, my dear precious brother!"

In Yiddish Meyer answered, "Sam, my dear brother. Sam, my dear, dear brother. How—"

He was interrupted by a click, and the Buenos Aires operator spoke rapidly to Meyer in Spanish. Meyer answered her excitedly. She spoke to him again, and again he answered her heatedly. She said something firm and curt to him.

"Hello, hello, whatsa matter?" Sam hollered.

"Whatsa matter, whatsa matter?" cried Nettie in Sam's ear.

"She should have a stroke the operator," Sam exclaimed.

"Just a moment, please," said the operator to Sam.

There was some conversation in Spanish between the Buenos Aires operator and the Miami operator. Then the Miami operator said, "Mr. Sam Mashoulam?"

"Yes, yes, yes."

"I'm sorry," she said in a firm voice. "You can't talk Yiddish to Mr. Meyer Mashoulam in Buenos Aires. You must carry on the conversation in Spanish or English."

"What? What?" Sam yelled, bewildered. "I'm talking to my brother Meyer I didn't see him thirty years already."

"You must carry on the conversation in Spanish or English," the operator repeated.

"Please, Irving," said Sam to his son, "you take the telephone. I can't understand."

"Hello," said Irving.

"You must carry on the conversation in Spanish or English," the operator said again.

Irving was interested. "Why?"

"There is a state of emergency in Argentina," the operator explained. "All foreign phone calls are being monitored. Therefore, they must be in Spanish or English. Since Mr. Meyer Mashoulam says he cannot speak English, Mr. Sam Mashoulam must speak Spanish if he wishes to talk to Mr. Meyer Mashoulam."

"What does she say she should drop dead the operator?" Sam asked his son.

"Just a minute," Irving told the operator. He turned to Sam. "She says you hafta talk Spanish if you want to talk to Uncle Meyer."

"Spanish!" Sam and Nettie screamed.

"She says you hafta talk Spanish otherwise you can't talk to Uncle Meyer."

"She should be able to eat like I can talk Spanish the operator," said Sam. "Tell her I didn't see my brother Meyer already thirty years."

Irving told her.

"I'm sorry," said the operator. "You will have to carry on the conversation in Spanish or English. And please hurry your call. The lines are needed."

"Irving!" exclaimed Nettie. "Didn't you study Spanish in the school? I remember I gave you two dollars you should buy a Spanish book."

"So talk to Meyer," said Sam, pushing Irving's face into the mouthpiece.

Irving answered, "It's a coupla years already since I took Spanish. Besides, I got kicked out of the class."

"The book! The book! The Spanish book I gave you two dollars you should buy. It's in the closet, cellar, someplace. Get the book. You'll talk from the book."

"I dunno where it is," said Irving, "and besides—"

Nettie flew into action. "I'll look in the closet. You look in the cellar a big box by the dill pickles all fulla books." She shoved Irving toward the basement stairs. "Sam, you hold the phone."

Nettie ran into the front closet while Sam, miserable and perspiring, held the phone. "Mr. Sam Mashoulam?" said the operator, "You'll have to hurry, please."

"Whatsa matter it's burning by you?" Sam snapped. "Wait a minute."

Nettie roared through the closet, tipping over box after box filled with newspapers, magazines, photographs, receipted bills, curtain fittings, candlesticks, baby clothes, citizenship papers and an occasional schoolbook of Irving's.

In the basement Irving was lifting grimy books out of a cardboard box, glancing at them quickly and flinging them to the floor.

"Mr. Sam Mashoulam?" said the operator. "I can only wait a moment longer. War needs the wires."

"All right. All right. A minute," Sam answered. "Nettie! Irving! You sleeping to hell goddam it?"

Nettie emerged from the closet with hair askew, dress ripped and face streaked with dirt. "Not in the closet," she announced. She ran for the basement.

"Argentina they had to call. Meyer they had to call," wailed Sam. "All day I'm standing on my feet they're falling off the arches cutting hair shaving faces trying to make a living I should come home at night to a nice—"

"If you don't begin very soon, I'll have to disconnect you," said the operator after another minute.

"Shut up, you Spanish!" Sam shrieked.

The basement door opened and Irving raced out waving a book. Nettie puffed behind, calling. "We found it. We found it."

Sam shoved the telephone into Irving's hand. "Quick!"

"Hello," gasped Irving. "Okay, connect me with Buenos Aires. I'll talk Spanish."

Irving nervously thumbed through the Spanish grammar as the connection was renewed. "I ain't so sure," he said to his father. "It's been a long time ago and besides I got kicked out of the class."

"Here is Mr. Meyer Mashoulam," said the operator.

"¿Sam? ¿Sam?" asked Uncle Meyer in Buenos Aires.

"Salud," said Irving. "Lo Irving."

"¿Irving?" asked Uncle Meyer. "¿Quién?"

"Irving," repeated Irving. "Irving Mashoulam." He turned quickly to the glossary in back of the book. "Hijo Sam."

"Ah, hijo," said Uncle Meyer. He proceeded to ask rapidly how were father and mother and was everything all right and why did they call. He was happy to hear from them, but perhaps, God forbid, something was wrong. ¿Eh?

Irving didn't understand a word. "¿Qué?" he said.

Uncle Meyer repeated.

Irving shook his head. "I told you," he said to Sam, "it's been a long time ago and besides I got kicked—"

"Talk, for God's sake, talk!" Sam bellowed. "You got a book, talk."

Irving looked through the glossary for "uncle." "Tío," he said, "Lo Irving."

"I understand," said Uncle Meyer in Spanish. "You are Irving, the son of Sam. ¿But how does it go with you and your father and mother? ¿Is something, God forbid, wrong?"

Irving shook his head. "Lo Irving," he repeated. "Irving Mashoulam. Lo Irving."

"Lo Irving! Lo Irving!" Sam screamed: "Is that all it says in that book?" He snatched the Spanish book from Irving's hand. "Here," he said, opening the book to the chapter on the subjunctive mood, "say this."

Irving shrugged. "Wear your overcoat," he said in Spanish. "Do not sit down. Long live the king. We want Joseph to study to be a lawyer. I need a bookkeeper who has good handwriting. ¿Do you permit me to smoke?"

"¿What? ¿What?" said Meyer in Buenos Aires. "I don't understand. ¿Joseph? ¿Bookkeeper? ¿Lawyer? ¿Smoke? ¿What are you saying? I don't understand. ¿Who is this?"

"Lo Irving," said Irving.

"Again with the Lo Irving!" Sam roared. He tore the book from Irving once more and opened it to the section on infinitive, gerund and past participle. "Read," he commanded Irving.

"I caught the car by running," said Irving in Spanish. "The laws are decreed by Congress. Wishing is the business of idlers. Returning to Rome, I ran across Mary. Knowing your lessons is the only guarantee of scholastic success."

Sam nodded approvingly as he listened to the Spanish.

"Sitting and dreaming is not working and doing," continued Irving. "To skate on the ice one must first have the equipment. Watching the impressive historic ruins stood two young women."

Sam turned another page, to the passive voice. "Go ahead," he said.

"The ocean was crossed by Lindbergh in an airplane," Irving told his Uncle Meyer. "The soldier was wounded by a bullet. Mary was invited to the dance. Catherine was not invited to the dance."

"¿What? ¿What?" shouted Uncle Meyer. "¿What is this ghastly joke? ¿Who is this? I spit in your milk."

"One eats well here," Irving went on. "The criminal is taken before the judge.

The criminals are taken before the judges. Lincoln was loved by all. Lo Irving."

"Your time is up," said the operator.

The next morning as Sam shaved Mr. Katz, his first customer, he said, "By the way, I talked to my brother last night."

"So?" said Mr. Katz.

"In Buenos Aires, Argentina," Sam said, laying a hot towel on Mr. Katz's face.

"In Buenos Aires, Argentina!" came the muffled exclamation.

"In Buenos Aires, Argentina," Sam repeated and lifted the towel so he could see Mr. Katz's face.

ANDRÉ MAUROIS

An Idea for a Story

THE other day I was thinking of the general laws governing a type of writing which I have always liked, while trying to make a story out of a subject which had amused me. This is the subject: Sexual pleasure has been the basis of an entire civilization, which began about the twelfth century and now seems on the decline. It is possible to argue indefinitely about these two dates, but not, I think, about the phenomenon itself, the birth of romantic love and its astounding influence on the art and morals of Europe. It is rather extraordinary, I said to myself, that a simple physical need should have given rise to such complex emotions and should be the subject of almost every artistic masterpiece, whereas other needs, equally urgent, like hunger and thirst, have remained rather primitive with most people.

A moment's reflection showed me that the difference is easily explained by the completely egotistic satisfaction of hunger and thirst. The civilizing and aesthetic value of love lies in the fact that it presupposes the harmony of two human beings, and that, from the time when both were free, owing to the relative emancipation of women, every kind of harmony and discord entered into their agreement. If human beings had been so constructed, I thought, that the satisfaction of thirst was only possible or agreeable between two people, then thirst would have been the cause of devastating passion and the subject of sublime masterpieces.

Why, I thought, should it not be possible to imagine a race so formed and governed by such desires, and to endow another form of desire with all the passion of love? Then I saw an island on which people like ourselves were living, but they had on their right arm a growth like a breast, only smaller, culminating in a nipple. I could see that this growth enabled them to satisfy each other's thirst, and the picture was somewhat revolting.

I was immediately confronted by a physiological difficulty. Was it not an unlikely supposition that food which was assimilable could come from a creature of the same species?

If these people could live only on the food which they gave each other, where did the liquid they secreted originally come from? Suppose that they secreted this liquid as plants produce sap. But plants draw their sustenance from the earth and from the heat of the sun. Should I endow the inhabitants of my

July, 1934

island with green hair and vegetal functions? The more I thought of it the more I could see that the difficulty was not so great as I had imagined. These creatures could feed through the mouth and the digestive tract as we do, but they would require as some sort of supplementary nourishment this juice produced by the human body, just as children need animal milk, and ants need the liquid secreted by plant-lice.

The idea of the island suggested two characters which I had already invented for "The Voyage to the Island of the Articoles," a young French sailor, whom I called Pierre Chambrelan, and his wife, whose name, I believe, was Anne. It was easy to imagine, as Swift did for Gulliver, that these two people, having left the island of the Articoles, had visited other unknown countries, and that one of these was the island on which my monsters lived with breasts on their arms. It was necessary to give these people a name, so I thought it would be natural and euphonic to call them the Erophagi. Erotophagi was a more correct derivation, but pleased me less. I decided that Pierre Chambrelan and his wife, on leaving the Articoles, should arrive at the island of the Erophagi.

At the beginning of the story it would have been clumsy to reveal to the hero and to the reader the key of the narrative and the symbols on which the fiction was based. In the earlier chapters the secret of the intimate life of the Erophagi must not be apparent to the travellers. They must be impressed by the astounding immodesty of this race. The Erophagi would be nudists, a fact explicable by the warmth of the climate, but they would wear on their shoulders an armlet embroidered with lovely ornaments. They would attach no importance to the gestures of physical love, which took place in public amidst general indifference. It would be the custom of the island for people to ask their friends to come and make love, just as we invite people to come to dinner. The Erophagi would be surprised and shocked by the repugnance of Pierre and Anne towards these collective amusements. They would accuse the travellers of not understanding the most innocent joys of humanity.

Gradually the travellers would discover that young Erophagi couples met several times a day and hid themselves in their rooms, and that it was forbidden, in fact inconceivable, to disturb them. "With such freedom, what on earth can they find to do in secret?" Anne and Pierre Chambrelan asked in astonishment. Another phenomenon which seemed curious to them was that these immodest people have a curiously localized form of modesty, which is in their right shoulder. Everybody, both men and women, always keep the top of their right arm covered up. This is all the more extraordinary because these people spend most of their time in the sea. But then both sexes wear bathing armlets, which are swollen out by a curious protuberance. On the beach strict notices declare that bathing with bare shoulders is prohibited.

It is easy to imagine the episodes which would lead the travellers to discover the truth. Suddenly the secret life of the Erophagi would be revealed. They would discover that every Erophagus, man or woman, secretes in the arm a liquid which another person can absorb by suction. This liquid, whose taste is delicious, and which is not otherwise obtainable in nature, is essential to the life of the Erophagi. If they are deprived of it, they do not die, but become prematurely old and are afflicted by slow and deadly diseases.

Obviously the problem is more complicated than would appear from this first outline. If each of these creatures could derive the necessary liquid from any other, then no deep feelings would be aroused by this simple physiological need, but the drama of their lives consists in the fact that, although the chemical composition of the individual liquids is very similar, and an unaccustomed palate could not distinguish one from the other, they are not interchangeable to a sensitive Erophagus, and most of them are highly sensitive. It is probable that the decided taste which each individual shows for the liquid secreted by a given person could be explained by an analysis of the liquid itself, if our knowledge of chemistry were more exact. It is reasonable to suppose that every organism requires certain juices to complete and maintain itself. The person who can supply those juices becomes indispensable. It is not surprising that an Erophagus should become desperately attached to that person and establish relationships as lasting and as tender as our love. These relationships are based, not on sexual pleasure, but on the exchange of perfectly assorted liquids.

It is easy to understand that such powerful sentiments should produce modesty. Hence the armlets. When two Erophagi withdraw to a room, as the travellers observe, it is always for one of these brachial feasts, which they call unions, and which are, as a matter of fact, a kind of union in normal cases, because the position of these breasts enable the Erophagi to enjoy their pleasures simultaneously. The great Erophagi novelists have no objection to describing sexual relations, and these books are permitted to children, but the description of a brachial feast is considered obscene, and the best authors avoid it.

It is not difficult to imagine the dramas which our travellers would witness, and which would permit them to study the sentimental life of a people so different from ourselves. The fundamental reason for amorous complications with the Erophagi, as with ourselves, is unshared feeling. Sometimes an Erophagus will have a great desire for the liquid of another, but the latter would have no feeling for the liquid secreted by the former. Then there would be the spectacle of an unfortunate human being, hungry and thirsty, importuning a reluctant Erophagus who would find the scene of an unshared brachial feast boring and ridiculous. In certain cases sickness and age would bring about profound changes in the composition of the liquids and destroy relations which had hitherto seemed solid. In other cases a relationship which had begun by an intense mutual delight in this exchange of liquids would become difficult and painful, because one of the lovers, tired of a too familiar savour, would look elsewhere for new sensations, whereas the other, endowed with a more constant taste, would ask nothing better than that their relationship should continue.

Pierre Chambrelan would notice with interest that the usual duration of a passion among the Erophagi is about the same as with ourselves. It varies considerably, and oscillates between a week and ten years. Certain Erophagi who are restless or blasé need a new liquid almost every day. But Anne would discover old couples still thirsting for each other after fifty years of happiness. What are fundamentally relationships of nourishment become the basis of spiritual unions, of tender affections and friendships. Marriage among the Erophagi, whose legal forms resemble our own, is always based on such feelings and never on sexual relations, which are entirely free. Nevertheless, jealousy, among them as among ourselves, often assumes extreme forms and concentrates upon actions which are regarded with indifference by normal people. For example, some Erophagi would prevent their wives from making love with a stranger, just as certain husbands in our countries prevent their wives from dining alone with a man friend. But legal adultery does not exist, unless there has been an exchange of liquids and the parties have been caught in the act of having a brachial feast.

The consequences, so far as the education of children is concerned, are curious, since the children are in the charge of the state, and married life rests upon an entirely different basis. Differences of sex play no part in the marriages of the Erophagi. A man may marry a man, or a woman a woman. In many cases however, when a marriage takes place between people of different sex, sexual relations may complete those of nourishment, perhaps thereby rendering the union more perfect. But that is always a secondary matter, just as a common liking for certain foods may be an additional bond between two lovers among us.

To sum up: the ideas which give its value to love, that is to say, the idea of sin and the idea that only a given individual can satisfy us, though associated with a different desire in the minds of the Erophagi, produce the same results as with us. The romantic story of nutrition follows with them practically the same course as the romantic story of reproduction does with us. Their art, which is very remarkable, has been entirely inspired by the need to sublimate impossible thirsts.

The religion of the Erophagi is also a sublimation of this instinct, a phenomenon which Paul Valéry divined, without knowing the Erophagi, when he said: "Hunger and thirst have not degenerated into sentiment and idolatry. Why? But sex has become a demigod. Perhaps even God."

Having reached this point in my reflections on the Erophagi, I decided not to write their story.

ILKA CHASE

◀————————————————————————————————▶

It Was Good Enough for Father

WE OF the twentieth century like to look back patronizingly at past generations; they, poor souls, did the best they could with the means at hand, but we—let's admit it—are far more advanced. Just consider all the mechanical goodies we have! Everything these days is a great deal bigger and faster than our ancestors ever dreamed of!

Well, we do have bigger things, and certainly faster ones. Better too, in many ways. It would be ridiculous to deny or to decry industrial and scientific advancement, though it's true that, thanks to one or two of our progressive items, we're subjected to forms of torture that former generations (those old stick-in-the-muds) never had to endure. We have, among other so-called advantages, the telephone—an instrument that rings constantly when we crave silence and maintains an infuriating silence when we want it to ring.

In the old days there were no telephones, no cellophane, no indoor plumbing. There weren't any psychoanalysts either; the madhouses were less crowded and the divorce courts weren't jammed to the rafters. Yes, our ancestors may have lacked many modern improvements, but yet, sorry bunglers though they were, they had an insight, a psychological understanding, and an appreciation of human well-being so profound as to make fools of us moderns. They knew, for example, that women need men and men need women and that the interdependence of the sexes must be recognized if a marriage is to succeed.

And so they invented a device known as the double bed.

Today we are more progressive than our forefathers, more sanitary, more civilized. Today we have twin beds—and a self-imposed exile they are, a folly for which there can be no praise. We have but to consider where they are most in use to ask ourselves in horror why we give them house room. Where are they used? They're used in hospitals, in prisons, in insane asylums, that's where! And fifty per cent of the people occupying them there probably wouldn't be in them if they hadn't used them at home.

What has happened to us that we no longer realize the double bed is more thrill-inducing than the airplane, more comforting than steam heat, more engrossing than television? The freedom, the companionship, the moments of lyric tenderness implicit in the double bed rank among life's great experiences. Occupied by two sympathetic members of the opposite sex, the double bed

July, 1948

yields the nearest facsimile of complete joy we may reasonably expect on earth.

A close rapport is likely to occur in a double bed—indeed it is to be hoped for —but to think only of sex in this connection is to think of a skeleton, to ignore the glowing flesh and garments of happiness.

Man is an animal. So, fortunately, is woman. Why then, when it is easily obtainable, deprive ourselves of our greatest animal comfort—the proximity, the touch of the creature we love? Curiously enough, this animal instinct in humans is the soil from which evolves the most exquisite bloom we are capable of: love for another. For those who love each other, the spirit and the flesh are inseparably allied, and it seems highly unlikely that, as some moderns claim, connubial desire is kept alive through physical separation. Will a husband and wife seem less familiar, more alluring to one another, if they occupy separate beds? If so, wouldn't separate rooms be even better? And if that's an improvement, how about separate houses? And then maybe separate cities? Different countries? "Darling, how appealing you are when I'm in Saskatchewan and you're in Tanganyika!" Unless the flint strike the steel, whence the spark? What about that?

If the love two people bear each other is a living thing by day, it is fostered and intensified by their sharing a double bed at night.

Many couples, vaguely aware of this, experiment with that unsatisfactory compromise, twin beds side by side, joined by the same headboard. What is the comfort in being joined by a headboard and separated by the covers? This system is perhaps a little better than twin beds separated by the night table, but so little as to make scant difference.

A great attraction of a double bed for the married is its face-saving property. It is kind to one's pride. It is a breach-healer par excellence. Most married differences start out not too seriously—a chip off here, a small dig there, and the first thing you know one partner's feelings are hurt and the other is angry. Suppose this hapless couple is sleeping in twin beds. What happens? The undressing, washing, tooth-brushing routine is gone through, the aggrieved wife flounces to her single pallet and the husband either slams up the window in furious silence or asks savagely if she minds if they get a little fresh air in here to blow away some of this nonsense. He then plunks himself down on the edge of his bed, kicks off his slippers, swings his legs in, draws up the covers, punches his pillow into a knot as unyielding as his mood, and ostentatiously turns his back on the blossom he not so long ago promised to love and cherish until death. The silence is broken only by the click of the light switch as the wife snaps it off and her exasperated exclamation, throbbing with more drama than a three-act play: "Of course! Leave *everything* to me."

Under these circumstances, it is a long time before either of them gets to sleep, though it may be safely said that the husband, a grosser spirit, will eventually get there first. In the meantime the darkness is taut as a fiddle string. Then gradually, as the hours slip by, each one will be thinking, "The hell with this silly business, why don't we kiss and forget?" But each one is damned if he (and the term is used generically) will be first to get up, cross the infinity which is the three-and-a-half feet separating the beds, and snuggle in beside his indubitably erring but still beloved spouse. As a result the couple wakens in the morning after a restive night as out of tune as when they went to bed. By the time the husband gets home in the evening, the wife has had time to think up a lot of other grievances; and the first thing you know, space permitting, one or the other of them has moved out of the nuptial chamber and the rift is widened for fair.

With contiguous beds, the situation is ameliorated but it is still not good, since any move for a rapprochement must be telegraphed, the magnanimous partner (as he will think of himself)—or the crow-eating one (as he thinks he will be considered)—having either to get up and go around the beds or tug at the covers of his own and then of his partner's in order to slip from one to the other. This is a deliberate gesture and takes doing.

But in the double bed! How simple, how natural, how unintentional! The lights are extinguished and the tension prevails, but not for long. A tentative toe is stretched toward the center. Quite by accident it touches a leg. Well, even in the heat of battle nothing was said about the other party's being physically repugnant. There is no real need to draw one's toe back again. It stays. One is conscious of a gentle return pressure. A hand, by chance, brushes a shoulder, two heads draw nearer, an arm reaches out . . . It is an endearing arrangement. And even if the reconciliation doesn't happen before going to sleep, where there has been physical contact rest is broken. Two are likely to wake in the deep darkness. Things are different in the dark: those who went to bed as strangers waken as lovers, and pride and bitterness and anger are daylight demons.

The most general objection to the communal couch seems to be that many people feel they cannot sleep in the same bed with another person. This argument is not to be lightly brushed aside. Actually, three-quarter beds and standard doubles are small for two people. There is nothing so restful as kicking space, and nothing more conducive to resentment than the feeling that one must budge only with caution for fear of disturbing another person. Then, too, it is maddening, as one slips into the gauzy borderland of sleep, to have the bed leap under a sudden flounce or to have an arm flop across one's face or to receive a sharp gouge in the ribs from an elbow. Nor does it give rise to gentle thoughts of love to waken chilled to the marrow, exposed to the winds of heaven, while one's unconscious spouse slumbers blissfully at one's side wrapped snug and mummylike in all the blankets. Also there is no denying that many wives are prey to peckish morning moods when they have been kept awake at night by that calliope with the cutout open which is a snoring husband. Sometimes he may be throttled without total extinction, or rubber stoppers in wifely ears may mute the racket (there is a nasty rumor afloat that some husbands are driven to them too); but, where such treatment fails, even twin beds won't help. Despite love and longing, separate rooms may be the only answer. Let us turn in sorrow from this insoluble problem and its painful solution.

There are those who complain that double beds tend to sag in the middle and that both occupants are likely to spend their nights rolling downhill to bump into each other at the bottom, getting thoroughly awake as they haul themselves back up the slope, and then repeating the performance all over again. To those who demur on this score we give short shrift. Keep the springs and mattress in good repair, and it won't happen.

In fact, to all objections, barring the noise of snoring, there is a shining answer: the outsize double bed, the jumbo job that anyone can obtain with patience, guile, and some money. A bed seven feet square is a domain of flawless delight. In such a bed one is a property owner roaming the lower forty, solitary if one wishes it, in easy contact with fellow man or fellow woman when the spirit moves. Either partner may curl into a ball or lie spread-eagle, secure in the knowledge that his spouse is undisturbed, unaware during his most restless gyrations.The feeling of freedom and at the same time of coziness that one experiences in this broad pasturage is delightful. There is so much room that even disciplinarian dog lovers, the kind who say with suspicious firmness, "I'm crazy about dogs, but I do not approve of them on beds," may alibi Rover's presence on those very premises with the explanation that they didn't know he was there.

One shocking thing about the movies is that sight of a double bed strikes horror in the heart of the Johnston Office. For a community as concerned about public morals as Hollywood, it's interesting to note that if figures tended to show that fewer divorces occur among couples using double beds than among those occupying twin beds or separate rooms, then Hollywood itself is instrumental in the breakup of countless homes. For Hollywood sets fashions, and many Americans follow slavishly.

Struggling to understand the point of view of the censors, we can't help wondering what is supposed to be "dirty" about a double bed? Or "suggestive"? for countless generations men and women have slept in them, and the children of the household grew up thinking of them—if they thought at all—as symbols of family unity. Father and Mother shared a bed. Why wouldn't they? It was one of the most commonplace and sweetest facts of life. It was the custom in every country of the world and among all classes for hundreds of years. Then came Hollywood and couples in the movies sleep on measly single beds (which, mark you, are separated by two or three feet).

As we have acknowledged, there are arguments against double beds, but they have nothing to do with morals. When the double bed is outsize, they are chiefly economic. Though initial price is steep, it is not prohibitive. The fly drops into the ointment later. Upkeep! That is expensive, because the furnishings for this mammoth cot—mattress pads, sheets, blankets, blanket covers, quilts and spreads—have to be specially made. It takes a lot of goods, blankets, blanket covers, quilts, but, fortunately, an electric blanket does away with layers of wool and down quilts and provides bug-snugness in zero weather. The electric blanket, which seemed originally designed for slow torture, has evolved into the sleeper's boon. And with dual control for double beds, the harmony it creates among married couples is so marked that Nevada will soon be looking for clients. The great he-man who spurns comfortable warmth as something effeminate can virtually put his master switch in reverse and manufacture a row of icicles while the little hot dish at his side turns hers on full strength and sizzles cheerily through the night.

It is true that maids are likely to complain when first confronted with the task of making up the mastodon and to mutter that some people are crazy—"that's what, crazy,"—but as a matter of fact the task is not as ardous as it seems, and moving the bed is child's play, since the box springs are set on wheels. That is of no practical importance, of course, because it never occurs to maids to move beds for cleaing purposes in any event; but, should the mistress be fired with enthusiasm, it's a handy device.

The continuing headache is the laundries. They don't complain, laundries don't, but they take one look at those sheets, which are only slightly larger than the movie screen in Radio City Music Hall, and add a few naughts to the bill. It's worth it, though. Such drawbacks as these are far outweighed by the joys, a fact that seems to be dawning on more and more people. One large department store reports a new ratio of more than three double beds sold for every pair of twins.

It is, after all, a simple mathematical computation. Eight hours out of every twenty-four we devote to sleep. Since time flies so quickly, how practical it is— and how delightful—to spend a third of our lives on the double!

You've Had a Few If —

YOU HAVE been worrying about economizing, and it suddenly occurs to you that you saved twelve dollars yesterday on the new overcoat you bought and that there's always the possibility that you'll be getting a raise soon.

You find yourself thinking up forceful rebuttals for an argument you lost the other day, an argument which, at the time, didn't seem particularly important.

You hold eight diamonds to the ten, jack, a singleton spade and four small clubs and bid one heart, figuring that, although you are vulnerable, a psychic bid, in an effort to save rubber, is a fine strategic move.

There is a fly in your drink, but instead of taking the trouble to remove it, you quaff down your drink, merely taking the precaution to avoid consuming the fly in the process.

You sign your name to bar checks at a slightly increased speed.

You find yourself speaking with extra distinctness to certain elderly persons whom you know to be opposed to the consumption of alcohol.

You say: "Thank you very much" to servants who do you special favors instead of "Thanks."

The first act of the play strikes you as excellent, some of the gags drawing hearty laughter from you, but you wish the act would finish so that you could go out and get a drink.

You are driving a car, and have several passengers. You keep a reasonably brisk pace, but slow down carefully for all intersections, watch the road ahead of you intently, and sound your horn at any cars or pedestrians who might suddenly do something queer.

You are at the club, due for a formal dinner party at quarter of eight. You have figured on three-quarters of an hour for bathing and getting into evening attire. Now you are confident that you can do it in twenty-five minutes.

You had intended taking your leave of her in the cocktail lounge, explaining that you had to go back to the office and work. You take another look at her, and suggest dinner.

You go into considerable details in describing a local golf tournament you won, and which, at the time, seemed very much of a pushover.

The first thing you get, when you switch on the radio, is a jazz orchestra. You

January, 1937

remark that they are playing a swell tune. It happens to be one which you have heard five or six times previously without being impressed.

You start arguing politics, and make dogmatic statements about economics and sociology although you are by nature a cautious person who customarily qualifies all statements in such a fashion that you always have an out.

You debate with yourself seriously whether quarter of twelve in the evening is too late to call her up and ask for a date.

The score is seven to seven, and the opponents have the ball on your team's six yard-line, first down. You have very little fear that they will score.

You tell that story in mixed company—the one which, when you first heard it, seemed slightly dubious for such an occasion.

You check up on your cigarette supply, and take steps, if necessary, to make sure that you won't suddenly be caught somewhere without an immediately available smoke.

It is just before dinner, and your host, passing dividends, has just emptied the shaker. You fail to catch a question from the lady on the sofa next to you because you are wondering if the host will get out to the kitchen to mix another batch before the maid comes in and announces dinner.

You hold forth at some length on various celebrities you have encountered lately although you are chronically a person who is impressed by few of them and who actively dislikes the majority.

When you take your leave of the party, you ask the Petersons for dinner without first consulting your wife, although you know what that's going to get you as soon as you are outside the door.

Dancing with a girl twenty years your junior you try that step which you have seen her Yale escort execute with such precision—and you aren't displeased with the result.

The canapé plate comes around to you with one remaining morsel on it. Your hostess says: "Don't be shy about taking the last one," and you reply: "I should say not," seize it, and devour it at a gulp.

Customarily you would walk three blocks and take the subway to get to the place where you are destined. You hail a taxi, and reflect that some psychologist has claimed that it is good for the morale to indulge in a bit of luxury once in a while.

Your companion is a man who has the reputation of being able to consume gallons without batting an eye. You pull a face as long as your arm, talk in a semi-whisper, and discuss business conditions with him.

You think it might be fun to send a telegram to somebody.

You are a writer, and always on the lookout for ideas. A remark, dropped by one of your companions, gives you one that you are sure can't possibly fail to click. You search in your pocket for a piece of paper, and, if successful, jot down a memo on it.

You sit down at the piano, reel off a couple of tunes, and feel that you **are** going pretty well. You are delighted when somebody makes a request.

You suddenly encounter some friends of yours who have been on another party. You study them intently for a moment or so, wondering whether they are tight.

Your empty cocktail glass has been on the mantelpiece. Seeing your host approaching in your general direction with the shaker, you pick up your glass and hold it—not *too* pointedly of course—in front of you.

You are in the process of mixing another Tom Collins for yourself. It seems like too much trouble to bother with the lemon squeezer, so you seize half a lemon between your fingers, and squeeze a few drops of juice into your glass. The result tastes all right, although, when starting fresh, you customarily use all the juice you can get out of a whole lemon.

A companion is dissertating at some length on one of his favorite theories. While he is in the process, you think of an objection. He keeps on talking, and, when he finally stops, you find that you have temporarily forgotten the point you intended to make.

You ask the orchestra leader to play several of your favorite tunes, and don't give a moment's thought as to whether this is a place where you are supposed to tip for such a favor.

If the leader complies with your request, you tell your partner that it is your favorite tune, despite the fact that there are some two dozen over the past ten or fifteen years which you would be hard put to choose between.

You are at the bar with various friends, and are joined by a fellow who consistently snubbed you in college. You talk for a while, and it occurs to you that you have been all wrong in thinking him a snob. It was probably, you decide, just that he was shy.

You reflect that it's a good thing that tomorrow is Sunday.

Although it is below freezing, you are sure it won't hurt you to go down to the corner for more fizz water without putting on a coat and hat.

You tell yourself that anyway you've at least got to admit that she has a good figure, haven't you?

The Williams kid, who usually makes a hell of a pest of himself whenever you go over there, strikes you as a pretty smart youngster, and you engage in a lengthy conversation with him, even to the extent of inquiring what he learned in school today.

You anxiously watch your wife's actions, and hope she's feeling pretty good too.

You are a senior in college with an important final exam due tomorrow. You find yourself reflecting that many old grads have told you that out in the business world a diploma doesn't mean a thing. It's the associations you've made in college that count.

You have five minutes to make your train. You're sure you'll make it.

ROBERT HENDERSON

The Pre-Occupation of New York

It HAS since been conclusively established that, early in the summer of 1940, New York City was attacked, captured and abandoned by a coalition of foreign powers, but at the time hardly anybody knew it. The radicals insisted even then that it was so, the Left press printing headlined accounts of the occupation of the city by fascists. The Dies Committee discovered it, too, and the conservative papers featured each day the overthrow of the government by Reds. But the people just took quick glances at the headlines and, secure in the thought that everything was in its normal state, went about their business.

In mid-May the Army had been flying menacingly up and down Brooklyn and dropping bombs on patches of water far out at sea, on the theory that the coast was being harried by an imaginary fleet representing three imaginary Powers. Thus, when the forces of the Three Powers really did arrive a few weeks later, the Army was in practice but exhausted, and most of the population was in the midst of sitting out a heat wave in air-cooled picture houses.

At first the Powers merely sent a fleet of planes to reconnoiter and perhaps provoke incidents. Office workers later recalled having heard them come over the city, but since they just sounded like other planes, no one paid any attention to them except to grumble and shut the windows, or to gaze at them and say, "It must be cool up there."

The planes came over again on the following day, dropping leaflets urging the city to get rid of its oppressors and threatening it with wholesale desolation in the event of its keeping them. On the whole, these merely served to litter the streets. One stenographer, a Miss Fairbanks, seeing a handful of them fluttering down on lower Broadway asked, "Where's the parade?"

And her girl companion replied, "I don't hear any band, do you?"

In the midtown district a man picked up one of the leaflets, and his wife said, "What's that Arthur?"

He answered, "A handbill, I guess."

His wife said, "Well, throw it away, then, Arthur."

The evening papers reported that handbills had been distributed by planes that afternoon, and rejoiced editorially in the freedom of the press enjoyed by America, pointing that such a thing could not have happened in Rome or Moscow—or in Berlin if it weren't for the British Royal Air Force.

April, 1940

Bombing began that night, the raiders using delayed-fuse bombs of extra-ordinary power. When the R.C.A. Building suddenly and noisily swelled and burst at the bottom, the upper fifty stories dropping sheer and true into ruin, passersby paused to stare, halting traffic for over an hour. A taxi driver commented, "Always tearing stuff down!"

The cop he was talking to said, "They ought to watch what they're doing."

There were other direct hits, but none so spectacular. At the seventh detona-tion, a salesgirl sitting quietly in her room on West Twenty-first Street looked up from the day's society pages and remarked, "My God, you can't hear your-self think around here!"

The Army's planes went up the following morning to investigate, and were at once attacked by the invaders. The battle raged for several hours, just east of the city. Because it was Saturday, most of the city's inhabitants had left for the country or for Coney Island, but the remainder were in Central Park. An elderly gentleman taking a constitutional with a sheep dog, was approached by a nurse-maid who was watching the battle and had become curious. "What's it all about?" she asked.

"Something about the Fair," the man said.

Two of the planes went down in flames, trailing spirals of smoke. The child in the nurse's charge remarked to his playmate, "Pepsi-Cola is better."

That night the Army's searchlights played back and forth across the sky. Broadway was thrown into a mild turmoil, as it was generally supposed that a great new motion picture must be having its world première; and autograph collectors poured into Times Square from all parts of the five boroughs, many casual theatre-goers being trampled to death.

Meanwhile troops were being landed at the Battery, preparatory to the oc-cupation of the city, which was to take place the next morning. At eight a.m., the First Army entered the city and invited the Powers to follow, check the work of subversive agencies, liberate and pacify the island, and make arrange-ments for the enlightenment of its citizens.

At eleven a.m., the Second Army lined lower Broadway and Fifth Avenue. At noon, the Third Army escorted the Three Dictators up these thoroughfares to the deafening shouts of the First and Second Armies. There were a number of bands.

The stenographer, Miss Fairbanks, said to her girl friend, "Look, that must be that parade," and began throwing ticker-tape out the window while her girl friend tore up telephone books.

"That was Friday," the other girl said.

"I don't know, was it?" said Miss Fairbanks. "Well, parades—!"

The pageantry of the Occupation lasted throughout the day. People in the downtown offices spent the first hours at the windows waving happily, and at about three o'clock most of the offices closed. Everybody started to go home, but it was impossible to cross Fifth Avenue, so most of the people went to bars instead, shaking their heads and chuckling tolerantly. One man said, "You would have thought those Legionnaires would have got tired by now."

The bartender replied, "Did you hear where one of them rode a horse into City Hall and said he was the Mayor? Probly drunk."

The Occupation continued for several weeks. Martial law was declared and troops took over the duties of the police, causing many traffic complications by constantly raising their hands in salute. Otherwise the new conditions went unnoticed, except for a decree closing places of amusement at 10 p.m., which resulted in a brisk boom for the night spots. When the doors of one club were closed at the required hour—thereafter to be opened only to customers—one business man set his drink down and remarked, "My God, you would think we had Prohibition again!"

To which a bystander replied hotly, "Well, what was wrong with Prohibition?"

The ballots of the plebiscite, which was held early in July, required a simple "yes" or "no" to the question of *anschluss*. The voters trooped obediently to the polls, some only complaining that it was hot for November, and some complaining about other things.

As one couple approached an East Side polling place, the woman said, "Arthur, how do you know what these bond issues are *about*?"

Her husband answered, "What's the difference? It's just a new way to waste the taxpayers' money. Some third party is behind it."

"Republicans?" his wife asked.

But it was generally felt, what with the sick voters being brought from the hospitals and the dead ones from the record-books, that clean government must be saved and Tammany crushed once and for all. As a Mr. Borchard of Central Park West put it, "This is what comes of having those fellows in Washington. Who does he think he is, Mussolini?"

It was an enormously successful election, the results being heavily in favor of Mr. Roosevelt, with Benny Goodman, Joe DiMaggio, and Raymond Gram Swing dividing the minorities evenly among them. The question of *anschluss* was ignored completely. There was a jubilant crowd in Times Square, cheering everything, and while the enthusiasm was at its height the invaders crept, shuddering, to their ships.

◄ —— ►

The Bourbon Lake

" 'Tis a vacation we're beginning, Michael, not an auto race," admonished Mary. Michael Flynn's foot obediently retreated on the accelerator and the near scenery became visible as the car slowed down.

"Was that a route marker?"

"Slow it down a bit more, Mike," said James O'Hannion, "and I'll watch for the next. Eileen, my dear, will you examine the map again?"

"Perhaps you'll examine it yourself, Mr. O'Hannion," said Eileen. "More complaints I've never heard than the last time I examined it."

"You know very well my glasses are packed in the trunk," said James O'Hannion. "Just hold it right side up, Eileen, and look for Stroudsburg."

"Is it near Provincetown?" asked Eileen after diligent examining. "That would be Route Six."

"Is there blue all around it?" asked James sweetly.

"Yes," said the happy Eileen.

"Well, that's the Atlantic Ocean, and you're on Cape Cod," said James. "Eileen, my sweet, just because you're holding the map flat on your lap does not mean your finger must travel toward the front of the car."

"But that's the direction we're going."

"Then turn the map around and read the names of the towns upside down, Eileen, my dear!"

"Glasses or no glasses, you can take the—"

"Stroudsburg, Mrs. O'Hannion," said Michael hopefully. Eileen compressed her lips, glared at her husband, and bent over the map again. Mary leaned over and helped. Finally, they turned the map around and began pushing their fingers toward the front of the car. James sighed and looked at the road ahead.

"Trenton?" ventured Mary.

"Stroudsburg," repeated Michael. "But you're getting close."

"Did you check to see if I have enough underwear?" asked O'Hannion, suddenly worried about the safety of a small bottle that he had secreted in his bag. Eileen looked up from the map.

"Yes, Jim," she said sweetly. "You'll have enough. I took out one little item and was able to squeeze in two more sets."

January, 1952

"That was most thoughtful," O'Hannion murmured, sinking lower until his head rested on the back of the seat. Neon flashes of red and yellow reflected in the windshield and then fled past them on the right, disappearing into the blackness. "I wonder if the boys are at Casey's now," he mused.

"You'll not miss them for two weeks," said Eileen.

"Two weeks," whispered O'Hannion mournfully. "And me with only underwear in me bag."

"Did you find Stroudsburg?" Michael demanded.

Early the next morning, James O'Hannion and Michael Flynn were ejected from their respective doors of the big double cabin.

"A walk, you say!" Michael glared at Mary who, arms folded, barred the door against his return to bed. "A walk can be a dangerous thing. A man must work his way into these vacations gradually. A fast walk at this stage of the game is liable to set me poor heart to beating something scandalous and do more harm than good."

"Then take a slow walk," advised Mary.

"And don't head for the nearest tavern," added Eileen, stepping out onto the porch.

"No worry there," said Mary Flynn, laughing. The men looked at her suspiciously.

"Have you lost your mind?" asked Eileen. "These are our husbands."

"While they carried the suitcases in last night, I had a little talk with Mr. Drummond," explained Mary. "After asking about linen and food facilities, I inquired about saloons. There isn't a one on any road around here. He said no tavern was ever able to exist in this vicinity."

James reached out to steady himself against the porch and Michael's mouth dropped open.

"No taverns," mourned Michael.

"Away with you," said Eileen. "Ponder the unhappy news while you walk, if you will. Mary and I have to pay our respects to the neighbors."

The stunned men turned slowly and trudged away into the bright Saturday sunlight. The path led past other cabins and circled toward a souvenir shop and small restaurant. There it divided, one side heading for tennis courts and a volleyball area, the other branching off toward the woods and fields. Michael and James stopped at the fork.

"Would you be caring for a brisk tussle of volleyball?" asked Michael forlornly.

"I would not," said James. "Now a good game of shuffleboard at Casey's—"

"We should have investigated beforehand," said Michael.

"Who would think it?" said James. "A vacation place with no saloon. A man could die of thirst. Michael, my old friend, two gentlemen are about to play tennis. Watching them will make me sweat. Let's try this path."

They walked slowly, in single file, heads bowed and feet kicking up dust. The dirt path became grassy and they wandered through woods and up and down hills. It was on the summit of one of the hills that James stopped and grasped Michael's arm.

"Me mind is playing tricks on me," he said. "The miserable thoughts I've been thinking have made something snap."

"What makes you say that?" asked Michael.

"I just smelled Casey's," said James.

"I don't suppose the women would consider cutting the vacation short if we convinced them you were going crazy," muttered Michael.

"Hallucinations. I never thought it would happen to an O'Hannion," whispered James.

Deep in thought, they resumed walking. Michael led the way along the narrow path and, when he stopped suddenly, James walked into his back.

"What is it?"

" 'Tis catching, James," said Michael, sniffing the air.

"Casey's?"

Michael nodded and James quickly elevated his nose and began sniffing deeply.

"Hard to tell," said James. "Something seems to dilute the odor."

"Fresh air, apparently," said Michael.

"Sh-h," cautioned James. "I have the scent."

"Might our reasoning be wrong?" he wondered. "Perhaps there is a tavern in the neighborhood and Mr. Drummond does not know it. Hold the scent, James boy. As of this moment, you are our bird dog. Fetch."

James O'Hannion started forward. Michael followed closely. They walked briskly, like men with a purpose in life.

" 'Tis no bird dog I'm needing now," said Michael, twitching his nose. "This is the strongest smelling tavern I have ever met."

The odor of whiskey hung heavily in the air and the two men were running as they came over a small rise in the land. No tavern graced the foreground. Instead they faced a pretty lake surrounded by woods.

"We must be crazy, Michael," said James. "Our minds have snapped at the same instant."

"At least we will go together."

" 'Tis not only my nose, but my eyes that have gone back on me," said James. "It was always my belief that lakes are blue."

"Have you ever seen one before?"

"In the park."

"Ha!" scoffed Michael. "A tame lake. This is a wild lake. There's no reason why they shouldn't come in different colors."

"Very pretty, it is. Sort of a reddish, deep amberish color."

They walked to the shore line and breathed deeply.

"Wild lakes smell better than park lakes," said James. "Look over there. Nature for sure."

He pointed along the shore line where a tree grew at the edge of the lake.

A beaver sat against the tree. His broad tail spread out before him, he rested on his rump, and his back leaned against the trunk of the tree. Occasionally, the animal dipped a paw into the lake and then brought it to its mouth. Then the paw was licked diligently and thoroughly.

"What kind of a beast is it?" asked O'Hannion.

"Perhaps we can sneak up on it and examine it at close range," said Michael. Immediately, he began to tiptoe toward the animal. James followed him. The beaver watched them approach. It closed its eyes to mere slits and waited. The men stood on each side staring down at it.

"I have been led to believe that wild beasts can easily sense the approach of human beings. This one appears to be sleeping." Michael glared at the beaver. James knelt and peered into the beaver's face. Slowly, the animal opened and closed one eye.

"He winked at me," James announced.

"Your insanity has gone beyond safe limits. Beasts like this do not wink. Sit still, me boy."

Michael dipped his cupped hands into the lake.

"Drink," he urged. "Perhaps it will clear your head."

James obediently sipped from his friend's hands. He licked his lips and frowned.

"Do you think you could dip me a tiny bit more?"

Michael obliged and James sipped again. Then he groaned.

"Order the strait jacket, Michael, old friend. I am completely gone."

Michael and the beaver studied James.

"Why do you say that?" asked Michael.

"The lake water tastes like bourbon," whispered James.

He leaned forward and dipped some up with his own hands.

"Bourbon," he said definitely.

Michael quickly tried some and immediately sat on the other side of the beaver. After five minutes of concerted dipping by the three of them, the beaver rolled himself forward, stumbled over O'Hannion's feet, and ambled away.

"Drunk," observed James. Michael nodded between dips.

After ten minutes had passed, Michael leaned back against the tree and studied the scene.

"Mr. O'Hannion, observe the size of this fine body of bourbon. 'Tis not necessary to dip so fast. We shall not run out."

"You're right," said James. "There is tomorrow to think of. And the day after that."

"And two delightful weeks. Even applying ourselves to the task, I doubt we'll make much of a dent in it."

Late in the afternoon, arm in arm, they weaved up the little rise in the land and headed back along the path.

"Memorize every living bush," cautioned Michael.

"Those that I can see," muttered James.

When they finally reached the fork in the path near the tennis courts they stopped.

"It is an unhappy fact that the length of the trip has a bit of a sobering action," observed Flynn.

"Perhaps that is for the best," said James. "It would never do for our wives to decide to leave this Utopia in the woods."

"A wise thought. And tomorrow we must remember to bring paper cups. Me hand doesn't hold a satisfactory amount."

"A lake of bourbon," sighed James happily. "You know, 'twas only last Sunday that Father Riley was saying that he felt I would have a wonderful time on my vacation. I wonder how he knew?"

"A fine man, Father Riley. I don't doubt for a moment that he prayed for us," said Michael. "I am almost out of peppermints, James. Tomorrow morning we will buy more in the restaurant."

They walked briskly along the path to the cabin. Eileen and Mary were on the big porch.

"The wanderers return," said Eileen. "We thought you might have considered a suicide pact after hearing the unhappy news."

"To what do you have reference, Mrs. O'Hannion?" asked Michael.

"I refer to the absence of a bar, Mr. Flynn."

"A bar?" said James, in a surprised voice. "Do you mean to imply that we are incapable of existing without a bar?"

"You've never managed to exist without one before," said Eileen. "And you needn't act surprised."

"When you're out in the woods communing with nature, there is no need for stimulants," said Michael.

"Communing," echoed Mary Flynn sarcastically. "'Tis a Boy Scout I've married. Did you find the moss on the trees?"

"It may be of interest to you to know that on this very day James and I studied a beast at close hand," Michael told her.

"I've done that myself for a number of years," said Mary.

"Make fun if you will," said James. "This beast was a very fine example of nature. Small and furry. Perhaps a mink."

"Then maybe you can trap a fur coat for me," said Eileen. "But one thing, I'm glad you're seeing small furry beasts instead of snakes and pink elephants."

Mary and Eileen had little trouble getting Michael and James out of the cabin the next morning. The two men enjoyed their breakfast and then announced intentions of going for another walk. Before their wives had recovered from the shock, Michael and James were in the small restaurant near the fork in the path. There they put in a supply of peppermints, sandwiches, and paper cups. Then they started along the trail that led to the bourbon lake.

"Let's take our time, James, lad. Drinking too early in the morning is supposed to be unhealthy," Michael said.

"That is probably a rumor started by our wives," answered James. "But you're right. There's no need to hurry."

They strolled leisurely through the woods, here nodding a cordial good morning to a busy robin, and here shouting a gay "Hello!" to a startled rabbit. Every so often, one of them would elevate his nose and sniff deeply. Then he would smile, nod happily to the other, and both would step forward with confidence. The bourbon lake was waiting, covered with sunlit amber ripples, as they came over the last hill.

"Beautiful," breathed Michael.

"Like a dream," said James.

They walked to the tree by the whiskey's edge and looked for their friend. The beaver wasn't around, so they settled down and made themselves comfortable. Admirably, they refrained from immediately breaking into the carton of paper cups. The sun was warm and they closed their eyes. Half an hour later, a myopic kingfisher flew overhead and thought he saw something swimming in the strangely colored lake. The splash of his sudden dive awakened Michael, who opened his eyes just in time to watch the bedraggled bird break the surface and try to hoist himself into the air. His tail feathers dragged alarmingly, and, after struggling for thirty feet, the kingfisher settled on the shore. The bird turned and examined this strange lake. Slowly and suspiciously, he lowered his long beak into the liquid and then tilted back his plumed head. As Michael watched, the bird rose into the air, circled over the lake, closed his wings, and dove. Michael closed his eyes as the bird disappeared in a golden spray of sun and bourbon.

"Much too early," he muttered.

On Wednesday afternoon, James and Michael had a bad moment. They were barely into their second cupful when it began to rain. They huddled under the tree and glared at the shower.

"Do you realize what it's doing?" asked James.

"I do," answered Michael. "It's dy-luting the bourbon."

"And yet, it must have happened before."

"Perfectly true, but I don't particularly care for the idea."

When the rain eased up, they hesitantly tried the cups again. Their smiles returned.

"It must be a very fine brand to defy the elements and retain its flavor and body," breathed Michael reverently.

"Besides," observed James, "it would take a lot of rain to turn this lake into a highball."

On Thursday, they watched a deer run into the lake to avoid hounds that bayed in the distance. The animal got in as far as his knees and then stopped. He dipped his muzzle into the amber fluid and jerked his head back. A second try provided a longer drink. The third drink did it. The noise of the dogs was much louder as the deer stalked out of the lake, testing the weight of his antlers. The baying of the two hounds turned into joyous yelps as they burst out of the foliage and saw their quarry facing them. But before they were halfway to him they realized that, for the first time in their long careers, they were confronted by a different end of the animal. The end that they saw was coming instead of going, had pointed horns instead of a white flag, and wore a hungry, undeerlike gleam in its eyes. The two dogs halted abruptly and looked around anxiously for their owner. Unfortunately, he was far behind them, so they hurried back for further instructions. The deer rumbled after them, but suddenly remembered the lake, and turned to investigate the neighborhood with a view toward making it his permanent abode.

On Friday, James and Michael had another visitor. It was Mr. Drummond, proprietor of their vacation spot. He walked slowly along the shore line and settled down beside the two drinkers. The Scotsman removed his cap, selected a cup, and helped himself to a good portion of the lake.

"So you've found our lake," he said softly.

"That we have," said Michael.

"Aye," said Mr. Drummond.

There was a long silence while the three of them took on fuel.

"And now you can under-r-stand why no taver-r-n can make good in this neighborhood."

"That we can," said James.

"Aye," said Mr. Drummond.

"We walked around the lake," Michael said, "and we saw no stream leading into it. It is something I would like to see—a stream of bourbon."

"Aye," mused Mr. Drummond. "But you won't see it. This lake comes out of the ground. We have figur-r-ed that somewhere below is a deposit of decayed vegetation. Instead of becoming oil, this vegetation fer-r-mented and distilled itself ver-r-y obligingly into good liquor."

"What a wonderful thing Nature is," marveled O'Hannion, reaching out with his cup.

"You like Bourbon," observed Mr. Drummond.

"Considerably," said James.

"You picked the right year to visit with us," said Mr. Drummond. "Each year it is different. Some time next Friday, all this bourbon will run back into the gr-r-ound. It is a phenomenon that happens ever-r-y year on the same date, a convenient arrangement for last-minute filling of jugs and gallon jars. Then, ear-r-ly in the spring, the lake fills up again."

"A day of great rejoicing, I imagine," said Michael.

"Aye," said Mr. Drummond. "And suspense. You see, each year the lake changes. A differ-r-ent liquor."

"You don't say," said James.

Mr. Drummond looked at him.

"A differ-r-ent liquor," he repeated.

"What was last year?" asked James.

"Irish," said Mr. Drummond.

There was a silence beneath the tree. Finally Michael spoke.

"A year late we are. In the midst of all this happiness I feel a great sadness. Perhaps I am ungrateful, but Irish whiskey—"

"Don't be too unhappy," said Mr. Drummond, grinning. "Irish may come again next year. But if it follows the schedule—no."

"Schedule?" asked Michael.

"Aye," said Mr. Drummond. "We figur-r-e that the differ-r-ent pools beneath the surface require a certain number of years in which to renew themselves. For a number of years they have been following in turn with few exceptions."

"What is due next year?" asked James.

"Applejack," said Mr. Drummond happily.

Michael and James nodded approvingly.

"We will be back."

"Unless your wives hear about it," observed Mr. Drummond slyly, refilling his cup.

"Is there danger of their hearing about it?" asked Michael.

"I'm afr-r-aid there is," said Mr. Drummond. "Unfortunately, the women of the vicinity are aware of the lake. They are likely to mention it."

"We will tackle that problem when it rears its ugly head," said Michael.

"Fine," said Mr. Drummond. "Do you have another cup handy? This one has spr-r-ung a leak."

When Michael and James weaved their way back to the cabin, they found Eileen and Mary in excellent spirits.

"We had a fine time today," bubbled Eileen. "A party we were invited to. And Mrs. Drummond served a delicious punch."

"Punch?" whispered Michael.

"Yes," gurgled Mary. "It was called Old Fashioneds."

Michael passed his hand over his eyes.

"The crisis is almost upon us, James boy," he whispered.

The crisis arrived on Monday morning. Mary and Eileen had spent the week end exploring all the delights of the punch called Old Fashioneds. On Monday, however, they found themselves in the swamp all such explorers must cross. Mary woke up holding her head. Half an hour later, she compared notes with Eileen.

"I feel exactly the way Michael has looked on occasion," she wailed.

"Is your hair pressing down on the top of your head like mine?" asked Eileen unhappily.

"I wonder if we were drinking whiskey?" Mary groaned.

Michael and James watched unhappily from the door.

"This is quite liable to create a bad effect in Eileen's subconscious," whispered James.

" 'Tis Mary's conscious I am worrying about," said Michael.

The women squinted against the sunlight toward the big Drummond cabin and then at Michael and James.

"Don't leave until we get back," ordered Mary. "Understand?"

Michael nodded quickly and the wives hurried away. The men sat on the porch steps.

"Is this the end?"

"We must meet it bravely, if it is," said Michael.

" 'Tis a coward I am, Michael. I feel like throwing myself into the lake and never coming up again."

"A beautiful thought, James boy, but we are men. We must face this thing like men. Forget the lake."

"Forget the lake?" asked James, astounded. "Sacrilege! I could as soon blow up Casey's."

"Would you torture yourself by remembering?" asked Michael. "When our wives return—"

He stopped suddenly and stared toward the Drummond cabin. Mr. Drummond was helping Mary and Eileen down the porch steps. He pointed them toward their own place and propelled gently. Eileen walked a few steps, then turned and blew a kiss to the little Scotsman. Gallantly, he returned the motion. She spun again and endeavored to walk completely over Mary, who stood, with crossed eyes, contemplating a big yellow butterfly that hovered an inch beyond her nose. The insect was fascinated by the aroma that Mary exhaled. As Eileen walked into her, Mary let out her breath; the butterfly folded its wings and joyfully collapsed. The women laughed and, arm in arm, strode at various angles toward the cabin. Their husbands rose slowly, unable to speak because their mouths were open too wide.

" 'Twas nothing serious, Jimmy dear," called Eileen.

"Nothing that couldn't be cured by a wonderful morning drink," hummed Mary. "It has a funny name. The hair—"

"—of the dog," said James and Michael in unison.

"That's it," whooped Mary. She and Eileen laughed until they nearly fell down. The men led them to wicker chairs. Michael motioned with his head and, a few minutes later, James followed him around the side of the cabin.

"We have been delivered," Michael announced. "Father Riley must have worked overtime."

"While I do not approve of women making fools of themselves with drink," observed James, "the question arises, how are we going to keep them this way?"

Eileen's voice floated harmoniously around the corner.

"Jimmy! Jim-m-my! Can you hear me, dear?"

"Yes—dear," called James.

"Before you take your walk, please carry our Thermos jug over to Mr. Drub— to Mr. Drummond's. He promised to fill it up to the brim with punch. You won't forget, will you?"

"No, Eileen. I won't forget," James called happily.

"To the brim," Mary repeated.

"The brim," Michael said.

When they reached the lake, they found Mr. Drummond and the beaver seated by the tree. The beaver, grumbling a bit, moved over to make room for the newcomers.

"Pardon me," said James, leaning forward with his paper cup. The beaver closed its eyes resignedly until the man leaned back out of its way.

"Mr. Drummond," Michael said, "we have much to thank you for."

"Aye," agreed the smiling Mr. Drummond. "Our cour-r-rse is clear. The remainder of your stay will be a happy one, I'm sure."

"Let us drink to that," said James.

The three men and the beaver dipped into the bourbon lake.

"About our reservations for next year," began Michael.

"Your wives took care of that this mor-r-ning when they came over for the cure."

By four o'clock all of them could stand, but only one could walk. That was the beaver, and he fell into the lake on his way to his dam.

Freehand Fables

Here is a picture of a cow.
The cow is on roller-skates.
That dark piece which looks like Australia
  proves that the cow is a Holstein,
  because Holsteins have dark pieces.
There is some doubt about the cow's
  other two legs.
If the cow expects to go where she is
  looking she'd better get her feet
  pointed in the same direction.
We think that is the tail on top of the
  cow: or, it might be someone in the
  back of the class who wants to ask a
  question.
If the cow would shave her ears once in
  a while, she wouldn't look so much
  like a cactus grove.
That is all.

Here are the hare and the tortoise.
They are resting after their race.
They are resting on top of a street car.
They have a hell of a nerve. They must
  think all the motorman has to do is
  drive them around while they cool off.
The motorman is a working man.
He has no time for shillyshallying.
It is an outrage. They should be forced
  to ride inside.
(The hare could let his ears go out a
  window) Something should be done
  about it.
Where is the conductor, anyway?

January, 1936

Here is a picture of a house.
It has nice trees near it.
Birds in these trees would be a menace
   to sleep.
Maybe it is just as well. If a man walked
   in his sleep he would fall down that
   cliff.
That funny thing on the left is the porch.
It ought to be on the house, but it is not.
What a crazy house!

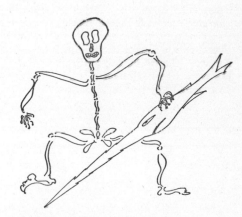

Here is the picture of a horse.
The horse is a long, lean thoroughbred.
He is listening in on a stethoscope.
Look closely, for horses do not often
   listen in on stethoscopes.
The horse looks puzzled.
We are puzzled, too. We wonder what
   in hell the horse expects to hear on a
   stethoscope dangling in the air.
He must think he is a radio set, or
   something.
No wonder he is thin and has ears like
   a dog.

Here is a picture of a skeleton.
He has a swordfish in his hand.
The skeleton means death.
The swordfish means war.
There is an old saying (I think) that
   those who live by the swordfish, die by
   the swordfish.
That is hard on the sea bass, who live
   right by the swordfish.
The skeleton should be in a closet.

Here is a picture of a pig.
He is a pig with possibilities. Any pig
  who can wear a tuxedo like that has
  possibilities.
Or, if it isn't a tuxedo and is only a dark
  suit, more power to him.
It is clear that he is a headwaiter, since
  he is pointing out a table.
No one we ever saw could fit at that
  damn table.
It is too much to expect.
But the pig expects it.
Let him sit at his own lousy table.

Here is a picture of a hippopotamus.
Hippopotamuses eat hay.
If this one thinks he can find hay at the
  96th street subway station, he's crazy.
The people on the station have no hay;
  they are waiting for a Broadway local.
Even with lights on, a hippopotamus
  would not look like a local.
He should be in the zoo, where it would
  not cost a nickel to see him.
Anyway, the tracks must hurt his feet.
He would be better off dead.
Just wait until the local comes.

Here is a picture of a train, Number 11.
It is three minutes behind time.
Someone should tell the engineer to
  hurry up.
Nobody on a train wants to be late.
Maybe there is not much coal. The coal
  car looks pretty flimsy.
There is smoke, though.
The engine looks like our janitor.
He is usually late, too.

SECTION FIVE

Largely About Women

INTRODUCTION

It SEEMS a bit late in the game to be coming up with any stop-press revelation to the effect that the Magazine for Men is not, necessarily, the magazine for misogynists. But in the early days whenever we allowed a feminine by-line to creep in, as we did in a piece that was a collaboration between Scott and Zelda Fitzgerald, or when we let an ad in for a woman's product, there was immediate and lasting hell to pay in *The Sound and the Fury*.

We reasoned with the boys to the effect that if this were a men's magazine in the narrowest sense, we couldn't consistently permit any references to women, either textual or pictorial, anywhere in its pages. Then we'd have a man's magazine and we wonder who'd read it. As it is, it's a magazine for men and, logically enough, it's largely about women. You can't reasonably object to pictures of and words about women in the advertising section if you don't object to them in the editorial portion. Then, too, if you know anything about magazines at all, you know that there are two ways you pay to read a magazine. First you pay by buying the magazine, but foremost you pay by exposing yourself, not to say responding, to its advertisements. Well, the unfair fact about the magazine for men in the past was that women were the half-paying readers. Women do read the magazine. You can't stop them. Saying that it is "for men only" merely

heightens their interest. We couldn't see why the men should go on paying full tariff while the women were getting by on a half-fare basis. The magazine isn't edited for women and won't be. Maybe after a while they'll get tired of it. And maybe they'll get tired of it sooner if the advertising pages begin catering to them, making the magazine seem less like forbidden fruit.

We thought that last, especially, was a happy thought for the die-hard contingent, but it didn't hold the Furymen for long. We got by for a while with ads for things like perfume, that conceivably could be classified under the heading of handy knowledge for men wondering What To Give Her. But when women's hat ads crept in, where the context of the copy showed the use of the second person pronoun to be indisputably feminine, the uproar was redoubled, and all our explaining was futile. The boys were obviously convinced that the poor old magazine was destined to become about as feminine as a back-room bar, a prize-fight or a barber shop.

They were right, too. As early as our first issue we had said that the general magazines, in the mad scramble to increase the women readership that seemed to be so highly prized by national advertisers, had bent over backward in catering to the special interests and tastes of the feminine audience, and that this tendency had reached the point where the male reader, in looking through what purported to be a general magazine, was made to feel like an intruder upon gynecic mysteries. And we had promised that this was one magazine that was going to try to be general but was determined to stay masculine.

Pinned down on what we stood for and whom, if anybody in particular, we were trying to gripe, we said that *Esquire's* platform would have to read something like this: *Esquire* stands for anything that will afford amusement to men of intelligence. We don't mean "gentlemen," as such, or "intellectuals," as such. Nor, when we say "men of intelligence" are we thinking of men of any one particular level as far as educacational background is concerned. We

mean, simply, any and all men who have adult minds. We have known woodsmen who possessed this intelligence, and Ph.D.'s who lacked it. And as for griping anybody, *Esquire* is crusading neither for nor against anything or anybody. It simply refuses to be bound—not to say hog-tied—by any delicate consideration for the feelings or prejudices of its minorities, however vociferous they may be.

Number-one spot among Esquire's "minorities," indubitably, was held by women, and vociferous they were indeed. Judge for yourself, gentle reader, in this last section, how well or ill we kept our promise as to the way they would be treated in our pages.

BETTY SOUTH

◀——————————————————————————————▶

The Secret of Love:
Have American Girls Forgotten?

THE Army transport was on her way to New York from Bremerhaven. She was loaded with Army officers and their dependents, war department civilians, G.I.s, alien brides and American children born in Germany.

The voyage was boring. Army transports aren't much fun. The only thing to do to pass the ten or eleven days at sea is to talk. So Julia Norfield and I talked.

"Is your husband still in Germany, Julia, or did he go on home ahead of you?" I asked her.

"I'm one of those fräulein widows," she said.

The look on my face made her smile a little even before I croaked out, "You?" It was hard to believe. Julia Norfield had taffy-colored hair. Her face was small and well-made. She was full of sparkle and wit. Her clothes were expensive and smart and fitted her trim figure perfectly.

"You're wondering what she had that I haven't got, aren't you? Well, that's what I'd like to know. And what hundreds of American wives in Germany would like to know. How do you explain it? What do these women have that makes a man like my husband ask me for a divorce?"

Her husband had been an officer in the U.S. Army. They had been married almost thirty years and had two grown children. The son was on assignment with the Occupation Forces in Germany. The daughter was engaged to an Army officer. Captain Norfield was assigned to duty in Germany in 1945.

"I should have thought the military would have kept them from living together."

"The Army condones this thing, Betty. Officers of high rank are doing it. A close friend of my husband's refused to help me. He wouldn't do anything on my behalf, because he is sleeping with a friend of hers himself. The Army doesn't care."

How familiar it sounded. Another American man stationed in Germany, seemingly happily married for years, forsaking country, wife, children, even deserting the Army itself, to live in comfortable sin with a German woman.

I counted all the others I had known about in the three years I had spent with the American Occupation Forces in Germany.

February, 1951

There had been, first, the boss of one of my best friends. He had been sent to Germany in 1945, and lived in happy sin until 1949, when his wife took the bull by the horns and insisted that she join him, for she thought it odd that he did not ask her to come. When she arrived in Germany it did not take her long to discover that he had a young fräulein. She tried everything she knew to win him back, but in the end went back to America, defeated. He had been a colonel in the American Army. They were married twenty-some years and had an attractive daughter, just out of finishing school. His wife and daughter begged him, reasoned with him, ranted at him, wept. But his only thought was how he could get a divorce and stay in Germany with his "Erika."

Then there was the American official who had attained status in the educational field in America. He was a man of intelligence and ability. In 1947 he took his family to Germany, and in 1949 his wife and children returned to the United States because they could no longer bear the humiliation of his open affair with "Hildegard." He was still over there the last I knew.

I remembered a young Army civilian, formerly a combat M.P., who had a wife and two children in the States, but who had never returned from Europe after the war. He was living with a fräulein in a couple of rooms over a cheap tavern. His wife had to take legal action to get child support out of him. He wasn't embarrassed or ashamed. He was concentrating on just one thing: How to stay in Germany with "Ursula."

Of course, I could not forget the day at lunch in the mess hall when the men figured out on the tablecloth the percentage of American personnel in our agency alone in Nürnberg who were "shacked up" with German girls and had already fathered one or two babies. It was 25 per cent of our personnel, and several of them had wives and children at home.

My thoughts went further back, to 1947, when aboard the Orient Express on my way to Prague on leave I met the young wife of a sergeant stationed in Germany. She, too, was going to Prague, on vacation by herself, and because she was lonely and I was a stranger and it didn't matter, she told me the same story. Her man had the fräulein neatly installed as maid in their quarters when she had arrived, and she didn't know for weeks that there was anything between them.

"I'm going back to the States next month," she had said. "But before I go I'm spending some of his money to see Europe."

And there were countless other instances. It was an old story to me after three years. It didn't seem to matter what kind of men they were or what their station. Officers, civilians, educated, ignorant, well-bred, ill-bred—no matter. American marriages in occupied Germany were collapsing left and right because of the German fräulein.

What *was* their power? What *did* they have that the American women lacked? Was it just a natural evil of any occupation that made the conquered women throw themselves at the conquerors? Or was it really something basic that the American wives failed in that made their men such easy prey to German women?

I had heard it hashed over many times by the American bachelor girls employed by the Occupation Forces. Most of them dismissed it as just out-and-out sex.

"They're whores, that's all," I had heard them comment often.

"No self-respecting American woman would sleep with a man for a carton of cigarettes."

"They'll go to bed with anybody who buys 'em a decent meal. Where could an American man get that at home?"

Of course, this reasoning might have answered for some of the bachelors and confirmed woman chasers. But it did not solve the problem of the married man who was breaking up his family, or the young Americans who were living quietly, unmarried, with their German girls and helping to raise their own German-born babies. For a carton of cigarettes they had bought family responsibility. Their pay checks were now going for toys and baby milk instead of nylons and lipsticks. And the boys were contented. They were not running out on the girls.

It was not as if there were no American girls there to date, either. Our Occupation Forces employ thousands of American girls. But these same girls who were calling the fräuleins bad names were sitting alone in their billets on week nights, and going to the G.I. movies in crowds of five or six on week ends. It was a rare thing to see an American bachelor out for a night with an American girl.

My thoughts had raced through all this while Julia stood at the porthole watching the green sea hiss and boil away from the side of the moving ship.

"Was she pretty, Julia?"

"I only saw her once. But all the gossips said she wasn't."

"Well, none of the husband-stealers I've seen were great beauties. I guess it's not looks."

"No," she answered, "it's not. Why, some of these women couldn't get to first base in America on their looks or their figures. Have you seen these alien brides on this ship? Do they look like charmers?"

I had to admit that they did not. Yet, Julia had found out that two of them had married divorced Americans. Divorced *after* the men had met the girls.

Julia turned from the porthole.

"I met a colonel in the lounge last night. He's been stationed in Berlin for three years and he's going home to get a divorce and go back and marry his fräulein. Let's ask him in here tonight for a drink. Let's try to get him to give us an American man's viewpoint on these damn fräuleins."

So the colonel came, and he was worth listening to. There was a quiet air of assurance about him that gave one the feeling that he was master of his thoughts.

"I think I can tell you what it is you want to know," he began, after unimportant chitchat had broken the ice, and Julia had put the question squarely before him, telling him in a few words what had happened to her marriage. "Briefly—and actually you can't be brief about it—it's this: European women, not just the German fräulein, but European women in general, make a man feel comfortable. I don't mean just by putting his pipe and his slippers by his chair. My wife always did that in Detroit. She was a good cook, too, and she was interested in my success. I mean something else. They give him a feeling of ease. A man isn't under a strain with a European woman."

"What kind of strain do you mean?" Julia asked. "I never noticed that my husband was strained in my company."

"Perhaps you couldn't see it, Mrs. Norfield. May I speak to you frankly?"

"I want you to," Julia answered eagerly.

"I think it's entirely possible that your husband was under rather a severe strain with you. I've watched you in the lounge. You're an attractive woman. Any man would notice you. You look expensive. But when I first saw you I thought to myself, 'Now there's a gal who can take care of herself. I'll bet none of these jokers fool her.' You see, I didn't have the urge to come over and sit down by you because your air of self-sufficiency scared me out. I was actually afraid you'd think I was a stupid fool trying to make time with you, and you look much too smart to put up with anything like that. I wonder if your self-sufficiency wasn't a little tough on your husband sometimes? I wonder if he didn't feel a lot of the time that he wasn't too important to you? Do you actually think that he thought you needed him?"

"If you mean by that, did I ever put on the clinging-vine act, the answer is 'no.' Is that the secret of the European woman? Does she play it smart and look and act dumb so you great big men will feel more great and big?" Julia's voice was edgy.

"No, that's not it, Mrs. Norfield. She doesn't have to act. She really feels that way. She is dependent on her man. You see, Mrs. Norfield, our highly prized 'American way of life' has made our women aggressive and hard. You are not truly feminine any more. You've lost your *gentleness*. You want to be 'smart' and you've become brittle. You want to 'get somewhere' and you've gotten hard. In your determination to be independent and compete with men you've sacrificed your *womanliness*. When a man is with a woman, he doesn't want to compete with her."

"He wants to be lord and master, doesn't he?" The tone of Julia's voice was cutting.

"If you want to put it that way, yes. There is that in the man which must feel that he's dominating a woman. In fact, it's absolutely necessary for most men. Do you find that thought irritating? Certainly after the years of marriage you had this is not a new proposition to you."

"Oh, it's not new. I went through thirty years of it. I practically knocked myself out letting him think he was wearing the pants in the family."

"There. You have touched the center, Mrs. Norfield. You 'let him think' he was boss. You knew all the time that he wasn't. Deep down in his subconscious he felt it. But he didn't realize it until he went to Germany and experienced what it is really like to live with a woman who is content to be just a woman and who thought he was wonderful because he was her man. She did not try to make him over. She took him as he was and built her life around him so that they became like one. Such an experience fills a man with happiness and a sense of importance that he won't give up."

"Won't you admit that these European women are getting plenty out of the American men in exchange for this cozy feeling they're dishing out? You don't think American men are being taken for suckers, do you?"

"Sure, I think some of them are. The same ones would be suckers at home for a clever woman. But these fräuleins don't seem to be clever. It doesn't seem like an act. Their sincerity is natural and deep-seated. It's part of them."

I was ready to chime in by this time. "I think I follow all this lofty talk about our lack of gentleness and femininity. I believe you when you say we're too aggressive. But I want to ask you, man to man, isn't the real reason American men prefer European women to us that they wait on you body and soul? Don't they polish your shoes, run all your errands, make all your bargains on the black market, protect you from chiselers among their own people, cook only for your taste, go only where you want to go, pack all the luggage, make the house to please you, and sleep with you when and how you want it? Honestly now, Colonel, isn't that what you really like about these women?"

He thought a moment. "Yes, I suppose that is true, as far as it goes. They spoil us."

"Servants. They're just your servants," Julia spat out. "Do you think any educated American woman in this day and age would kowtow to a man like that?"

He chuckled, but his eyes were wise. "That, Mrs. Norfield, is your answer as to why American men are deserting their wives over here to live with foreign women. Waiting on a man's personal needs is only an outward manifestation of the way they feel about men. You get no pleasure out of waiting on a man. You think it's out-of-date. You want him to wait on you. That's where your European sister beats your time. She *likes* it. She does not have a false sense of what you call 'self-respect.' She has, rather, a sense of intimacy with her husband, of belonging to him and that he belongs to her. She doesn't feel like his servant—just as much as a person is never a servant to himself. They have a feeling of oneness, a fusion of mood and spirit."

"Don't you feel just a little bit like a heel, asking your wife for a divorce so you can go back to Berlin and marry this girl?" Julia prodded, unimpressed.

"In a way I do, yes," he answered. "But I am forty-nine years old, Mrs. Norfield. Life is truly short. I want what I have found. I never experienced the peace with my wife that I have had with this woman. I have been comfortable and at ease and in love with her for three years, and I like *myself* for the first time I can remember. I didn't know it was possible to have such a combination of companionship and love and to live so entirely without strain and tension. I have decided I owe it to myself to fight to keep this. I'll pay any price."

"No matter who may get hurt," Julia finished for him.

"Yes."

"And what you've told us is how the rest of these men feel? Is that what makes them ask for a divorce and stay over?"

"That's as near as I can come to telling you why they do it, Mrs. Norfield. I think I've talked too much. Good night. . . ."

ANONYMOUS

◄——————————————————————————————►

The Wench Is Not Amused

Any girl, if the body she possesses isn't actually deformed and the face badly moth-bitten, is going to become acquainted with the gentle art of seduction fairly early in life. As for myself, I've had what I now recognize as more than my share of experience.

Not at the risk of sounding vain, because I know I am vain, I'll say that when men look at me in the street I know why. They've good reason to. In 1930, when the agency I was working for folded, I posed for several commercial photographers. I've seen strange men studying my picture in a magazine and, though their eyes generally started at the ankles and worked up by degrees, I'm pleased to admit that they looked twice at the face, too. And I've read a book, I dance well because I love it, I know how to listen as well as talk, I can tell a touchback from a safety, I can hold my likker as well as my men—when I want to—and I know most of the right words. I seldom buy my own dinner.

I know that sounds conceited as the devil but, darn it, it's true. I'll lay twenty to one I can make any nine out of ten males, provided they are neither puling infants nor doddering antiquarians, ask for my phone number within any given half-hour.

So, when I say I've had more than the average experience with the technique of seduction (horrible phrase) I think I'm stating a simple truth.

When a gal is first turned loose in the world of man the game of seduction— win, lose or draw—is pretty exciting. And it continues to be for some years. At first, either your parents or your school keep you under observation and you're only exposed to younger men. Their approach, naturally, isn't as polished as that which you'll encounter later. Also, the fact that you are under some sort of surveillance means that you'll be exposed only occasionally and for brief periods of time and not to the extensive and intensive campaigns you'll have to face when you become what is so quaintly known as a "bachelor girl." During my last four years of school, a year abroad, and my first three or four years in New York I must admit that I thoroughly enjoyed the whole tiresome process; particularly so when I learned that, so long as I kept my head, the game could be played according to my own rules without ever hurting the boy friend's sense of masculine superiority in the least.

It was always a thrilling battle and the campaign itself was often more

February, 1937

exciting than the storming, or attempted storming, of one's last citadel. How many times I've lost in this warfare is entirely a matter of my own business. But I will say this: no campaigner, no matter how hardened, ever overcame my last line of defense unless I deliberately chose that he should—and that can hardly be counted a total defeat.

In the past year, sadly enough, I've come to realize that what was once an enthralling game is now a dead bore. And I contend it's all the men's fault. A seduction should be above all things glamorous and exciting. But can there be glamour in a story repeated a dozen, yea a hundred times? Can glamour be expected to survive the hundredth ardent whispering of non-poetic, time-worn words? Can there be excitement in a card game played eternally, with both players forever holding the same cards? There cannot!

Why don't men vary their approaches? Damn it, haven't they any originality? Must they be so monotonous?

Why is it that each man has at his command three or four of the seven standard approaches to seduction and selects his approach according to what he fondly believes to be his shrewd analysis of the character of the wench he is lusting for?

This is all wrong. And something should be done about it. Why don't men realize that an injection of originality or novelty into their love-making will get them further with the gal of their temporary choice than any pet phrases or standard passes the gibbering idiots can produce?

Repetition is so damned boring. The fun is all gone if, after the first kiss and the first declamation, you can, from past experience, anticipate practically every word and gesture that is to follow, be it a one night stand or a three week siege. And that isn't right—sex should be fun.

If you're a girl who hasn't given this matter any objective thought, stop now and take stock. You'll be saddened and disillusioned to see what well-worn ruts your young men pursue.

And you, lad, believing yourself to be a Casanova as you do, cast your eyes over the following catalog—and blush for your sex's limitations. Blush, too, for yourself, for you have nothing more on the ball than any other man. You're unoriginal and trite. That swell build-up you were planning to use tonight and which you rather expected to send darling little Jean into a swoon will be the same build-up John used on her two months ago, Paul the week before, Ronald last year, and so on back to the days when she bought her first lipstick and lace panties. And you actually expected her to fall for it tonight? Fooey! Those girlish peals of laughter will probably be at you, rather than with you. But you have only to get yourself a new approach, my lad, really new, and your path will be paved with recumbent maidens.

The following list contains what I've found to be the seven fundamental approaches. There are, of course, variants but they are all variants of these basic seven. At least, my own experience and the experience of the attractive girls I know leads me to believe that this is a complete list. If it isn't, I've been neglected and I resent that. And if the young man will step forward to present credentials proving that he is in possession of an Approach Number Eight I'll be glad to meet him on his home grounds, winner take all.

APPROACH ONE
The Crudest

Simple, and very raw. The idea is for the male to ply you with likker until you lose control. The man who uses this approach is obviously a louse, obviously without resources, and so unsubtle that he is easily seen through and a cinch to out-smart. This technique is so bad it doesn't merit serious discussion. The only ones who will succumb to this attack are the completely foolish, those who are particularly light-headed drinkers, and potential nymphomaniacs.

APPROACH TWO
The Cheapest

As crude in its way as One. This man tries to get at you through passionate declarations of love. He may even plead with you to marry him, *sometime* soon. Meanwhile, since you are already man and wife in the eyes of God or, at the very least, two hearts that beat as one—how about it? The man who uses these tactics is probably an even greater louse than the likker-plying male. The "I-love-you"-chanted-soulfully method will succeed only with susceptible virgins (any age) and those stridently emotional wenches of meager intelligence whose *métier* in life is rocking the cradle. The gal who has been around will merely enjoy her laugh, when approached in this manner, and promptly send the man back to the minor leagues, where he belongs.

APPROACH THREE
The Ham-iest

The long-bearded "misunderstood husband" gag. No elucidation is needed. Only fools fall for this chestnut and it is doubtful if, after falling, they deserve any sympathy. It has been my experience that married men are seldom worth the trouble. It is generally wisest to send them home to the little woman, in short order.

APPROACH FOUR
The Outright Purchase

Like the Greeks, they come bearing gifts; generally expensive and so tendered that it is possible for the semi-prostitute to accept her wages without feeling too professional. The man who pulls this one isn't fooling. He means business and wants it tacitly understood that there are to be no strings attached to this business deal. And he is intelligent enough to know that the average female is capable of very long distance rationalizing and thus can graciously and right-eously accept a fur coat or a diamond ring whereas she would regard the offer of actual cash as a terrific insult. This system, probably because it has a sound economic and not emotional basis, is liable to work with any of us who haven't been born heiresses. If the man is anywhere near as attractive as his gift it is sometimes necessary for a gal to summon up her last bit of will power to say "No." But it is usually worth it, if only to preserve those few remaining shreds of self respect.

APPROACH FIVE
The Big Brother Act

This predatory gent is an insidious operator where the unwary female is concerned. In the first place, he is patient. This, in itself, is unusual enough to throw you off. He starts off on a "just friends" basis and worms his way into your heart as a confidant and pal. Before you know it you are, on those odd nights, telling him all about your joys or sorrows with whichever Tom, Dick or Harry you are at the moment involved. He is very sweet, sympathetic and understanding. But he is playing a waiting game. He knows that eventually, human nature being what it is, there'll be a bust-up between you and the boy of the moment . . . and when it comes you'll find his broad shoulder there for you to weep on. You weep and you weep. You're on the rebound and desperately in need of masculine comforting. And suddenly you find that you're getting it in a very big, and totally unexpected way. And because you are weak and blue and emotionally drained and in need of some male tenderness you all at once become aware of the fact that your Big Brother is much sweeter and more desirable than you had ever found him to be before. And if he realizes this at the same time that you awaken . . . you're lost. When he puts on the pressure you're defenseless. I know that this approach depends upon extenuating circumstances but they occur far more frequently than one ever suspects. And a girl on the rebound is in no fit condition to put up an adequate defense. My only solution is this: never trust a man who tries to build up a *platonic* friendship with you. At the time it may seem to you that it would be *such* a relief to know a man like that, but you can with impunity bet your last garter-belt that you're wrong because, some place in the back of his mind, he'll have an idea or two . . .

APPROACH SIX
The Pseudo-Sophisticated

This approach has three subdivisions but they are all based on the same fundamental sophistry:

6-A. *The Philosophical.* The life-is-real, life-is-earnest, opportunity-knocks-but-once, so grab-each-fleeting-moment-while-you-may school. This is, of course, the veriest hokum, fit only for children in their teens. Every woman beyond the age of adolescence knows that this unique opportunity the gentleman is so magnanimously offering her is an opportunity that knocks all too damn frequently. Why any man who isn't completely witless ever thinks a girl will believe him to be the only one who will ever offer her a chance to indulge in a life of sin is beyond me. So, girls, the next time a man pulls this "Tonight is ours!" line on you, control your laughter, let him down gently, and send him on his way. The stronger sex? Physically, yes.

6-B. *The Pagan.* This lad is likely to have long hair. He has read *Ulysses* and has a glib knowledge of neo-realistic painting or something of that sort. He thinks very highly of individualism and can quote Nietzsche's remarks about the Superman (himself). He tells you that the old, conventional moral standards of our fathers are outmoded (news to you?) and insists that today we see such things as sexual relations with a new vision, a proper perspective. "After all, we want each other, and what is there to stop us?" he asks. "Aren't we free people, free to live our own lives?" You are also free to point out to him that "we want each other" is taking altogether too much for granted. You explain, in as tactful and gentle terms as the situation requires, that a fairly ardent kiss or two, permitted in a moment of weakness, doesn't exactly establish the fact that you are willing to turn over the body beautiful. He'll never believe, of course, that it wasn't your inhibitions which prevented you from succumbing and he'll go on his way, still proud of his free and soaring spirit, in search of a girl with low heels and spectacles, who thinks Communism would be nice. And he'll say to her, "Look at Russia," and get away with it. I don't want to look at Russia. Blouses and smocks? Not with my torso.

6-C. *The Physical.* Whereas the first chap in this category went at you on a philosophical plane, so-called, and the second tried to weaken you on moral and individualistic grounds he "Physical" lad goes to the root of the matter and attacks you with body blows. His weapons are psychiatry, Freudian psychology and your glands. These physical realists always have your well being at heart. They explain at great length that sex is an appetite which must be satisfied if one isn't to become a victim of all sorts of fetishes and suppressed desires. Now, no girl would want to become amorous in public with a Shetland pony or become addicted to horsewhipping her grandmother. It isn't being done. The obvious solution is to permit whichever physical realist is at the moment spouting his propaganda to come between you and the tragedies of perversion. The whole affair is, of course, to be conducted in your own best interests.

We may very well be animals and victims of appetites which must be satisfied in order to prevent complexes and frustrations. I'm willing to admit that the boys may have something there. But, so far, I've been able to order my own meals and I think I'll continue to do so. When I'm hungry I'll eat, if the proper food is available, and no one is going to force improperly prepared food on me when I'm not hungry . . . and my grandmother will have to take her chances.

APPROACH SEVEN
The "Forcing" Method

Or perhaps I should call it the cat-and-mouse attack. In any event, the glib gentleman who works this approach on you is primarily concerned with forcing you to make the final move and "Safety First" is obviously his motto.

The opening lines generally read something like this, "I don't love you and I know you don't love me—but I can't help wanting you. Why pretend? I think you're swell—sex excluded—but you're so damned attractive that, no matter how hard I try, when I'm with you I want you." Then he adds, oh very frankly and fairly, "I like you so much that I have to be honest with you. If I continue to see

you I'll make love to you, I can't help myself. If you want me to stop coming
around, now that you know, you've only to say so." The only catch in this last
speech is that he only produces it when he is pretty damn sure that you like him
a lot and enjoy being with him. Of course you, liking him as you do and feeling on safe terrain because he hasn't so much as touched you, laugh it off and
take your chances.

But after a night or two of conversation in the same vein but growing progres-
sively more intense, the chances are that he will kiss you; ardently, of course, and
probably with considerable finesse—and you've given the inch that may cost you
your virtue.

Gently and insidiously the campaign progresses. Each night it will become
a little more intense and each night your defenses will fall back an inch or two.
But he will never use force, never put on any obvious pressure. Each time you
feel called upon to say "Stop," he'll stop—to your growing annoyance. And,
though you probably won't realize it, that is one word you'll come to use less
and less frequently.

Slowly and inevitably the tide, to use a figure of speech, creeps up and up until
that night when you've forgotten even the meaning of the word—and then the
louse stops of his own accord!

The speeches at this point are liable to be on the impassioned side and to deal
at some length with his desire for you and your many darling qualities and so on
far into the night. Eventually he gets around to asking you if you, too, desire him.
After what has just transpired you wonder if he is a complete idiot, then reassure
him in your own subtle way.

This generally calls for a clinch and the addition of fuel to the flame. After a
proper interval he pulls the Remorse-stop. It goes something like this and is
generally delivered in a somewhat throaty voice, "I want you *soooo* much
(pause) but I can't let you do this unless you are sure in your own mind. We're
excited now, my dear (he's telling you!), and I wouldn't want you to do anything
you'd later regret. I want you more than anyone I've ever known (this is
standard; note careful evasion of the word *love*), but this is too beautiful an
adventure to rush into headlong." While you're wondering just how he would
have you rush into said adventure he makes a suggestion, "Sleep on it tonight
and think it over in the clear light of day, tomorrow. We'll meet for dinner,
and then you can give me your decision."

You agree, and this leads to another scene that wouldn't get by the Will
Hays' office and considerable incoherent and what he thinks is poetic talk
about how much he hopes you'll feel tomorrow night as you do tonight.

Then to the much discussed sleep and "thinking (if any) in the light of day."
It would serve the gent right if the daylight led to a decision he wouldn't like
but for some darned reason it seldom does.

When you meet him the next night he is pretty solemn about the whole thing
(but you can be sure he'll give you the best dinner he can afford, with a rather
obvious emphasis on the wine list). Once you get back to whichever apartment
is the scene of combat you'll find that tenderness is the preliminary mood of the

evening. He may not use his arms and hands as they were intended to be used at all, but if he does he'll be very, very gentle. In desperation you finally take him by the hand, figuratively speaking, and lead him to the bedroom.

It may be several days before you begin to realize that you've been *had* in more ways than one. And if this realization doesn't come to you shortly you are in an even worse position because you've been had so thoroughly that your heart may well be in your young man's hands—and that is one section of your anatomy which should remain permanently yours.

There is a mild variant to this approach. In this method the man, at the critical point, doesn't suggest a little daylight thought on the subject but, instead, goes dramatic and says, "No, this can't be. The price you pay is too large," or words to that effect. It works out in exactly the same way. One says, "Perhaps," and the other says, "No," and in the end you are unconsciously forced into taking them both by the hand . . .

This is probably the most difficult form of seduction to work clear of—because you've been allowed to work yourself into it.

These are the standardized versions of sexual Blind Man's Buff, Tag, You're It, or whatever you want to call it, as I know them. There are probably others, depending on race, color or previous condition of servitude, but I wager that they in their way are just as standardized. What to do about it?

Sometimes I think I'd rather be attacked. Or at least meet a man direct enough to say bluntly and without preamble, "I think you're swell and I'd like to make love to you. I warn you, if you say no I'll ask you the same thing tomorrow night. What will it be, milady's boudoir or the movies?"

The hell of it is, experience has so conditioned me that I'd probably choose the movies and be forced to sit through a Hollywood version of the preliminaries of one of the stereotyped brands of seduction I've listed. There's no escape.

ROBERT C. RUARK

What Hath God Wrought?

THE American woman, by her own admission, is the loveliest, smartest (chic-wise), most intelligent, healthiest, richest, tallest, best-fed, best-housed, most-worshiped, most-pampered female on the face of the globe. God and *Good Housekeeping* watch over her home. Santa Claus, Cupid and the Easter bunny are solidly in her corner.

According to her mood, she smells like date night in a harem or a breath of British spring. Nothing she owns ever fades, rips or shrinks. Psychiatrists and agony columnists worship at her feet, to tell her how wonderful she is. All our communications—newspapers, magazines, radio, television, moving pictures— fawn on her. Her marriages are made in heaven, and when a spate of heavenly bliss exhausts itself, special couturières deck her in costumes which blend a maidenly regret at (his) failure with a spicy tinge of harlotry, designed to snare a new candidate for ecstasy. Her sons become Presidents, and her daughters are all Senators and spot-welders. She is never, never wrong, even when she *is* wrong.

Yet she is very possibly the unhappiest creature on the face of the globe at this writing, because she is undecided as to just what and where she is in the scheme. She is on the verge of destroying her basic commodity out of sheer envious ego. As she grasps the gavel and strides toward the rostrum, her lacy handkerchief flutters unnoticed to the floor, and this makes her weep. She is on the way to becoming a definite third sex, having progressed too far to retreat, out of vanity, while simultaneously striving to preserve that which she had and is now in process of losing.

The American woman is finally trapped in a snare of her own devising, and you can read the box score of futility every morning on the third and fifth pages of the tabloids.

Let us dissect this frail creature, victim of her own intolerant ambition, but first let us establish that she has reversed her role.

Sometime back a suburban father eavesdropped a game of House, time-honored sport of the tots, in which his young son, a hearty, sturdy boy in the prime of childhood, was playing hard to get.

"Come on, Jimmy," a little girl neighbor said. "I'll be the mama, you be the papa."

October, 1950

616

"No," said Jimmy. "I want to be the mama."

"But Jimmy," the little girl said, "mammas is girls. Papas is boys. I'm a girl and you're a boy."

"I don't care," Jimmy replied, stoutly. "Mama is the boss in our house, and I want to be the boss or I won't play."

This particular father went away shaking his head, wondering to what state matrimony had come if even the children were cognizant of the change of status. His wonderment was upheld, the same week, when Miss Bette Davis of the films split for the umpteenth time with the man who was then her husband, William Grant Sherry. It was Mr. Sherry, a retired athlete who paints for fun, who did the wailing.

He said he stayed home all day, doing the housework, while Miss Davis toiled at the studios. He made the beds and swept and washed the dishes, he said, and he even pressed Miss Davis' frocks. He had her slippers ready and a fine dinner, prepared with his own hands, smoking on the stove when Miss Davis came home from the jute mills, and what do you know? Sometimes she didn't even kiss him.

"I am a man who needs lots of affection," Mr. Sherry said, stifling a sob.

But he did not pack his clothes in a huff, and buzz off to a hotel, his club, or the apartment of a friend. Miss Davis moved out, leaving the lorn husband to brood in *both* their houses.

This is complete reversal of form. A short time ago, the lady told the judge the sad story about how she washed and worked and slaved over a hot iron all day, how she never got to the movies, how she was starved for affection, and how that uppercase bum either buried his snoot in the papers, went out with the fellows or fell asleep in his easy chair as soon as supper was finished. Judge grants the divorce, and the old man goes to live outside the nest, until a property settlement is made and it is established who gets custody of the cat. But under the current system Junior has to play Mama in the home. It's the only way he gets to wear the pants, and I largely blame the gentleman for letting the broads get out of hand.

I never bought that old axiom about keeping 'em pregnant and barefooted, in order to insure peace in the dovecote, and even came out, once, in favor of letting women eat at the same table with the menfolk. Time has proved me wrong. The initial mistake was made in treating women like people. We did them no favor when we allowed them the rights and privileges of the male, while subjecting them to few of the penalties of masculinity. Crammed with propaganda and still giddy from political emancipation, Madame Housewife has got entirely too big for her panty girdle. I even recall a note from a couple of years back saying that Ronald Reagan and Jane Wyman had been divorced, after eight years of marriage, for "political" differences. Nowhere in a marriage ceremony will you find a clause which says "love, honor, cherish and vote the straight Democratic and/or Republican ticket."

Misplaced kindness to the female over the last few years has given woman time to think, which is tragic, because womankind has not yet learned to separate thought from intuition. She gets mad at Henry Wallace and burns the eggs. She becomes outraged about Harry Truman and recalls the ancient lipstick smear on Father's collar; she broods of the injustice of stag barrooms and cuffs the kids.

So many labor-saving devices to save her toil have been invented that she greets the cocktail hour as fresh as a sailor on leave. She is the authority on the atom; the FEPC; the Communists and the ECA. She knows everything, and ties her opinion to her own emotions, so that a momentary malaise will set her off onto a witch hunt over the plight of the female Mohammedan.

The American male is finding it increasingly difficult to be believably tender to a creature who knows everything and is little loath to admit it, in a high, shrill voice. He finds it difficult to pat the posterior of a mate who turns his parlor into a debating stand, and who is painfully insistent that she can do everything better than he can—or is mad and broody about the fact that she can't but won't admit it.

It is an unfortunate truth that the American woman continues to regard herself as a willowy sprite, subject to swoon, even though she may be six feet tall, with the muscles of a rassler and the appetite of a goat. One of the greatest ills of matrimony today is the lady's erroneous infatuation with herself as a faery queen, destined to dwell forever in a rosy fog of amorous foolishness.

Anyone who has ever lived with a dame knows women to be generally stronger than mules, with limitless endurance and nerves of wrought steel. Her demands on her husband are generally more economic than romantic, but she is so fattened on soap operas, romantic novels and the cosmetic advertisements that she whimpers with dissatisfaction and brands her husband a lousy lover. She inflicts on her serf a stifling possessiveness that would soak the starch from Don Juan, but she still wants to live in gooey bliss, with her stevedorish qualities unrecognized and her vestigial maidenhood enhanced by imposed delusion.

"Love me, you bum!" she shrieks, scourging him to the connubial cot with a whip. "Love me like Gable, or I will cut off your allowance. Love me or I will quit work. Love me or I will resign from Congress. I am smarter than you are and make more dough than you do and my friends are nicer than your friends, you seedy tramp, so kiss me sweet or I will not let you go to the ball game Saturday."

Faced with this interpretation of love's young dream, Father sinks deeper and deeper into the hockey scores and the financial page. Finally, in order to escape a sweeping lecture on the failure of our program in China, he seeks the company of something soft, fluffy and brainless, and they ring up another divorce on the cash register of disenchantment. This leaves one more lonely dame with a fistful of Canasta cards, wondering what she did wrong, and why that ungrateful beast had the unmitigated gall to spurn her charms for a moron who was also her physical inferior.

I submit it is getting tougher and tougher to fondle a female who is apt to be busy in the brain about her career, her clubs, her charity chores (fruit of boredom with what we used to call "woman's lot"), her involvements and her ideological commitments. Speaking for me, if I make a pass at something, I am not reaching for the Heart Fund or the Helen Gahagan-for-Senator Committee. I am reaching for a dame, with all the logical fixtures of same, except a runaway intellect that distracts her from the business at hand.

The capsuling of one of the many salient faults of the female came up a few months back in Congress, when the Senate passed something called Amendment 22 to the Constitution, but with a rider. This was a bill which would bestow on the female Equal Rights. The bill passed the Senate when Senator Carl Hayden stuck on a footnote to the effect that woman was granted complete equality before the law, but that nothing in the Amendment would "impair any rights, benefits or exemptions now or hereafter conferred by law upon persons of the female sex." It was noted that while half of the female lobby was for full passage of the equality bill, the other half was strongly against it. The negative half reflected a denial of responsibility for legal equality, while wishing to retain all the perquisites of the male. The Senate version clad women with complete legal trousers, but immunized her from a kick in the pants, no matter how well-deserved.

Under complete equality, the chances are there would be no rape. Laws against rape were written into the books in order to protect a weaker sex, which was regarded as chattel, and hence unable to protect itself. Men are not generally receptive, today, to alimony if a marriage turns sour. Under Amendment 22, with no rider, an embittered he-spouse might be able to sue and collect. The same would apply to breach-of-promise suits. You get spurned by a legal equal, boys, and you institute proceedings for heart balm. This the girls don't crave.

So many little treasured feminine prerogatives would go by the board. It would be okay to kiss and tell or even brag, and in the presence of the lady, because you are no longer protecting the good name of a fluffy monopolistic minority. You are merely discussing a business dealing with an equal.

The deadly female weapon of à la carte fainting and ready tears would become obsolescent. The silly business of leaping on chairs at the sight of a mouse would be regarded as no longer amusing or cute. Come down off that chandelier on your own time, Toots. You got up there by yourself. Hatpins and umbrellas in the eye would subject the lady fair to a punch in the snoot. No, sir. They don't really want equality. They want all theirs and all ours, and that is why they are a touch addled at the moment.

A subtle poison spreads among women who have flunked the romance course through their own inability to decide who runs the roost. This is especially noticeable among the middle and upper-middle classes, and is most evident at the female get-together—the hen lunch, the Canasta party, the distaff cocktail fight. You may observe there, to the horror of a masculine eavesdropper, the complete, clinical casualness of the rap against man.

His infidelities are retailed to all the eager hens. The worthlessness of men in general is stressed. Vivid details of his inadequacies in the mattress department are recounted with a lack of delicacy that would shock a commercial traveler. Seldom, except among the coarsest of males, would you hear such a caddish concert of carnal particulars as at a hen luncheon, with the girls' tongues loosened by the third Martini. This poison spreads even to the happy, well-adjusted wife or sweetheart, who is contaminated merely by the presence of the cobras who are heartsick at their own failure to hold onto their fellow. Miss Clare Boothe Luce, as I recall, pointed this up a generation ago when she did a play called *The Women*.

End product of this wholesale knock is that the gals who came in happy go away disturbed. Most women are gifted with total recall, and an ability to color said recall according to their mood, so that the husband who comes happily home in the expectancy of a decent meal and a little peace suddenly finds himself set upon by a harridan with hooked fingernails, angered anew at an old and minor transgression that may have been a mutual joke for months or years.

In justice to the woman, it must be said that the husband and lover has been something less than 4.0 in recent years, and has provided plenty of room for a dainty beef. But in justice to the man it also must be said that he has been dealing with a brand-new commodity—the "new" woman—recently, and is honestly baffled. If this makes him something less than an ardent lover and a considerate playmate, you can barely blame him. He courted a maid and watched her turn into a complicated machine—jealous of his masculinity and envious of his immunity from the pangs of childbirth and the heat of the cookstove.

Discontent is the seed which has flowered into the present schism between boy and girl. This discontent was watered and tended by the arm-wavers and the experts, the psychiatrists, authors and agitators who discovered a ripe field for exploitation among the females. Our women are in the analysis stage now—no action is good enough to stand on its own as natural and uncontrived. The unnecessary second guessing of sex has turned it from a thing of simple enjoyment into a clinical horror of deep-rooted complexes and over-expectation and self-questioning and clinical apparatus until the process of climbing into the hay with a lady love resembles a tryst less than an experiment in biochemistry. The agony columns themselves, cluttered with half-baked psychiatric advice by unfrocked chiropractors, are enough to wreck the soundest liaison in the world if taken seriously. The scores of women's magazines have made everything from menstruation to eyebrow-plucking such a vast and complicated mystery, in a big-business sense, and have showered so much expert advice on the female, that she now regards herself as a laboratory of mingled emotion and intricate machinery.

The books that are written by lady authors with definable mustaches and flat bustlines are generally contrived to set up a reaction of self-question, to breed dissatisfaction with that old cliché—woman's lot. In nearly all I have read, the man becomes a sort of villain whose prime purpose is to wreak as much misery upon woman in general as he can. This in itself is an evidence of the jealousy of unfulfilled females who were unable to muster up enough allure to snag a provider, and have been shouting sour grapes, clothed in pseudoscientific jargon, ever since. Only trouble is that a vast number of normally handsome, intelligent, sexually attractive women take an old maid's (male or female) rationalizations seriously, and begin to brood about the leanness of their lives. It is comparable to the spoken poison the disenchanted ex-wives drench their friends with at the tea parties and hen lunches.

Woman's lot, alongside man's, is about an even shake, but there has always been a repressed desire in most gals—until they find out how good they got it—to kiss their elbow and turn into a boy. This is maybe because the boy takes the active approach to the girls, while the girls—legend says—were supposed to sit demurely by and be asked. This applies no longer, so now we have a picture of an awkward female who wants to take the masculine initiative while maintaining a maidenly coyness in her life with the opposite sex, and it just don't work. There is a deep-seated shyness in man, bred out of generations of folkway, that turns him out of the path of the aggressive woman. Man has one pride—masculinity. When you encroach on that pride you have lost a lover, and gained a son. Women who discover themselves married to sons shortly find they are living on alimony or sharing a room with another girl friend who made the same mistake.

Pants are a terrific symbol in today's strife between the sexes. Science has shown that there is room for only one person in the same pair of pants. No seat is so voluminous, no legs are so wide, that they will contain a man and wife, a swain and his maid. Womankind, reaching avidly for Pappy's britches, is in process of achieving such a sweeping triumph that she can wear her new splendor in lonely grandeur.

If there is one thing an average (average to mean normal as we know normalcy from a standpoint of sex, economics and personality) man cannot stand from a lass is competition on his own terrain. He will go for tantrums and tears, for a burned dinner and a sloppily kept home, for hysteria and hurled crockery, so long as the lady in question refrains from competition on what he feels is a masculine plane. Competition will curdle the sweetest romance, because competition is what the old boy gets all day long in the trade marts, and what he needs least when he takes off his work clothes and arrays himself in lover's lingerie. When a man pursues a maid, when a man marries a woman, he seeks many things, but competition is the last thing he wants to find beneath the frills. This is why so few minglings of top careers last as marriages except in lip-service, or joke, form.

I would say, too, that man possesses a much more basic morality than modern woman, and is more easily shocked by breaches of same. With the "new" equality has come a flaunting, by the females, of old concepts of copybook morality, and the cockbird finds himself shocked to the gizzard by the naked social unmorality of the emancipated dame who figures she can do *anything* better than he can.

The domination of man by woman in our time has been predicated on gentle deception on the part of the girls, and when they quit leading us down the path we are prone to buck and shy and finally to bolt. The new woman, unless she watches her step, is going to find herself emancipated right out of business, because most of her glamorous mystery has been betrayed in recent years, and she has sacrificed femininity for masculine vanity in fields outside her accepted orbit. Nobody ever comes to see a magician when they know all his tricks.

And it may be said, too, that in the recent frantic rush to top the male animal in his own domain, the she-creature has appeared as something of a fool.

GEORGE JEAN NATHAN

Sweet Faces and Foul Minds

THAT, taking one with another, women's minds are less clean than men's is a fact which, while sufficiently recognized by men in the mass, has yet strangely, so far as I know, not found its commentator and analyst on paper. We have had a few general epigrams on the subject, and we have thought, now and again, that we were about to read some sharp and penetrating statement on the matter, but in both cases delicate evasion and polite half-statement have been the only reward of our curiosity. In the interest of lovely truth, therefore, let us make bold to pursue the inquiry a bit further.

Any man who moves about in feminine society and who is not deaf in both ears can testify to the fact that women's conversation, whatever the specific nature of its initial impulse, sooner or later is inevitably bound to get around to sex. The manoeuvre may be contrived indirectly and with a certain spurious show of neo-Victorian modesty in some instances, but once it gains a measure of confidence it stalks into the topic like a bouncer into a barroom. Whereas men, when they enter into the subject, customarily enter into it, often somewhat disconcertingly, with what may metaphorically be described as both feet, women begin by skirting around its edges, by tossing out innuendo, and by playing ping-pong with suggestiveness before getting to the main business of the conversational meeting. A man will say, frankly, openly, and plainly, what is in his mind; a woman will by verbal by-play and insinuation convert what would otherwise be forthrightly clean into something that is vaguely dirty. Women seldom, in sex matters, use the straight-forward, clean-cut, appropriate terms. They rely upon circumlocutions and synonyms which, like burlesque show strippers, are twice as suggestive as the naked words. They drape their colloquies in gauze veils and, slowly and with deliberately timed oral movements and gestures, remove them, to their twofold—or sevenfold—eroticism.

For this, the still remaining double standard of sex—it still remains for all the vociferous verbal and physical promiscuity of a relative handful of females and for all the editorial fulminations in liberal publications edited by unwanted old maids or fed-up married men who have eyes for their stenographers and obliquely wish to give their wives the gate—the still operative double standard, as I say, is doubtless responsible. Women, under its terms, are denied the privilege of directness and honesty and must perforce take refuge in an arsenal of allusive hints and winks. Their thoughts may be the same as men's thoughts, but the forbidden direct articulation of them serves by repression to make them gradually stagnant and fungus-covered. A man, as the saying is, gets them off his chest and is done with them; a woman is not equally permitted to get them off her mind, and there they remain to crawl about with their increasingly slimy worminess.

This enforced repression seeking vicarious outlet is indicated, among other things, by the stuff that women read. Who are the chief consumers of cheap sex novels and the magazines of so-called "snappy" fiction? The sales statistics show, and emphatically, that they are women—young, medium, and pretty old. The phrase, "shop-girl fiction," tells its own story. On the higher literary but equally sexy level, who have been and are the chief worshipers of D. H. Lawrence, particularly in his "Lady Chatterley's Lover" mood? The answer is too obvious to be recorded.

Women think of sex in the daytime as well as at night, whereas men in general seldom find their thoughts hovering about the topic when the sun is shining. Even Frenchmen and the Viennese hardly begin before twilight. And speculation is inflammation. I have known many men in my lifetime, but I have yet to encounter one who talked or thought about sex at lunch. The majority of women, on the other hand, even those who work for a living, allow their imaginations and conversation to play around it from the first application of the morning lipstick to the last dab of cold cream at night. Like hatred, sex must be articulated or, like hatred, it will produce a disturbing internal malaise. The edicts of polite society are responsible to no small degree for women's dirty minds.

Any psychoanalyst or practitioner of psychopathology will tell you that, out of every ten customers and patients, nine are women. And out of the nine, at least eight will be found to be troubled with sex complexes. These sex complexes, the aforesaid professors need hardly tell you, are the result of repressions, and the aforesaid repressions are responsible for all kinds of mental quirks. The injunction, "Get it out of your mind," suggests the nature of the mind and its thoughts. These thoughts are not healthy, but diseased. Concentration on sex, though sometimes unsuspected, has brought with it a species of mental corruption.

Plays dealing with abnormality always find their chief customers among women. When "The Captive" was, previous to its enforced withdrawal by the police, shown in New York, the box-office statistics revealed that five women to every man attended it, and the matinées were patronized almost exclusively by women.

Such pornographic literary trash as Elinor Glyn's "Three Weeks," Ethel M. Dell's "The Sheik" and Arlen's "The Green Hat" finds itself in the best-seller class solely because of women.

The sex moving pictures, with Mae West's alone excepted (and they are humorous rather than erotically stimulating), are patronized overwhelmingly, the exhibitor's records assure us, by women.

The heroines of men are Joan of Arc, Florence Nightingale and Edith Cavell. The heroines of women are Du Barry, Pompadour and Gabriele d'Annunzio.

I have lately had the privilege of scrutinizing the account books of the four leading purveyors of so-called erotica in New York City. Not the cheap dispensers of contemptible pink-backs, but the sellers of books, that, for one reason or another, are not supposed to be read by the moral element in the community. The account books of the first, covering the period from January first, 1934, to July first, 1934, showed that his customers numbered 1,810 women as against 254 men. The books of the second, covering a like period, showed 927 women as against 46 men. Those of the third, covering the time between January first, 1934, to September first, 1934, showed 737 women and only 34 men. And those of the fourth, covering the period from February first, 1934, to August first, 1934, disclosed 462 women as against just 14 men. I am not acquainted with the sellers of pink-backs and so, unfortunately, cannot offer statistics in that quarter. But the story on the somewhat higher sexy level is sufficiently illuminating. Men usually outgrow their taste for pornography after they have completed, at an early age, the prescribed course of "Only a Boy," "Fanny Hill," and "Green Girls in Paris." But women's taste for pornography seems seldom to abate.

Perhaps in no clearer way may we appreciate the dubious quality of the feminine mind than by referring to the question of motion picture censorship and observing the peculiar aberrations of that mind when it serves on the various state censorship committees whose business it is to pass on the morality of the films. Through various esoteric channels, I have managed to glean certain facts and certain information in this direction that offer tasty reading. I herewith present my findings:

1. The male members of three of these censorship boards—there are state boards at the present time in New York, Maryland, Virginia, Ohio, Kansas, Pennsylvania, and for Sunday films, in Massachusetts—found nothing particularly dirty in such words and phrases as "naked," "twin beds," "mistress," "birth control" and "long, lonely nights," but were compelled to demand their deletion upon the insistence of women members of the boards.

2. It was the women on the boards of two state censorship bodies who, against the male members' indifference, forced the elimination from certain films of such innocent spectacles as women's under-clothing hanging on a clothes line and a husband appearing in his wife's presence in his B. V. D.'s.

3. The deletion of such childishly harmless lines as "I wonder if Molly's mother has told her everything (spoken by the husband on his wedding night), as "You made her so dizzy she had to go in and lie down" (spoken after a kiss), as "I'm from America"—"What part?"—"All of me," as "If you think Americans are good at the Black Bottom, just watch those Africans," and as "Come in, young man. Don't be frightened. It's much warmer here than on the balcony," were all ordered out not by the male members but by the female.

4. Although the male censors could not discern anything excessively foul in a view of a nude little baby, of a girl sitting on a couch with a man's head in her lap, of a man in pajamas, of a girl drawing her feet up on a bench, of

nightgowns arranged on a bed, of a nude figure carved on a pipe, and of table book-ends showing a female figure's single nude breast, the women censors apparently could.

5. The censorship ladies also saw something extremely filthy in the following lines: "Corinne thinks a mistress is something you read about in a French novel"; "You know, experience should have taught you, my dear, that the name Smith is always suspicious on the hotel register"; "You mustn't think of the man in me, only the artist"; "It wasn't love"; "What's your name?" "Eve," "Mine's Adam"; "Is friend husband out of town again?"; and "This girl, painted as a harlot, met death with a smile."

Under beautiful rose-beds, it would seem, there are often sewers.

ELLIOT PAUL

Gertrude, Alas, Alas

Two Cockneys in a railway car got into an argument as to whether a very respectable-looking man with a clerical collar, sitting at the other end of the car, was or was not the Archbishop of York. They made a bet and one Cockney walked the length of the car, apologized, told the solid-looking citizen about the bet, and waited hopefully for an answer.

The gentleman in question looked severely at the Cockney over the rim of his pince-nez and said: "B——r off, will you!"

The Cockney went back and said to his friend, who had bet that the stranger was not the Archbishop of York: "He won't tell us."

I am reminded of that story whenever it is suggested to me that Gertrude Stein has been perpetrating a hoax for the last forty years. A few feature writers have asked her that question point-blank. She has always avoided answering the question.

Her closest companion for more than two decades has been Alice B. Toklas, whom Gertrude has made almost as famous as herself. Gertrude dominates Alice, makes all the decisions, takes all the praise or blame. Throughout their career, Alice has graciously accepted the role of disciple, with no expressed wishes of her own, never questioning Gertrude's judgment or whims. She has never ventured to give advice, or even traffic directions when Gertrude was driving their Model T Ford. When others are present, Alice frequently addresses Gertrude as "Lovey," and if this is not done for effect, it is practically the only thing not done for effect by either of them lo, these many years. They believe in doing things for effect, and that the effect should be mildly provocative and confusing. That is the way Gertrude likes to live.

Having a comfortable income from sources that require no care, Gertrude could have lived almost any way she wanted to. She excelled in philosophy as a favorite student of William James at Radcliffe, and was one of the most promising students of brain surgery and related sciences at Johns Hopkins. She proved, while still in school, that she could write clearly, convincingly and well and could find a ready market for her works. Any of the careers suggested by those beginnings seemed too easy to Gertrude. She knew there were plenty of conscientious writers and gifted scientists. What she did not see, as a young woman in looking around her, was a single human who seemed to be doing what he or she pleased, without dictation or hindrance. She was not willing to admit that a woman with moderate means, good health and fair intelligence could not live for herself and amuse herself without an illusion that she was essential to society.

"Nothing is meaningless if one likes to do it," she once said.

Wars, depressions, artistic and literary storms, and revolutions come and go. She remains the same—solitary (except for Alice who has practically submerged herself in Gertrude's personality), mysterious, forceful and conspicuous. I doubt if Garbo, Shaw or Einstein has had more publicity. Gertrude frankly loves it. But she has never gone out of her way to get it. Publicists have always come to her. And while they came to scoff, they remained to admire and went away with a haunting feeling that they had been in contact with one of America's most remarkable women of all time. They never knew any more about her writing or her intentions than when they arrived. But she is always so charming, so witty, so kindly and tolerant, so versatile, so unexpectedly diverse in her interests, that it takes a dull person, indeed, not to find some common ground with Miss Stein.

In saying that she was "solitary," I don't mean to suggest that Gertrude has not had plenty of company. Probably she entertained more Americans, from all walks of life, in her Rue de Fleurus studio, between World Wars I and II, than any other American celebrity. And I keep referring to her as "American" in spite of the fact that she has made but one short visit to America in the last forty years. Characteristically, Gertrude remained where she was and let America come to her. She speaks French with an American inflection and a slight flavor of the California she abandoned as a girl. She looks, as Jimmy Cagney remarked, very much like Spencer Tracy and dresses quite as informally.

Not a few of the American "exiles" in the carefree and foolhardy 1920's played the heavy man of letters in the most flamboyant European style. Wherever you found Ludwig Lewisohn, for instance, you would be sure to encounter a flock of writers with various accents, haircuts, and axes to grind. The talk would be of the latest editions or translations of the work of *le maître* (the master) and, in so far as the satellites dared, of the latest editions or translations of their own works, if any. In groups of the advance guard, like the Surrealists, literary talk was taboo. The few timid Americans who were admitted to the circle sat very still and listened to the Gauleiter, who then was André Breton. The talk was of revolution and violence, although Stalin had declined to admit them in a body to the Party. When Gertrude Atherton or chaps like Thornton Wilder disembarked, they saw to it that they were met by reporters of the New York *Herald* and the Chicago *Tribune*, and, if possible, the humbler Paris *Times* and the ultra-British *Daily Mail*. They were listed as "among those present" at the teas and receptions given by the late Mrs. E. Berry Wall, Mrs. Tryphosa Bates-Bachelor and the other prevailing lionesses of the American colony's high society. Although Gertrude Stein was on speaking terms with almost all the ambitious women who wanted to boost their social standing by giving free handouts to the French, Austrian, Spanish and Russian aristocracy, she never took them seriously and never permitted them to exploit her fame or popularity or amazing conversation. As a matter of fact, Gertrude was on speaking terms with the genuine French old families who seldom, if ever, received Americans. Gertrude endeared herself to these descendants of noblemen who still loved France by her work for the French wounded and later the American wounded in World War I, during which she raised a great deal of money and herself drove an ambulance at the front.

It is almost maddening to think that a writer of her talent should have seen so much so well and should have stubbornly refused to write about it. I have seldom felt sadder than when I read Gertrude's *Wars I Have Seen*. In danger every moment as a famous Jewish fugitive from the Nazis who occupied her province in the east of France, knowing the intimate reactions of the people of the region in which Stendhal found his characters for *The Red and the Black*, Miss Stein, approaching the biblical age, turns out an inconsequential, almost meaningless book which tells us next to nothing. I suppose that is Gertrude's own affair. Anyway, it is consistent with her personal philosophy.

I have never met an intelligent person of either sex, or in any social or economic or artistic bracket, who did not enjoy talking with Gertrude Stein. It is not going too far to class her with Oscar Wilde or Mark Hanna as a conversationalist. She does not spark off wisecracks, like Groucho Marx, or play on words like James Joyce.

Whatever was said to her started an interesting train of associations on which she improvised in a masterful way. She had very few opinions, no zeal about politics, her scientific background was sound and modern but she seldom drew upon that. Sherwood Anderson, Ernest Hemingway, Professor Robert A. Millikan, Josephine Baker, Harold Ickes, Paul Valéry, Doctor Coué, Picasso, Charles Steinmetz, Ponzi, Havelock Ellis, Dean Inge, Frank Harris, Leopold Stokowski, the Sitwells, George Gershwin, Hendrik Van Loon, Oscar Levant, the late Gen. Summerall, Madame Schiaparelli, Helena Rubinstein, Edward G. Robinson—the list is endless—sat at Miss Stein's feet and listened with pleasure. And seldom or never on the special subjects they knew as a trade. Gertrude had no theories about economic or social progress. She pretended not to care for music. The work of other writers held little interest for her, either the classical, the standard or her contemporaries. Her name was constantly being linked with that of James Joyce, as a rampant modernist. Actually, she had never read Joyce, and he told me quite frankly that he hadn't read Gertrude.

Gertrude was at home nearly every afternoon for "tea." It was in those tranquil hours, from four to dinnertime at seven, when the world's intelligentsia flowed through the Rue de Fleurus studio. On the walls were renowned Picassos, the Cézannes, and paintings by Gris, Renoir, Matisse, and Tchelitchev. The guests Gertrude favored were maneuvered by Alice into seats that afforded the best view of Picasso's portrait of Gertrude, and the Cézanne *Woman in the Arm Chair*. These were the No. 1 and No. 2 spots and the initiated knew well that they were to defer for the time being to those who occupied them. A very highranking place was one from which Picasso's *Rose Nude* and *Blue Boy* appeared to best advantage.

Alice, on these occasions, was magnificent. I have never seen such skill as she had in shifting guests for Gertrude's comfort and convenience. Somehow, just before any given person was about to weary Gertrude, Alice had him or her in tow and the seat near the throne was being occupied by someone Alice had chosen and propelled there. The refreshments consisted of tea made and poured by Alice, and the strongest liquor distilled in France and probably anywhere in the world, a special "Marc de Bourgogne," with a handwritten label, about eighty years old. This was a test Gertrude applied to anyone who preferred liquor to tea. The primary sensation, on taking a sip of it, was like swallowing a lighted kerosene lamp. I have seen many accomplished drinkers, and even pronounced alcoholics, gasp, blink, shudder and wipe their eyes. A second later, however, when the rare old flavor asserted itself, the most eloquent looks of appreciation would follow, but no remarks. The sight of Gertrude, placidly sipping hers as if nothing were more natural in the world, discouraged comment.

Somehow, the choice of beverages, the suave, slightly smoky souchong and the ruggedest strong spirits known to man, reveals much about Gertrude's personality. With her, there is no middle ground. The effect was well-calculated, as was everything else in the Stein household, to let Gertrude keep the floor and Alice control the disposition of the guests. I can never remember seeing anyone drunk at one of Gertrude's teas. If a guest arrived with a few too many under his belt, one shot of that phenomenal *Marc* straightened him out. If a guest arrived empty, one drink of Gertrude's potent liquor did not suggest another. Incidentally, Gertrude is a true connoisseur of food and wine. I have known her, while Mathilde, her famous cook, was busy in the kitchen and Alice was dutifully typing such gems as *Nearly All of it to be as a Wife Has a Cow, A Love Story*, to journey by bus all the way across Paris to a certain bakery near La Porte St. Denis to buy exactly the kind of Spanish pastry she wanted for dessert.

It is a legend among Gertrude's friends that Alice has never made an error in typing. I can only testify that in the years I was handling Gertrude's contributions to the magazine, *transition*, every page was letter-perfect. When the first number of *transition* was published, Gertrude complained that the text of her *An Elucidation* had been garbled. We found that a French printer had reversed typewritten pages two and three and none of us had noticed the difference. We were obliged to issue a supplement to transition No. 1, containing *An Elucidation* with pages two and three in their proper order. This was commented upon all over England, America, and France, and resulted in a landslide of free publicity. Many of my cynical acquaintances accused me then and still believe that the error was made purposely in order to stir up comment.

Part of Gertrude's tradition was to break off friendships from time to time purely, I think, for variety's sake. Hemingway was banished from Gertrude's presence in 1928 because he had achieved too much financial success by profiting from Gertrude's teachings. Tchelitchev, then a struggling young painter, became *persona non grata*, along with his companion, Allen Tanner, shortly after he had painted a portrait of Alice which accentuated a slight cast in her eye. One young poet who for a time was seen almost daily with Gertrude and Alice was abruptly dismissed when he returned from a two weeks' vacation with a bride of whom Gertrude did not approve. Of course, it always fell to Alice to pronounce these sentences of exile. She would call the disfavored one on the telephone and say sweetly, "I wanted to inquire how you are, because I suppose that Lovey and I will not be seeing you again."

Those who think that only workers should eat have long been indignant about Miss Stein. It is true that nearly half a century of writing has brought her very little money. However, if she had to, Gertrude could earn large sums in several ways. Her art collection, which she bought for a song at the time when others less discerning were ridiculing the Impressionists and Post-Impressionists, is worth well over a million dollars today and is intact. Her lecture tour in the middle thirties in the United States was a financial success. In fact, she was the rage. Her opera, *Four Saints in Three Acts*, to which Virgil Thomson contributed the music, did not do badly. She has lectured and received respectful attention on the subject of English composition and literature at both Oxford and the Sorbonne. I have already said that she reads no fiction except her own, but she has always been an omnivorous reader of autobiographies, biographies, and letters. She insists that only this form of literature is helpful in understanding life, history, and her own "art for art's sake."

Her first book, *Three Lives*, is stark, unadorned, unpretentious realism, and no one should forget that it antedates Dreiser's *American Tragedy*. It appeared, unheralded, when American literary taste was Victorian and "icky" to a degree that now seems nothing short of comical. *Three Lives* won instant praise from the brave and discerning critics who must have long realized that the prevailing brand of corn some day would have to be supplanted by something reflecting modern trends. A fair sample of what readers of books and magazines relished in the period that preceded Miss Stein's little, down-to-earth gem about three servant girls is this quotation, taken from *Barriers Burned Away* by E. P. Roe.

"Dennis was no faint shadow of a man who had frittered away in numberless flirtations what little heart he originally had. He belonged to the male species, with something of the pristine vigor of the first man, who said of the one woman in the world, 'This is now bone of my bones, and flesh of my flesh,' and one whom he had first seen but a few short months since now seemed to belong to him by the highest and divinest right. But could he ever claim his own?"

Picture the devotees of E. P. Roe suddenly confronted with the following, from Miss Stein's *Tender Buttons*.

> "Chicken is a dirty word
> Chicken is a dirty third.
> Chicken is a dirty bird."

Naturally, the public yelled murder. The bulk of it is still yelling, and Miss Stein is going serenely on. About once every five years, lately, she has put out a book advertised by her publisher as "intelligible." Examples are *The Auto-biography of Alice B. Toklas* and *Wars I Have Seen*.

Her best-known story is entitled *Miss Furr and Miss Skeene* and in it she manages to convey a lot about the futile goings-on of a couple of American women abroad by using, repeating, inverting and varying the phrase: "They were gay there."

In her longest book, *The Making of Americans*, which dates back to 1920, she elaborates on a pet idea of hers, namely, that only the middle-class is important. That infuriates the champions of the proletariat, and the aristocrats as well. Also, in this book, Miss Stein insists that there are only twenty-six kinds of human faces, and that any face may be definitely classified. When asked to explain a Picasso exhibition of ultra-Cubist paintings she calmly remarked, "There are no feet in nature," as if that settled the whole thing.

Miss Stein is a preposterous woman, the reader will say. She is conceited, overbearing, frivolous, selfish, egotistical, pretentious, exotic, eccentric, unimportant. Her friends will add that she is stimulating, full of common sense, that she has a zest for life and lives it well. Anyone will have to admit that she has held more than her share of the public attention nearly half a century and is still going strong. And whenever a reader is willing to throw away her entire product, he is likely to reconsider when he finds a passage like this, from *Wars I Have Seen*.

"Of course there are a good many times when there is no war just as there are a good many times when there is a war. To be sure when there is a war the years are longer that is to say the days are longer the months are longer are much longer but the weeks are shorter that is what makes a war."

Miss Stein's book for children, entitled *The World is Round*, contains gems like this.

> "Here I am.
> When I wish a dish
> I wish a dish of ham.
> When I wish a little wish
> I wish that I was where I am."

In *Geography and Plays* one finds lines like: "Toasted Suzie is my ice cream."

From *Studies in Conversation*: "A god-mother to her god-mother. A god-father to him, his god-father. A god-father, a god-mother, her god-mother, his god-father, his god-mother, her god-father, her god-mother his god-father. So and so. So and so is his god-father. And so her god-mother, as god-mother. God-mother to whom and when."

She likes oil paintings because "there is no air in them." The motto on her stationery is "A rose is a rose is a rose."

After the fall of Paris, it was a common G.I. experience to encounter Gertrude strolling along a boulevard. The boys could usually recognize her by the queer, dunce-shaped hat she wore. In any event, she was likely to introduce herself, for an American uniform was an open invitation to drop in for a visit at a Gertrude soirée, where Picasso was usually an added attraction. Many a soldier left a Stein session bewildered by an experience that was moving and impressive, yet somehow as confusing as one of Gertrude's more abstruse passages.

Now that World War II is over, she is back in Paris, giving sage advice to American veterans. "Boys," she said, recently, "if one of you wants to be a plumber, he doesn't have to be the best plumber. To be a good plumber is enough."

Well. Lots of the boys get plenty of advice that makes less sense than that.

RICHARD E. LAUTERBACH

The Legend of Dorothy Parker

THERE is a plump little dark-haired lady now nearing fifty-one who might have been America's greatest woman writer if she had only held her tongue. As it is, her four thin volumes of verse and her three slim collections of short stories are credentials enough for a place close to the pinnacle.

Dorothy Parker, the reluctant wizard of the wonderful wisecrack, has only herself and her friends to blame for her brilliant failure as a literary giant. The things she said and the things they said she said were her undoing. If it had been less easy to talk so well, then perhaps all the rich promise of her quick eye for people, of her tightly tuned ear for language, might have been put on paper, bound into novels, produced as plays. But her skill in fencing with a rapier tongue swept her, too young, to a select literary heaven—whence the bright intellectuals of the gay twenties trumpeted her glib glory.

With such a build-up it was never possible for a fundamentally ease-loving person to cast aside her oral slings and arrows in favor of solid, earthy work. When motivated by love or hunger she penned perfectly cadenced, bitter little verses, or occasional short stories. She became in her heyday the symbol of supersophistication.

Describing herself and other female writers of the old "smartypants" school, Mrs. Parker observed:

"We were gallant, hard-riding and careless of life. We were little black eyes that had gone astray . . . a sort of Ladies' Auxiliary of the Legion of the Damned."

The reputation for the wondrous wisecrack, which changed the course of Dorothy Parker's career before it ever matured, is not entirely her fault. In Hollywood they tell a story about Sam Goldwyn having dinner with Mrs. Parker. During the meal he turned to her and asked, "Do you really say all those things which the papers report that you say?" Dorothy smiled, batted her long black lashes and parried, "Do you?"

In both instances the answer is "No." Any anecdote about a Hollywood producer with a garbled vocabulary and a genius for *non sequitur* is eventually retold about Goldwyn. And for twenty years most quotable *bon mots* emanating from U. S. literary circles were attributed to Dorothy Parker.

The concoction which Alexander Woollcott labelled an odd blend of

"Little Nell and Lady Macbeth" was born Dorothy Rothschild on August 22, 1893, at West End, N. J. Her father was Jewish, her mother was Scotch. When Dorothy was very young, her mother died and she was taken to a convent in New York, from which she remembers only that if you spit on a pencil eraser it will erase ink. She was, by her own description, a plain, disagreeable child with stringy hair and a yen to write verse. Her unhappy stay at the convent culminated in her dismissal for writing an essay which the Mother Superior considered horribly unfunny.

Deciding that Dorothy wasn't going to become a teacher, her father did not put her back in school, hoping she would soon marry and therefore not require a complete education. Dorothy beguiled her way into a job writing fashion captions for Vogue at the lavish salary of ten dollars a week. On the side she swelled that income by writing and selling light verse and playing the piano for a children's dancing class.

While she was struggling along at Vogue, she married Edwin Parker, a handsome young man from Connecticut whom she had known most of her life. He was a Wall Street broker, serious and correct. They lived together for four or five hilarious days until his division sailed for France. When he came back two years later the Parkers began rollicking down the high, wide and handsome speak-easy road that smashed so many marriages in the twenties.

After the Armistice Mrs. Parker shifted her talents from Vogue to Vanity Fair. This urbane monthly, under the editorship of Frank Crowninshield, was then publishing the work of such writers as Heywood Broun, Edna St. Vincent Millay, John Dos Passos, Stephen Leacock, Floyd Dell, F. Scott Fitzgerald, Walter Lippmann, James Branch Cabell, Ernest Boyd, John V. A. Weaver, Donald Ogden Stewart and Grantland Rice. Working in almost glorious anonymity, Mrs. Parker earned twenty-five dollars a week, wrote picture captions with an exact count of 14½ which had to have a punch in them, and was friendly with a young pundit named Bob Benchley.

Mrs. Parker soon became the perfect lunching companion for Vanity Fair editors. Addicted to plain suits and cute little red hats, she was shy, a good listener and minxy rather than devastating with her modest sense of humor.

In those Prohibition days the bright young people drank their lunches and feasted on dry wit. Mrs. Parker learned fast, both in and out of the office. In a few months she was not only doing all the Vanity Fair picture captions but also writing articles under pseudonyms. She became increasingly popular with the staff, especially with Benchley, who was managing editor, and Robert Sherwood, dramatic editor. Mrs. Parker made a practice of calling them "Mr. Benchley" and "Mr. Sherwood," which she still does as a gag.

Mrs. Parker wasn't exactly fired from Vanity Fair in 1921. She wrote tartly and with restrained sophistication about most of the New York matters which she examined and reviewed for the magazine. But the storm began to brew almost immediately after she started to grind out sharp play reviews as a pinch hitter for P. G. Wodehouse, who was on his summer vacation. She hit too hard. Editor Crowninshield fretted over her biting dissections and lightning really struck when she reviewed Billie Burke's performance in W. Somerset Maugham's *Caesar's Wife*, saying, "Miss Burke, in the role of the young wife, looks charmingly youthful. She is at her best in her more serious moments; in her desire to convey the girlishness of the character, she plays her lighter scenes rather as if she were giving an impersonation of Eva Tanguay." (Miss Tanguay was a vaudeville performer with wild, wooly hair who sang a song called *I Don't Care*.) When Crowninshield received angry letters from Florenz Ziegfeld, David Belasco and Charles Dillingham, he suggested to Benchley that Mrs. Parker be taken off reviews. Benchley next day offered his resignation, hoping that such a decisive action would change the editor's mind. He was quite surprised when Crowninshield shook his hand and said, "Gee, Bob, I'm sorry to see you go." Whereupon Benchley and Parker quit, formed a writing team, opened an "oversized broom closet" office in the Metropolitan Opera building. They called the firm "Utica Drop Forge and Tool Co., Benchley and Parker, Presidents," but never had enough money to pay for having the name lettered on the door. They tried doing a play, but the problem of naming the characters held up that project interminably. Dorothy suggested calling them 1, 2, 3, 4, 5, but found that stage directions like "1 moves upstage while 2 shrinks against backdrop," were more like bad chess than good theatre.

Mrs. Parker, with an office, a typewriter and an appetite, finally starved herself into writing. She did some play reviews for *Ainslee's* and began turning out a little fiction. It took her then, as now, as long as a month to smooth the prose of one very short story. She spent most of her sober hours dreaming up new excuses for not working. A favorite was writing menus on a large mirror, of fancy luncheons she'd like to eat. The first two paragraphs of a Parker book review stayed in the typewriter until the paper yellowed and crumpled. The other president of the Utica Drop Forge was no more assiduous. The first line of a Benchley essay beginning, "Now that wages are coming down," stayed in his typewriter so long that wages were going up again before he got around to finishing it. This line became a running gag for Mrs. Parker, who would prefix every remark on the social scene with, "Now that wages are coming down." It invariably made Benchley sick with laughter.

In 1923 they gave up their office and later wangled space at the old humorous weekly, *Life*, edited by Bob Sherwood, who had quit *Vanity Fair* a few weeks before Parker and Benchley.

During these years Mrs. Parker's reputation as a wag began spreading, largely because she had two of New York's brightest circles acting as her personal publicists. One was the Algonquin crowd which included Franklin P. Adams, Alexander Woollcott, Heywood Broun and others. They met at the Algonquin Hotel for lunch, and each day carried away with them the latest and brightest Parkerisms. F.P.A. spread the pointed word in his column and at his regular poker games with Broadway celebrities. Woollcott, who made his reputation out of the conversation of others, delighted in conveying Parker's remarks back to the people they were directed against. This luncheon group, originally self-christened "The S. J. Kaufman Post of the American Legion," grew into what was known as the "Critics' Round-table." The table grew larger, and when curious crowds began to flock to the Algonquin to listen, the regulars went back to eating in speak-easies for privacy.

Another more Bohemian group gathered at the studio of Neysa McMein, a cover artist. Mrs. Parker frequented these alcoholic teas, and finally took an apartment under Neysa's studio, which complicated the Parkers' already confused home life. They were finally divorced in 1928.

Sophisticated magazines were carrying an occasional Dorothy Parker poem or sketch. In 1924 Elmer Rice suggested they collaborate on dramatizing one of her stories. The play, called *Close Harmony*, ran four weeks. On the fourth Wednesday Mrs. Parker wired Benchley collect: "CLOSE HARMONY DID A COOL NINETY DOLLARS AT THE MATINEE. STOP. ASK THE BOYS IN THE BACK ROOM WHAT THEY WILL HAVE."

The publication of *Enough Rope* in 1926 firmly established Mrs. Parker as a poet. By 1927 the book had gone into eight printings and hit a record high for U.S. poetry sales. It is still selling today.

But most of the smart set were talking about Mrs. Parker's unrhymed witticisms rather than her verses. Woollcott gave the kiss of fame to her bright sayings at a week-end house party which he attended with Mrs. Parker. They were thrown in with a motley group of guests who bathed infrequently. When Woollcott wondered where they came from and where they might be found at other times, Mrs. Parker whispered, "I think that they crawl back into the woodwork."

Inspecting the inadequate washing facilities on that same week end, Woollcott noted an aging toothbrush hanging on the wall above the chipped basin. "What do you suppose our hostess does with that?" Woollcott asked. Mrs. Parker, after a moment's study, answered, "I think she rides it on Hallowe'en."

The upshot of a long series of verbal bull's-eyes was the formulation of a group known as "Woollcott's Vigilantes," banded together in self-protection. Anyone who heard a Parker crack about one of the others would report it immediately. It made for some fine fights.

Very early in her career the literary and theatrical crowd liked to be "in the know" by tagging Dorothy Parker's name onto every new crackling gag. Her fame and her stories traveled abroad and came back. Mrs. Parker feels that her act was never as good as her billing. She even indicates that there mightn't have been an act at all if it hadn't been for Benchley. This Benchley stoutly denies. Furthermore, he states categorically that Mrs. Parker, when sober, has never made an unfunny crack. Most of the second-rate ad libs repeated with her by-line are misquotations or not hers at all. Recently columnists, especially Winchell, have been prone to quote Dorothy Parker on topics probably dreamed up by an overanxious press agent. This is always a source of annoyance to Mrs. Parker.

Even the late Alex Woollcott once wrote a nostalgic story about Mrs. Parker in which he claimed that she had MEN painted on the door of her office just to break the monotony. Actually, Mrs. Parker only talked of doing it.

While hardened to the inferior stories propelled by the magic of her name, Mrs. Parker still winces when something she really authored is credited to another. It was Mrs. Parker who reacted to the news of President Coolidge's death with the cool, "How do they know?" On a magazine piece on Wilson Mizner this tidbit was thrust into his mouth.

Another thing which arouses her ire is a misquotation of:

> *Men seldom make passes*
> *At girls who wear glasses.*

She resents the use of the word "never" instead of "seldom." She often wears glasses herself.

Many of Mrs. Parker's genuine gems are lost to readers because they are too frank to print. Fortunately, her present husband, Alan Campbell, occasionally overhears a good one and repeats it. One example has to do with his wife's comment on a lady politician whose character was being gleefully shredded over martinis. One of the women at the cocktail party said in her defense, "But really, she's awfully kind to her inferiors."

Mrs. Parker quipped, "Where does she find them?"

Until 1925 Mrs. Parker worked on the old *Life* doing articles, stories and reviews. Shortly after the *New Yorker* began publication she moved her acid pen over there, and portioned out her weekly vitriol against the puny efforts of the publishing industry in reviews signed "Constant Reader." Once, at the end of a criticism of A. A. Milne's sugar-saturated whimsy, she recorded the fact that "Tontant Weader fwowed up."

During the next decade Mrs. Parker did a great deal of traveling abroad, and her interest in things international developed apace. At least one of the periodic European junkets had a higher purpose. In 1937 she went to Spain "without any axe to grind" to see what and wherefore of the bitter Civil War. Writing about her experiences afterward, she said: "I didn't bring messages from anybody. I am not a member of any political party. The only group I have ever been affiliated with is that not especially brave little band that hid its nakedness of heart and mind under the out-of-date garment of a sense of humor. I heard someone say, and so I said it, too, that ridicule is the most effective weapon. . . . Well, now I know . . . ridicule may be a shield, but it is not a weapon."

When she came back, firmly convinced of the Loyalist cause, she worked hard to arouse U. S. sympathy against the Fascists. All her scorn was turned into this channel, against the isolationists, the fence sitters. At a party given by Leon Henderson in Washington she sat on a piano and pleaded for funds for Spanish children. Her words moved her so she cried. When a photographer tried to get a picture of her misery, Henderson threw him out bodily. At that party Mrs. Parker declared soberly, "A humorist in this world is whistling by the loneliest graveyard and whistling the saddest song. There is nothing funny in the world any more."

The trip to Spain crystallized a social consciousness which Mrs. Parker had been nicely sublimating since she was a child. Occasionally it cropped up in her short stories or over some dramatic incident. She was arrested in 1927 for "sauntering and loitering" near the scene of the Sacco-Vanzetti trial in Boston, although her active participation was no greater than that of hundreds of liberal intellectuals. She had merely marched in a protest parade.

Mrs. Parker recalls the first incident in her life which caused her to think of humanity in social terms. One wintry day she stood at the window of an apartment on West 72nd Street with her aunt who pointed at the poor, tired old men shoveling the streets clean during a snowstorm. The aunt remarked to her young charge that thanks were due to God for sending the snow as it gave the unemployed an opportunity to work. The child Dorothy thought that men ought to have the *chance* to work even in good weather.

After Spain Mrs. Parker's writing became more serious but there was little market for it. Editors wanted the charming, sophisticated Dorothy Parker, the old brittle stories, the nostalgic moon-calf poems. This reaction only soured her more completely on humor and light verse. Invited by The Congress of American Writers in 1939 to talk at their poetry session, she entitled her discourse, "Sophisticated Verse and *the Hell with It*."

She turned her old ruthlessness on the glittering adjectives used to describe her own work. "Out in Hollywood where the streets are paved with Goldwyn," she remarked, "the word 'sophisticate' means, very simply, 'obscene.' A sophisticated story is a dirty story. Some of that meaning has wafted eastward and got itself mixed up into the present definition. So that a 'sophisticate' means: one who dwells in a tower made of a DuPont substitute for ivory and holds a glass of flat champagne in one hand and an album of dirty post cards in the other."

With these words Dorothy Parker completely turned her back on New York, her old hangouts and cronies. She and her second husband buckled down to work in Hollywood. Looking back now on her collections of verse and short stories, Mrs. Parker takes pride only in *Soldiers of the Republic*, a singularly effective story about Spain. But she is far better known than many fine authors who have published a hundred times as much. Her publisher estimates that on a per word basis she is probably the world's highest paid writer. Her poems and stories appear repeatedly in collected volumes and anthologies, and stories are constantly adapted for radio and stage.

Her verse has been all things to all critics: "sly and philosophical" to Russell Crouse, "robust" to Laurence Stallings, "biting and terse" to Henry Hazlitt, and to Woollcott a "potent distillation of nectar and wormwood, of ambrosia and deadly nightshade." Her prose to Robert Sherwood was the "superior of Ernest Hemingway added to Ring Lardner added to Aldous Huxley added to Rebecca West."

But at bridge parties and stag dinners Mrs. Parker is not remembered as the author of the O. Henry prize-winning story, *Big Blonde,* or as the dialogue writer for *Pride of the Yankees.* She's the wisecrack artist who summed up Channing Pollock's *The House Beautiful* as "the play lousy," who said of Katharine

Hepburn's acting, "she runs the gamut of emotions from A. to B." She's the mistress of the deadly verbal thrust who wired a famous actress when that thespian finally had a baby (after making conspicuous entrances during her prolonged pregnancy) "GOOD WORK WE ALL KNEW YOU HAD IT IN YOU." Dorothy Parker's work has been heavily conditioned by four men in her life. When her early marriage with Edwin Parker floated on the rocks, she fell in love with Charles MacArthur, now married to Helen Hayes. Three years of that bred only frustration and a volume of bitter love poems. The next heartthrob was John Garrett, a socialite. The third was John McClain, a reporter, about whose Victor Maturish framework Mrs. Parker made the classic crack, "His body has gone to his head." Her second husband, Alan Campbell, is number four. They were married in 1933 when he was playing juvenile leads in summer stock. While Campbell was touring in Denver, Mrs. Parker received an offer for them to go to Hollywood. They borrowed money to buy a second-hand flivver and drove to the Coast. They soon drove a Packard and lived in a mansion.

Up until this second marriage Mrs. Parker's life had been a series of high plateaus between heartbreaks. She usually crawled out of the pits slowly, pulling herself up by a series of bitter verses, stories and parties. Since she achieved comparative stability with Campbell, the plateaus have leveled out, the bitter verses swell up no more, the stories are so much drudgery and the parties are less frequent. With Campbell in the Army some of her "old friends" hope that the literary output will start again.

After nine years of being one of Hollywood's most highly paid scenarists, Mrs. Parker's scorn for the tinselled town has not abated. She believes one of the troubles with the movies is "that everybody in Hollywood thinks he can write, including the producers. I don't believe the films have anything to do with writing except in a crossword puzzle kind of way. Writing a script is drawing together a lot of ends which can be worked into a moving picture."

Parker and Campbell have collaborated on tough, realistic pictures like *Mary Burns, Fugitive*, gay, screwball items like *Hands Across the Table* and *The Moon's Our Home*, serious Hollywood self-analysis like *A Star is Born*; ironically their biggest box-office draw was the saccharine *Sweethearts*, a 1938 musical hit with Nelson Eddy and Jeanette MacDonald. The Campbells sweated out their time in the studios like so many days in purgatory to pay for their earthly bills. The only picture that gave Mrs. Parker any satisfaction "aside from the check every week" was the scenario for Lillian Hellman's *The Little Foxes*.

After the filming of this stage hit had started, she received a frantic phone call in the middle of the night from Producer Sam Goldwyn. "I've seen the rushes," he shouted, "and that picture's communistic, it's communism pure and simple I tell you."

"But, Sam," Mrs. Parker remonstrated gently and with inspiration, "the story is set in the early 1900's. There wasn't any communism then."

"Thank God," Goldwyn exclaimed. He hung up, contented.

While her husband, a lieutenant in the Air Forces, shuttled around for training, Mrs. Parker lived in a dowdy two-room apartment in a New York apartment hotel, which she aptly described as "the kind of a hotel where businessmen install their mothers and then run."

In the Army, Campbell although he has a solid reputation of his own as a writer, finds most soldiers know of his wife. They refer to her as a "newspaper-woman" and occasionally confuse her with Dorothy Thompson. This confusion, incidentally, is shared by hundreds of others—to the delight of neither Dorothy.

Dorothy Parker still has her old charm. Her conversation is animated, intelligent, not unkindly. She is short, about five feet, with dark hair that bommerbangs over her forehead, large dark eyes and a tired look. She has a nervous, shy, gamin manner relieved by a quick, warm smile. Her voice has an unusual timbre, sometimes throaty, sometimes high. No one has ever heard Mrs. Parker laugh at one of her fabulous wisecracks. She just goes on with the conversation as if she had only said, "How do you do?"

She still likes dachshunds and Hemingway, cries very easily, is extremely generous and intensely self-deprecating, avoids publicity, likes to be lazy.

She is still the center of any room full of people. This, she says, has always upset her. "How would you like to walk into a party and have a dozen women look up and say with their eyes, 'So you're Dorothy Parker. I dare you to say something nasty.'" The tragedy is that Mrs. Parker loves being with people, dreads the fact that her reputation precedes and follows her. On one occasion at a first night the woman next to her turned and asked, "Are you Dorothy Parker?" In self-defense, Mrs. Parker said, "Yes, do you mind?"

Mrs. Parker would gladly trade her secure niche as a foremost American wit for one thick, solid, earthy, realistic masterpiece. She would gladly forget her own prediction:

> "Three be the things I shall have till I die:
> Laughter and hope and a sock in the eye."

She would even hurl mud at her own epitaph, EXCUSE MY DUST. But somehow she can no longer kid herself. Her contribution to the 20th Century Culture, unless she should reverse her field, is the elevation of the wisecrack from the speak-easy barroom to the level of Bartlett's *Familiar Quotations*.

GEORGE A. McNAMARA

◄───►

Essay on Jiggling

SPRING is here. The girls have emerged from their winter cocoons of cloth and fur and the jiggle is once more abroad in the land. All winter long the jiggle, that gayest decoration of the public scene, that champagne of movement which can be accomplished only by the human female, has been obscured from the public gaze by heavy fabrics and voluminous draperies. With the coming of spring, it has blossomed forth once more, lightly clothed in gay prints, to charm and adorn a drab and care-worn world. It gets more delighted attention than all of Mother Earth's new-born and colorful horticultural display. It inspires more of the bubbly, electric feeling of well-being than all of the conventional, publicized harbingers of spring together. Everybody sees the jiggling and each one is charmed by it. But no one has a kind word to say for it. It is treated as an infirmity, partly physical and partly moral and better not spoken of at all. Even the poets ignore it. They twang their lyres to the birds and the bees, the sunshine and the trees, they make grateful mention of the maiden herself, her eyes and her sighs, her dresses and her tresses but they say nothing at all about her pleasingly complicated mode of locomotion. They, like everyone else, avoid jiggling, in words, if not in flesh.

This graceless convention has penetrated even to the irresponsible and care-free as I learned one day when I made, to a very young lady, a light and passing allusion to the girls' jiggling. She looked concerned for a moment. Then she leaned closer to me and in a confidential voice she implied a mild reproof. "They can't help it," she whispered. She sat back with such a pleased air of having been helpful and informative upon a delicate subject that only a brute could have said he thanked God they couldn't help.

This hypocritical shushing of something everyone sees and enjoys is a vestige of puritanism still successfully murdering the esthetic and charming. A lovely girl makes pleasant and cheerful any scene at all and she confers a favor upon each person who sees her. People look at her and after her because the sight of her pleases them. And she pleases them with no cold and static beauty.

The museums are full of classic marble compositions but their aisles are empty except for a few nearsighted grinds hunting for culture. She offers living beauty, youth in motion, cheerful and hopeful and gay. However serious her errand she proceeds to its discharge by a series of complicated evolutions which make everybody who sees her feel better. She jiggles. And in spite of all the shushing, in spite of her own earnest endeavors to proceed in only one direction at one time, various portions of her persist in swinging along on their own harmonic lines of motion. And the faster she hurries, the faster she jiggles. Even the Board of Education which has ruined more young women than any other force or agency is helpless before the jiggle and its young teachers are as entertaining as they are instructive. Advancing years, of course, take away their entertaining qualities and their cheerfulness but advancing years would do that almost as quickly without any help from the Board. The essential point is that all the girls, however admonished or instructed, continue to jiggle for the delight of the common people without any sanction from society or any intention of their own. Everybody sees it and enjoys it but only God approves of it.

In view of the conspiracy of silence on the subject, it is remarkable that we have such a word as jiggle. The meaning of the word is definite and widely under-understood—jiggling is what happens when a young woman walks. Or turns or bends or reaches or stamps her foot. And she approaches the absolutely ultimate in jiggling when she runs. Hers is a purely human achievement in this machine age. Machines may shake, they may vibrate or oscillate but they can never, never jiggle.

Although the meaning of the word is clear and definite, it is difficult to describe the jiggle because it is an integral part of the intricate succession of exercises by which women propel themselves from one spot to another. Of course women wiggle and the wiggling causes jiggling but the wiggling is beside the point. Wiggling is neither here nor there, we will confine ourselves to jiggling. A jiggle occurs when some portion of the body, having been left behind when the major portion was in motion and wishing to catch up, gives a sprightly bounce. In its anxiety not to be left alone, it overleaps its proper position and finding itself without support from the main body, it quickly retires too far, whereupon a secondary jiggle ensues. It is all liveliness and eagerness and gaiety. And as some parts are sliding back while others are catching up, each in its own tempo and arc, yet all somehow holding to the central movement, the effect is indescribably spirited and jolly. It is a symphony of motion *allegretto*, a symphony of joy and hope, a symphony with a message. It says in the language of the emotions, which is the proper language of a symphony, that it is not good for man to use all his energies in the grubby business of acquiring goods or to give all his thought to the injustices of society or to the dour contemplation of the future of his race. It presents, most appealingly, the lovely and the lively. And it makes plain that these things, with the good nature inherent in them, can give more happiness than all the efficiency and forethought in the world. Everybody sees the girls walking along and everybody is pleased and cheered up.

And the remarkable part of it is that the girls themselves have little to do with the cheer and good feeling they disseminate. Young ladies are essentially serious creatures. They lay deep plans for the most trifling adventures and they worry enormously over the most trivial eventualities. It is only their bodies which are lively and irresponsible and which, by their antics, keep them smiling and gay.

And all the attractiveness they bring to the public scene is due to their brightness and eagerness and their general effect of uncontrollable but charming activity.

Consider Lois as she hurries to the office at a canter. She is all anxiety at what the boss will have to say if she is late. She is possessed of one idea. She is feverish with haste and concern. But does she present a picture of harassed distraction? Not at all, not at all. Her garments have been chosen in a more leisurely moment for their brightness and appeal. Her face and hair and hat have been pleasingly tended. But more than all this, she moves so brightly and eagerly in a fascinating blend of so many small, epicycloidal lines of motion that the effect is entrancing—she jiggles. Who shall say how many worn householders have brightened at the sight and having felt the blue devils within them weaken for a moment, gritted their teeth and resolved to hold onto the ancestral home in Teaneck? Or how many fat industrialists, gloomily contemplating the state of business and tempted to dump a line on the market, have held their hands at the vague memory of a vast and promising busyness recently beheld? The industrialists may not remember but the vast busyness was just Lois and her sisters trotting, very seriously, about their inconsequential affairs. And these are no special instances for there are girls like Lois jiggling up and down every street and avenue, every lane and highway in the country, broadcasting a message of joy and hope. Spring is here.

It is a melancholy thought that each one of them will, some day, lose her jiggle. With advancing years the jiggle becomes a menace. A woman is in grave danger of flying to pieces. To prevent any such unpleasantness, she binds herself into one solid, inelastic lump and thereafter jiggles no more.

With her person in close and continual restraint, she carries on under difficulties particularly in warm weather. No longer does she scatter good cheer all about but saves her smiles until the favor she wishes is most immediate. And then, one awful day, comes the realization that nobody looks at her any more. Nobody even listens to her. This soul-shaking irreparable loss of her audience so deranges her psyche that she develops the disposition and facial expression of a spitting cobra. In her confusion of spirit, she falls into futile vindictiveness and she treats each member of the calloused and inattentive human race with the screeching animosity she formerly showed only to mice, snakes and things that crawled out from under flat stones. Animosity and vindictiveness are catching and as she composes twenty-five per cent of our population, her unsettling effect on the body politic is enormous. We are able to maintain a stable form of government only because all males engaged in her service have adopted a universal incantation which, muttered to themselves immediately upon her departure, exorcises the residue of her visit and leaves them free to be bland and conciliatory to the next customer.

A world from which the jiggle had been removed and all women were like that is an impossibility. Nobody would ever have any children. The will to live would be irritated right out of the human race and no one would wait for his physical envelope to wear out before having a look at the next world.

It is sufficiently distressing to remember that is the state to which all the happy, smiling girls about us must some day come. But let us be glad we have them with us, to brighten and animate the daily scene for a short time, before they settle down to being a helpmate for some one man and a nest of scorpions to everyone else in the world. Let us be glad their lively mode of locomotion is largely outside their control and not to be modified by any silly notions which staid elders may put in their heads. And lastly let us be glad for the gay, lively, hopeful air which they disseminate through a medium which so successfully attracts the eye. For though you may never have noticed the great social significance of the jiggle, you do notice the jiggle itself. And so does your old man. Spring is here.

ANONYMOUS

◀━━━━━━━━━━━━━━━━━━━━━━━━━━━━━━━━▶

They Order It Better in France

I took a friend, a Frenchman, who happens to be in New York, out to lunch. We went to a certain restaurant on East Fifty-fifth Street where I knew the food was good and the place itself quiet. Always a few people; never a crowd.

We had some business to discuss.

At the table on our right were three very pretty women. No one likes looking at a pretty woman better than I do.

At the table on our left, were three women, one a girl as pretty as paint. One blonde and smart. The third a brunette. That was all right for me too. I like a feminine background for a business talk.

Opposite us were several couples. A woman per couple; I didn't notice them at first.

We ordered our luncheon.

Knowing my friend, and my France, I expected we'd start off with a certain amount of appreciation of so much female beauty, near by. Actually, I myself am not a bad judge of feminine looks: and of what used to be called "It."

So I gave my friend a lead.

"Pretty, isn't she? The girl in the red scarf?"

He didn't answer at once. I'd forgotten in my long absence from France that I'd asked a question which would immediately provoke expert reflection before I got a considered opinion.

My friend the Frenchman looked at the pretty girl and then said:

"Y . . . yes. She is *pretty*," in a tone implying that that was all that could be said about her.

"Why I think she's *awfully* pretty," I defended; "she looks like Myrna Loy."

He agreed, helping himself to *hors d'oeuvres*, that she was like Myrna Loy. "But Myrna Loy is not 'excitante' (i.e., physically disturbing)," he said.

"Well then," I said, "perhaps you prefer the woman next her? The blonde with the gold clips in her sweater?"

Again the pause. Then:

"She has very pretty eyes, and mouth. But I am afraid of something in her . . ."

"What?"

He slightly shook his head and bit an olive. "I am afraid that she would be less well naked. She does not look well formed. I detest experiencing the hip bones of a woman."

By now my host instinct was roused; and, feeling that I wanted to make him feel properly entertained, I hastened to offer him the third woman at the table, a perfectly ravishing little brunette, plump enough to obviate the risk of anyone experiencing any bones anywhere. "What about her?" I said.

She was sitting near to us so we had an excellent view of her.

"She is *better*. She is much better. A pretty nose, and a ravishing smile. A charming little stomach. Only I'm afraid of one thing about her. . . . She has an expression, a look, which is too—intelligent! A look that is more observant than warm. . . . A warm look in a woman is a great thing, with an intellectual woman one arrives with difficulty at great pleasures! . . . Now, that woman opposite," he said. "She has atrocious arms, but she has a little vicious air which pleases me! One sees very well that she understands Love."

I looked at her. To me she was large and frog-faced. I could imagine "love" with her being about as satisfying as with a Fifth Avenue bus. . . . I turned my eyes to the table at our right. The waiter brought our steaks. I realized it would be some time before we got around to talking "business." So I picked him yet another daisy. "Well now *there*," I insisted, "is an absolutely *glorious girl*. You couldn't see anything easier to look at anywhere!"

She was, too. A blonde, tall, with a divine figure. She was sitting sort of away from the table, sprawling like a schoolgirl and smoking cigarettes. As far as I was concerned, she was tops. And I envied the man who had put a big sapphire ring on her engagement finger.

My French friend looked her over. His contemplative glance raked her from the top of her perfectly heavenly little head, down to the tips of her pumps. Finally he conceded, as he cut his steak across—"She has excellent thighs . . . *altogether* charming thighs," then, having eaten two mouthfuls, while he stared at the woman, of the couple opposite us, whom I hardly noticed, for the good reason that she wasn't too easy to look at, he said,

"Now *there*—my friend—*Voila une bonne affaire!*"

So I took a look. She was a square-rigged dame with a brownish skin, a large mouth, her eyes made up black all around. She wasn't chic, and she wasn't by any means young. She seemed to be eating well and laughing a great deal.

But when a Frenchman gives a lady the once over and says, "*C'est une bonne affaire*," which roughly translates "She has boudoir talent" you needn't have any more doubts about her. Because he's one of a nation of Experts! And if you ask him why he thinks so, he can give you a highly reasoned bit of anatomical chapter and verse to demonstrate the amorous capabilities of the question. For instance a good curve in and out at the back of the waist is an encouraging sign . . . whereas thin arms and wrists are very discouraging and mean "coldness." A good firm neck and not too much length of leg, is what is wanted. And the face must be *lively*. But it must *not* be intellectual. "Too intellectual for pleasure" is a well-known dismissal for girls with college honors. And a certain amount of plumpness is liked. Though a girl I know was told by her French boyfriend, "You are a little too fat, chérie. I prefer it for love. But it is not becoming when you are dressed." Another symptom that raises hope is a readiness to laugh. A woman who laughs easily is easy to love!

The fact is that the Frenchman's eye in the matter of picking a lady is very highly trained to discern ability for love. (Put it that way!) He can pick a girl the way an Englishman of a certain type picks a horse—he sees the "points" right away that are going to guarantee him satisfaction. The whole American idealization of "Dream Girls," "Pretty Kids" and what not, doesn't enter his consciousness. The Frenchman's looking for a good time; not for a picture to hang over his bed—which all means that he's got a lot less liking than we tender-hearted, misty-eyed Americans have for "baby" qualities in girls. He isn't captivated by big eyes and lisps and bows and what not. (Something symptomatic, I always think, this calling a girl "Baby.") And in fact his whole idea about the "right age" for a woman to be is practically opposite to ours.

I suppose The Traveling Salesman in any country is probably about as good an index as you can get of average taste in girls for any nation. (Except in England where the salesmen are called Commercial Travelers and go to Temperance Inns and spend their evenings talking to one another!) But when the American salesman gets to talking to you, you soon can tell what sort of dames he looks for when he arrives at his destination, because he never talks about anything else.

Roughly speaking his ideal is something young enough and coy and fluffy. . . . And if she's not such hotstuff really when he gets down to it—well then he gets an enormous kick out of the idea (seldom correct) that she's a virgin! It's wonderful what a sense of outraging Innocence will do for the Nordic man's self esteem. The Tired Business Man likes to think of his love of the moment as his "little girl" and a certain newspaper lately gave great prominence to a gentleman in a western state who achieved the enviable feat of combining age and good-citizenship by marrying a girl eleven years old. Incidentally, he was backed up by his mother-in-law who declared her profound certainty that the Almighty was tickled to death by the marriage.

But our French friends like it all the other way. "Ripeness" is one of the things they're after. Most Frenchmen will assert that a woman isn't worth considering until she's thirty. Vintage Women in fact. And whereas a pair of sheer stockings, a pinafore and a baby-blue hair riband symbolizes our own Ideal of Womanhood, you've only got to read *Chéri*—that stirring description of an idyll between a boy of sixteen and a lady of (certainly) fifty, to realize how Grandmothers get Glorified in France—when every fresh wrinkle is a path of mystery, and a double chin does for the Frenchman what a double Scotch does for us—makes him feel better just to think about it.

However—the Frenchman's a practical man. He has his "ideal" but he knows he doesn't meet it every day. And in the meantime he isn't going to waste his opportunities. So he doesn't, as we're apt to do, keep on kidding himself that every new girl *is* an ideal. On the contrary. He's a cheerful realist. He's trained to spot the redeeming graces as adroitly as a highly bred pig sniffs truffles. And faced with the homeliest dame he'll work over her until he can say, "Yes—she's certainly homely, but she has 'delightful ears' "; or "an exciting back to her neck"; or "provocative biceps." And the worst he cares to admit about any woman is "Yes, she is very ugly, but she has 'something' *(Elle a quelque chose)."* And if you get him in a cynical but wholesome mood he'll indicate that after all, "All cats are grey at night!"

The same practical view which prompts him to make the best of what he gets, and never to leave a lady unturned, so to speak, had an instructive influence a year ago on the conduct of the big strikes in Paris, France.

When the Trades Union Leaders ordered a sit-down strike and got the men in the factories, they sent out motor lorries from Paris full of the gayest possible gals—to sit in with them.

Which seems to be an idea anyway for Brightening Up Industrial Disputes. (American Labor Leaders please copy.)